continued on back

Sampling Techniques

A WILEY PUBLICATION IN APPLIED STATISTICS

Sampling Techniques
second edition

WILLIAM G. COCHRAN

Professor of Statistics
Harvard University

John Wiley & Sons, Inc.

New York · London · Sydney

ISBN 0 471 16238 8

LIBRARY OF CONGRESS CATALOG CARD NUMBER: 63-7553

PRINTED IN THE UNITED STATES OF AMERICA

to Betty

Preface

The purpose of this book is to present a comprehensive account of sampling theory as it has been developed for use in sample surveys, with illustrations to show how the theory is applied in practice and with a supply of exercises to be worked by the student. My hope is that the book will be useful both as a text for a course on sample surveys in which the major emphasis is on theory and for individual reading by the student who does not have access to formal instruction.

The minimum mathematical equipment necessary for an easy understanding of the proofs is a knowledge of differential calculus as far as the determination of maxima and minima (using Lagrange multipliers where required), plus a familiarity with elementary algebra and especially with the handling of relatively complicated algebraic summations. Knowledge of the laws of probability for finite sample spaces, including combinatorial probabilities, the properties of expected values, and conditional probability, is extremely helpful. On the statistical side, the book presupposes an introductory course which covers such topics as means and standard deviations, the normal, binomial, and multinomial distributions, confidence limits, Student's t-test, linear regression, and the simpler types of analysis of variance. Occasionally, more advanced results from statistics are used, since I have tried to point out the relation between sample survey theory and the main stream of statistical theory. In the early parts of the book each step in a proof should be readily apparent from the previous steps: towards the end, where proofs are more condensed, a little work with paper and pencil may be necessary to follow some of the steps in detail.

The order of presentation of topics in this edition is essentially the same as in the first edition, most theorems retaining their old numbers. Chapter 5 on stratification, which was already undesirably long in the first edition, has, however, been split into two chapters. The present Chapter 5 contains

vii

the older, standard results. A new Chapter 5A is devoted to the numerous specialized topics that are necessary for the most efficient use of stratification. A further change in order is that an introduction to ratio estimates is now included in Chapters 2 and 3 instead of being postponed to Chapter 6. This change was made because ratio estimates are found in practice, often in disguised form, even in the simplest types of survey, so that an early introduction to them seemed advisable. The teacher who prefers to postpone this subject until Chapter 6 may, of course, continue to do so.

Many sections have been added at appropriate places to cover results published since the writing of the first edition in 1951–1952. Since these developments are quite miscellaneous, the new sections are indicated by an asterisk in the table of contents. Some of the major topics are as follows. Several sections are devoted to the statistical methods that apply when survey results are to be presented separately for specified subdivisions of the population (for example, persons of different ages or house owners and renters) and when comparisons among these subdivisions are wanted for analytical reasons. In stratified sampling newer work deals with the construction of strata and the choice of number of strata, with the optimum sample sizes in individual strata when specified levels of precision are to be attained for each of several variables and with two-way stratification when the sample is small. A summary is given of the extensive recent researches on sampling without replacement when primary units are selected with unequal probabilities. The study of nonsampling errors has produced new methods of investigating the effectiveness of call-backs, as compared with other techniques for reducing the bias due to nonresponse, and new methods of gathering data that throw light on the contribution of errors of measurement to the total errors in estimates made from surveys.

Some of the new sections are intended to fill gaps in presentation that were pointed out by teachers who have used this book or were suggested by my own experience. In two-stage sampling, for instance, the variance formulas are given separately for each of the principal methods of sample selection and estimation, and the efficiency of self-weighting estimates is discussed in greater detail. Although these formulas can be deduced from one or two general theorems, the convenience of having the explicit results readily available appeared worth the extra space required. Many old sections have been rewritten to include new developments or to clarify the presentation. The number of exercises has more than doubled.

The present edition is about one third larger than the first. I view this growth with mixed feelings. Even in the first edition it was difficult to cover all the material in a one-term course of lectures while leaving time for case studies of actual surveys in the fields of interest of the students. However, the sections have been prepared so that many can be omitted, or condensed to a brief statement of results, without creating difficulties in reading later parts of the book. Although the choice of topics for discussion will be governed by the views of the teacher and by the level of preparation and fields of application of the students, the following suggestions are made of sections that may be omitted or condensed in an introductory course: 2.8, 2.13, 2.14; 3.9, 3.11; 4.6, 4.7; 5.8, 5.9; 5A.1, 5A.3, 5A.4, 5A.5, 5A.10, 5A.12; 6.4, 6.5, 6.9, 6.13, 6.14, 6.15, 6.17; 7.4, 7.5, 7.7, 7.8, 7.9; 8.5, 8.6, 8.8, 8.11, 8.12; 9.5, 9.6, 9.11, 9.12, 9.13; 10.7, 10.8, 10.9, 10.10; 11.7, 11.9, 11.16; 12.5, 12.6, 12.7, 12.8; 13.5, 13.7, 13.15, 13.16.

Dr. Alva L. Finkner and Dr. Emil H. Jebe prepared a large part of the lecture notes from which the first edition was written, and Dr. F. C. Cornell, Dr. J. A. Doull, and Dr. Finkner kindly gave their permission to quote data from surveys. Some investigations, both theoretical and applied, that served as background material were made possible by a research contract with the Office of Naval Research, U. S. Navy Department. In the preparation of the present edition the secretarial staff of the Department of Statistics, Harvard University, performed nobly in typing, and generous assistance in proofreading was given by Mrs. Cleo Youtz and by any graduate students who had the ill-fortune to pass my office door during the critical time-period. The author index was prepared by Miss Susan Rogers and the answers to exercises checked by Mr. P. S. R. Sambasiva Rao. I have received much stimulating discussion of recent trends in sampling from colleagues Lyle D. Calvin, R. M. Cyert, W. Edwards Deming, Tore Dalenius, Morris H. Hansen, Herman O. Hartley, William N. Hurwitz, Leslie Kish, William G. Madow, and Frederick F. Stephan. To all these persons, named or unnamed, I would like to express my thanks.

Cambridge, Massachusetts   WILLIAM G. COCHRAN
November 1962

Contents

Asterisk denotes sections that are new in this edition.

CHAPTER 1

Introduction

1.1 ADVANTAGES OF THE SAMPLING METHOD

Our knowledge, our attitudes, and our actions are based to a very large extent on samples. This is equally true in everyday life and in scientific research. A person's opinion of an institution that conducts thousands of transactions every day is often determined by the one or two encounters which he has had with the institution in the course of several years. The traveler who spends 10 days in a foreign country and then proceeds to write a book telling the inhabitants how to revive their industries, reform their political system, balance their budget, and improve the food in their hotels is a familiar figure of fun. But in a real sense he differs from the political scientist who devotes 20 years to living and studying in the country only in that he bases his conclusions on a much smaller sample of experience and is less likely to be aware of the extent of his ignorance. In science and human affairs alike we lack the resources to study more than a fragment of the phenomena that might advance our knowledge.

Until the last 30 years little attention was given to the problems of how to obtain a good sample and how to draw sound conclusions from the results. This does not matter so long as the material from which we are sampling is uniform, so that any kind of sample gives almost the same results. Laboratory diagnoses about the state of our health are made from a few drops of blood. This procedure is based on the assumption that the circulating blood is always well mixed and that one drop tells the same story as another—an assumption which we as laymen fervently hope is correct. But when the material is far from uniform, as is often the case, the method by which the sample is obtained is critical, and the study of techniques that ensure a trustworthy sample becomes important.

This book contains an account of the body of theory that has been built up to provide a background for good sampling methods. In most of the applications for which this theory was constructed, the aggregate about

1

which information is desired is finite and delimited—the inhabitants of a town, the machines in a factory, the fish in a lake. In some cases it may seem feasible to obtain the information by taking a complete enumeration or census of the aggregate. Administrators accustomed to dealing with censuses were at first inclined to be suspicious of samples and reluctant to use them in place of censuses. Although this attitude no longer persists, it may be well to list the principal advantages of sampling as compared with complete enumeration.

Reduced Cost

If data are secured from only a small fraction of the aggregate, expenditures are smaller than if a complete census is attempted. With large populations, results accurate enough to be useful can be obtained from samples that represent only a small fraction of the population. In the United States the most important recurrent surveys taken by the government use samples of around 100,000 persons, or about one person in 1800. Surveys used to provide facts bearing on sales and advertising policy in market research may employ samples of only a few thousand.

Greater Speed

For the same reason, the data can be collected and summarized more quickly with a sample than with a complete count. This is a vital consideration when the information is urgently needed.

Greater Scope

In certain types of inquiry highly trained personnel or specialized equipment, limited in availability, must be used to obtain the data. A complete census is impracticable: the choice lies between obtaining the information by sampling or not at all. Thus surveys which rely on sampling have more scope and flexibility regarding the types of information that can be obtained. On the other hand, if accurate information is wanted for many subdivisions of the population, the size of sample needed to do the job is sometimes so large that a complete enumeration offers the best solution.

Greater Accuracy

Because personnel of higher quality can be employed and given intensive training and because more careful supervision of the field work and processing of results becomes feasible when the volume of work is reduced, a sample may actually produce more accurate results than the kind of complete enumeration that can be taken.

1.2 SOME USES OF SAMPLE SURVEYS

To an observer of developments in sampling over the last 10 years the most striking feature is the rapid increase in the number and types of surveys taken by sampling. The Statistical Office of the United Nations publishes reports from time to time on "Sample Surveys of Current Interest" conducted by member countries. The 1960 report lists surveys from 52 countries. Many of these surveys seek information of obvious importance to national planning on such topics as agricultural production and land use, unemployment and the size of the labor force, industrial production, wholesale and retail prices, health status of the people, and family incomes and expenditures. But more specialized inquiries can also be found: for example, housing and social problems of old people (Austria), rural debt (Ceylon), the cost of housebuilding (Czechoslovakia), the ages of elementary-school pupils (Italy), the effects of television on school children (Netherlands), the domestic working conditions of housewives (Sweden), the characteristics and recruitment of foster mothers (United Kingdom), the use of technical information by small industry (United Kingdom), and the employment of scientists and engineers by industry (United States).

Sampling has come to play a prominent part in national decennial censuses. In the United States a 5% sample was introduced into the 1940 Census by asking extra questions about occupation, parentage, fertility, etc., of those persons whose names fell on two of the 40 lines on each page of the schedule. The use of sampling was greatly extended in 1950. From a 20% sample (every fifth line) information was obtained on items such as income, years in school, migration, and service in armed forces. By taking every sixth person in the 20% sample, a further sample of $3\frac{1}{3}\%$ was created to give information on marriage and fertility. A series of questions dealing with the condition and age of housing was split into five sets, each set being filled in at every fifth house. Sampling was also employed to speed up publication of the results. Preliminary tabulations for many important items, made on a sample basis, appeared more than a year and a half before the final reports.

This process continued in the 1960 Census. Except for certain basic information required from every person for constitutional or legal reasons, the whole census was shifted to a 25% sample basis, only one household in four receiving the complete schedule. This change, accompanied by greatly increased mechanization, resulted in much earlier publication and substantial savings.

On a smaller scale, local governments—city, state, and county—are making increased use of sample surveys to obtain information needed for future planning and for meeting pressing problems. In the United States most large cities have commercial agencies that make a business of planning and conducting sample surveys for clients.

The operation known as market research is heavily dependent on the sampling approach. Estimates of the sizes of television and radio audiences for different programs and of newspaper and magazine readership (including the advertisements) are kept continually under scrutiny. Manufacturers and retailers want to know the reactions of people to new products or new methods of packaging, their complaints about old products, and their reasons for preferring one product to another.

Business and industry have many uses for sampling in attempting to increase the efficiency of their internal operations. The important areas of quality control and acceptance sampling are outside the scope of this book. But, obviously, decisions taken with respect to level or change of quality or to acceptance or rejection of batches are well grounded only if results obtained from the sample data are valid (within a reasonable tolerance) for the whole batch. The sampling of records of business transactions (accounts, payrolls, stock, personnel)—usually much easier than the sampling of people—can provide serviceable information quickly and economically. Savings can also be made through sampling in the estimation of inventories, in studies of the condition and length of the life of equipment, in the inspection of the accuracy and rate of output of clerical work, in investigating how key personnel distribute their working time among different tasks, and, more generally, in the new field known as operations research. The books by Deming (1960) and Slonim (1960) contain many interesting examples showing the range of applications of the sampling method in business.

Opinion, attitude, and election polls, which did much to bring the technique of sampling before the public eye, continue to be a popular feature of newspapers. In the field of accounting and auditing, which has employed sampling for many years, a new interest has arisen in adapting modern developments to the particular problems of this field. The status of sample surveys as evidence in lawsuits has also been subject to lively discussion.

Sample surveys can be classified broadly into two types—*descriptive* and *analytical*. In a descriptive survey the objective is simply to obtain certain information about large groups: for example, the numbers of men, women, and children who view a television program. In an analytical survey, comparisons are made between different subgroups of the population, in order to discover whether differences exist among them that may enable us to form or to verify hypotheses about the forces at work in the population. The Indianapolis fertility survey, for instance, was an attempt to determine the extent to which married couples plan the number and spacing of children, the husband's and wife's attitudes toward this planning, the reasons for these attitudes, and the degree of success attained (Kiser and Whelpton, 1953).

The distinction between descriptive and analytical surveys is not, of course, clear-cut. Many surveys provide data that serve both purposes. Along with the rise in the number of descriptive surveys, there has, however, been a noticeable increase in surveys taken primarily for analytical purposes, particularly in the study of human behavior and health. Surveys of the teeth of school children before and after fluoridation of water, of the death rates and causes of death of people who smoke different amounts, and the huge study of the effectiveness of the Salk polio vaccine may be cited.

The success of the sample survey has led to its employment in estimating some unusual items: for example, the lengths of cigarette butts, the number of flies in a town, the number of signatures to a petition that were not actually written by the persons whose names appear, and the number of people who can fold their tongues. These items were relevant, respectively, to studies of the relation of lung cancer and smoking, of the effectiveness of fly spraying, of the legality of a petition, and of the inheritance of tongue folding—although the last item has not, to my knowledge, been the subject of an extensive survey.

1.3 THE PRINCIPAL STEPS IN A SAMPLE SURVEY

As a preliminary to a discussion of the role that theory plays in a sample survey, it is useful to describe briefly the steps involved in the planning and execution of a survey. Surveys vary greatly in their complexity. To take a sample from 5000 cards, neatly arranged and numbered in a file, is an easy task. It is another matter to sample the inhabitants of a region where transport is by water through the forests, where there are no maps, where 15 different dialects are spoken, and where the inhabitants are very suspicious of an inquisitive stranger. Problems that are baffling in one survey may be trivial or nonexistent in another.

The principal steps in a survey are grouped somewhat arbitrarily under 11 headings.

Objectives of the Survey

A lucid statement of the objectives is most helpful. Without this, it is easy in a complex survey to forget the objectives when engrossed in the details of planning, and to make decisions that are at variance with the objectives.

Population to be Sampled

The word *population* is used to denote the aggregate from which the sample is chosen. The definition of the population may present no problem, as when sampling a batch of electric light bulbs in order to estimate the average length of life of a bulb. In sampling a population of farms, on the other hand, rules must be set up to define a farm, and borderline cases arise. These rules must be usable in practice: the enumerator must be able to decide in the field, without much hesitation, whether or not a doubtful case belongs to the population.

The population to be sampled (the *sampled* population) should coincide with the population about which information is wanted (the *target* population). Sometimes, for reasons of practicability or convenience, the sampled population is more restricted than the target population. If so, it should be remembered that conclusions drawn from the sample apply to the sampled population. Judgment about the extent to which these conclusions will also apply to the target population must depend on other sources of information. Any supplementary information that can be gathered about the nature of the differences between sampled and target population may be helpful.

Data to be Collected

It is well to verify that all the data are relevant to the purposes of the survey and that no essential data are omitted. There is frequently a tendency, particularly with human populations, to ask too many questions, some of which are never subsequently analyzed. An overlong questionnaire lowers the quality of the answers to important as well as unimportant questions.

Degree of Precision Desired

The results of sample surveys are always subject to some uncertainty because only part of the population has been measured and because of errors of measurement. This uncertainty can be reduced by taking larger samples and by using superior instruments of measurement. But this usually costs time and money. Consequently, the specification of the degree of precision wanted in the results is an important step. This step is the responsibility of the person who is going to use the data. It may present difficulties, since many administrators are unaccustomed to thinking in terms of the amount of error that can be tolerated in estimates, consistent with making good decisions. The statistician can often help at this stage.

Methods of Measurement

There may be a choice of measuring instrument and of method of approach to the population. Data about a person's state of health may be obtained from statements that he makes or from a medical examination. The survey may employ a self-administered questionnaire, an interviewer who reads a standard set of questions with no discretion, or an interviewing process that allows much latitude in the form and ordering of the questions. The approach may be by mail, by telephone, by personal visit, or by a combination of the three. Much study has been made of interviewing methods and problems [see, e.g., Hyman (1954) and Payne (1951)].

A major part of the preliminary work is the construction of record forms on which the questions and answers are to be entered. With simple questionnaires, the answers can sometimes be precoded—that is, entered in a manner in which they can be routinely transferred to mechanical equipment. In fact, for the construction of good record forms, it is necessary to visualize the structure of the final summary tables that will be used for drawing conclusions.

The Frame

Before selecting the sample, the population must be divided into parts which are called *sampling units*, or *units*. These units must cover the whole of the population and they must not overlap, in the sense that every element in the population belongs to one and only one unit. Sometimes the appropriate unit is obvious, as in a population of light bulbs, in which the unit is the single bulb. Sometimes there is a choice of unit. In sampling the people in a town, the unit might be an individual person, the members of a family, or all persons living in the same city block. In sampling an agricultural crop, the unit might be a field, a farm, or an area of land whose shape and dimensions are at our disposal.

The construction of this list of sampling units, called a *frame*, is often one of the major practical problems. From bitter experience, samplers have acquired a critical attitude toward lists that have been routinely collected for some purpose. Despite assurances to the contrary, such lists are often found to be incomplete, or partly illegible, or to contain an unknown amount of duplication. A good frame may be hard to come by when the population is specialized, as in populations of bookmakers or of people who keep turkeys. Jessen (1955) presents an interesting method of constructing a frame from the branches of a fruit tree.

Selection of the Sample

There is now a variety of plans by which the sample may be selected. For each plan that is considered, rough estimates of the size of sample can be made from a knowledge of the degree of precision desired. The relative costs and time involved for each plan are also compared before making a decision.

The Pretest

It has been found useful to try out the questionnaire and the field methods on a small scale. This nearly always results in improvements in the questionnaire and may reveal other troubles that will be serious on a large scale, for example, that the cost will be much greater than expected.

Organization of the Field Work

In extensive surveys many problems of business administration are met. The personnel must receive training in the purpose of the survey and in the methods of measurement to be employed and must be adequately supervised in their work. A procedure for *early* checking of the quality of the returns is invaluable. Plans must be made for handling nonresponse, that is, the failure of the enumerator to obtain information from certain of the units in the sample.

Summary and Analysis of the Data

The first step is to edit the completed questionnaires, in the hope of amending recording errors, or at least of deleting data that are obviously erroneous. Decisions about tabulating procedure are needed in cases in which answers to certain questions were omitted by some respondents or were deleted in the editing process. Thereafter, the tabulations which lead to the estimates are performed. Different methods of estimation may be available for the same data.

In the presentation of results it is good practice to report the amount of error to be expected in the most important estimates. One of the advantages of probability sampling is that such statements can be made, although they have to be severely qualified if the amount of nonresponse is substantial.

Information Gained for Future Surveys

The more information we have initially about a population, the easier it is to devise a sample that will give accurate estimates. Any completed sample is potentially a guide to improved future sampling, in the data that it supplies about the means, standard deviations, and nature of the variability of the principal measurements and about the costs involved in getting the data. Sampling practice advances more rapidly when provisions are made to assemble and record information of this type.

There is another important respect in which any completed sample facilitates future samples. Things never go exactly as planned in a complex survey. The alert sampler learns to recognize mistakes in execution and to see that they do not occur in future surveys.

1.4 THE ROLE OF SAMPLING THEORY

This list of the steps in a sample survey has been given in order to emphasize that sampling is a practical business, which calls for several different types of skill. In some of the steps—the definition of the population, the determination of the data to be collected and of the methods of measurement, and the organization of the field work—sampling theory plays at most a minor role. Although these topics are not discussed further in this book, their importance should be realized. Sampling demands attention to all phases of the activity: poor work in one phase may ruin a survey in which everything else is done well.

The purpose of sampling theory is to make sampling more efficient. It attempts to develop methods of sample selection and of estimation that provide, at the lowest possible cost, estimates that are precise enough for our purpose. This principle of specified precision at minimum cost recurs repeatedly in the presentation of theory.

In order to apply this principle, we must be able to predict, for any sampling procedure that is under consideration, the precision and the cost to be expected. So far as precision is concerned, we cannot foretell exactly how large an error will be present in an estimate in any specific situation, for this would require a knowledge of the true value for the population. Instead, the precision of a sampling procedure is judged by examining the frequency distribution generated for the estimate if the procedure is applied again and again to the same population. This is, of course, the standard technique by which precision is judged in statistical theory.

A further simplification is introduced. With samples of the sizes that are common in practice, there is often good reason to suppose that the sample estimates are approximately normally distributed. With a normally distributed estimate, the whole shape of the frequency distribution is known if we know the mean and the standard deviation (or the variance). A considerable part of sample survey theory is concerned with finding formulas for these means and variances.

One difference between sample survey theory and the classical theory of sampling is that the populations in survey work contain a *finite* number of units. The methods used to prove theorems are different, and the results are slightly more complicated, when sampling is from a finite instead of an infinite population. For practical purposes these differences in results for finite and infinite populations are seldom important. Whenever the size of the sample is small (in terms of the number of primary sampling units) relative to the size of the population, results derived from an infinite population are fully adequate. In general, results for finite populations are presented in this book. In some of the more difficult problems, the theory for infinite populations is used to simplify the presentation.

1.5 PROBABILITY SAMPLING

All sampling procedures for which a theory has been developed have the following mathematical properties in common.

1. We are able to define the set of distinct samples, $S_1, S_2, \cdots, S_v$, which the procedure is capable of selecting if applied to a specific population. This means that we can say precisely what sampling units belong to S_1, to S_2, and so on. For example, suppose that the population contains six units, numbered 1 to 6. A common procedure for choosing a sample of size 2 gives three possible candidates—$S_1 \sim (1, 4)$; $S_2 \sim (2, 5)$; $S_3 \sim (3, 6)$. Note that not all possible samples of size 2 need be included.

2. Each possible sample S_i has assigned to it a known probability of selection π_i.

3. We select one of the S_i by a process in which each S_i receives its appropriate probability π_i of being selected. In the example we might assign equal probabilities to the three samples. Then the draw itself can be made by choosing a random number between 1 and 3. If this number is j, S_j is the sample that is taken.

4. The method for computing the estimate from the sample must be stated and must lead to a unique estimate for any specific sample. We may declare, for example, that the estimate is to be the average of the measurements on the individual units in the sample.

For any sampling procedure that satisfies these properties, we are in a position to calculate the frequency distribution of the estimates it generates if repeatedly applied to the same population. For we know how frequently any particular sample S_i will be selected, and we know how to calculate the estimate from the data in S_i. It is clear, therefore, that a sampling theory can be developed for any procedure of this type, although the details of the development may be intricate.

The term *probability sampling* refers to a procedure of this type. This is, of course, not the only way in which a sample can be drawn. The following are some common types of nonprobability sampling.

1. The sample is restricted to a part of the population that is readily accessible. A sample of coal from an open wagon may be taken from the top 6 to 9 inches.

2. The sample is selected haphazardly. In picking ten rabbits from a large cage in a laboratory, the investigator may take those that his hands rest on, without conscious planning.

3. With a small but heterogeneous population, the sampler inspects the whole of it and selects a small sample of "typical" units—that is, units that are close to his impression of the average of the population. This method is sometimes called *judgment* or *purposive selection*.

4. The sample consists essentially of volunteers, in studies in which the measuring process is unpleasant or troublesome to the person being measured.

Under the right conditions, any of these methods can give useful results. They are not, however, amenable to the development of a sampling theory, since no element of random selection is involved. About the only way of examining how good one of them may be is to find a situation in which the results are known, either for the whole population or for a probability sample, and make comparisons. Even if a method appears to do well in one such comparison, this does not guarantee that it will do well under different circumstances.

In practice we seldom draw a probability sample by writing down the S_i and π_i as outlined above. This is intolerably laborious with a large population, where a sampling procedure may produce billions of possible samples. The draw is most commonly made by specifying probabilities of inclusion for the individual units and drawing units, one by one or in groups until the sample of desired size and type is constructed. For the purposes of a theory it is sufficient to know that we could write down the S_i and π_i if we wanted to and had unlimited time.

1.6 USE OF THE NORMAL DISTRIBUTION

As mentioned previously, the samples in surveys are often large enough so that an estimate made from them is approximately normally distributed. Further, with probability sampling, we have formulas that give the mean and variance of the estimate. Consider first *unbiased* estimates. An estimate $\hat{\mu}$ given by a sampling plan is called an unbiased estimate of some population characteristic μ if the mean value of $\hat{\mu}$, taken over all possible samples, is equal to μ. In the notation of section 1.5, this condition may be written

$$E(\hat{\mu}) = \sum_{i=1}^{v} \pi_i \hat{\mu}_i = \mu$$

where $\hat{\mu}_i$ is the estimate given by the ith sample. The symbol E, which stands for "the expected value of," is used frequently.

Suppose that we have taken a sample by a procedure known to give unbiased estimates and have computed the sample estimate $\hat{\mu}$ and its standard deviation $\sigma_{\hat{\mu}}$ (often called, alternatively, its standard error). How good is the estimate? We cannot know the exact value of the error of estimate

$(\hat{\mu} - \mu)$, but from the properties of the normal curve the chances are

0.32 (about 1 in 3) that the absolute error $|\hat{\mu} - \mu|$ exceeds $\sigma_{\hat{\mu}}$

0.05 (1 in 20) that the absolute error $|\hat{\mu} - \mu|$ exceeds $1.96\sigma_{\hat{\mu}} \doteq 2\sigma_{\hat{\mu}}$

0.01 (1 in 100) that the absolute error $|\hat{\mu} - \mu|$ exceeds $2.58\sigma_{\hat{\mu}}$

For example, if a probability sample of the records of batteries in routine use in a large factory shows an average life $\hat{\mu} = 394$ days, with a standard error $\sigma_{\hat{\mu}} = 4.6$ days, the chances are 99 in 100 that the average life in the population of batteries lies between

$$\hat{\mu}_L = 394 - (2.58)(4.6) = 382 \text{ days}$$

and $\qquad \hat{\mu}_U = 394 + (2.58)(4.6) = 406 \text{ days}$

The limits, 382 days and 406 days, are called lower and upper *confidence limits*. With a single estimate from a single survey, the statement "μ lies between 382 and 406 days" is not certain to be correct. The "99% confidence" figure implies that if the same sampling plan were used many times in a population, a confidence statement being made from each sample, about 99% of these statements would be correct and 1% wrong. When sampling is being introduced into an operation in which complete censuses have previously been used, a demonstration of this property is sometimes made by drawing repeated samples of the type proposed from a population for which complete records exist, so that μ is known (see, e.g., Trueblood and Cyert, 1957). The practical verification that approximately the stated proportion of statements is correct does much to educate and reassure administrators about the nature of sampling. Similarly, when a single sample is taken from each of a series of different populations, about 95% of the 95% confidence statements are correct.

The preceding discussion assumes that $\sigma_{\hat{\mu}}$, as computed from the sample, is known exactly. Actually, $\sigma_{\hat{\mu}}$, like $\hat{\mu}$, is subject to a sampling error. With a normally distributed variable, tables of Student's t distribution are used instead of the normal tables to calculate confidence limits for μ when the sample is small. Replacement of the normal table by the t table makes almost no difference if the number of degrees of freedom in $\sigma_{\hat{\mu}}$ exceeds 60. With certain types of stratified sampling and with the method of replicated sampling (section 13.14) the degrees of freedom are small and the t table is needed.

1.7 BIAS AND ITS EFFECTS

In sample survey theory it is necessary to consider biased estimates for two reasons.

1. In some of the most common problems, particularly in the estimation of ratios, estimates that are otherwise convenient and suitable are found to be biased.

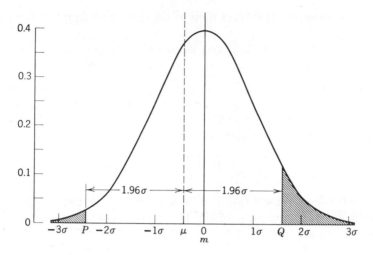

Fig. 1.1 Effect of bias on errors of estimation.

2. Even with estimates that are unbiased in probability sampling, errors of measurement and nonresponse may produce biases in the numbers that we are able to compute from the data. This happens, for instance, if the persons who refuse to be interviewed are almost all opposed to some expenditure of public funds, whereas those who are interviewed are split evenly for and against.

To examine the effect of bias, suppose that the estimate $\hat{\mu}$ is normally distributed about a mean m which is a distance B from the true population value μ, as shown in Fig. 1.1. The amount of bias is $B = m - \mu$. Suppose that we do not know that any bias is present. We compute the standard deviation σ of the frequency distribution of the estimate—this will, of course, be the standard deviation about the mean m of the distribution, not about the true mean μ. We are using σ in place of $\sigma_{\hat{\mu}}$. As a statement about the accuracy of the estimate, we declare that the probability is 0.05 that the estimate $\hat{\mu}$ is in error by more than 1.96σ.

We will consider how the presence of bias distorts this probability. To do this, we calculate the true probability that the estimate is in error by more than 1.96σ, where error is measured from the true mean μ. The two tails of the distribution must be examined separately. For the upper tail, the probability of an error of more than $+1.96\sigma$ is the shaded area above Q in Fig. 1.1. This area is given by

$$\frac{1}{\sigma\sqrt{2\pi}} \int_{\mu+1.96\sigma}^{\infty} e^{-(\hat{\mu}-m)^2/2\sigma^2} \, d\hat{\mu}$$

Put $\hat{\mu} - m = \sigma t$. The lower limit of the range of integration for t is

$$\frac{\mu - m}{\sigma} + 1.96 = 1.96 - \frac{B}{\sigma}$$

Thus the area is

$$\frac{1}{\sqrt{2\pi}} \int_{1.96-(B/\sigma)}^{\infty} e^{-t^2/2} \, dt$$

Similarly, the lower tail, that is, the shaded area below P, has an area

$$\frac{1}{\sqrt{2\pi}} \int_{-\infty}^{-1.96-(B/\sigma)} e^{-t^2/2} \, dt$$

From the form of the integrals it is clear that the amount of disturbance depends solely on the ratio of the bias to the standard deviation. The results are shown in Table 1.1.

TABLE 1.1

EFFECT OF A BIAS B ON THE PROBABILITY OF AN ERROR
GREATER THAN 1.96σ

B/σ	Probability of Error		Total
	$< -1.96\sigma$	$>1.96\sigma$	
0.02	0.0238	0.0262	0.0500
0.04	0.0228	0.0274	0.0502
0.06	0.0217	0.0287	0.0504
0.08	0.0207	0.0301	0.0508
0.10	0.0197	0.0314	0.0511
0.20	0.0154	0.0392	0.0546
0.40	0.0091	0.0594	0.0685
0.60	0.0052	0.0869	0.0921
0.80	0.0029	0.1230	0.1259
1.00	0.0015	0.1685	0.1700
1.50	0.0003	0.3228	0.3231

For the total probability of an error of more than 1.96σ, the bias has little effect provided that it is less than one-tenth of the standard deviation. At this point the total probability is 0.0511 instead of the 0.05 which we think it is. As the bias increases further, the disturbance becomes more serious. At $B = \sigma$, the total probability of error is 0.17, more than three times the presumed value.

The two tails are affected differently. With a positive bias, as in this example, the probability of an underestimate by more than 1.96σ shrinks rapidly from the presumed 0.025 to become negligible when $B = \sigma$. The probability of the corresponding overestimate mounts steadily. In most applications the total error is the primary interest, but occasionally we are particularly interested in errors in one direction.

As a working rule, the effect of bias on the accuracy of an estimate is negligible if the bias is less than one tenth of the standard deviation of the estimate. If we have a biased method of estimation for which $B/\sigma < 0.1$, where B is the absolute value of the bias, it can be claimed that the bias is not an appreciable disadvantage of the method. Even with $B/\sigma = 0.2$, the disturbance in the probability of error is modest.

In using these results, a distinction must be made between the two sources of bias mentioned at the beginning of this section. With biases of the type that arise in estimating ratios, an upper limit to the ratio B/σ can be found mathematically. If the sample is large enough, we can be confident that B/σ will not exceed 0.1. With biases caused by errors of measurement or nonresponse, on the other hand, it is usually impossible to find a guaranteed upper limit to B/σ that is small. This troublesome problem is discussed in Chapter 13.

1.8 THE MEAN SQUARE ERROR

In order to compare a biased estimate with an unbiased estimate, or two estimates that have different amounts of bias, a useful criterion is the mean square error (MSE) of the estimate, measured from the population value that is being estimated. Formally,

$$\text{MSE}(\hat{\mu}) = E(\hat{\mu} - \mu)^2 = E[(\hat{\mu} - m) + (m - \mu)]^2$$

$$= E(\hat{\mu} - m)^2 + 2(m - \mu)E(\hat{\mu} - m) + (m - \mu)^2$$

$$= (\text{variance of } \hat{\mu}) + (\text{bias})^2$$

the cross-product term vanishing since $E(\hat{\mu} - m) = 0$.

Use of the MSE as a criterion of the accuracy of an estimate amounts to regarding two estimates that have the same MSE as equivalent. This is not strictly correct because the frequency distributions of errors $(\hat{\mu} - \mu)$ of different sizes will not be the same for the two estimates if they have different amounts of bias. It has been shown, however, by Hansen, Hurwitz, and Madow (1953) that if B/σ is less than about $\frac{1}{2}$ the two frequency distributions are almost identical in regard to *absolute* errors $|\hat{\mu} - \mu|$ of different sizes. Table 1.2 illustrates this result.

Even at $B/\sigma = 0.6$, the changes in the probabilities as compared with those for $B/\sigma = 0$ are slight.

Because of the difficulty of ensuring that no unsuspected bias enters into estimates, we shall usually speak of the *precision* of an estimate rather than

TABLE 1.2

PROBABILITY OF AN ABSOLUTE ERROR $\geq 1\sqrt{MSE}$,
$1.96\sqrt{MSE}$ AND $2.576\sqrt{MSE}$

Probability

B/σ	$1\sqrt{MSE}$	$1.96\sqrt{MSE}$	$2.576\sqrt{MSE}$
0	0.317	0.0500	0.0100
0.2	0.317	0.0499	0.0100
0.4	0.319	0.0495	0.0095
0.6	0.324	0.0479	0.0083

its *accuracy*. Accuracy refers to the size of deviations from the true mean μ, whereas precision refers to the size of deviations from the mean m obtained by repeated application of the sampling procedure.

EXERCISES

1.1 Suppose that you were using sampling to estimate the total number of words in a book that contains illustrations.
(a) Is there any problem of definition of the population? (b) What are the pros and cons of (1) the page, (2) the line, as a sampling unit?

1.2 A sample is to be taken from a list of names that are on cards (one name to a card) numbered consecutively in a file. Each name is to have an equal chance of being drawn in the sample. What problems arise in the following common situations? (a) Some of the names do not belong to the target population, although this fact cannot be verified for any name until it has been drawn. (b) Some names appear on more than one card. All cards with the same name bear consecutive numbers and therefore appear together in the file. (c) Some names appear on more than one card, but cards bearing the same name may be scattered anywhere about the file.

1.3 The problem of finding a frame that enables the sample to be drawn inexpensively is often an obstacle. What kinds of frames might be convenient for the following surveys? Have the frames any serious weaknesses? (a) A survey of stores that sell luggage in a large city. (b) A survey of the kinds of articles left behind in subways or buses. (c) A survey of persons bitten by snakes during the last year.

1.4 A city directory, four years old, lists the addresses in order along each street, and gives the names of the persons living at each address. For a current interview survey of the people in the city, what are the deficiencies of this frame? Can they be remedied by the interviewers during the course of the field work? In using the directory, would you draw a list of addresses (dwelling-places) or a list of persons?

1.5 In estimating by sampling the actual value of the small items in the inventory of a large firm, the actual and the book value were recorded for each item in the sample. For the total sample, the ratio of actual to book value was 1.021, this estimate being approximately normally distributed with a standard error of 0.0082. If the book value of the inventory is $80,000, compute 95% confidence limits for the actual value.

⁎ 1.6 Frequently data must be treated as a sample, although at first sight they appear to be a complete enumeration. A proprietor of a parking lot finds that business is poor on Sunday mornings. After 26 Sundays in operation, his average receipts per Sunday morning are exactly $10. The standard error of this figure, computed from week-to-week variations, is $1.2. The attendant costs $7 each Sunday. The proprietor is willing to keep the lot open at this time if his expected future profit is $5 per Sunday morning. What is the confidence probability that the long-term profit rate will be at least $5? What assumption must be made in order to answer this question?

⁎ 1.7 In Table 1.2, what happens to the probability of exceeding $1\sqrt{\text{MSE}}$, $1.96\sqrt{\text{MSE}}$ and $2.576\sqrt{\text{MSE}}$ when B/σ tends to infinity, i.e., when the MSE is due entirely to bias? Do your results agree with the directions of the changes noted in Table 1.2 as B/σ moves from 0 to 0.6?

1.8 When it is necessary to compare two estimates that have different frequency distributions of errors ($\hat{\mu} - \mu$), it is occasionally possible, in specialized problems, to compute the cost or loss that will result from an error ($\hat{\mu} - \mu$) of any given size. The estimate that gives the smaller expected loss is preferred, other things being equal. Show that if the loss is a quadratic function $\lambda(\hat{\mu} - \mu)^2$ of the error, we should choose the estimate with the smaller mean square error.

REFERENCES

Deming, W. E. (1960). *Sample design in business research*. John Wiley and Sons, New York.

Hansen, M. H., Hurwitz, W. N., and Madow, W. G. (1953). *Sample survey methods and theory*. John Wiley and Sons, New York, Vol. I, p. 58.

Hyman, H. H. (1954). *Interviewing in social research*. University of Chicago Press.

Jessen, R. J. (1955). Determining the fruit count on a tree by randomized branch sampling. *Biometrics*, **11**, 99–109.

Kiser, C. V., and Whelpton, P. K. (1953). Résumé of the Indianapolis study of social and psychological factors affecting fertility. *Population Studies*, **7**, 95–110.

Payne, S. L. (1951). *The art of asking questions*. Princeton University Press.

Slonim, M. J. (1960). *Sampling in a nutshell*. Simon & Schuster, New York.

Trueblood, R. M., and Cyert, R. M. (1957). *Sampling techniques in accounting*. Prentice-Hall, Englewood Cliffs, N. J.

U. N. Statistical Office (1960). *Sample surveys of current interest*. Eighth Report.

CHAPTER 2

Simple Random Sampling

2.1 SIMPLE RANDOM SAMPLING

Sample surveys deal with samples drawn from populations which contain a finite number N of units. If these units can all be distinguished from one another, the number of distinct samples of size n that can be drawn from the N units is given by the combinatorial formula

$$\binom{N}{n} = {}_NC_n = \frac{N!}{n!\,(N-n)!} \tag{2.1}$$

For example, if the population contains five units denoted by A, B, C, D, and E, there are 10 different samples of size 3, as follows:

ABC	ABD	ABE	ACD	ACE
ADE	BCD	BCE	BDE	CDE

Note that the same letter is not allowed to occur twice in the sample. No attention is paid to the order in which the letters occur in the sample, the six samples ABC, ACB, BAC, BCA, CAB, and CBA being considered identical.

Simple random sampling is a method of selecting n units out of the N such that every one of the ${}_NC_n$ samples has an equal chance of being chosen. This type of sampling is sometimes called *random sampling*. Since the word *random* is used in the literature in many different senses, an extra qualifying adjective is advisable. Some writers prefer the phrase *unrestricted random sampling*.

In practice a simple random sample is drawn unit by unit. The units in the population are numbered from 1 to N. A series of random numbers between 1 and N is then drawn, either by means of a table of random numbers or by placing the numbers 1 to N in a bowl and mixing thoroughly. If the bowl is used, n numbers are drawn out in succession. The units which bear these numbers constitute the sample. At any stage in the draw, this

18

process gives an equal chance of selection to all numbers not previously drawn. It is easy to verify that all $_NC_n$ possible samples have an equal chance.

When a number has been drawn from the bowl, it is not replaced, since this might allow the same unit to enter the sample more than once. For this reason the sampling is described as *without replacement*. Similarly, if a table of random numbers is employed, a number that has been drawn previously is ignored. Sampling with replacement is entirely feasible but except in special circumstances is seldom used, since there seems little point in having the same unit twice in the sample.

Other methods of sampling are often preferable to simple random sampling on the grounds of convenience or of increased precision. Simple random sampling serves best to introduce sampling theory.

2.2 DEFINITIONS AND NOTATION

In a sample survey we decide on certain properties which we attempt to measure and record for every unit that comes into the sample. These properties of the units are referred to as *characteristics* or more simply as *items*.

The values obtained for any specific item in the N units that comprise the population are denoted by $y_1, y_2, \cdots, y_N$. The corresponding values for the units in the sample are denoted by $y_1, y_2, \cdots, y_n$, or, if we wish to refer to a typical sample member, by y_i ($i = 1, 2, \cdots, n$). Note that the sample will not consist of the *first* n units in the population, except in the instance, usually rare, in which these units happen to be drawn. If this point is kept in mind, my experience has been that no confusion need result.

Capital letters refer to characteristics of the *population* and *lower case* letters to those of the *sample*. For totals and means we have the following definitions:

Population	Sample
Total: $Y = \sum\limits^{N} y_i = y_1 + y_2 + \cdots + y_N$	$\sum\limits^{n} y_i = y_1 + y_2 + \cdots + y_n$
Mean: $\overline{Y} = \dfrac{y_1 + y_2 + \cdots + y_N}{N} = \dfrac{\sum\limits^{N} y_i}{N}$	$\bar{y} = \dfrac{y_1 + y_2 + \cdots + y_n}{n} = \dfrac{\sum\limits^{n} y_i}{n}$

Although sampling is undertaken for many purposes, interest centers most frequently on four characteristics of the population.

1. Mean $= \overline{Y}$ (e.g., the average number of children per school).
2. Total $= Y$ (e.g., the total number of acres of wheat in a region).
3. Ratio of two totals or means $R = Y/X = \overline{Y}/\overline{X}$ (e.g., ratio of liquid assets to total assets in a group of families).

4. Proportion of units which fall into some defined class (e.g., proportion of people with false teeth).

Estimation of the first three quantities is discussed in this chapter.

The symbol $\frown$ denotes an estimate of a population characteristic made from a sample. In this chapter only the simplest estimates are considered:

Estimate

Population mean $\bar{Y}$	$\hat{\bar{Y}} = \bar{y}$ = sample mean
Population total Y	$\hat{Y} = N\bar{y} = N\sum_{}^{n} y_i/n$
Population ratio R	$\hat{R} = \bar{y}/\bar{x} = \sum_{}^{n} y_i \Big/ \sum_{}^{n} x_i$

In $\hat{Y}$ the factor N/n by which the sample total is multiplied is sometimes called the *expansion* or *raising* or *inflation* factor. Its inverse n/N, the ratio of the size of the sample to that of the population, is called the *sampling fraction* and is denoted by the letter f.

2.3 PROPERTIES OF THE ESTIMATES

The precision of any estimate made from a sample depends both on the method by which the estimate is calculated from the sample data and on the plan of sampling. To save space we sometimes write of "the precision of the sample mean" or "the precision of simple random sampling," without specifically mentioning the other fundamental factor. This has been done, we hope, only in instances in which it is clear from the context what the missing factor is. When studying any formula that is presented, the reader should make sure that he knows the specific method of sampling and method of estimation for which the formula has been established.

In this book a method of estimation is called *consistent* if the estimate becomes exactly equal to the population value when $n = N$, that is, when the sample consists of the whole population. For simple random sampling it is obvious that $\bar{y}$ and $N\bar{y}$ are consistent estimates of the population mean and total, respectively. Consistency is a desirable property of estimates. On the other hand, an inconsistent estimate is not necessarily useless, since it may give satisfactory precision when n is small compared to N. Its utility is likely to be confined to this situation. For another definition of consistency in a finite population, see Hansen, Hurwitz, and Madow, (1953).

As we have seen, a method of estimation is *unbiased* if the average value of the estimate, taken over all possible samples of given size n, is exactly equal to the true population value. If the method is to be unbiased without qualification, this result must hold for any population of finite values y_i and for any n. To investigate whether $\bar{y}$ is unbiased with simple random sampling, we calculate the value of $\bar{y}$ for all $_NC_n$ samples and find the average of the estimates. The symbol E denotes this average over all possible samples.

Theorem 2.1. The sample mean $\bar{y}$ is an unbiased estimate of $\bar{Y}$.
Proof. By its definition

$$E\bar{y} = \frac{\sum \bar{y}}{_NC_n} = \frac{\sum (y_1 + y_2 + \cdots + y_n)}{n[N!/n!\,(N-n)!]} \tag{2.2}$$

where the sum extends over all $_NC_n$ samples. To evaluate this sum, we find out in how many samples any specific value y_i appears. Since there are $(N-1)$ other units available for the rest of the sample and $(n-1)$ other places to fill in the sample, the number of samples containing y_i is

$$_{N-1}C_{n-1} = \frac{(N-1)!}{(n-1)!\,(N-n)!} \tag{2.3}$$

Hence

$$\sum (y_1 + y_2 + \cdots + y_n) = \frac{(N-1)!}{(n-1)!\,(N-n)!}(y_1 + y_2 + \cdots + y_N)$$

From (2.2) this gives

$$E\bar{y} = \frac{(N-1)!}{(n-1)!\,(N-n)!}\,\frac{n!\,(N-n)!}{nN!}(y_1 + y_2 + \cdots + y_N)$$

$$= \frac{(y_1 + y_2 + \cdots + y_N)}{N} = \bar{Y} \tag{2.4}$$

Corollary. $\hat{Y} = N\bar{y}$ is an unbiased estimate of the population total Y.

A less cumbersome proof of theorem 2.1 is obtained as follows. Since every unit appears in the same number of samples, it is clear that

$$E(y_1 + y_2 + \cdots + y_n) \text{ must be some multiple of } y_1 + y_2 + \cdots + y_N \tag{2.5}$$

The multiplier must be n/N, since the expression on the left has n terms and that on the right has N terms. This leads to the result.

2.4 VARIANCES OF THE ESTIMATES

The variance of the y_i in a finite population is usually defined as

$$\sigma^2 = \frac{\sum\limits_{1}^{N} (y_i - \bar{Y})^2}{N} \tag{2.6}$$

As a matter of notation, results are presented in terms of a slightly different expression, in which the divisor $(N - 1)$ is used instead of N. We take

$$S^2 = \frac{\sum_1^N (y_i - \bar{Y})^2}{N - 1} \tag{2.7}$$

This convention has been used by those who approach sampling theory by means of the analysis of variance. Its advantage is that most results take a slightly simpler form. Provided that the same notation is maintained consistently, all results are equivalent in either notation.

We now consider the variance of $\bar{y}$. By this we mean $E(\bar{y} - \bar{Y})^2$ taken over all $_NC_n$ samples.

Theorem 2.2. The variance of the mean $\bar{y}$ from a simple random sample is

$$V(\bar{y}) = E(\bar{y} - \bar{Y})^2 = \frac{S^2}{n} \frac{(N - n)}{N} = \frac{S^2}{n}(1 - f) \tag{2.8}$$

where $f = n/N$ is the sampling fraction.
Proof.

$$n(\bar{y} - \bar{Y}) = (y_1 - \bar{Y}) + (y_2 - \bar{Y}) + \cdots + (y_n - \bar{Y}) \tag{2.9}$$

By the argument of symmetry used in relation (2.5), it follows that

$$E[(y_1 - \bar{Y})^2 + \cdots + (y_n - \bar{Y})^2] = \frac{n}{N}[(y_1 - \bar{Y})^2 + \cdots + (y_N - \bar{Y})^2] \tag{2.10}$$

and also that

$$E[(y_1 - \bar{Y})(y_2 - \bar{Y}) + (y_1 - \bar{Y})(y_3 - \bar{Y}) + \cdots + (y_{n-1} - \bar{Y})(y_n - \bar{Y})]$$
$$= \frac{n(n - 1)}{N(N - 1)}[(y_1 - \bar{Y})(y_2 - \bar{Y}) + (y_1 - \bar{Y})(y_3 - \bar{Y})$$
$$+ \cdots + (y_{N-1} - \bar{Y})(y_N - \bar{Y})] \tag{2.11}$$

In (2.11) the sums of products extend over all pairs of units in the sample and population, respectively. The sum on the left contains $n(n - 1)/2$ terms and that on the right $N(N - 1)/2$ terms.

Now square (2.9) and average over all simple random samples. Using (2.10) and (2.11), we obtain

$$n^2 E(\bar{y} - \bar{Y})^2 = \frac{n}{N}\left\{(y_1 - \bar{Y})^2 + \cdots + (y_N - \bar{Y})^2\right.$$
$$\left. + \frac{2(n - 1)}{N - 1}[(y_1 - \bar{Y})(y_2 - \bar{Y}) + \cdots + (y_{N-1} - \bar{Y})(y_N - \bar{Y})]\right\}$$

Completing the square on the cross-product term, we have

$$n^2 E(\bar{y} - \bar{Y})^2 = \frac{n}{N} \left\{ \left(1 - \frac{n-1}{N-1} \right) [(y_1 - \bar{Y})^2 + \cdots + (y_N - \bar{Y})^2] \right.$$

$$\left. + \frac{n-1}{N-1} [(y_1 - \bar{Y}) + \cdots + (y_N - \bar{Y})]^2 \right\}$$

The second term inside the curly bracket vanishes, since the sum of the y_i equals $N\bar{Y}$. Division by n^2 gives

$$V(\bar{y}) = E(\bar{y} - \bar{Y})^2 = \frac{N-n}{nN(N-1)} \sum_{i=1}^{N} (y_i - \bar{Y})^2 = \frac{S^2}{n} \frac{(N-n)}{N}$$

Corollary 1. The standard error of $\bar{y}$ is

$$\sigma_{\bar{y}} = \frac{S}{\sqrt{n}} \sqrt{(N-n)/N} = \frac{S}{\sqrt{n}} \sqrt{1-f} \qquad (2.12)$$

Corollary 2. The variance of $\hat{Y} = N\bar{y}$, as an estimate of the population total Y, is

$$V(\hat{Y}) = E(\hat{Y} - Y)^2 = \frac{N^2 S^2}{n} \frac{(N-n)}{N} = \frac{N^2 S^2}{n} (1-f) \qquad (2.13)$$

Corollary 3. The standard error of $\hat{Y}$ is

$$\sigma_{\hat{Y}} = \frac{NS}{\sqrt{n}} \sqrt{(N-n)/N} = \frac{NS}{\sqrt{n}} \sqrt{1-f} \qquad (2.14)$$

2.5 THE FINITE POPULATION CORRECTION

For a random sample of size n from an infinite population, it is well known that the variance of the mean is σ^2/n. The only change in this result when the population is finite is the introduction of the factor $(N-n)/N$. The factors $(N-n)/N$ for the variance and $\sqrt{(N-n)/N}$ for the standard error are called the *finite population corrections* (fpc). They are given with a divisor $(N-1)$ in place of N by writers who present results in terms of σ. Provided that the sampling fraction n/N remains low, these factors are close to unity, and the size of the population as such has no direct effect on the standard error of the sample mean. For instance, if S is the same in the two populations, a sample of 500 from a population of 200,000 gives almost as precise an estimate of the population mean as a sample of 500 from a population of 10,000. Persons unfamiliar with sampling often find this result very difficult to believe, and indeed it is remarkable. To them it seems intuitively obvious that, if information has been obtained about only a very small fraction of the population, the sample mean just cannot be accurate. It is instructive for the reader to consider why this point of view is erroneous.

In practice the fpc can be ignored whenever the sampling fraction does not exceed 5% and for many purposes even if it is as high as 10%. The effect of ignoring the correction is to overestimate the standard error of the estimate $\bar{y}$.

The following theorem, which is an extension of theorem 2.2, is not required for the discussion in this chapter, but it is proved here for later reference.

Theorem 2.3. If y_i, x_i are a pair of variates defined on every unit in the population and $\bar{y}$, $\bar{x}$ are the corresponding means from a simple random sample of size n, then their *covariance*

$$E(\bar{y} - \bar{Y})(\bar{x} - \bar{X}) = \frac{N - n}{nN} \frac{1}{N - 1} \sum_{i=1}^{N} (y_i - \bar{Y})(x_i - \bar{X}) \quad (2.15)$$

This theorem reduces to theorem 2.2 if the variates y_i, x_i are equal on every unit.

Proof. Apply theorem 2.2 to the variate $u_i = y_i + x_i$. The population mean of u_i is $\bar{U} = \bar{Y} + \bar{X}$, and theorem 2.2 gives

$$E(\bar{u} - \bar{U})^2 = \frac{N - n}{nN} \frac{1}{N - 1} \sum_{i=1}^{N} (u_i - \bar{U})^2$$

that is,

$$E[(\bar{y} - \bar{Y}) + (\bar{x} - \bar{X})]^2$$
$$= \frac{N - n}{nN} \frac{1}{N - 1} \sum_{i=1}^{N} [(y_i - \bar{Y}) + (x_i - \bar{X})]^2 \quad (2.16)$$

Expand the quadratic terms on both sides. By theorem 2.2,

$$E(\bar{y} - \bar{Y})^2 = \frac{N - n}{nN} \frac{1}{N - 1} \sum_{i=1}^{N} (y_i - \bar{Y})^2$$

with a similar relation for $E(\bar{x} - \bar{X})^2$. Hence these two terms cancel on the left and right sides of (2.16). The result of the theorem (equation 2.15) follows from the cross-product terms.

2.6 ESTIMATION OF THE STANDARD ERROR FROM A SAMPLE

The formulas for the standard errors of the estimated population mean and total are used primarily for three purposes: (1) to compare the precision obtained by simple random sampling with that given by other methods of sampling, (2) to estimate the size of the sample needed in a survey that is being planned, (3) to estimate the precision actually attained in a survey that has been completed. The formulas involve S^2, the population variance. In practice this will not be known, but it can be estimated from the sample data. The relevant result is stated in theorem 2.4.

Theorem 2.4. For a simple random sample

$$s^2 = \frac{\sum_1^n (y_i - \bar{y})^2}{n - 1}$$

is an unbiased estimate of

$$S^2 = \frac{\sum_1^N (y_i - \bar{Y})^2}{N - 1}$$

Proof. We may write

$$s^2 = \frac{1}{n - 1} \sum_{i=1}^n [(y_i - \bar{Y}) - (\bar{y} - \bar{Y})]^2$$

$$= \frac{1}{n - 1} \left[\sum_{i=1}^n (y_i - \bar{Y})^2 - n(\bar{y} - \bar{Y})^2 \right]$$

Now average over all simple random samples of size n. By the argument of symmetry used in theorem 2.2,

$$E\left[\sum_{i=1}^n (y_i - \bar{Y})^2 \right] = \frac{n}{N} \sum_{i=1}^N (y_i - \bar{Y})^2 = \frac{n(N - 1)}{N} S^2$$

by the definition of S^2. Further, by theorem 2.2,

$$E[n(\bar{y} - \bar{Y})^2] = \frac{N - n}{N} S^2$$

Hence

$$E(s^2) = \frac{S^2}{(n - 1)N} [n(N - 1) - (N - n)] = S^2 \qquad (2.17)$$

Corollary. Unbiased estimates of the variances of $\bar{y}$ and $\hat{Y} = N\bar{y}$ are

$$v(\bar{y}) = s_{\bar{y}}^2 = \frac{s^2}{n} \left(\frac{N - n}{N} \right) = \frac{s^2}{n} (1 - f) \qquad (2.18)$$

$$v(\hat{Y}) = s_{\hat{Y}}^2 = \frac{N^2 s^2}{n} \left(\frac{N - n}{N} \right) = \frac{N^2 s^2}{n} (1 - f) \qquad (2.19)$$

For the standard errors we take

$$s_{\bar{y}} = \frac{s}{\sqrt{n}} \sqrt{1 - f}, \qquad s_{\hat{Y}} = \frac{Ns}{\sqrt{n}} \sqrt{1 - f} \qquad (2.20)$$

These estimates are slightly biased: for most applications the bias is unimportant.

The reader should note the symbols employed for true and estimated variances of the estimates. Thus for $\bar{y}$ we write

true variance: $\qquad\qquad V(\bar{y}) = \sigma_{\bar{y}}^2$

estimated variance: $\qquad v(\bar{y}) = s_{\bar{y}}^2$

2.7 CONFIDENCE LIMITS

It is usually assumed that the estimates $\bar{y}$ and $\hat{Y}$ are normally distributed about the corresponding population values. The reasons for this assumption and its limitations are considered in section 2.13. If the assumption holds, lower and upper confidence limits for the population mean and total are as follows:

Mean:

$$\hat{\bar{Y}}_L = \bar{y} - \frac{ts}{\sqrt{n}}\sqrt{1-f}, \qquad \hat{\bar{Y}}_U = \bar{y} + \frac{ts}{\sqrt{n}}\sqrt{1-f} \qquad (2.21)$$

Total:

$$\hat{Y}_L = N\bar{y} - \frac{tNs}{\sqrt{n}}\sqrt{1-f}, \qquad \hat{Y}_U = N\bar{y} + \frac{tNs}{\sqrt{n}}\sqrt{1-f} \qquad (2.22)$$

The symbol t is the value of the normal deviate corresponding to the desired confidence probability. The most common values are

Confidence probability (%)	50	80	90	95	99
	0.67	1.28	1.64	1.96	2.58

If the sample size is less than 60, the percentage points may be taken from Student's t table with $(n-1)$ degrees of freedom, these being the degrees of freedom in the estimated variance s^2. The t distribution holds exactly only if the observations y_i are themselves normally distributed and N is infinite. Moderate departures from normality do not affect it greatly. For small samples with very skew distributions, special methods are needed.

Example. Signatures to a petition were collected on 676 sheets. Each sheet had enough space for 42 signatures, but on many sheets a smaller number of signatures had been collected. The numbers of signatures per sheet were counted on a random sample of 50 sheets (about a 7% sample), with the results shown in Table 2.1.

Estimate the total number of signatures to the petition and the 80 per cent confidence limits.

The sampling unit is a sheet, and the observations y_i are the numbers of signatures per sheet. Since about half the sheets had the maximum number of signatures, 42, the data are presented as a frequency distribution. Note that the original distribution appears to be far from normal, the greatest frequency being at the upper end. Nevertheless, there is reason to believe from experience that the means of samples of 50 are approximately normally distributed.

We find

$$n = \sum f_i = 50, \qquad y = \sum f_i y_i = 1471, \qquad \sum f_i y_i^2 = 54{,}497$$

Hence the estimated total number of signatures is

$$\hat{Y} = N\bar{y} = \frac{(676)(1471)}{50} = 19{,}888$$

For the sample variance s^2 we have

$$s^2 = \frac{1}{n-1}[\sum f_i(y_i - \bar{y})^2] = \frac{1}{n-1}\left[\sum f_i y_i{}^2 - \frac{(\sum f_i y_i)^2}{\sum f_i}\right]$$

$$= \frac{1}{49}\left[54{,}497 - \frac{(1471)^2}{50}\right] = 229.0$$

From (2.22) the 80% confidence limits are

$$19{,}888 \pm \frac{tNs}{\sqrt{n}}\sqrt{1-f} = 19{,}888 \pm \frac{(1.28)(676)(15.13)\sqrt{1-0.0740}}{\sqrt{50}}$$

This gives 18,107 and 21,669 for the 80% limits. A complete count showed 21,045 signatures.

TABLE 2.1

RESULTS FOR A SAMPLE OF 50 PETITION SHEETS

Number of Signatures y_i	Frequency f_i
42	23
41	4
36	1
32	1
29	1
27	2
23	1
19	1
16	2
15	2
14	1
11	1
10	1
9	1
7	1
6	3
5	2
4	1
3	1
	50

2.8 AN ALTERNATIVE METHOD OF PROOF

Cornfield (1944) suggested a method of proving the principal results for simple random sampling without replacement that enables us to use standard results from infinite population theory. Let a_i be a random variate which takes the value 1 if the ith unit is in the sample and the value 0 otherwise. The sample mean $\bar{y}$ may be written

$$\bar{y} = \frac{1}{n} \sum_{i=1}^{N} a_i y_i \qquad (2.23)$$

where the sum extends over all N units in the population. In this expression the a_i are random variables and the y_i are a set of fixed numbers.

Clearly

$$\Pr(a_i = 1) = \frac{n}{N}, \qquad \Pr(a_i = 0) = 1 - \frac{n}{N}$$

Thus a_i is distributed as a binomial variate in a single trial, with $P = n/N$. Hence

$$E(a_i) = P = \frac{n}{N} \qquad V(a_i) = PQ = \frac{n}{N}\left(1 - \frac{n}{N}\right) \qquad (2.24)$$

To find $V(\bar{y})$ we need also the covariance of a_i and a_j. The product $a_i a_j$ is 1 if the ith and jth unit are both in the sample and is zero otherwise. The probability that two specific units are both in the sample is easily found to be $n(n-1)/N(N-1)$. Hence

$$\mathrm{Cov}\,(a_i a_j) = E(a_i a_j) - E(a_i)E(a_j)$$

$$= \frac{n(n-1)}{N(N-1)} - \left(\frac{n}{N}\right)^2 = -\frac{n}{N(N-1)}\left(1 - \frac{n}{N}\right) \qquad (2.25)$$

Applying this approach to find $V(\bar{y})$, we have from (2.23),

$$V(\bar{y}) = \frac{1}{n^2}\left[\sum_{i=1}^{N} y_i^2 V(a_i) + 2\sum_{i<j}^{N} y_i y_j \,\mathrm{Cov}\,(a_i a_j)\right]$$

$$= \frac{1-f}{nN}\left(\sum y_i^2 - \frac{2}{N-1}\sum y_i y_j\right)$$

using (2.24) and (2.25). Completing the square on the cross-product term gives

$$V(\bar{y}) = \frac{1-f}{nN}\left(\frac{N}{N-1}\sum y_i^2 - \frac{1}{N-1}Y^2\right)$$

$$= \frac{1-f}{n(N-1)}\sum(y_i - \bar{Y})^2 = \frac{(1-f)S^2}{n}$$

The method gives easy proofs of theorems 2.3 and 2.4. It may be used to find higher moments of the distribution of $\bar{y}$, although for this purpose a method given by Tukey (1950), with further development by Wishart (1952), is more powerful.

A similar approach applies when sampling is with replacement. In this event the ith unit may appear $0, 1, 2, \cdots, n$ times in the sample. Let t_i be the number of times that the ith unit appears in the sample. Then

$$\bar{y} = \frac{1}{n} \sum_{i=1}^{N} t_i y_i \tag{2.26}$$

Since the probability that the ith unit is drawn is $1/N$ at each draw, the variate t_i is distributed as a binomial number of successes out of n trials with $p = 1/N$. Hence

$$E(t_i) = \frac{n}{N}, \qquad V(t_i) = n\left(\frac{1}{N}\right)\left(1 - \frac{1}{N}\right) \tag{2.27}$$

Jointly, the variates t_i follow a multinomial distribution. For this,

$$\text{Cov}\,(t_i t_j) = -\frac{n}{N^2} \tag{2.28}$$

Using (2.26), (2.27), and (2.28), we have, for sampling with replacement,

$$V(\bar{y}) = \frac{1}{n^2}\left[\sum_{i=1}^{N} y_i^2 \frac{n(N-1)}{N^2} - 2\sum_{i<j}^{N} y_i y_j \frac{n}{N^2}\right]$$

$$= \frac{1}{nN}\sum_{i=1}^{N}(y_i - \bar{Y})^2 = \frac{\sigma^2}{n} = \frac{N-1}{N}\frac{S^2}{n}$$

2.9 ESTIMATION OF A RATIO

Frequently the quantity that is to be estimated from a simple random sample is the ratio of two variables both of which vary from unit to unit. In a household survey examples are the average number of suits of clothes per adult male, the average expenditure on cosmetics per adult female, and the average number of hours per week spent watching television per child aged 10 to 15. In order to estimate the first of these items, we would record for the ith household ($i = 1, 2, \cdots, n$) the number of adult males x_i who live there and the total number of suits y_i that they possess. The population parameter to be estimated is the ratio

$$R = \frac{\text{total number of suits}}{\text{total number of adult males}} = \frac{\displaystyle\sum_{1}^{N} y_i}{\displaystyle\sum_{1}^{N} x_i}$$

The corresponding sample estimate is

$$\hat{R} = \frac{\displaystyle\sum_{1}^{n} y_i}{\displaystyle\sum_{1}^{n} x_i} = \frac{\bar{y}}{\bar{x}}$$

Examples of this kind occur frequently when the sampling unit (the household) comprises a group or cluster of elements (adult males) and our interest is in the population mean *per element*. Ratios also appear in many other applications, for example, the ratio of loans for building purposes to total loans in a bank or the ratio of acres of wheat to total acres on a farm.

The sampling distribution of $\hat{R}$ is more complicated than that of $\bar{y}$ because both the numerator $\bar{y}$ and the denominator $\bar{x}$ vary from sample to sample. In small samples the distribution of $\hat{R}$ is skew and $\hat{R}$ is usually a slightly biased estimate of R. In large samples the distribution of $\hat{R}$ tends to normality and the bias becomes negligible. The following approximate result will serve for most purposes: the distribution of $\hat{R}$ is studied in more detail in Chapter 6.

Theorem 2.5. If variates y_i, x_i are measured on each unit of a simple random sample of size n, assumed large, the variance of $\hat{R} = \bar{y}/\bar{x}$ is approximately

$$V(\hat{R}) \doteq \frac{1-f}{n\bar{X}^2} \frac{\sum\limits_{i=1}^{N}(y_i - Rx_i)^2}{N-1} \tag{2.29}$$

where $R = \bar{Y}/\bar{X}$ is the ratio of the population means and $f = n/N$.
Proof.

$$\hat{R} - R = \frac{\bar{y}}{\bar{x}} - R = \frac{\bar{y} - R\bar{x}}{\bar{x}} \tag{2.30}$$

If n is large, $\bar{x}$ should not differ greatly from $\bar{X}$. The approximation consists in replacing $\bar{x}$ by $\bar{X}$ in the denominator of (2.30). This gives

$$\hat{R} - R \doteq \frac{\bar{y} - R\bar{x}}{\bar{X}} \tag{2.31}$$

Now average over all simple random samples of size n.

$$E(\hat{R} - R) \doteq \frac{E(\bar{y} - R\bar{x})}{\bar{X}} = \frac{\bar{Y} - R\bar{X}}{\bar{X}} = 0 \tag{2.32}$$

since $R = \bar{Y}/\bar{X}$. This shows that to the order of approximation used here $\hat{R}$ is an unbiased estimate of R.

From (2.31) we also obtain the result

$$V(\hat{R}) = E(\hat{R} - R)^2 \doteq \frac{1}{\bar{X}^2} E(\bar{y} - R\bar{x})^2$$

The quantity $\bar{y} - R\bar{x}$ is the sample mean of the variate $d_i = y_i - Rx_i$, whose population mean $\bar{D} = \bar{Y} - R\bar{X} = 0$. Hence we can find $V(\hat{R})$ by applying theorem 2.2 for the variance of the mean of a simple random sample to the variate d_i and dividing by $\bar{X}^2$. This gives

$$V(\hat{R}) \doteq \frac{1}{\bar{X}^2} E(\bar{y} - R\bar{x})^2 = \frac{1}{\bar{X}^2} \frac{S_d^{\,2}}{n} (1 - f)$$

$$= \frac{1 - f}{n\bar{X}^2} \frac{\sum_{i=1}^{N}(d_i - \bar{D})^2}{(N - 1)} = \frac{1 - f}{n\bar{X}^2} \frac{\sum_{i=1}^{N}(y_i - Rx_i)^2}{N - 1}$$

This completes the proof.

The way in which theorem 2.5 was proved is worth noting. It was shown that the formula in theorem 2.2 for the variance of the sample mean $\bar{y}$ gives the formula for the approximate variance of the ratio $\bar{y}/\bar{x}$, if the variate y_i is replaced by the variate $(y_i - Rx_i)/\bar{X}$. The same result, or its natural extension, holds also in more complex sampling situations and is used frequently later in this book.

As a sample estimate of

$$\frac{\sum_{i=1}^{N}(y_i - Rx_i)^2}{N - 1}$$

it is customary to take

$$\frac{\sum_{i=1}^{n}(y_i - \hat{R}x_i)^2}{n - 1}$$

This estimate can be shown to have a bias of order $1/n$.

For the estimated standard error of $\hat{R}$, this gives

$$s(\hat{R}) = \frac{\sqrt{1 - f}}{\sqrt{n}\,\bar{X}} \sqrt{\frac{\sum(y_i - \hat{R}x_i)^2}{n - 1}} \qquad (2.33)$$

If $\bar{X}$ is not known, the sample estimate $\bar{x}$ is substituted in the denominator.

The quickest way to compute $s(\hat{R})$ on a desk machine is to express it as

$$s(\hat{R}) = \frac{\sqrt{1 - f}}{\sqrt{n}\,\bar{X}} \sqrt{\frac{\sum y_i^{\,2} - 2\hat{R}\sum y_i x_i + \hat{R}^2 \sum x_i^{\,2}}{n - 1}} \qquad (2.34)$$

Example. Table 2.2 shows the number of persons (x_1), the weekly family income (x_2), and the weekly expenditure on food (y) in a simple random sample of 33 low-income families. Since the sample is small, the data are intended only to illustrate the calculations.

Estimate from the sample (*a*) the mean weekly expenditure on food per family, (*b*) the mean weekly expenditure on food per person, (*c*) the percentage of the income that is spent on food. Compute the standard errors of these estimates.

Weekly Expenditure on Food per Family. This is the ordinary sample mean

$$\bar{y} = \frac{907.2}{33} = \$27.49$$

By theorem 2.2 (ignoring the fpc) its standard error is

$$s_{\bar{y}} = \frac{1}{\sqrt{n}}\sqrt{\frac{\sum(y_i - \bar{y})^2}{n-1}} = \frac{1}{\sqrt{n(n-1)}}\sqrt{\sum y_i^2 - \frac{(\sum y_i)^2}{n}}$$

$$= \frac{1}{\sqrt{(33)(32)}}\sqrt{28,224 - (907.2)^2/33} = \$1.76$$

(The uncorrected sum of squares 28,224 is given underneath Table 2.2).

TABLE 2.2

SIZE, WEEKLY INCOME, AND FOOD COST OF 33 FAMILIES

Family Number	Size x_1	Income x_2	Food Cost y	Family Number	Size x_1	Income x_2	Food Cost y
1	2	62	14.3	18	4	83	36.0
2	3	62	20.8	19	2	85	20.6
3	3	87	22.7	20	4	73	27.7
4	5	65	30.5	21	2	66	25.9
5	4	58	41.2	22	5	58	23.3
6	7	92	28.2	23	3	77	39.8
7	2	88	24.2	24	4	69	16.8
8	4	79	30.0	25	7	65	37.8
9	2	83	24.2	26	3	77	34.8
10	5	62	44.4	27	3	69	28.7
11	3	63	13.4	28	6	95	63.0
12	6	62	19.8	29	2	77	19.5
13	4	60	29.4	30	2	69	21.6
14	4	75	27.1	31	6	69	18.2
15	2	90	22.2	32	4	67	20.1
16	5	75	37.7	33	2	63	20.7
17	3	69	22.6				
				Total	123	2394	907.2

$\sum x_1^2 = 533,$ $\sum x_2^2 = 177,254,$ $\sum y^2 = 28,224$

$\sum x_1 y = 3595.5,$ $\sum x_2 y = 66,678$

Weekly Expenditure on Food per Person. Since the size of family varies, the estimate is a ratio of two variables,

$$\hat{R}_1 = \frac{\sum y}{\sum x_1} = \frac{907.2}{123} = \$7.38 \text{ per person}$$

The sums of squares and products needed to compute $S(\hat{R})$ by (2.34) are found under Table 2.2. We need in addition

$$2\hat{R}_1 = 14.7512, \qquad \hat{R}_1^2 = 54.3996, \qquad \bar{x}_1 = 3.7273$$

Extra decimals are carried in $\hat{R}_1$, $2\hat{R}_1$, $\hat{R}_1^2$ to preserve accuracy.
Hence from (2.34)

$$s(\hat{R}_1) = \frac{1}{\sqrt{33}(3.7273)}\sqrt{\frac{(28,224) - (14.7512)(3595.5) + (54.3996)(533)}{32}}$$

$$= \$0.534.$$

Percentage of Income Spent on Food. This again is a ratio of two variables

$$\hat{R}_2 = 100\frac{\sum y}{\sum x_2} = \frac{(100)(907.2)}{2394} = 37.9\%$$

By (2.34) the reader may verify that the standard error is 2.38%.

2.10 ESTIMATES OF MEANS OVER SUBPOPULATIONS

In many surveys, estimates are made for each of a number of classes into which the population is subdivided. In a household survey separate estimates might be wanted for families with 0, 1, 2, . . . children, for owners and renters, or for families in different occupation groups. The term *domains of study* has been given to these subpopulations by the U.N. Subcommission on Sampling (1950).

In the simplest situation each unit in the population falls into one of the domains. Let the jth domain contain N_j units, and let n_j be the number of units in a simple random sample of size n that happen to fall in this domain. If y_{jk} $(k = 1, 2, \cdots, n_j)$ are the measurements on these units, the population mean $\bar{Y}_j$ for the jth domain is estimated by

$$\bar{y}_j = \sum_{k=1}^{n_j} \frac{y_{jk}}{n_j} \tag{2.35}$$

At first sight $\bar{y}_j$ seems to be a ratio estimate as in section 2.9, for, although n is fixed, n_j will vary from one sample of size n to another. The complication of a ratio estimate can be avoided by considering the distribution of $\bar{y}_j$ over samples in which both n and n_j are fixed.

In the totality of samples with given n and n_j the probability that any specific set of n_j units from the N_j units in domain j is drawn is

$$\frac{{}_{N-N_j}C_{n-n_j}}{{}_{N-N_j}C_{n-n_j} \cdot {}_{N_j}C_{n_j}} = \frac{1}{{}_{N_j}C_{n_j}}$$

Since each specific set of n_j units from domain j can appear with all selections of $(n - n_j)$ units from the $(N - N_j)$ that are not in domain j, the numerator above is the number of samples containing a specified set of n_j, and the denominator is the total number of samples. It follows that theorems 2.1, 2.2, and 2.4 apply to the y_{jk} if we put n_j for n and N_j for N.

From theorem 2.1: $\bar{y}_j$ is an unbiased estimate of $\bar{Y}_j$ (2.36)

From theorem 2.2: the standard error of $\bar{y}_j$ is $\dfrac{S_j}{\sqrt{n_j}}\sqrt{1 - (n_j/N_j)}$ (2.37)

where

$$S_j{}^2 = \sum_{k=1}^{N_j} \frac{(y_{jk} - \bar{Y}_j)^2}{N_j - 1} \tag{2.38}$$

From theorem 2.4: An estimate of the standard error of $\bar{y}_j$ is

$$\frac{s_j}{\sqrt{n_j}}\sqrt{1 - (n_j/N_j)} \tag{2.39}$$

where

$$s_j{}^2 = \sum_{k=1}^{n_j} \frac{(y_{jk} - \bar{y}_j)^2}{n_j - 1} \tag{2.40}$$

If the value of N_j is not known, the quantity n/N may be used in place of n_j/N_j when computing the fpc. (With simple random sampling, n_j/N_j is an unbiased estimate of n/N.)

2.11 ESTIMATES OF TOTALS OVER SUBPOPULATIONS

In a firm's list of accounts receivable, in which some accounts have been paid and some not, we might wish to estimate by a sample the total dollar amount of unpaid bills. If N_j (the number of unpaid bills in the population) is known, there is no problem. The sample estimate is $N_j\bar{y}_j$ and its conditional standard error is N_j times expression (2.37).

Alternatively, if the total amount receivable in the list is known, a ratio estimate can be used. The sample gives an estimate of the ratio (total amount of unpaid bills)/(total amount of all bills). This is multiplied by the known total amount receivable in the list.

If neither N_j nor the total receivables is known, these estimates cannot be made. Instead, we multiply the sample total of the y's over units falling in the jth domain by the raising factor N/n. This gives the estimate

$$\hat{Y}_j = \frac{N}{n}\sum_{k=1}^{n_j} y_{jk} \tag{2.41}$$

We shall show that $\hat{Y}_j$ is unbiased and obtain its standard error over repeated samples of size n. The device of keeping n_j fixed as well as n does not help in this problem.

In presenting the proof we revert to the original notation, in which y_i is the measurement on the ith unit in the population. Define for every unit in the population a new variate $y_i{}'$, where

$$y_i{}' = \begin{cases} y_i & \text{if the unit is in the } j\text{th domain,} \\ 0 & \text{otherwise} \end{cases}$$

The population total of the $y_i{}'$ is

$$\sum_{i=1}^{N} y_i{}' = \sum_{j\text{th dom}} y_i = Y_j$$

In a simple random sample of size n, $y_i{}' = y_i$ for each of the n_j units that lie in the jth domain; $y_i{}' = 0$ for each of the remaining $n - n_j$ units. If $\bar{y}'$ is the ordinary sample mean of the $y_i{}'$, the quantity

$$N\bar{y}' = \frac{N}{n}\sum_{i=1}^{n} y_i{}' = \frac{N}{n}\sum_{k=1}^{n_j} y_{jk} = \hat{Y}_j$$

This result shows that the estimate $\hat{Y}_j$ as defined in equation (2.41) is N times the sample mean of the $y_i{}'$.

In repeated samples of size n we can clearly apply theorems 2.1, 2.2, and 2.4 to the variates $y_i{}'$. These show that $\hat{Y}_j$ is an unbiased estimate of Y_j with standard error

$$\sigma(\hat{Y}_j) = \frac{NS'}{\sqrt{n}}\sqrt{1 - (n/N)} \tag{2.42}$$

where S' is the population standard deviation of the $y_i{}'$. In order to compute S', we regard the population as consisting of the N_j values y_i that are in the jth domain and of $N - N_j$ zero values. Thus

$$S'^2 = \frac{1}{N-1}\left(\sum_{j\text{th dom}} y_i^2 - \frac{Y_j^2}{N}\right) \tag{2.43}$$

From theorem 2.4 a sample estimate of the standard error of $\hat{Y}_j$ is

$$s(\hat{Y}_j) = \frac{Ns'}{\sqrt{n}}\sqrt{1 - (n/N)} \tag{2.44}$$

In computing s', any unit not in the jth domain is given a zero value. Some students seem to have a psychological objection to doing this, but the method is sound.

The methods of this and the preceding section also apply to surveys in which the frame used contains units that do not belong to the population as it has been defined. An example illustrates this application.

Example. From a list of 2422 minor household expenditures a simple random sample of 180 items was drawn in order to estimate the total spent for operation of the household. Certain types of expenditure (on clothing and car upkeep) were not considered relevant. Of the 180 sample items, 152 were relevant. The sum and uncorrected sum of squares of the relevant amounts (in dollars) were as follows:

$$\sum y_i' = 343.5, \qquad \sum y_i'^2 = 1491.38$$

Estimate the total expenditure for household operation and give the standard error of the estimate.

$$\hat{Y}_j = \frac{N}{n} \sum_{i=1}^{n} y_i' = \frac{(2422)(343.5)}{180} = \$4622$$

From (2.44)

$$s(\hat{Y}_j) = \frac{Ns'}{\sqrt{n}} \sqrt{1 - (n/N)}$$

In computing s' we regard our sample of 180 items as having 28 zeros. Hence

$$s'^2 = \frac{1}{(179)}\left(\sum y_i'^2 - \frac{(\sum y_i')^2}{180}\right)$$

$$= \frac{1}{(179)}\left(1491.38 - \frac{(343.5)^2}{180}\right) = 4.670$$

Finally,

$$s_{\hat{Y}_j} = (2422)\sqrt{\frac{4.670}{180}\left(1 - \frac{180}{2422}\right)} = \$375$$

The estimate is not precise, its coefficient of variation 375/4622 being about 8%.

In this example expenditures on car upkeep and clothing were excluded as not relevant and therefore were scored as zeros in the sample. In some applications it is known in advance that certain units in the population contribute nothing to the total that is being estimated. For instance, in a survey of stores to estimate total sales of luggage, some stores do not handle luggage; certain area sampling units for farm studies contain no farms. Sometimes it is possible, by expenditure of effort, to identify and count the units that contribute nothing, so that in our notation $(N - N_j)$, hence N_j, is known.

Consequently it is worth examining by how much $V(\hat{Y}_j)$ is reduced when N_j is known. If N_j is not known, then from (2.42)

$$V(\hat{Y}_j) = \frac{N^2 S'^2}{n}\left(1 - \frac{n}{N}\right)$$

If $\bar{Y}_j$ and S_j are the mean and standard deviation in the domain of interest (i.e., among the nonzero units) the reader may verify that

$$(N - 1)S'^2 = (N_j - 1)S_j^2 + N_j \bar{Y}_j^2\left(1 - \frac{N_j}{N}\right)$$

Since terms in $1/N_j$ and $1/N$ are nearly always negligible,

$$S'^2 \doteq P_j S_j^2 + P_j Q_j \overline{Y}_j^2 \qquad (2.45)$$

where $P_j = N_j/N$ and $Q_j = 1 - P_j$. This gives

$$V(\hat{Y}_j) \doteq \frac{N^2}{n} (P_j S_j^2 + P_j Q_j \overline{Y}_j^2)\left(1 - \frac{n}{N}\right) \qquad (2.46)$$

If nonzero units are identified, we draw a sample of size n_j from them. The estimate of the domain total is $N_j \bar{y}_j$ with variance

$$V(N_j \bar{y}_j) = \frac{N_j^2}{n_j} S_j^2\left(1 - \frac{n_j}{N_j}\right) = \frac{N^2}{n_j} P_j^2 S_j^2\left(1 - \frac{n_j}{N_j}\right) \qquad (2.47)$$

The comparable variances are (2.46) and (2.47). In (2.46) the average number of nonzero units in the sample of size n is nP_j. If we take $n_j = nP_j$ in (2.47), so that the number of nonzeros to be measured is about the same with both methods, (2.47) becomes

$$V(N_j \bar{y}_j) = \frac{N^2}{n} P_j S_j^2\left(1 - \frac{n}{N}\right) \qquad (2.48)$$

The ratio of the variances (2.48) to (2.46) is

$$\frac{V(N_j \text{ known})}{V(N_j \text{ not known})} = \frac{S_j^2}{S_j^2 + Q_j \overline{Y}_j^2} = \frac{C_j^2}{C_j^2 + Q_j}$$

where $C_j = S_j/\overline{Y}_j$ is the coefficient of variation among the nonzeros. As might be expected, the reduction in variance due to a knowledge of N_j is greater when the proportion of zero units is large and when y_j varies relatively little among the nonzero units. For further study of this problem, see Jessen and Houseman (1944).

2.12 COMPARISONS BETWEEN DOMAIN MEANS

Let $\bar{y}_j$, $\bar{y}_k$ be the sample means in the jth and kth of a set of domains into which the units in a simple random sample are classified. The variance of their difference is

$$V(\bar{y}_j - \bar{y}_k) = V(\bar{y}_j) + V(\bar{y}_k)$$

This formula applies also to the difference between two ratios $\hat{R}_j$ and $\hat{R}_k$.

One point should be noted. It is seldom of scientific interest to ask whether $\overline{Y}_j = \overline{Y}_k$ because these means would not be exactly equal in a finite population, except by a rare chance, even if the data in both domains were drawn at random from the same infinite population. Instead, we test the null hypothesis that the two domains were drawn from *infinite* populations having the same mean. Consequently we omit the fpc when computing $V(\bar{y}_j)$ and $V(\bar{y}_k)$, using the formula

$$V(\bar{y}_j - \bar{y}_k) = \frac{S_j^{\,2}}{n_j} + \frac{S_k^{\,2}}{n_k}$$

2.13 VALIDITY OF THE NORMAL APPROXIMATION

Confidence that the normal approximation is adequate in most practical situations comes from a variety of sources. In the theory of probability much study has been made of the distribution of means of random samples. It has been proved that for any population which has a finite standard deviation the distribution of the sample mean tends to normality as n increases (see, e.g., Feller, 1957). This work relates to infinite populations.

For sampling without replacement from finite populations, Hájek (1960) has given necessary and sufficient conditions under which the distribution of the sample mean tends to normality, following work by Erdös and Rényi (1959) and Madow (1948). Hájek assumes a sequence of values n_v, N_v tending to infinity in such a way that $(N_v - n_v)$ also tends to infinity. The measurements in the vth population are denoted by y_{vi}, $(i = 1, 2, \cdots, N_v)$. For this population, let $S_{v\tau}$ be the set of units in the population for which

$$|y_{vi} - \bar{Y}_v| > \tau\sqrt{n_v(1 - f_v)}S_v$$

where $\bar{Y}_v$, S_v, f_v are the population mean, s.d. and fpc, and τ is a number > 0. Then the Lindeberg-type condition

$$\lim_{v \to \infty} \frac{\sum\limits_{S_{v\tau}}(y_{vi} - \bar{Y}_v)^2}{(N_v - 1)S_v^{\,2}} = 0$$

is necessary and sufficient to ensure that $\bar{y}_v$ tends to normality with the mean and variance given in theorems 2.1 and 2.2.

This imposing body of knowledge leaves something to be desired. It is not easy to answer the direct question: "For this population, how large must n be so that the normal approximation is accurate enough?" Nonnormal distributions vary greatly both in the nature and in the degree of their departure from normality. In sampling practice it cannot be assumed that the frequency distributions will all be reasonably close to normality. The distributions of many types of economic enterprise (stores, chicken farms, towns) exhibit a marked positive skewness, with a few large units and many small units. The same kind of skewness is displayed by some biological populations (e.g., the number of rats or flies per city block).

As an illustration of a positively skewed distribution, Fig. 2.1 shows the

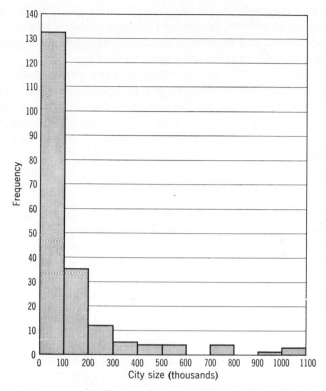

Fig. 2.1. Frequency distribution of sizes of 196 United States cities in 1920.

frequency distribution of the numbers of inhabitants in 196 large United States cities in 1920. (The four largest cities, New York, Chicago, Philadelphia, and Detroit, were omitted. Their inclusion would extend the horizontal scale to more than five times the length shown and would, of course, greatly accentuate the skewness.) Figure 2.2 shows the frequency

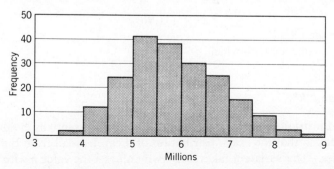

Fig. 2.2 Frequency distribution of totals of 200 simple random samples with $n = 49$.

distribution of the total number of inhabitants in each of 200 simple random samples, with $n = 49$, drawn from this population. The distribution of the sample totals, and likewise of the means, is much more similar to a normal curve but still displays some positive skewness.

In any discussion of the validity of the normal approximation we must define what it means to say that the normal approximation is "accurate enough." In sample surveys the normal approximation is used primarily to calculate confidence limits. When 95% confidence limits are computed for the population mean $\bar{Y}$ by the normal approximation, we make the following statement:

$$\bar{y} - 1.96s_{\bar{y}} < \bar{Y} < \bar{y} + 1.96s_{\bar{y}} \tag{2.49}$$

With repeated sampling, we claim that statements of this kind will be wrong only 5% of the time. Consequently we might say that the normal approximation is accurate enough if such statements are in fact wrong between 4 and 6% of the time. The choice of the numbers 4 and 6 is arbitrary: some workers may be satisfied with wider limits.

From the study of theoretical distributions that are skewed and from the results of sampling experiments on actual skewed populations, some statements can be made about what usually happens to confidence probabilities when we sample from positively skew populations. The sample size is assumed large enough so that the distribution of $\bar{y}$ shows some approach to normality, as in Fig. 2.2. The statements are as follows:

1. The frequency with which the assertion

$$\bar{y} - 1.96s_{\bar{y}} < \bar{Y} < \bar{y} + 1.96s_{\bar{y}}$$

is wrong is usually higher than 5%.

2. The frequency with which

$$\bar{Y} > \bar{y} + 1.96s_{\bar{y}}$$

is *greater* than 2.5%.

3. The frequency with which

$$\bar{Y} < \bar{y} - 1.96s_{\bar{y}}$$

is *less* than 2.5%.

As an illustration, consider a variate y which is essentially binomially distributed, so that the exact distribution of $\bar{y}$ can be read from the binomial tables. The variate y takes only two values—the value h with probability P and the value 0 with probability Q. The population mean is

$\bar{Y} = Ph$. A simple random sample of size n shows a units which have the value h and $n - a$ units which have the value 0. For the sample,

$$\sum y = ah, \qquad \bar{y} = \frac{ah}{n}$$

$$(n - 1)s^2 = \sum y^2 - n\bar{y}^2 = ah^2 - \frac{a^2h^2}{n}$$

$$s_{\bar{y}}^2 = \frac{s^2}{n} = \frac{h^2}{n^2}\frac{a(n - a)}{n - 1}$$

Hence 95% confidence limits for $\bar{Y}$ are

$$\bar{y} \pm 1.96 s_{\bar{y}} = \frac{h}{n}\left[a \pm 1.96\sqrt{\frac{a(n - a)}{n - 1}}\right] \tag{2.50}$$

Let $n = 400$, $P = 0.1$. Then $\bar{Y} = 0.1h$. By trial we find that if $a = 29$ in expression (2.50) the upper confidence limit is $39.18h/400 = 0.098h$, whereas $a = 30$ gives $40.34h/400 = 0.101h$. Hence any value of $a \le 29$ gives an upper confidence limit that is too low. Similarly we find that if $a \ge 54$ the lower limit is too high.

The variate a follows the binomial distribution with $n = 400$, $P = 0.1$. The tables (Harvard Computation Laboratory, 1955) show that

Pr (stated upper limit too low) = Pr ($a \le 29$) = 0.0357
Pr (stated lower limit too high) = Pr ($a \ge 54$) = 0.0217

Pr (confidence statement wrong)   = 0.0574

The total probability of being wrong is not far from 0.05. In more than 60% of the wrong statements, the true mean is higher than the stated upper limit.

There is no safe general rule as to how large n must be for use of the normal approximation in computing confidence limits. For populations in which the principal deviation from normality consists of marked positive skewness, a crude rule which I have occasionally found useful is

$$n > 25G_1^2$$

where G_1 is Fisher's measure of skewness (Fisher, 1932).

$$G_1 = \frac{E(y_i - \bar{Y})^3}{\sigma^3} = \frac{1}{N\sigma^3}\sum_{i=1}^{N}(y_i - \bar{Y})^3$$

This rule is designed so that a 95% confidence probability statement will be wrong not more than 6% of the time. It is derived mathematically by assuming that any disturbance due to moments of the distribution of $\bar{y}$ higher than the third is negligible. The rule attempts to control only the *total* frequency of wrong statements, ignoring the direction of the error of estimate.

By calculating G_1, or an estimate, for a specific population, we can obtain a rough idea of the sample size needed for application of the normal approximation to compute confidence limits. The result should be checked by sampling experiments whenever possible.

Example. The data in Table 2.3 show the numbers of acres devoted to crops

TABLE 2.3

FREQUENCY DISTRIBUTION OF ACRES IN CROPS ON 556 FARMS

Class Intervals (acres)	Coded Scale y_i	Frequency f_i	$f_i y_i$	$f_i y_i^2$	$f_i y_i^3$
0–29	−0.9	47	−42.3	38.1	−34.3
30–63	0	143	0	0	0
64–97	1	154	154	154	154
98–131	2	82	164	328	656
132–165	3	62	186	558	1,674
166–199	4	33	132	528	2,112
200–233	5	13	65	325	1,625
234–267	6	6	36	216	1,296
268–301	7	4	28	196	1,372
302–335	8	6	48	384	3,072
336–369	9	2	18	162	1,458
370–403	10	0	0	0	0
404–437	11	2	22	242	2,662
438–471	12	0	0	0	0
472–505	13	2	26	338	4,394
Totals		556	836.7	3,469.1	20,440.7

$$E(y_i) = \overline{Y} = \frac{836.7}{556} = 1.50486$$

$$E(y_i^2) = \frac{3469.1}{556} = 6.23939$$

$$E(y_i^3) = \frac{20,440.7}{556} = 36.76385$$

$$\sigma^2 = E(y_i^2) - \overline{Y}^2 = 3.97479$$

$$\kappa_3 = E(y_i - \overline{Y})^3 = E(y_i^3) - 3E(y_i^2)\overline{Y} + 2\overline{Y}^3$$
$$= 15.411$$

$$G_1 = \frac{\kappa_3}{\sigma^3} = \frac{15.411}{7.925} = 1.9$$

on 556 farms in Seneca County, New York. The data come from a series of studies by West (1951), who drew repeated samples of size 100 from this population and examined the frequency distributions of $\bar{y}$, s, and Student's t for several items of interest in farm management surveys.

The computation of G_1 is shown under the table. The computations are made on a coded scale, and, since G_1 is a pure number, there is no need to return to the original scale. Note that the first class-interval was slightly different from the others.

Since $G_1 = 1.9$, we take as a suggested minimum n

$$n = (25)(1.9)^2 = 90$$

For samples of size 100, West found with this item (acres in crops) that neither the distribution of $\bar{y}$ nor that of Student's t differed significantly from the corresponding theoretical normal distributions.

Good sampling practice tends to make the normal approximation more valid. Failure of the normal approximation occurs mostly when the population contains some extreme individuals which dominate the sample average when they are present. However, these extremes also have a much more serious effect of increasing the variance of the sample and decreasing the precision. Consequently, it is wise to segregate them and make separate plans for coping with them, perhaps by taking a complete enumeration of them if they are not numerous. This removal of the extremes from the main body of the population reduces the skewness and improves the normal approximation. This technique is an example of stratified sampling, which is discussed in Chapter 5.

2.14 EFFECT OF NON-NORMALITY ON THE ESTIMATED VARIANCE

One effect of non-normality is that the estimated variance s^2 may be more highly variable from sample to sample than we expect if we assume that we are sampling from a normal distribution. For any infinite population, the variance of s^2 in random samples of size n is (Fisher, 1932)

$$V(s^2) = \frac{2\sigma^4}{n-1} + \frac{\kappa_4}{n} \tag{2.51}$$

The first term after the equality sign is the value that the variance of s^2 has when the parent distribution is normal. The second term represents the effect of non-normality. The quantity κ_4 is Fisher's fourth cumulant (Fisher, 1932) and is given by

$$\kappa_4 = E(y_i - \bar{Y})^4 - 3\sigma^4$$

Note that skewness in the original distribution, as measured by G_1, does not affect the stability of s^2: the important factor is the *fourth* moment in the parent population.

The cumulant κ_4 is zero for a normal distribution. It may take either positive or negative values in other distributions, but in those encountered in sampling practice κ_4 appears to be positive much more often than negative and may have a high value for some parent distributions.

We may write (2.51) as

$$V(s^2) = \frac{2\sigma^4}{n-1}\left(1 + \frac{n-1}{2n}\frac{\kappa_4}{\sigma^4}\right) = \frac{2\sigma^4}{n-1}\left(1 + \frac{n-1}{2n}G_2\right)$$

where $G_2 = \kappa_4/\sigma^4$ is Fisher's measure of kurtosis (*loc. cit*). The quantity inside the parentheses shows the factor by which the variance of s^2 is inflated owing to non-normality. Note that the factor is almost independent of n, so that the inflation remains even with large samples.

For West's data on farm acres in crops (Table 2.3), the value of G_2 will be found to be about 6. Thus $V(s^2)$ is close to four times as large as would be assumed if we regarded the original distribution of acres in crops as normal. In his sampling studies West found a similar inflation in the variance of the standard deviation s in three items he tested. The ratio of $V(s)$ to the theoretical variance of s from a normal population was 3.7 for acres in crops, 2.1 for total acres operated, and 13.7 for productive-man-work units. (By theory this ratio should be roughly the same for s as for s^2.)

The relevance of these results in practical sampling is that we sometimes use values of s^2 to compare the precision of one method of sampling with that of another or to estimate the sample size needed to attain a specified degree of precision in $\bar{y}$ (see Chapter 4). For these purposes it is well to have some idea of the precision of the estimate s^2, particularly if it has been calculated from rather scanty data. As the previous results indicate, use of the "normal" formula for appraising the variance of s^2 may give a very misleading impression of the stability of s^2.

EXERCISES

2.1 In a population with $N = 6$ the values of y_i are 8, 3, 1, 11, 4, and 7. Calculate the sample mean $\bar{y}$ for all possible simple random samples of size 2. Verify that $\bar{y}$ is an unbiased estimate of $\bar{Y}$ and that its variance is as given in theorem 2.2.

2.2 For the same population, calculate s^2 for all simple random samples of size 3 and verify that $E(s^2) = S^2$.

2.3 If random samples of size 2 are drawn with replacement from this population, show by finding all possible samples that $V(\bar{y})$ satisfies the equation

$$V(\bar{y}) = \frac{\sigma^2}{n} = \frac{S^2}{n}\frac{(N-1)}{N}$$

2.4   A simple random sample of 30 households was drawn from a city area containing 14,848 households. The numbers of persons per household in the sample were as follows:

5, 6, 3, 3, 2, 3, 3, 3, 4, 4, 3, 2, 7, 4, 3, 5, 4, 4, 3, 3, 4, 3, 3, 1, 2, 4, 3, 4, 2, 4

Estimate the total number of people in the area and compute the probability that this estimate is within $\pm 10\%$ of the true value.

2.5   In a study of the possible use of sampling to cut down the work in taking inventory in a stock room, a count is made of the value of the articles on each of 36 shelves in the room. The values to the nearest dollar are as follows.

29, 38, 42, 44, 45, 47, 51, 53, 53, 54, 56, 56, 56, 58, 58, 59, 60, 60,

60, 60, 61, 61, 61, 62, 64, 65, 65, 67, 67, 68, 69, 71, 74, 77, 82, 85.

The estimate of total value made from a sample is to be correct within $200, apart from a 1 in 20 chance. An advisor suggests that a simple random sample of 12 shelves will meet the requirements. Do you agree?

$$\sum y = 2138, \qquad \sum y^2 = 131,682$$

2.6   After the sample in Table 2.1 (p. 27) was taken, the number of completely filled sheets (with 42 signatures each) was counted and found to be 326. Use this information to make an improved estimate of the total number of signatures and find the standard error of your estimate.

2.7   From a list of 468 small two-year colleges a simple random sample of 100 colleges was drawn. The sample contained 54 public and 46 private colleges. Data for number of students (y) and number of teachers (x) are shown below.

	n	$\sum (y)$	$\sum (x)$
Public	54	31,281	2,024
Private	46	13,707	1,075

	$\sum (y^2)$	$\sum (yx)$	$\sum (x^2)$
Public	29,881,219	1,729,349	111,090
Private	6,366,785	431,041	33,119

(a) For each type of college in the population, estimate the ratio (number of students)/(number of teachers). (b) Compute the standard errors of your estimates. (c) For the public colleges, find 90% confidence limits for the student/teacher ratio in the whole population.

2.8   In the preceding example test at the 5% level whether the student/teacher ratio is significantly different in the two types of colleges.

2.9   For the public colleges, estimate the total number of teachers (a) given that the total number of public colleges in the population is 251, (b) without knowing this figure. In each case compute the standard error of your estimate.

2.10   The table below shows the numbers of inhabitants in each of the 197 United States cities which had populations over 50,000 in 1940. Calculate the standard error of the estimated total number of inhabitants in all 197 cities for the following methods of sampling: (a) a simple random sample of size 50, (b) a sample which includes the five largest cities and is a simple random sample of size 45 from the remaining 192 cities, (c) a sample which includes the nine largest cities and is a simple random sample of size 41 from the remaining cities.

FREQUENCY DISTRIBUTION OF CITY SIZES

Size Class (1000's)	f	Size Class (1000's)	f	Size Class (1000's)	f
50–100	105	550–600	2	....	....
100–150	36	600–650	1	1500–1550	1
150–200	13	650–700	2	....	....
200–250	6	700–750	0	1600–1650	1
250–300	7	750–800	1	....	....
300–350	8	800–850	1	1900–1950	1
350–400	4	850–900	2	....	....
400–450	1	900–950	0	3350–3400	1
450–500	3	950–1000	0	....	....
500–550	0	1000–1050	0	7450–7500	1

Gaps in the intervals are indicated by ....

2.11　Calculate the coefficient of skewness G_1 for the original population and for the population remaining after removing (a) the five largest cities, (b) the nine largest cities.

√ • 2.12　A small survey is to be taken to compare home-owners with renters. In the population about 75% are owners, 25% are renters. For one item the variance is thought to be about 15 for both owners and renters. The standard error of the difference between the two domain means is not to exceed 1. How large a sample is needed (a) if owners and renters can be identified in advance of drawing the sample, (b) if not. (An approximate answer will do in (b); an exact discussion requires binomial tables.)

√ 2.13　A simple random sample of size 3 is drawn from a population of size N with replacement. Show that the probabilities that the sample contains 1, 2, and 3 different units (for example, aaa, aab, abc, respectively) are,

$$P_1 = \frac{1}{N^2}, \qquad P_2 = \frac{3(N-1)}{N^2}, \qquad P_3 = \frac{(N-1)(N-2)}{N^2}$$

As an estimate of $\bar{Y}$ we take $\bar{y}'$, the unweighted mean over the different units in the sample. Show that the average variance of $\bar{y}'$ is

$$V(\bar{y}') = \frac{(2N-1)(N-1)S^2}{6N^2}$$

One way to do this is to show that

$$V(\bar{y}') = S^2 \left(\frac{N-1}{N} P_1 + \frac{N-2}{2N} P_2 + \frac{N-3}{3N} P_3 \right)$$

Hence show that $V(\bar{y}') < V(\bar{y})$, where $\bar{y}$ is the ordinary mean of the n observations in the sample. The result that $V(\bar{y}') < V(\bar{y})$ for any $n > 2$ was proved by Raj and Khamis (1958).

✓ • 2.14 Two dentists A and B make a survey of the state of the teeth of 200 children in a village. Dr. A selects a simple random sample of 20 children and counts the number of decayed teeth for each child, with the following results:

Number of decayed teeth/child	0	1	2	3	4	5	6	7	8	9	10
Number of children	8	4	2	2	1	1	0	0	0	1	1

Dr. B, using the same dental techniques, examines all 200 children, recording merely those who have no decayed teeth. He finds 60 children with no decayed teeth.

Estimate the total number of decayed teeth in the village children, (a) using A's results only; (b) using both A's and B's results. (c) Are the estimates unbiased? (d) Which estimate do you expect to be more precise?

• 2.15 A company intends to interview a simple random sample of employees who have been with it more than five years. The company has $1000 to spend, and each interview costs $10. There is no separate list of employees with more than five years service, but a list can be compiled from the files at a cost of $200. The company can either (a) compile the list and interview a simple random sample drawn from the eligible employees or (b) draw a simple random sample of all employees, interviewing only those eligible. The cost of rejecting those not eligible in the sample is assumed negligible.

Show that for estimating a total over the population of eligible employees, plan (a) gives a smaller variance than plan (b) only if $V_j < 2\sqrt{Q_j}$, where V_j is the coefficient of variation of the item among eligible employees and Q_j is the proportion of noneligibles in the company. Ignore the fpc.

REFERENCES

Cornfield, J. (1944). On samples from finite populations. *Jour. Amer. Stat. Assoc.*, **39**, 236–239.

Erdös, P., and Rényi, A. (1959). On the central limit theorem for samples from a finite population. *Pub. Math. Inst. Hungarian Acad. Sci.*, **4**, 49–57.

Feller, W. (1957). *An introduction to probability theory and its applications.* John Wiley and Sons, New York, second edition.

Fisher, R. A. (1932). *Statistical methods for research workers.* Oliver and Boyd, Edinburgh, fourth edition.

Hájek, J. (1960). Limiting distributions in simple random sampling from a finite population. *Pub. Math. Inst. Hungarian Acad. Sci.*, **5**, 361–374.

Hansen, M. H., Hurwitz, W. N., and Madow, W. G. (1953). *Sample survey methods and theory.* John Wiley and Sons, New York, Vol. II.

Harvard Computation Laboratory (1955). Tables of the cumulative binomial probability distribution. Harvard University Press, Cambridge, Mass.

Jessen, R. J., and Houseman, E. E. (1944). Statistical investigations of farm sample surveys taken in Iowa, Florida and California. *Iowa Agr. Exp. Sta. Res. Bull.* 329.

Madow, W. G. (1948). On the limiting distributions of estimates based on samples from finite universes. *Ann. Math. Stat.*, **19**, 535–545.

Raj, Des, and Khamis, S. H. (1958). Some remarks on sampling with replacement. *Ann. Math. Stat.*, **29**, 550–557.

Tukey, J. W. (1950). Some sampling simplified. *Jour. Amer. Stat. Assoc.*, **45**, 501–519.

U.N. Statistical Office (1950). The preparation of sample survey reports. Stat. Papers series C no. 1.

West, Q. M. (1951). *The results of applying a simple random sampling process to farm management data.* Agricultural Experiment Station, Cornell University.

Wishart, J. (1952). Moment-coefficients of the k-statistics in samples from a finite population. *Biometrika*, **39**, 1–13.

CHAPTER 3

Sampling for Proportions and Percentages

3.1 QUALITATIVE CHARACTERISTICS

Sometimes we wish to estimate the total number, the proportion, or the percentage of units in the population which possess some characteristic or attribute or fall into some defined class. Many of the results regularly published from censuses or surveys are of this form, for example, numbers of unemployed persons, the percentage of the population that is native-born. The classification may be introduced directly into the questionnaire, as in questions that are answered by a simple "yes" or "no." In other cases the original measurements are more or less continuous, and the classification is introduced in the tabulation of results. Thus we may record the respondents' ages to the nearest year but publish the percentage of the population aged 60 and over.

Notation. We suppose that every unit in the population falls into one of the two classes C and C'. The notation is as follows:

Number of units in C in		Proportion of units in C in	
Population	Sample	Population	Sample
A	a	$P = A/N$	$p = a/n$

The sample estimate of P is p, and the sample estimate of A is Np or Na/n. In statistical work the *binomial* distribution is often applied to estimates like a and p. As will be seen, the correct distribution for finite populations is the *hypergeometric*, although the binomial is usually a satisfactory approximation.

3.2 VARIANCES OF THE SAMPLE ESTIMATES

By means of a simple device it is possible to apply the theorems established in Chapter 2 to this situation. For any unit in the sample or

49

population, define y_i as 1 if the unit is in C and as 0 if it is in C'. For this population of values y_i, it is clear that

$$Y = \sum_1^N y_i = A \tag{3.1}$$

$$\bar{Y} = \frac{\sum_1^N y_i}{N} = \frac{A}{N} = P \tag{3.2}$$

Also, for the sample,

$$\bar{y} = \frac{\sum_1^n y_i}{n} = \frac{a}{n} = p \tag{3.3}$$

Consequently the problem of estimating A and P can be regarded as that of estimating the total and mean of a population in which every y_i is either 1 or 0. In order to use the theorems in Chapter 2, we first express S^2 and s^2 in terms of P and p. Note that

$$\sum_1^N y_i{}^2 = A = NP, \qquad \sum_1^n y_i{}^2 = a = np$$

Hence

$$S^2 = \frac{\sum_1^N (y_i - \bar{Y})^2}{N - 1} = \frac{\sum_1^N y_i{}^2 - N\bar{Y}^2}{N - 1}$$

$$= \frac{1}{N - 1}(NP - NP^2) = \frac{N}{N - 1} PQ \tag{3.4}$$

where $Q = 1 - P$. Similarly

$$s^2 = \frac{\sum_1^n (y_i - \bar{y})^2}{n - 1} = \frac{n}{n - 1} pq \tag{3.5}$$

Application of theorems 2.1, 2.2, and 2.4 to this population gives the following results for simple random sampling of the units that are being classified.

Theorem 3.1.   The sample proportion $p = a/n$ is an unbiased estimate of the population proportion $P = A/N$.

Theorem 3.2.   The variance of p is

$$V(p) = E(p - P)^2 = \frac{S^2}{n}\left(\frac{N - n}{N}\right) = \frac{PQ}{n}\left(\frac{N - n}{N - 1}\right) \tag{3.6}$$

using (3.4).

Corollary 1. If p and P are the sample and population *percentages*, respectively, falling into class C, (3.6) continues to hold for the variance of p.

Corollary 2. The variance of $\hat{A} = Np$, the estimated total number of units in class C, is

$$V(\hat{A}) = \frac{N^2 PQ}{n}\left(\frac{N - n}{N - 1}\right) \tag{3.7}$$

Theorem 3.3. An unbiased estimate of the variance of p, derived from the sample, is

$$v(p) = s_p^{\,2} = \frac{N - n}{(n - 1)N}\, pq \tag{3.8}$$

Proof. In the corollary of theorem 2.4 it was shown that for a continuous variate y_i an unbiased estimate of the variance of the sample mean $\bar{y}$ is

$$v(\bar{y}) = \frac{s^2\,(N - n)}{n}\frac{}{N} \tag{3.9}$$

For proportions, p takes the place of $\bar{y}$, and in (3.5) we showed that

$$s^2 = \frac{n}{n - 1}\, pq \tag{3.10}$$

Hence

$$v(p) = s_p^{\,2} = \frac{N - n}{(n - 1)N}\, pq$$

It follows that if N is very large relative to n, so that the fpc is negligible, an unbiased estimate of the variance of p is

$$\frac{pq}{n - 1}$$

This result may appear puzzling to some readers, since the expression pq/n is almost invariably used in practice for the estimated variance. The fact is that pq/n is not unbiased even with an infinite population.

Corollary. An unbiased estimate of the variance of $\hat{A} = Np$, the estimated total number of units in class C in the population, is

$$v(\hat{A}) = s_{Np}^{\,2} = \frac{N(N - n)}{n - 1}\, pq \tag{3.11}$$

Example. From a list of 3042 names and addresses, a simple random sample of 200 names showed on investigation 38 wrong addresses. Estimate the total number of addresses needing correction in the list and find the standard error of this estimate. We have

$$N = 3042, \qquad n = 200, \qquad a = 38, \qquad p = 0.19$$

The estimated total number of wrong addresses is

$$\hat{A} = Np = (3042)(0.19) = 578$$

$$s_{\hat{A}} = \sqrt{[(3042)(2842)(0.19)(0.81)/199]} = \sqrt{6685} = 81.8$$

Since the sampling ratio is under 7%, the fpc makes little difference. To remove it, replace the term $N - n$ by N. If, in addition, we replace $n - 1$ by n, we have the simpler formula

$$s_{Np} = N\sqrt{pq/n} = (3042)\sqrt{(0.19)(0.81)/200} = 84.4$$

This is in fairly close agreement with the previous result, 81.8.

The preceding formulas for the variance and the estimated variance of p hold only if the *units* are classified into C or C' so that p is the ratio of the number of units in C in the sample to the total number of units in the sample. In many surveys each unit is composed of a group of elements, and it is the elements that are classified. A few examples are as follows:

Sampling Unit	Elements
Family	Members of the family
Restaurant	Employees
Crate of eggs	Individual eggs
Peach tree	Individual peaches

If a simple random sample of units is drawn in order to estimate the proportion P of *elements* in the population that belong to class C, the preceding formulas do not apply. Appropriate methods are given in section 3.12.

3.3 THE EFFECT OF P ON THE STANDARD ERRORS

Equation (3.6) shows how the variance of the estimated percentage changes with P, for fixed n and N. If the fpc is ignored, we have

$$V(p) = \frac{PQ}{n}$$

The function PQ and its square root are shown in Table 3.1. These functions may be regarded as the variance and standard deviation, respectively, for a sample of size 1.

TABLE 3.1

VALUES OF PQ AND $\sqrt{PQ}$

P = Population percentage in class C

P	0	10	20	30	40	50	60	70	80	90	100
PQ	0	900	1600	2100	2400	2500	2400	2100	1600	900	0
$\sqrt{PQ}$	0	30	40	46	49	50	49	46	40	30	0

The functions have their greatest values when the population is equally divided between the two classes, and are symmetrical about this point. The standard error of p changes relatively little when P lies anywhere between 30 and 70%. At the maximum value of $\sqrt{PQ}$, 50, a sample size of 100 is needed to reduce the standard error of the estimate to 5%. To attain a 1% standard error requires a sample size of 2500.

This approach is not appropriate when interest lies in the total *number* of units in the population which are in class C. In this event it is more natural to ask: Is the estimate likely to be correct to within, say, 7% of the true total? Thus we tend to think of the standard error expressed as a fraction or percentage of the true value, NP. The fraction is

$$\frac{\sigma_{Np}}{NP} = \frac{N\sqrt{PQ}}{\sqrt{n}NP}\sqrt{\frac{N-n}{N-1}} = \frac{1}{\sqrt{n}}\sqrt{\frac{Q}{P}}\sqrt{\frac{N-n}{N-1}} \qquad (3.12)$$

This quantity is usually called the *coefficient of variation* of the estimate. If the fpc is ignored, the coefficient is $\sqrt{Q/nP}$. The ratio $\sqrt{Q/P}$, which might be considered the coefficient of variation for a sample of size 1, is shown in Table 3.2.

TABLE 3.2

VALUES OF $\sqrt{Q/P}$ FOR DIFFERENT VALUES OF P

P = Population percentage in class C

P	0	0.1	0.5	1	5	10	20
$\sqrt{Q/P}$	∞	31.6	14.1	9.9	4.4	3.0	2.0

P	30	40	50	60	70	80	90
$\sqrt{Q/P}$	1.5	1.2	1.0	0.8	0.7	0.5	0.3

For a fixed sample size, the coefficient of variation of the estimated total in class C decreases steadily as the true percentage in C increases. The coefficient is high when P is less than 5%. Very large samples are needed for precise estimates of the total number possessing any attribute that is rare in the population. For $P = 1\%$, we must have $\sqrt{n} = 99$ in order to reduce the coefficient of variation of the estimate to 0.1 or 10%. This gives a sample size of 9801. Simple random sampling, or any method of sampling that is adapted for general purposes, is an expensive method of estimating the total number of units of a scarce type.

3.4 THE BINOMIAL DISTRIBUTION

Since the population is of a particularly simple type, in which the y_i are either 1 or 0, we can find the actual frequency distribution of the estimate p and not merely its mean and variance.

The population contains A units that are in class C and $N - A$ units in C', where $P = A/N$. If the first unit that is drawn happens to be in C, there will remain in the population $A - 1$ units in C and $N - A$ in C'. Thus the proportion of units in C, after the first draw, changes slightly to $(A - 1)/(N - 1)$. Alternatively, if the first unit drawn is in C', the proportion in C changes to $A/(N - 1)$. In sampling without replacement, the proportion keeps changing in this way throughout the draw. In the present section these variations are ignored, that is, P is assumed constant. This amounts to assuming that A and $N - A$ are both large relative to the sample size n.

With this assumption, the process of drawing the sample consists of a series of n trials, in each of which the probability that the unit drawn is in C is P. This situation gives rise to the familiar binomial frequency distribution for the number of units in C in the sample. The probability that the sample contains a units in C is

$$\Pr(a) = \frac{n!}{a!\,(n-a)!}\, P^a Q^{n-a} \tag{3.13}$$

From this expression we may tabulate the frequency distribution of a, of $p = a/n$, or of the estimated total Np.

There are three comprehensive sets of tables. All give P by intervals of 0.01. The ranges for n are as follows.

U.S. Bureau of Standards (1950):

$$n = 1(1)49, \text{ i.e., goes from 1 to 49 by intervals of 1.}$$

Romig (1952): $n = 50(5)100$.

Harvard Computation Laboratory (1955):
$$n = 1(1)50(2)100(10)200(20)500(50)1000$$

3.5 THE HYPERGEOMETRIC DISTRIBUTION

The distribution of p can be found without the assumption that the population is large in relation to the sample. The numbers of units in the two classes C and C' in the population are A and A', respectively. We shall calculate the probability that the corresponding numbers in the sample are a and a', where

$$a + a' = n, \qquad A + A' = N$$

In simple random sampling each of the $\binom{N}{n}$ different selections of n units out of N has an equal chance of being drawn. To find the probability wanted, we count how many of these samples contain exactly a units from C and a' from C'. The number of different selections of a units among the A that are in C is $\binom{A}{a}$, whereas the number of different selections of a' among A' is $\binom{A'}{a'}$. Each selection of the first type can be combined with any one of the second to give a different sample of the required type. The total number of samples of the required type is therefore

$$\binom{A}{a} \cdot \binom{A'}{a'}$$

Hence, if a simple random sample of size n is drawn, the probability that it is of the required type is

$$\Pr(a, a' \mid A, A') = \binom{A}{a} \cdot \binom{A'}{a'} \Big/ \binom{N}{n} \qquad (3.14)$$

This is the frequency distribution of a or np, from which that of p is immediately derivable. The distribution is called the *hypergeometric* distribution.

For computing purposes the hypergeometric probability (3.14) may be written as follows.

$$\frac{n!}{a!\,(n-a)!} \cdot \frac{A(A-1)\cdots(A-a+1)(A')(A'-1)\cdots(A'-a'+1)}{N(N-1)\cdots(N-n+1)}$$

$$(3.14)'$$

Example. A family of eight contains three males and five females. Find the frequency distribution of the number of males in a simple random sample of size 4. In this case

$$A = 3; \qquad A' = 5, \qquad N = 8; \qquad n = 4$$

From (3.14)′ the distribution of the number of males, a, is as follows:

a	Probability
0	$\dfrac{4!}{0!\,4!} \cdot \dfrac{5.4.3.2}{8.7.6.5} = \dfrac{1}{14}$
1	$\dfrac{4!}{1!\,3!} \cdot \dfrac{3.5.4.3}{8.7.6.5} = \dfrac{6}{14}$
2	$\dfrac{4!}{2!\,2!} \cdot \dfrac{3.2.5.4}{8.7.6.5} = \dfrac{6}{14}$
3	$\dfrac{4!}{3!\,1!} \cdot \dfrac{3.2.1.5}{8.7.6.5} = \dfrac{1}{14}$
4	Impossible $= 0$

The reader may verify that the mean number of males is $\frac{3}{2}$ and the variance is $\frac{15}{28}$. These results agree with the formulas previously established in section 3.2, which give

$$E(np) = nP = \frac{nA}{N} = \frac{(4)(3)}{8} = \frac{3}{2}$$

$$V(np) = nPQ \frac{N-n}{N-1} = 4 \cdot \frac{3}{8} \cdot \frac{5}{8} \cdot \frac{4}{7} = \frac{15}{28}$$

3.6 CONFIDENCE LIMITS

We first discuss the meaning of confidence limits in the case of qualitative characteristics. In the sample, a out of n fall in class C. Suppose that inferences are to be made about the number A in the population which falls in class C. For an upper confidence limit to A, we compute a value $\hat{A}_U$ such that for this value the probability of getting a or less falling in C in the sample is some small quantity α_U, for example, 0.025. Formally, $\hat{A}_U$ satisfies the equation

$$\sum_{j=0}^{a} \text{Pr}\,(j, n-j \mid \hat{A}_U, N - \hat{A}_U) = \alpha_U \qquad (3.15)$$

where Pr is the probability term for the hypergeometric distribution, as defined in (3.14).

When α_U is chosen in advance, (3.15) requires in general a nonintegral value of $\hat{A}_U$ to satisfy it, whereas conceptually $\hat{A}_U$ should be a whole number. In practice we choose $\hat{A}_U$ as the smallest integral value of A such that the left side of (3.15) is less than or equal to α_U. Similarly, the lower confidence limit $\hat{A}_L$ is the largest integral value such that

$$\sum_{j=a}^{n} \text{Pr}\,(j, n-j \mid \hat{A}_L, N - \hat{A}_L) \leq \alpha_L \qquad (3.16)$$

Confidence limits for P are then found by taking $\hat{P}_U = \hat{A}_U/N$, $\hat{P}_L = \hat{A}_L/N$.

Numerous methods are available for computing confidence limits.

Exact Methods

Chung and DeLury (1950) present charts of the 90, 95, and 99% limits for P for $N = 500$, 2500, and 10,000. Values for intermediate population sizes are obtainable by interpolation. Lieberman and Owen (1961) give tables of individual and cumulative terms of the hypergeometric distribution, but N extends only to 100.

The Normal Approximation

From (3.8) for the variance of p, one form of the normal approximation to the confidence limits for P is

$$p \pm \left[t\sqrt{1-f}\sqrt{pq/(n-1)} + \frac{1}{2n} \right] \qquad (3.17)$$

where $f = n/N$ and t is the normal deviate corresponding to the confidence probability. For those who prefer it, use of the more familiar term $\sqrt{pq/n}$ seldom makes an appreciable difference. The last term on the right is a correction for continuity. This produces only a slight improvement in the approximation. However, without the correction, the normal approximation usually gives too narrow a confidence interval.

The error in the normal approximation depends on all the quantities n, p, N, α_U, and α_L. The quantity to which the error is most sensitive is np or more specifically the number observed in the *smaller* class. Table 3.3

TABLE 3.3

Smallest Values of np for Use of the Normal Approximation

p	$np = $ Number Observed in the *Smaller* Class	$n = $ Sample Size
0.5	15	30
0.4	20	50
0.3	24	80
0.2	40	200
0.1	60	600
0.05	70	1400
~0*	80	∞

* This means that p is extremely small, so that np follows the Poisson distribution.

gives working rules for deciding when the normal approximation (3.17) may be used.

The rules in Table 3.3 are constructed so that with 95% confidence limits the true frequency with which the limits fail to enclose P is not greater than 5.5%. Further, the probability that the upper limit is below P is between 2.5 and 3.5%, and the probability that the lower limit exceeds P is between 2.5 and 1.5%.

Example 1. In a simple random sample of size 100, from a population of size 500, there are 37 units in class C. Find the 95% confidence limits for the proportion and for the total number in class C in the population. In this example

$$n = 100, \qquad N = 500, \qquad p = 0.37$$

The example lies in the range in which the normal approximation is recommended. The estimated standard error of p is

$$\sqrt{(1 - f)pq/(n - 1)} = \sqrt{(0.8)(0.37)(0.63)/99} = 0.0434$$

The correction for continuity, $1/2n$, equals 0.005. Hence the 95% limits for P are estimated as

$$0.37 \pm (1.96 \times 0.0434 + 0.005) = 0.37 \pm 0.090$$
$$\hat{P}_L = 0.280, \qquad \hat{P}_U = 0.460$$

The limits as read from the charts by Chung and DeLury are 0.285 and 0.462, respectively.

To find limits for the total number in class C in the population, we multiply by N, obtaining 140 and 230, respectively.

Binomial Approximations

When the normal approximation does not apply, limits for P may be found from the binomial tables (section 3.4) and adjusted, if necessary, to take account of the fpc. Table VIII₁ in Fisher and Yates's *Statistical Tables* (1957) gives binomial confidence limits for P for any value of n, and is a useful alternative to the ordinary binomial tables. Example 2 shows how the binomial approximation is computed.

Example 2. For another item in the sample in example 1, nine of the 100 units fall in class C. From Romig's table for $n = 100$ the 95% limits for P are found to be 0.041 and 0.165. (The Fisher-Yates tables give 0.042 and 0.164.) If f, the sampling fraction, is less than 5%, limits found in this way are close enough for most purposes. In this example, $f = 0.2$ and adjustment is needed.

To apply the adjustment, we shorten the interval between p and each limit by the factor $\sqrt{1 - f} = \sqrt{0.8} = 0.894$. The adjusted limits are as follows:

$$\hat{P}_L = 0.090 - (0.894)(0.090 - 0.041) = 0.046$$
$$\hat{P}_U = 0.090 + (0.894)(0.165 - 0.090) = 0.157$$

The limits read from the charts by Chung and DeLury are 0.045 and 0.157, respectively.

Example 3. In auditing records in which a very low error rate is demanded, the upper confidence limit for A is primarily of interest. Suppose that 200 of 1000 records are verified and that the batch of 1000 is accepted if no errors are found. Special tables have been constructed to give the upper confidence limit for the number of errors in the batch. A good approximation results from the following relation. The probability that no errors are found in n when A errors are present in N is, from the hypergeometric distribution,

$$\frac{(N - A)(N - A - 1) \cdots (N - A - n + 1)}{N(N - 1) \cdots (N - n + 1)} \doteq \left(\frac{N - A - u}{N - u}\right)^n$$

where $u = (n - 1)/2$. For example, with $n = 200$, $A = 10$, $N = 1000$, the approximation gives $(890.5/900.5)^{200}$, which is found by logs to be 0.107. Thus $A = 10$ (a 1% error rate) is approximately the 90% upper confidence limit for the number of errors in the batch.

3.7 CLASSIFICATION INTO MORE THAN TWO CLASSES

Frequently, in the presentation of results, the units are classified into more than two classes. Thus a sample from a human population may be arranged in 15 five-year age groups. Even when a question is supposed to be answered by a simple "yes" or "no," the results actually obtained may fall into four classes: "yes," "no," "don't know," and "no answer." The extension of the theory to such cases is illustrated by the situation in which there are three classes.

We suppose that the number falling in the ith class is A_i in the population and a_i in the sample, where

$$N = \sum A_i, \qquad n = \sum a_i, \qquad P_i = \frac{A_i}{N}, \qquad p_i = \frac{a_i}{n}$$

When the sample size n is small in relation to all the A_i, the probabilities P_i may be considered effectively constant throughout the drawing of the sample. The probability of drawing the observed sample is given by the *multinomial* expression

$$\Pr(a_i) = \frac{n!}{a_1! \, a_2! \, a_3!} P_1^{a_1} P_2^{a_2} P_3^{a_3} \tag{3.18}$$

This is the appropriate extension of the binomial distribution and is a good approximation when the sampling fraction is small.

The correct expression for the probability of drawing the observed sample is

$$\Pr(a_i \mid A_i) = \binom{A_1}{a_1}\binom{A_2}{a_2}\binom{A_3}{a_3} \Big/ \binom{N}{n} \tag{3.19}$$

This expression is the natural extension of (3.14), section 3.5, for the hypergeometric distribution. The numerator is the number of distinct samples of size n that can be formed with a_1 units in class 1, a_2 in class 2, and a_3 in class 3.

3.8 CONFIDENCE LIMITS WHEN THERE ARE MORE THAN TWO CLASSES

Two different cases must be distinguished.

Case 1. We calculate

$$p = \frac{\text{number in any one class in sample}}{n} = \frac{a_1}{n}$$

or

$$p = \frac{\text{total number in a group of classes}}{n} = \frac{a_1 + a_2 + a_3}{n}$$

In either of these situations, although the original classification contains more than two classes, p itself is obtained from a subdivision of the n units into only two classes. The theory already presented applies to this case. Confidence limits are calculated as described in section 3.6.

Case 2. Sometimes certain classes are omitted, p being computed from a breakdown of the remaining classes into two parts. For example, we might omit persons who did not know or gave no answer and consider the ratio of number of "yes" answers to "yes" plus "no" answers. Ratios that are structurally of this type are often of interest in sample surveys. The denominator of such a ratio is not n but some smaller number n'.

Although n' varies from sample to sample, previous results can still be used by considering the conditional distribution of p in samples in which both n and n' are fixed. This device was already employed in section 2.10. Suppose that

$$p = \frac{a_1}{a_1 + a_2}, \qquad n' = a_1 + a_2, \qquad n = a_1 + a_2 + a_3$$

so that a_3 is the number in the sample falling in classes in which we are not at the moment interested. Then, as shown in the next section, the conditional distribution of a_1 and a_2 is the hypergeometric distribution obtained when the sample is of size n' and the population of size $N' = A_1 + A_2$. Hence, from (3.17), the normal approximation to conditional confidence limits for $P = A_1/(A_1 + A_2)$ are

$$p \pm \left[t \sqrt{\left(1 - \frac{n'}{N'}\right) \frac{pq}{(n' - 1)}} + \frac{1}{2n'} \right] \qquad (3.20)$$

If the value of N' is not known, n/N may be substituted for n'/N' in the fpc term in (3.20).

3.9 THE CONDITIONAL DISTRIBUTION OF p

To find this distribution, we restrict our attention to samples of size n in which $n' = a_1 + a_2$ fall in classes 1 and 2. The number of distinct samples of this type is

$$\binom{N'}{n'}\binom{N - N'}{n - n'} = \binom{A_1 + A_2}{a_1 + a_2}\binom{A_3}{a_3} \tag{3.21}$$

Among these samples, the number which have a_1 in class 1 and a_2 in class 2 has already been given as the numerator in (3.19), section 3.7. Dividing this numerator by (3.21), we have

$$\Pr\left(a_1 \mid A_1, A_2, n, n'\right) = \binom{A_1}{a_1}\binom{A_2}{a_2} \Big/ \binom{A_1 + A_2}{a_1 + a_2} \tag{3.22}$$

This is an ordinary hypergeometric distribution for a sample of size n' from a population of size $N' = A_1 + A_2$.

Example. Consider a population that consists of the five units b, c, d, e, f, which fall in three classes.

Class	A_i	Units denoted by
1	1	b
2	2	c, d
3	2	e, f

With random samples of size 3, we wish to estimate $P = A_1/(A_1 + A_2)$, or in this case $\frac{1}{3}$. Thus $N = 5$ and $N' = 3$.

There are 10 possible samples of size 3, all with equal initial probabilities. These are grouped according to the value of n'.

$$n' = 1$$

Sample	a_1	a_2	p	Conditional Probability	$(p - P)$
bef	1	0	1	$\frac{1}{3}$	$\frac{2}{3}$
cef or *def*	0	1	0	$\frac{2}{3}$	$-\frac{1}{3}$

If samples are specified by the values of a_1, a_2, only two types are obtainable: $a_1 = 1$, $a_2 = 0$; $a_1 = 0$, $a_2 = 1$. Their conditional probabilities, $\frac{1}{3}$ and $\frac{2}{3}$, respectively, agree with the general expression (3.22). Further,

$$E(p) = \tfrac{1}{3}$$

$$\sigma_p^2 = \left(\frac{1}{3}\right)\left(\frac{4}{9}\right) + \left(\frac{2}{3}\right)\left(\frac{1}{9}\right) = \frac{6}{27} = \frac{2}{9}$$

The estimate p is unbiased, and its variance agrees with the general formula

$$\sigma_p{}^2 = \left(\frac{N'-n'}{N'-1}\right)\frac{PQ}{n'} = \left(\frac{3-1}{3-1}\right)\left(\frac{1}{3}\right)\left(\frac{2}{3}\right) = \frac{2}{9}$$

For $n' = 2$ there are six possible samples, which give only two sets of values of a_1, a_2.

$$n' = 2$$

Sample	a_1	a_2	p	Conditional Probability	$(p - P)$
bce, bcf, bde, or *bdf*	1	1	$\frac{1}{2}$	$\frac{2}{3}$	$\frac{1}{6}$
cde or *cdf*	0	2	0	$\frac{1}{3}$	$-\frac{1}{3}$

The estimate is again unbiased and its variance is

$$\sigma_p{}^2 = \left(\frac{2}{3}\right)\left(\frac{1}{36}\right) + \left(\frac{1}{3}\right)\left(\frac{1}{9}\right) = \frac{1}{18}$$

which may be verified from the general formula. Note that the variance is only one fourth of that obtained when $n' = 1$. In a conditional approach the variance changes with the configuration of the sample that was drawn.

For $n' = 3$, there is only one possible sample, *bcd*. This gives the correct population fraction, $\frac{1}{3}$. The conditional variance of p is zero, as indicated by the general formula, which reduces to zero when $N' = n'$.

3.10 PROPORTIONS AND TOTALS OVER SUBPOPULATIONS

If separate estimates are to be made for each of a number of subpopulations or domains of study to which the units in the sample are allotted, the results in sections 3.8 and 3.9 are applicable. The sample data may be presented as follows:

Class	Domain 1 C	C'	Domain 2 C	C'	$\cdots$	Domain k C	C'	Total
Number of units	a_1	a_1'	a_2	a_2'	$\cdots$	a_k	a_k'	n

Of the n units, $(a_1 + a_1')$ are found to fall in domain 1 and of these a_1 fall in class C. The proportion falling in class C in domain 1 is estimated by $p_1 = a_1/(a_1 + a_1')$. The frequency distribution and confidence limits for p_1 were discussed under Case 2 in sections 3.8 and 3.9.

For estimating the *total* number A_1 of units in class C in domain 1, there are two possibilities. If N_1, the total number of units in domain 1 in the population, is known, we may use the conditional estimate

$$\hat{A}_1 = N_1 p_1 = \frac{N_1 a_1}{a_1 + a_1'}$$

Its standard error is computed as

$$s(\hat{A}_1) = N_1\sqrt{1 - (n_1/N_1)}\sqrt{p_1 q_1/(n_1 - 1)}$$

where $n_1 = a_1 + a_1'$.

If N_1 is not known, the estimate is

$$\hat{A}_1' = \frac{Na_1}{n}$$

with estimated standard error

$$s(\hat{A}_1') = N\sqrt{1 - (n/N)}\sqrt{pq/(n - 1)}$$

where $p = a_1/n$.

3.11 COMPARISONS BETWEEN DIFFERENT DOMAINS

Since proportions are estimated independently in different domains, comparisons between such proportions are made by standard elementary methods. For example, to test whether the proportion $p_1 = a_1/(a_1 + a_1')$ differs significantly from the proportion $p_2 = a_2/(a_2 + a_2')$, we form the usual 2×2 table

	Domain 1	2
C	a_1	a_2
C'	a_1'	a_2'
Total	n_1	n_1'

The ordinary χ^2 test (Fisher, 1958) or the normal approximation to the distribution of $(p_1 - p_2)$ is appropriate. Similarly, comparisons among proportions for more than two domains are made by the methods for a $2 \times k$ contingency table.

Occasionally it is desired to test whether a_1 differs significantly from a_2; for example, whether the *number* of Republicans who favor some proposal is greater than the *number* of Democrats in favor. On the null hypothesis that these two numbers are equal in the population, the total $n' = a_1 + a_2$ in the two classes in question should divide with equal probability between the two classes. Consequently we may regard a_1 as a binomial number of successes in n' trials, with probability of success $\frac{1}{2}$ on the null hypothesis. It may be verified that the normal deviate (corrected for continuity) is

$$\frac{2(|a_1 - \frac{1}{2}n'| - \frac{1}{2})}{\sqrt{n'}}$$

3.12   ESTIMATION   OF   PROPORTIONS   IN   CLUSTER SAMPLING

As mentioned in section 3.2, the preceding methods are not valid if each unit is a cluster of elements and we are estimating the proportion of elements that fall into class C.

If each unit contains the same number m of elements, let $p_i = a_i/m$ be the proportion of elements in the ith unit that fall into class C. The proportion falling in C in the sample is

$$p = \frac{\sum a_i}{nm} = \frac{1}{n} \sum_{}^{n} p_i$$

that is, the estimate p is the unweighted mean of the quantities p_i. Consequently, if y_i is replaced by p_i, the formulas in Chapter 2 may be applied directly to give the true and estimated variance of p.

$$V(p) = \frac{1-f}{n} \frac{\sum_{}^{N}(p_i - P)^2}{N-1} \tag{3.23}$$

An unbiased sample estimate of this variance is

$$v(p) = \frac{1-f}{n} \frac{\sum_{}^{n}(p_i - p)^2}{n-1} \tag{3.24}$$

Example 1.   A group of 61 leprosy patients were treated with a drug for 48 weeks. To measure the effect of the drug on the leprosy bacilli, the presence of bacilli at six sites on the body of each patient was tested bacteriologically. Among the 366 sites, 153, or 41.8%, were negative. What is the standard error of this percentage?

This example comes from a controlled experiment rather than a survey, but it illustrates how erroneous the binomial formula may be. By the binomial formula we have $n = 366$ and

$$\text{s.e.} (p) = \sqrt{pq/(n-1)} = \sqrt{(41.8)(58.2)/365} = 2.58\%$$

Each patient is a cluster unit with $m = 6$ elements (sites). To find the standard error by the correct formula, we need the frequency distribution of the 61 values of p_i. It is more convenient to tabulate the distribution of y_i, the number of negative sites per patient. With p_i expressed in per cents, $p_i = 100y_i/6$. From the distribution in Table 3.4 we find $\sum fy^2 = 669$ and

$$\text{s.e.} (\bar{y}) = \sqrt{\frac{\sum f_i(y_i - \bar{y})^2}{n(n-1)}} = \sqrt{\frac{669 - [(153)^2/61]}{(61)(60)}} = 0.279$$

Hence

$$\text{s.e.} (p) = \frac{100}{6} \text{ s.e.} (\bar{y}) = 4.65\%$$

This figure is about 1.8 times the value given by the binomial formula. The binomial formula requires the assumption that results at different sites on the same patient are independent, although actually they have a strong positive correlation. The last line of Table 3.4 shows the expected numbers of patients

TABLE 3.4

NUMBER OF NEGATIVE SITES PER PATIENT

$y_i = 6p_i/100$	0	1	2	3	4	5	6	Total
f	17	11	4	4	7	14	4	61
fy_i	0	11	8	12	28	70	24	153
f_{exp}	2.3	10.1	18.3	17.6	9.6	2.8	0.3	61.0

with $0, 1, 2, \ldots$ negative sites, computed from the binomial $(0.58 + 0.42)^6$. Note the marked excesses of observed frequencies f of patients with zero negatives and with five and six negatives.

If the size of cluster is not constant, let m_i be the number of elements in the ith cluster unit and let $p_i = a_i/m_i$. The proportion of units falling in class C in the sample is

$$p = \frac{\sum\limits_{n} a_i}{\sum\limits_{n} m_i}$$

Structurally, this is a typical ratio estimate, discussed in section 2.9 and later in Chapter 6. It is slightly biased, though the bias is seldom likely to be of practical importance.

If we put a_i for y_i and m_i for x_i in (2.29), the approximate variance of p is

$$V(p) \doteq \frac{1-f}{n\bar{M}^2} \frac{\sum\limits^{N}(a_i - Pm_i)^2}{N-1}$$

where P is the proportion of elements in C in the population and $\bar{M} = \sum\limits^{N} m_i/N$ is the average number of elements per cluster. An alternative expression is

$$V(p) \doteq \frac{1-f}{n} \sum\limits^{N} \left(\frac{m_i}{\bar{M}}\right)^2 \frac{(p_i - P)^2}{N-1} \tag{3.25}$$

This form shows that the approximate variance involves a weighted sum of squares of deviations of the p_i from the population value P.

For the estimated variance we have

$$v(p) = \frac{1-f}{n\bar{m}^2} \frac{\sum a_i^2 - 2p \sum a_i m_i + p^2 \sum m_i^2}{n-1} \tag{3.26}$$

where $\bar{m} = \sum m_i/n$ is the average number of elements per cluster in the sample.

Example 2. A simple random sample of 30 households was drawn from a census taken in 1947 in wards 6 and 7 of the Eastern Health District of Baltimore. The population contains about 15,000 households. In Table 3.5 the persons in each household are classified (*a*) according to whether they had consulted a doctor in the last 12 months, (*b*) according to sex.

TABLE 3.5

DATA FOR A SIMPLE RANDOM SAMPLE OF 30 HOUSEHOLDS

Household Number	Number of Persons m_i	Number of		Doctor Seen in Last Year	
		Males	Females	Yes	No
		a_i		a_i	
1	5	1	4	5	0
2	6	3	3	0	6
3	3	1	2	2	1
4	3	1	2	3	0
5	2	1	1	0	2
6	3	1	2	0	3
7	3	1	2	0	3
8	3	1	2	0	3
9	4	2	2	0	4
10	4	3	1	0	4
11	3	2	1	0	3
12	2	1	1	0	2
13	7	3	4	0	7
14	4	3	1	4	0
15	3	2	1	1	2
16	5	3	2	2	3
17	4	3	1	0	4
18	4	3	1	0	4
19	3	2	1	1	2
20	3	1	2	3	0
21	4	1	3	2	2
22	3	2	1	0	3
23	3	2	1	0	3
24	1	0	1	0	1
25	2	1	1	2	0
26	4	3	1	2	2
27	3	1	2	0	3
28	4	2	2	2	2
29	2	1	1	0	2
30	4	2	2	1	3
Totals	104	53	51	30	74

Our purpose is to contrast the ratio formula with the inappropriate binomial formula. Consider first the proportion of people who had consulted a doctor. For the binomial formula, we would take

$$n = 104, \qquad p = \frac{30}{104} = 0.2885$$

Hence

$$v_{bin}(p) = \frac{pq}{n} = \frac{(0.2885)(0.7115)}{104} = 0.00197$$

For the ratio formula, we note that there are 30 clusters and take

$n = 30$

m_i = total number in ith household

a_i = number in ith household who had seen a doctor

$p = 0.2885$, as before

$\bar{m} = \frac{104}{30} = 3.4667$

$\sum a_i^2 = 86; \quad \sum m_i^2 = 404; \quad \sum a_i m_i = 113$

The fpc may be ignored. Hence, from (3.26),

$$v(p) = \frac{(86) - 2(0.2885)(113) + (0.2885)^2(404)}{(30)(29)(3.4667)^2} = 0.00520$$

The variance given by the ratio method, 0.00520, is much larger than that given by the binomial formula, 0.00197. For various reasons, families differ in the frequency with which their members consult a doctor. For the sample as a whole, the proportion who consult a doctor is only a little more than one in four, but there are several families in which every member has seen a doctor. Similar results would be obtained for any characteristic in which the members of the same family tend to act in the same way.

In estimating the proportion of males in the population, the results are different. By the same type of calculation, we find

binomial formula: $v(p) = 0.00240$

ratio formula: $v(p) = 0.00114$

Here the binomial formula *overestimates* the variance. The reason is interesting. Most households are set up as a result of a marriage, hence contain at least one male and one female. Consequently the proportion of males per family varies less from $\frac{1}{2}$ than would be expected from the binomial formula. None of the 30 families, except one with only one member, is composed entirely of males, or entirely of females. If the binomial distribution were applicable, with a true P of approximately $\frac{1}{2}$, households with all members of the same sex would constitute one quarter of the households of size 3 and one eighth of the households of size 4. This property of the sex ratio has been discussed by Hansen and Hurwitz (1942). Other illustrations of the error committed by improper use of the binomial formula in sociological investigations have been given by Kish (1957).

EXERCISES

• 3.1   For a population with $N = 6$, $A = 4$, $A' = 2$, work out the value of a for all possible simple random samples of size 3. Verify the theorems given for the mean and variance of $p = a/n$. Verify that

$$\frac{N - n}{(n - 1)N} pq$$

is an unbiased estimate of the variance of p.

• 3.2   In a simple random sample of 200 from a population of 2000 colleges, 120 colleges were in favor of a proposal, 57 were opposed, and 23 had no opinion. Estimate 95 % confidence limits for the number of colleges in the population that favored the proposal.

• 3.3   Do the results of the previous sample furnish conclusive evidence that the majority of the colleges in the population favored this proposal?

• 3.4   A population with $N = 7$ consists of the elements B_1, C_1, C_2, C_3, D_1, D_2, and D_3. A simple random sample of size 4 is taken in order to estimate the proportion of C's to C's + D's. Work out the conditional distributions of this proportion, p, and verify the formula for its conditional variance.

• 3.5   In the preceding exercise, what is the probability that a sample of size 4 contains B_1? Find the average variance of p over all simple random samples of size 4 and verify that this is $11/280$.

• 3.6   A simple random sample of 290 households was chosen from a city area containing 14,828 households. Each family was asked whether it owned or rented the house and also whether it had the exclusive use of an indoor toilet. Results were as follows:

	Owned		Rented		Total
	Yes	No	Yes	No	
Exclusive use of toilet	141	6	109	34	290

(a) For families who rent, estimate the percentage in the area with exclusive use of an indoor toilet and give the standard error of your estimate;   (b) estimate the total number of renting families in the area who do not have exclusive indoor toilet facilities and give the standard error of this estimate.

• 3.7   If, in example 3.6, the total number of renting families in the city area is 7526, make a new estimate of the number of renters without exclusive toilet facilities and give the standard error of this estimate.

3.8   For estimating the total number of units in class C in domain 1 (section 3.10), the estimate $\hat{A}_1 = N_1 p_1$ was recommended if N_1 were known, as against $\hat{A}_1' = Na_1/n$ if N_1 were not known. Ignoring the fpc, show that in large samples the ratio of the variance of $\hat{A}_1$ to that of $\hat{A}_1'$ is approximately $Q_1/(Q_1 + P_1\pi)$, where π is the proportion of the population that is not in domain 1, and P_1, as in section 3.10, is the proportion of the units in domain 1 that fall in class C. State the conditions under which knowledge of N_1 produces large reductions in variance.

3.9   In a simple random sample of size 5 from a population of size 30, no units in the sample were in class C. By the hypergeometric distribution, find the upper limit to the number A of units in class C in the population, corresponding to a one-tailed confidence probability of 95%. Find also the approximation to A_U obtained by computing the upper 95% binomial limit P_U and shortening the interval as described in section 3.6. Try also the method on p. 59.

• 3.10 A student health service has a record of the total number of eligible students N and of the total number of visits Y made by students during a year. Some students made no visits. The service wishes to estimate the mean number of visits Y/N_1 for the N_1 students who made at least one visit, but does not know the value of N_1. A simple random sample of n eligible students is taken. In it n_1 students out of the n made at least one visit and their total number of visits was y. Ignore the fpc in this question. (a) Show that y/n_1 is an unbiased estimate of Y/N_1 and that its conditional variance is S^2/n_1, where S^2 is the variance of the number of visits among students making at least one visit. (b) A second method of estimating Y/N_1 is to use $\hat{N}_1 = Nn_1/n$ as an estimate of N_1 and hence Yn/Nn_1 as an estimate of Y/N_1. Show that this estimate is biased and that the ratio of the bias to the true value Y/N_1 is approximately $(N - N_1)/nN_1$. Find an approximate expression for the variance of the estimate Yn/Nn_1 and show that the estimate in (a) has a higher variance if

$$S^2 > \frac{(N - N_1)n_1}{N_1 n}\left(\frac{Y}{N_1}\right)^2$$

Hint. If p is a binomial estimate of P, based on n trials, then approximately

$$E\left(\frac{1}{p}\right) = \frac{1}{P} + \frac{Q}{nP^2}, \qquad V\left(\frac{1}{p}\right) = \frac{Q}{nP^3}$$

• 3.11 Which of the two previous estimates seems more precise in the following circumstances? $N = 2004$, $Y = 3011$. The sample with $n = 100$ showed that 73 students made at least one visit. Their total number of visits was 152 and the estimated variance s^2 was 1.55.

3.12 A simple random sample of n cluster units, each with m elements, is taken from a population in which the proportion of elements in class C is P. As the intracluster correlation varies, what are the highest and lowest possible values of the true variance of p (the sample estimate of P) and how do they compare with the binomial variance? Ignore the fpc.

3.13 For the sample of 30 households in Table 3.5, the data shown (p. 70) refer to visits to the dentist in the last year. Estimate the variance of the proportion of persons who saw a dentist, and compare this with the binomial estimate of the variance.

› 3.14 In sampling for a rare attribute, one method is to continue drawing a simple random sample until m units that possess the rare attribute have been found (Haldane, 1945) where m is chosen in advance. If the fpc is ignored, prove that the probability that the total sample required is of size n is

$$\frac{(n - 1)!}{(m - 1)! (n - m)!} P^m Q^{n-m} \qquad (n \geq m)$$

where P is the frequency of the rare attribute. Find the average size of the total sample and show that $p = (m - 1)/(n - 1)$ is an unbiased estimate of P. (For further discussion, see Finney, 1949, and Sandelius, 1951, who considers a plan

Number of Persons	Dentist Seen		Number of Persons	Dentist Seen	
	Yes	No		Yes	No
5	1	4	5	1	4
6	0	6	4	4	0
3	1	2	4	1	3
3	2	1	3	1	2
2	0	2	3	0	3
3	0	3	4	1	3
3	1	2	3	0	3
3	1	2	3	1	2
4	1	3	1	0	1
4	0	4	2	0	2
3	1	2	4	0	4
2	0	2	3	1	2
7	2	5	4	1	3
4	1	3	2	0	2
3	0	3	4	0	4

in which sampling continues until either m has been found or the total sample size has reached a preassigned limit n_0.)

REFERENCES

Chung, J. H. and DeLury, D. B. (1950). *Confidence limits for the hypergeometric distribution.* University of Toronto Press.

Finney, D. J. (1949). On a method of estimating frequencies. *Biometrika,* **36,** 233–234.

Fisher, R. A. (1958). *Statistical methods for research workers.* Oliver and Boyd, Edinburgh, thirteenth edition, 21.

Fisher, R. A. and Yates, F. (1957). *Statistical tables for biological, agricultural and medical research.* Oliver and Boyd, Edinburgh, fifth edition.

Haldane, J. B. S. (1945). On a method of estimating frequencies. *Biometrika,* **33,** 222–225.

Hansen, M. H. and Hurwitz, W. N. (1942). Relative efficiencies of various sampling units in population inquiries. *Jour. Amer. Stat. Ass.,* **37,** 89–94.

Harvard Computation Laboratory (1955). *Tables of the cumulative binomial probability distribution.* Harvard University Press, Cambridge, Mass.

Kish, L. (1957). Confidence limits for clustered samples. *Amer. Soc. Rev.,* **22,** 154–165.

Lieberman, G. J., and Owen, D. B., (1961). *Tables of the hypergeometric probability distribution.* Stanford University Press.

National Bureau of Standards (1950). *Tables of the binomial probability distribution.* U. S. Government Printing Office, Washington, D. C.

Romig, H. G. (1952). *50–100 binomial tables.* John Wiley and Sons, New York.

Sandelius, M. (1951). Truncated inverse binomial sampling. *Skandinavisk Aktuarietidskrift,* **34,** 41–44.

CHAPTER 4

The Estimation of Sample Size

4.1 A HYPOTHETICAL EXAMPLE

In the planning of a sample survey, a stage is always reached at which a decision must be made about the size of the sample. The decision is important. Too large a sample implies a waste of resources, and too small a sample diminishes the utility of the results. The decision cannot always be made satisfactorily, for often we do not possess enough information to be sure that our choice of sample size is the best one. Sampling theory provides a framework within which to think intelligently about the problem.

A hypothetical example brings out the steps involved in reaching a solution. An anthropologist is preparing to study the inhabitants of some island. Among other things, he wishes to estimate the percentage of inhabitants belonging to blood group O. Cooperation has been secured so that it is feasible to take a simple random sample. How large should the sample be?

This question cannot be discussed without first receiving an answer to another question. How accurately does the anthropologist wish to know the percentage of people with blood group O? In reply he states that he will be content if the percentage is correct within $\pm 5\%$ in the sense that, if the sample shows 43% to have blood group O, the percentage for the whole island is sure to lie between 38 and 48.

To avoid misunderstanding, it may be advisable to point out to the anthropologist that we cannot absolutely guarantee accuracy within 5% except by measuring everyone. However large n is taken, there is a chance of a very unlucky sample that is in error by more than the desired 5%. The anthropologist replies coldly that he is aware of this, that he is willing to take a 1 in 20 chance of getting an unlucky sample, and that all he asks for is the value of n instead of a lecture on statistics.

We are now in a position to make a rough estimate of n. To simplify matters, the fpc is ignored, and the sample percentage p is assumed to be

71

normally distributed. Whether these assumptions are reasonable can be verified when the initial n is known.

In technical terms, p is to lie in the range $(P \pm 5)$, except for a 1 in 20 chance. Since p is assumed normally distributed about P, it will lie in the range $(P \pm 2\sigma_p)$, apart from a 1 in 20 chance. Further,

$$\sigma_p \doteq \sqrt{PQ/n}$$

Hence, we may put

$$2\sqrt{PQ/n} = 5 \quad \text{or} \quad n = \frac{4PQ}{25}$$

At this point a difficulty appears that is common to all problems in the estimation of sample size. A formula for n has been obtained, but n depends on some property of the population that is to be sampled. In this instance the property is the quantity P which we would like to measure. We therefore ask the anthropologist if he can give us some idea of the likely value of P. He replies that from previous data on other ethnic groups, and from his speculations about the racial history of this island, he will be surprised if P lies outside the range 30 to 60%.

This information is sufficient to provide a usable answer. For any value of P between 30 and 60, the product PQ lies between 2100 and a maximum of 2500 at $P = 50$. The corresponding n lies between 336 and 400. To be on the safe side, 400 is taken as the initial estimate of n.

The assumptions made in this analysis can now be re-examined. With $n = 400$ and a P between 30 and 60, the distribution of p should be close to normal. Whether the fpc is required depends on the number of people on the island. If the population exceeds 8000, the sampling fraction is less than 5% and no adjustment for fpc is called for. The method of applying the readjustment, if it is needed, is discussed in section 4.4.

4.2 ANALYSIS OF THE PROBLEM

The principal steps involved in the choice of a sample size are as follows:

1. There must be some statement concerning what is expected of the sample. This statement may be in terms of desired limits of error, as in the previous example, or in terms of some decision that is to be made or action that is to be taken when the sample results are known. The responsibility for framing the statement rests primarily with the persons who wish to use · the results of the survey, though they frequently need guidance in putting their wishes into numerical terms.

2. Some equation which connects n with the desired precision of the sample must be found. The equation will vary with the content of the

statement of precision and with the kind of sampling that is contemplated. One of the advantages of probability sampling is that it enables this equation to be constructed.

3. This equation will contain, as parameters, certain unknown properties of the population. These must be estimated in order to give specific results.

4. It often happens that data are to be published for certain major subdivisions of the population and that desired limits of error are set up for each subdivision. A separate calculation is made for the n in each subdivision, and the total n is found by addition.

5. More than one item or characteristic is usually measured in a sample survey: sometimes the number of items is large. If a desired degree of precision is prescribed for each item, the calculations lead to a series of conflicting values of n, one for each item. Some method must be found for reconciling these values.

6. Finally, the chosen value of n must be appraised to see whether it is consistent with the resources available to take the sample. This demands an estimation of the cost, labor, time, and materials required to obtain the proposed size of sample. It sometimes becomes apparent that n will have to be drastically reduced. A hard decision must then be faced—whether to proceed with a much smaller sample size, thus reducing precision, or to abandon efforts until more resources can be found.

In succeeding sections some of these questions are examined in more detail.

4.3 THE SPECIFICATION OF PRECISION

The statement of precision desired may be made by giving the amount of error that we are willing to tolerate in the sample estimates. This amount is determined, as best we can, in the light of the uses to which the sample results are to be put. Sometimes it is difficult to decide how much error *should* be tolerated, particularly when the results have several different uses. Suppose that we asked the anthropologist why he wished the percentage with blood group O to be correct to 5% rather than, say, 4 or 6%. He might reply that the blood group data are to be used primarily for racial classification. He strongly suspects that the islanders belong either to a racial type with a P of about 35% or to one with a P of about 50%. An error limit of 5% in the estimate seemed to him small enough to permit classification into one of these types. He would, however, have no violent objection to 4 or 6% limits of error.

Thus the choice of a 5% limit of error by the anthropologist was to some extent arbitrary. In this respect the example is typical of the way in which a limit of error is often decided on. In fact, the anthropologist was more certain of what he wanted than many other scientists and administrators will be found to be. When the question of desired degree of precision is first raised, such persons may confess that they have never thought about it and have no idea of the answer. My experience has been, however, that after discussion they can frequently indicate at least roughly the size of a limit of error that appears reasonable to them.

Further than this we may not be able to go in many practical situations. Part of the difficulty is that not enough is known about the consequences of errors of different sizes as they affect the wisdom of practical decisions that are made from survey results. Even when these consequences are known, however, the results of many important surveys are used by different people for different purposes, and some of the purposes are not foreseen at the time when the survey is planned. Therefore, an element of guesswork is likely to be prominent in the specification of precision for some time to come.

If the sample is taken for a very specific purpose, for example, for making a single "yes" or "no" decision or for deciding how much money to spend on a certain venture, the precision needed can usually be stated in a more definite manner, in terms of the consequences of errors in the decision. A general approach to problems of this type is given in section 4.9, which, although in need of amplification, offers a logical start on a solution.

4.4 THE FORMULA FOR *n* IN SAMPLING FOR PROPORTIONS

The units are classified into two classes, C and C'. Some margin of error d in the estimated proportion p of units in class C has been agreed on, and there is a small risk α which we are willing to incur that the actual error is larger than d; that is, we want

$$\Pr(|p - P| \geq d) = \alpha$$

Simple random sampling is assumed, and p is taken as normally distributed. From theorem 3.2, section 3.2,

$$\sigma_p = \sqrt{\frac{N - n}{N - 1}} \sqrt{\frac{PQ}{n}}$$

Hence the formula that connects n with the desired degree of precision is

$$d = t \sqrt{\frac{N - n}{N - 1}} \sqrt{\frac{PQ}{n}}$$

where t is the abscissa of the normal curve that cuts off an area α at the tails. Solving for n, we find

$$n = \frac{\dfrac{t^2 PQ}{d^2}}{1 + \dfrac{1}{N}\left(\dfrac{t^2 PQ}{d^2} - 1\right)} \tag{4.1}$$

For practical use, an advance estimate p of P is substituted in this formula. If N is large, a first approximation is

$$n_0 = \frac{t^2 pq}{d^2} = \frac{pq}{V} \tag{4.2}$$

where

$$V = \frac{d^2}{t^2} = \text{desired variance of the sample proportion}$$

In practice we first calculate n_0. If n_0/N is negligible, n_0 is a satisfactory approximation to the n of (4.1). If not, it is apparent on comparison of (4.1) and (4.2) that n is obtained as

$$n = \frac{n_0}{1 + (n_0 - 1)/N} \doteq \frac{n_0}{1 + (n_0/N)} \tag{4.3}$$

Example. In the hypothetical blood groups example we had

$$d = 0.05, \qquad p = 0.5, \qquad \alpha = 0.05, \qquad t = 2$$

Thus

$$n_0 = \frac{(4)(0.5)(0.5)}{(0.0025)} = 400$$

Let us assume that there are only 3200 people on the island. The fpc is needed, and we find

$$n = \frac{n_0}{1 + (n_0 - 1)/N} = \frac{400}{1 + \frac{399}{3200}} = 356$$

The formula for n_0 holds also if d, p, and q are all expressed as percentages instead of proportions. Since the product pq increases as p moves toward $\frac{1}{2}$, or 50%, a conservative estimate of n is obtained by choosing for p the value nearest to $\frac{1}{2}$ in the range in which p is thought likely to lie. If p seems likely to lie between 5 and 9%, for instance, we assume 9% for the estimation of n.

4.5 THE FORMULA FOR n WITH CONTINUOUS DATA

If $\bar{y}$ is the average of the observations from a simple random sample, we wish to have

$$\Pr\left(|\bar{y} - \bar{Y}| \geq d\right) = \alpha$$

where d is the chosen margin of error and α a small probability. We assume that $\bar{y}$ is normally distributed: from theorem 2.2, corollary 1, its standard error is

$$\sigma_{\bar{y}} = \sqrt{\frac{N-n}{N}} \frac{S}{\sqrt{n}}$$

Hence

$$d = t \sqrt{\frac{N-n}{N}} \frac{S}{\sqrt{n}} \tag{4.4}$$

This gives

$$n = \frac{\left(\dfrac{tS}{d}\right)^2}{1 + \dfrac{1}{N}\left(\dfrac{tS}{d}\right)^2}$$

As in the preceding section, we take as a first approximation

$$n_0 = \left(\frac{tS}{d}\right)^2 = \frac{S^2}{V} \tag{4.5}$$

This is adequate unless n_0/N is appreciable, in which event we compute n as

$$n = \frac{n_0}{1 + (n_0/N)} \tag{4.6}$$

If the population *total* Y is to be estimated with margin of error d, take as a first approximation

$$n_0 = \left(\frac{NtS}{d}\right)^2 = \frac{(NS)^2}{V}$$

instead of (4.5). Equation 4.6 remains unchanged.

Example. In nurseries that produce young trees for sale it is advisable to estimate, in late winter or early spring, how many healthy young trees are likely to be on hand, since this determines policy toward the solicitation and acceptance of orders. A study of sampling methods for the estimation of the total numbers of seedlings was undertaken by Johnson (1943). The data that follow were obtained from a bed of silver maple seedlings, 1 ft wide and 430 ft long. The sampling unit was 1 ft of the length of the bed, so that $N = 430$. By complete enumeration of the bed it was found that $\bar{Y} = 19$, $S^2 = 85.6$, these being the true population values.

With simple random sampling, how many units must be taken to estimate $\bar{Y}$ within 10%, apart from a chance of 1 in 20? From (4.5) we obtain

$$n_0 = \frac{t^2 S^2}{d^2} = \frac{(4)(85.6)}{(1.9)^2} = 95$$

Since n_0/N is not negligible, we take

$$n = \frac{95}{1 + \frac{95}{430}} = 78$$

Almost 20% of the bed has to be counted in order to attain the precision desired.

The formulas for n given here apply only to simple random sampling in which the sample mean is used as the estimate of $\bar{Y}$. The appropriate formulas for other methods of sampling and estimation are presented with the discussion of these techniques.

4.6 ADVANCE ESTIMATES OF POPULATION VARIANCES

The nursery example is atypical in that the population variance S^2 was known. In practice, there are four ways of estimating population variances for sample size determinations: (1) by taking the sample in two steps, the first being a simple random sample of size n_1 from which the value of S^2 or P and the required n will be obtained; (2) by the results of a pilot survey; (3) by previous sampling of the same or a similar population; and (4) by guesswork about the structure of the population, assisted by some mathematical results.

Method 1 gives the most reliable estimates of S^2 or P, but it is not often used since it slows up the completion of the survey. When the method is feasible, Cox (1952), following work by Stein (1945), shows how to compute n from A_1^2 or p_1 so that the final estimate $\bar{y}$ or p will have a preassigned variance V, a preassigned limit of error d, or a preassigned coefficient of variation. The first sample is assumed large enough to neglect terms of order $1/n_1^2$. A few results are quoted.

Estimation of $\bar{Y}$ with Variance V

If s_1^2 is the variance from the first sample, take additional units to make the total sample size

$$n = \frac{s_1^2}{V}\left(1 + \frac{2}{n_1}\right) \qquad (4.7)$$

The distribution of y is assumed to be approximately normal. If S were known exactly, the required sample size would be S^2/V. The effect of not knowing S is to increase the average size by the factor $(1 + 2/n_1)$.

Estimation of P with variance V

Let p_1 be the estimate of P from the first sample. The combined size of the first two samples should be

$$n = \frac{p_1 q_1}{V} + \frac{3 - 8p_1 q_1}{p_1 q_1} + \frac{1 - 3p_1 q_1}{V n_1} \qquad (4.8)$$

The first term on the right is the size required if P is known to be equal to p_1. With this method, the ordinary binomial estimate p made from the complete sample of size n is slightly biased. To correct for bias, take

$$\hat{P} = p + \frac{V(1 - 2p)}{pq}$$

Estimation of P with given $cv = \sqrt{C}$

Take

$$n = \frac{q_1}{Cp_1} + \frac{3}{p_1q_1} + \frac{1}{Cp_1n_1} \qquad (4.9)$$

The estimate is $\hat{P} = p - Cp/q$. In all three results given above the fpc is ignored.

Example. A sampler wishes to estimate P with a coefficient of variation of 0.1 (10%). He guesses that P will lie somewhere between 5 and 20%. This range is too wide to give a good initial estimate of the required n. Since the cv of P is $\sqrt{Q/nP}$, it is easily verified that $n = 400$ is adequate for $P = 20\%$, but $n = 1900$ will be needed if P is only 5%.

Accordingly, he takes an initial sample with $n_1 = 400$ and finds $p_1 = 0.105$. Since $\sqrt{C} = 0.1$, $C = 0.01$. Equation 4.9 gives

$$n = \frac{(0.895)}{(0.01)(0.105)} + \frac{3}{(0.0940)} + \frac{1}{(0.01)(42)} = 925$$

The combined sample gives $np = 88$; $p = 88/925 = 0.0951$. The correction for bias, Cp/q, amounts to 0.0011, giving a final estimate of 0.0940 or 9.4%.

The second method, a small pilot survey, serves many purposes, especially if the feasibility of the main survey is in doubt. If the pilot survey is itself a simple random sample, the preceding methods apply. But often the pilot work is restricted to a part of the population that is convenient to handle or that will reveal the magnitude of certain problems. Allowance must be made for the selective nature of the pilot when using its results to estimate S^2 or P. For instance, a common practice is to confine the pilot work to a few clusters of units. Thus the computed s^2 measures mostly the variation within a cluster and may be an underestimate of the relevant S^2. The relation between intra- and intercluster variation is discussed in Chapter 9. The same problem arises in cluster sampling for proportions, in which the formula pq/n may underestimate the effect of variation among clusters. Cornfield (1951) gives a good illustration of the estimation of sample size in cluster sampling for proportions.

Method 3—the use of results from previous surveys—points to the value of making available, or at least keeping accessible, any data on standard deviations obtained in previous surveys. Unfortunately, the cost of computing standard deviations in complex surveys is high, even with electronic machines, and frequently only those s.d.'s needed to give a rough idea of the precision of the principal estimates are computed and recorded. If suitable past data are found, the value of S^2 may require adjustment for time changes. With skew data in which $\bar{Y}$ is changing with time, S^2 is often found to change at a rate lying somewhere between $k\bar{Y}$ and $k\bar{Y}^2$, where k is a constant. Thus, if $\bar{Y}$ is thought to have increased by 10% in the time interval since the previous survey, we might increase our initial estimate of S^2 by 10 to 20%.

Finally, a serviceable estimate of S^2 can sometimes be made from relatively little information about the nature of the population. In early studies of the numbers of wireworms in soils, a tool was used to take a sample ($9 \times 9 \times 5$ in.) of the topsoil. For estimating n, the sampler needed to know the standard deviation of the number of wireworms found in a boring with the tool. If wireworms were distributed at random over the topsoil, the number found in a small volume would follow the Poisson distribution, for which $S^2 = \bar{Y}$. Since there might be some tendency for wireworms to congregate, it was decided to assume $S^2 = 1.2\,\bar{Y}$, the factor 1.2 being an arbitrary safety factor. Although $\bar{Y}$ was not known, the values of $\bar{Y}$ that are of economic importance with respect to crop damage could be delineated. These two pieces of information made it possible to determine sample sizes that proved satisfactory.

Deming (1960) shows how some simple mathematical distributions may be used to estimate S^2 from a knowledge of the range and a general idea of the shape of the distribution. If the distribution is like a binomial, with a proportion p of the observations at one end of the range and a proportion q at the other end, $S^2 = pqh^2$, where h is the range. When $p = q = \frac{1}{2}$, the value of $S^2 = 0.25h^2$ is the maximum possible for a given range h. Other useful relations are that $S^2 = 0.083h^2$ for a rectangular distribution, $S^2 = 0.056h^2$ for a distribution shaped like a right triangle, and $S^2 = 0.042h^2$ for an isosceles triangle.

These relations do not help much if h is large or poorly known. However, if h is large, good sampling practice is to stratify the population (Chapter 5) so that within any stratum the range is much reduced. Usually the shape also becomes simpler (closer to a rectangular) within a stratum. Consequently, these relations are effective in predicting S^2, hence n, within individual strata.

4.7 SAMPLE SIZE WITH MORE THAN ONE ITEM

In most surveys information is collected on more than one item. One method of determining sample size is to specify margins of error for the items that are regarded as most vital to the survey. An estimation of the sample size needed is first made separately for each of these important items.

When the single-item estimations of n have been completed, it is time to take stock of the situation. It may happen that the n's required are all reasonably close. If the largest of the n's falls within the limits of the budget, this n is selected. More commonly, there is a sufficient variation among the n's so that we are reluctant to choose the largest, either from budgetary considerations or because this will give an over-all standard of precision substantially higher than originally contemplated. In this event the desired standard of precision may be relaxed for certain of the items, in order to permit the use of a smaller value of n.

In some cases the n's required for different items are so discordant that certain of them must be dropped from the inquiry, for with the resources available the precision expected for these items is totally inadequate. The difficulty may not be merely one of sample size. Some items call for a different type of sampling from others. With populations that are sampled repeatedly, it is useful to amass information about those items that can be combined economically in a general survey and those that necessitate special methods. As an example, a classification of items into four types,

TABLE 4.1

An Example of Different Types of Item in
Regional Surveys

Type	Characteristics of Item	Type of Sampling Needed
1	Widespread throughout the region, occurring with reasonable frequency in all parts.	A general survey with low sampling ratio.
2	Widespread throughout the region but with low frequency.	A general survey, but with a higher sampling ratio.
3	Occurring with reasonable frequency in most parts of the region, but with more sporadic distribution, being absent in some parts and highly concentrated in others.	For best results, a stratified sample with different intensities in different parts of the region (Chapter 5). Can sometimes be included in a general survey with supplementary sampling.
4	Distribution very sporadic or concentrated in a small part of the region.	Not suitable for a general survey. Requires a sample geared to its distribution.

suggested by experience in regional agricultural surveys, is shown in Table 4.1. In this classification, a general survey means one in which the units are fairly evenly distributed over some region, as for example by a simple random sample.

4.8 SAMPLE SIZE WHEN ESTIMATES ARE WANTED FOR SUBDIVISIONS OF THE POPULATION

It is often planned to present estimates not only for the population as a whole but for certain subdivisions. If these can be identified in advance, as with different geographical regions, a separate calculation of n is made for each region. Suppose that the mean of each subdivision is to be estimated with a specified variance V. For the ith subdivision, we have $n_i = S_i^2/V$, so that the total sample size $n = \sum S_i^2/V$. The individual S_i^2 will, on the average, be smaller than S^2, the population variance, but often they are only slightly smaller. Thus, if there are k subdivisions, $n \doteq kS^2/V$, whereas if only the estimate for the population as a whole were wanted we would take $n = S^2/V$.

Thus if estimates with variance V are wanted for each of k subdivisions the sample size must be roughly k times as large as is needed for an over-all estimate of the same precision. This point tends to be overlooked in calculations of sample size by persons inexperienced in survey methods.

If the subdivisions represent classifications by variables such as age, sex, income, and years of schooling, the subdivision to which a person belongs is not known until the sample has been taken. Advance sample size estimates can still be made if the proportions π_i of the units that belong to the various subdivisions are known. If a simple random sample of size n is selected, the expected size of sample from the ith subdivision is $n\pi_i$. The average variance of the mean from this subdivision is

$$V(\bar{y}_i) = E\left(\frac{S_i^2}{n_i}\right) \doteq \frac{S_i^2}{n\pi_i}$$

if $n\pi_i$ is large. Hence we require $n \doteq S_i^2/\pi_i V$ in order to make $V(\bar{y}_i) = V$. If this is to hold for every subdivision,

$$n \doteq \max\left(\frac{S_i^2}{\pi_i V}\right) \doteq \frac{S^2}{V} \max\left(\frac{1}{\pi_i}\right)$$

If the subdivisions are approximately equal in size, $\pi_i \doteq 1/k$, but the factor $\max(1/\pi_i)$ can be considerably larger than k if some subdivisions are rare. In this event, we may either have to increase the value of V in this subdivision or find some way of identifying units in rare subdivisions in advance so that they can be sampled at a higher rate. The method of double sampling (Chapter 12) is sometimes useful for this purpose.

The demands on sample size are still greater in analytical studies in which the specifications are

$$V(\bar{y}_i - \bar{y}_j) \leq V$$

for every pair of subdivisions (domains). In this case

$$n \doteq \max_{i,j} \frac{1}{V}\left(\frac{S_i^2}{\pi_i} + \frac{S_j^2}{\pi_j}\right)$$

If the S_i^2 are not very different from S^2, n will be $2kS^2/V$ when the k domains are of equal size, and still greater otherwise. The effect of fpc terms, neglected in this discussion, is to reduce the required n's to some extent.

4.9 SAMPLE SIZE IN DECISION PROBLEMS

A more logical approach to the determination of sample size can sometimes be developed when a practical decision is to be made from the results of the sample. The decision will presumably be more soundly based if the sample estimate has a low error than if it has a high error. We may be able to calculate, in monetary terms, the loss $l(z)$ that will be incurred in a decision through an error of amount z in the estimate. Although the actual value of z is not predictable in advance, sampling theory enables us to find the frequency distribution $f(z, n)$ of z, which for a specified sampling method will depend on the sample size n. Hence the *expected loss* for a given size of sample is

$$L(n) = \int l(z)f(z, n)\, dz$$

The purpose in taking the sample is to diminish this loss. If $C(n)$ is the cost of a sample of size n, a reasonable procedure is to choose n to minimize

$$C(n) + L(n)$$

since this is the total cost involved in taking the sample and in making decisions from its results. The choice of n determines both the optimum size of sample and the most advantageous degree of precision.

Alternatively, the same approach can be presented in terms of the monetary *gain* that accrues from having the sample information, rather than in terms of the loss that arises from errors in the sample information. If monetary gain is used, we construct an expected gain $G(n)$ from a sample of size n, where $G(n)$ is zero if no sample is taken. We *maximize*

$$G(n) - C(n)$$

In this form the principle is equivalent to the rule in classical economics that profit is to be maximized.

The simplest application occurs when the loss function, $l(z)$, is λz^2, where λ is a constant. It follows that

$$L(n) = \lambda E(z^2)$$

For instance, if $\hat{\bar{Y}}$ is the sample estimate of $\bar{Y}$, and $z = \hat{\bar{Y}} - \bar{Y}$,

$$L(n) = \lambda V(\hat{\bar{Y}}) = \frac{\lambda S^2}{n} - \frac{\lambda S^2}{N}$$

if simple random sampling is used.

The simplest type of cost function for the sample is

$$C(n) = c_0 + c_1 n$$

where c_0 is the overhead cost. By differentiation, the value of n which minimizes cost plus loss is

$$n = \sqrt{\lambda S^2/c_1}$$

A more general form of this result is given by Yates (1960). The same analysis applies to any method of sampling and estimation in which the variance of the estimate is inversely proportional to n and the cost is a linear function of n.

Blythe (1945) describes the application of this principle to the estimation of the volume of timber in a lot for selling purposes (see exercise 4.11). Nordin (1944) discusses the optimum size of sample for estimating potential sales in a market which a manufacturer intends to enter. If the sales can be forecast accurately, the amount of fixed equipment and the production per unit period can be allocated to maximize the manufacturer's expected profit. Grundy et al. (1954, 1956) consider the optimum size of a second sample when the results of a first sample are already known.

This approach has received substantial further development from workers on statistical decision theory. Generalizations include the substitution of utility for money value as a scale on which to measure costs and losses, the explicit use of subjective prior information about unknown parameters by expressing this information as "prior" probability distributions of the unknown parameters, and the investigation of different types of cost and loss functions and of qualitative as well as quantitative data. For a comprehensive account of the method, see Raiffa and Schlaifer (1961). Although it is still not evident how frequently decision problems will be amenable to complete solution by this approach, the method has value in stimulating clear thinking about the important factors in a good decision. One area that appears suitable for applications is the sampling of lots of articles in a mass-production process in order to decide whether to accept or reject the lot on the basis of its estimated quality. Sittig (1951) considers the economics of sample-size determination, taking account of costs of inspection and the costs incurred through defective articles in accepted lots and good articles in rejected lots.

EXERCISES

- 4.1 In a district containing 4000 houses the percentage of owned houses is to be estimated with a s.e. of not more than 2% and the percentage of two-car households with a s.e. of not more than 1%. (The figures 2 and 1% are the absolute values, not the cv's.) The true percentage of owners is thought to lie between 45 and 65% and the percentage of two-car households between 5 and 10%. How large a sample is necessary to satisfy both aims?

- 4.2 In the population of 676 petition sheets (Table 2.1, page 27) how large must the sample be if the total number of signatures is to be estimated with a margin of error of 1000, apart from a 1 in 20 chance? Assume that the value of s^2 given on page 27 is the population S^2.

- 4.3 A survey is to be made of the prevalence of the common diseases in a large population. For any disease that affects at least 1% of the individuals in the population, it is desired to estimate the total number of cases, with a coefficient of variation of not more than 20%. (a) What size of simple random sample is needed, assuming that the presence of the disease can be recognized without mistakes? (b) What size is needed if total cases are wanted separately for males and females, with the same precision?

4.4 In a wireworm survey the number of wireworms per acre is to be estimated with a limit of error of 30%, at the 95% probability level, in any field in which wireworm density exceeds 200,000 per acre in the top 5 in. of soil. The sampling tool measures 9 × 9 × 5 in. deep. Assuming that the number of wireworms in a single sample follows a distribution slightly more variable than the Poisson, we take $S^2 = 1.2\bar{Y}$. What size of simple random sample is needed? (1 acre = 43,560 sq ft.)

- 4.5 The following coefficients of variation per unit were obtained in a farm survey in Iowa, the unit being an area 1 mile square (data of R. J. Jessen):

Item	Estimated cv (%)
Acres in farms	38
Acres in corn	39
Acres in oats	44
Number of family workers	100
Number of hired workers	110
Number of unemployed	317

A survey is planned to estimate acreage items with a cv of $2\frac{1}{2}$% and numbers of workers (excluding unemployed) with a cv of 5%. With simple random sampling, how many units are needed? How well would this sample be expected to estimate the number of unemployed?

4.6 By experimental sampling, the mean value of a random variate is to be estimated with variance $V = 0.0005$. The values of the random variate for the first 20 samples drawn are shown below. How many more samples are needed? (Use equation 4.7.)

Sample Number	Value of Random Variate	Sample Number	Value of Random Variate
1	0.0725	11	0.0712
2	0.0755	12	0.0748
3	0.0759	13	0.0878
4	0.0739	14	0.0710
5	0.0732	15	0.0754
6	0.0843	16	0.0712
7	0.0727	17	0.0757
8	0.0769	18	0.0737
9	0.0730	19	0.0704
10	0.0727	20	0.0723

4.7 A household survey is designed to estimate the proportion of families possessing certain attributes. For the principal items of interest, the value of P is expected to lie between 30 and 70%. With simple random sampling, how large are the values of n necessary to estimate the following means with a standard error not exceeding 3%? (a) the over-all mean P. (b) the *individual* means P_i for the income classes—under \$5000; \$5000 to \$10,000; over \$10,000. ($i = 1, 2, 3$). (c) the differences between the means ($P_i - P_j$) for every pair of the classes in (b). Give a separate answer for (a), (b), and (c). Income statistics indicate that the proportions of families with incomes in the three classes above are 50, 38, and 12%.

4.8 The four-year colleges in the United States were divided into classes of four different sizes according to their 1952–1953 enrollments. The standard deviations within each class are shown below.

	Class			
	1	2	3	4
Number of students	<1000	1000–3000	3000–10,000	over 10,000
S	236	625	2008	10,023

If you know the class boundaries but not the values of S, how well can you guess the S values by using simple mathematical figures (section 4.6)? No college has less than 200 students and the largest has about 50,000 students.

4.9 With a quadratic loss function and a linear cost function, as in section 4.9, S^2 is reduced to S'^2 by a superior sampling plan, c_0, c_1, and λ remaining unchanged. If n', V' denote the new optimum sample size and the accompanying $V(\hat{Y})$, show that $n' < n$ and that $V' < V$, provided that $n \leq N/2$.

4.10   If the loss function due to an error in $\bar{y}$ is $\lambda |\bar{y} - \bar{Y}|$ and if the cost $C = c_0 + c_1 n$, show that with simple random sampling, ignoring the fpc, the most economical value of n is

$$\left(\frac{\lambda S}{c_1 \sqrt{2\pi}}\right)^{2/3}$$

• 4.11   (Adapted from Blythe, 1945) The selling price of a lot of standing timber is UW, where U is the price per unit volume and W is the volume of timber on the lot. The number N of logs on the lot is counted, and the average volume per log is estimated from a simple random sample of n logs. The estimate is made and paid for by the seller and is provisionally accepted by the buyer. Later, the buyer finds out the exact volume purchased, and the seller reimburses him if he has paid for more than was delivered. If he has paid for less than was delivered, the buyer does not mention the fact.

Construct the seller's loss function. Assuming that the cost of measuring n logs is cn, find the optimum value of n. The standard deviation of the volume per log may be denoted by S and the fpc ignored.

REFERENCES

Blythe, R. H. (1945). The economics of sample size applied to the scaling of saw-logs. *Biom. Bull.*, **1**, 67–70.

Cornfield, J. (1951). The determination of sample size. *Amer. Jour. Pub. Health*, **41**, 654–661.

Cox, D. R. (1952). Estimation by double sampling. *Biometrika*, **39**, 217–227.

Deming, W. E. (1960). *Sample design in business research.* John Wiley and Sons, New York.

Grundy, P. M., Healy, M. J. R., and Rees, D. H. (1954). Decision between two alternatives—how many experiments? *Biometrics*, **10**, 317–323.

Grundy, P. M., Healy, M. J. R., and Rees, D. H. (1956). Economic choice of the amount of experimentation. *Jour. Roy. Stat. Soc.*, B, **18**, 32–55.

Johnson, F. A. (1943). A statistical study of sampling methods for tree nursery inventories. *Jour. Forestry*, **41**, 674–679.

Nordin, J. A. (1944). Determining sample size. *Jour. Amer. Stat. Assoc.*, **39**, 497–506.

Raiffa, H., and Schlaifer, R. (1961). *Applied statistical decision theory.* Harvard Business School, Boston.

Sittig, J. (1951). The economic choice of sampling system in acceptance sampling. *Bull. Int. Stat. Inst.*, **33**, V, 51–84.

Stein, C. (1945). A two-sample test for a linear hypothesis whose power is independent of the variance. *Ann. Math. Stat.*, **16**, 243–258.

Yates, F. (1960). *Sampling methods for censuses and surveys.* Charles Griffin and Co., London, Third Edition.

CHAPTER 5

Stratified Random Sampling

5.1 DESCRIPTION

In stratified sampling the population of N units is first divided into sub-populations of $N_1, N_2, \cdots, N_L$ units, respectively. These subpopulations are nonoverlapping, and together they comprise the whole of the population, so that

$$N_1 + N_2 + \cdots + N_L = N$$

The subpopulations are called *strata*. To obtain the full benefit from stratification, the values of the N_h must be known. When the strata have been determined, a sample is drawn from each, the drawings being made independently in different strata. The sample sizes within the strata are denoted by $n_1, n_2, \cdots, n_L$, respectively.

If a simple random sample is taken in each stratum, the whole procedure is described as *stratified random sampling*.

Stratification is a common technique. There are many reasons for this; the principal ones are the following:

1. If data of known precision are wanted for certain subdivisions of the population, it is advisable to treat each subdivision as a "population" in its own right.

2. Administrative convenience may dictate the use of stratification; for example, the agency conducting the survey may have field offices, each of which can supervise the survey for a part of the population.

3. Sampling problems may differ markedly in different parts of the population. With human populations, people living in institutions (e.g., hotels, hospitals, prisons) are often placed in a different stratum from people living in ordinary homes because a different approach to the sampling is appropriate for the two situations. In sampling businesses we may possess a list of the large firms, which are placed in a separate stratum. Some type of area sampling may have to be used for the smaller firms.

87

4. Stratification may produce a gain in precision in the estimates of characteristics of the whole population. It may be possible to divide a heterogeneous population into subpopulations, each of which is internally homogeneous. This is suggested by the name *strata*, with its implication of a division into layers. If each stratum is homogeneous, in that the measurements vary little from one unit to another, a precise estimate of any stratum mean can be obtained from a small sample in that stratum. These estimates can then be combined into a precise estimate for the whole population.

The theory of stratified sampling deals with the properties of the estimates from a stratified sample and with the best choice of the sample sizes n_h to obtain maximum precision. In this development it is taken for granted that the strata have already been constructed. The problems of how to construct strata and of how many strata there should be are postponed to a later stage (section 5A.6).

5.2   NOTATION

The suffix h denotes the stratum and i the unit within the stratum. The notation is a natural extension of that previously used. The following symbols all refer to stratum h:

$$N_h \qquad\qquad \text{total number of units}$$

$$n_h \qquad\qquad \text{number of units in sample}$$

$$y_{hi} \qquad\qquad \text{value obtained for the } i\text{th unit}$$

$$W_h = \frac{N_h}{N} \qquad\qquad \text{stratum weight}$$

$$f_h = \frac{n_h}{N_h} \qquad\qquad \text{sampling fraction in the stratum}$$

$$\bar{Y}_h = \frac{\sum_{i=1}^{N_h} y_{hi}}{N_h} \qquad\qquad \text{true mean}$$

$$\bar{y}_h = \frac{\sum_{i=1}^{n_h} y_{hi}}{n_h} \qquad\qquad \text{sample mean}$$

$$S_h{}^2 = \frac{\sum_{i=1}^{N_h} (y_{hi} - \bar{Y}_h)^2}{N_h - 1} \qquad\qquad \text{true variance}$$

Note that the divisor for the variance is $(N_h - 1)$.

5.3 PROPERTIES OF THE ESTIMATES

For the population mean per unit, the estimate used in stratified sampling is $\bar{y}_{st}$ (st for *stratified*), where

$$\bar{y}_{st} = \frac{\sum\limits_{h=1}^{L} N_h \bar{y}_h}{N} \tag{5.1}$$

where $N = N_1 + N_2 + \cdots + N_L$.

The estimate $\bar{y}_{st}$ is not in general the same as the sample mean. The sample mean, $\bar{y}$, can be written as

$$\bar{y} = \frac{\sum\limits_{h=1}^{L} n_h \bar{y}_h}{n} \tag{5.2}$$

The difference is that in $\bar{y}_{st}$ the estimates from the individual strata receive their correct weights N_h/N. It is evident that $\bar{y}$ coincides with $\bar{y}_{st}$ provided that in every stratum

$$\frac{n_h}{n} = \frac{N_h}{N} \quad \text{or} \quad \frac{n_h}{N_h} = \frac{n}{N} \quad \text{or} \quad f_h = f$$

This means that the sampling fraction is the same in all strata. This stratification is described as stratification with *proportional* allocation of the n_h. It gives a *self-weighting* sample. If numerous estimates have to be made, a self-weighting sample is time-saving.

The principal properties of the estimate $\bar{y}_{st}$ are outlined in the following theorems. The first two theorems apply to stratified sampling in general and are not restricted to stratified random sampling; that is, the sample from any stratum need not be a simple random sample.

Theorem 5.1. If in every stratum the sample estimate $\bar{y}_h$ is unbiased, then $\bar{y}_{st}$ is an unbiased estimate of the population mean $\bar{Y}$.

Proof.

$$E(\bar{y}_{st}) = E \frac{\sum\limits_{h=1}^{L} N_h \bar{y}_h}{N} = \frac{\sum\limits_{h=1}^{L} N_h \bar{Y}_h}{N}$$

since the estimates are unbiased in the individual strata. But the population mean $\bar{Y}$ may be written

$$\bar{Y} = \frac{\sum\limits_{h=1}^{L} \sum\limits_{i=1}^{N_h} y_{hi}}{N} = \frac{\sum\limits_{h=1}^{L} N_h \bar{Y}_h}{N}$$

This completes the proof.

Corollary. Since $\bar{y}_h$ is an unbiased estimate of $\bar{Y}_h$ for simple random sampling within strata, $\bar{y}_{st}$ is an unbiased estimate of $\bar{Y}$ for stratified random sampling.

Theorem 5.2. For stratified sampling, the variance of $\bar{y}_{st}$, as an estimate of the population mean $\bar{Y}$, is

$$V(\bar{y}_{st}) = \frac{\sum\limits_{h=1}^{L} N_h^2 V(\bar{y}_h)}{N^2} = \sum\limits_{h=1}^{L} W_h^2 V(\bar{y}_h) \tag{5.3}$$

where

$$V(\bar{y}_h) = E(\bar{y}_h - \bar{Y}_h)^2$$

There are two restrictions on the theorem: (a) $\bar{y}_h$ must be an unbiased estimate of $\bar{Y}_h$, and (b) the samples must be drawn independently in different strata.

Proof.

$$\bar{y}_{st} - \bar{Y} = \frac{\sum N_h \bar{y}_h}{N} - \frac{\sum N_h \bar{Y}_h}{N}$$

$$= \frac{\sum N_h(\bar{y}_h - \bar{Y}_h)}{N} \tag{5.4}$$

where the sum extends over all strata. Note that the error $(\bar{y}_{st} - \bar{Y})$ in the estimate is now expressed as a weighted mean of the errors of estimation which have been made within the individual strata. Hence

$$(\bar{y}_{st} - \bar{Y})^2 = \frac{\sum N_h^2(\bar{y}_h - \bar{Y}_h)^2}{N^2} + \frac{2 \sum N_h N_j(\bar{y}_h - \bar{Y}_h)(\bar{y}_j - \bar{Y}_j)}{N^2}$$

where the right-hand term extends over all pairs of strata.

We now average over all possible samples. For any cross-product term, we begin by keeping the sample in stratum h fixed, and average over all samples in stratum j. Since sampling is independent in the two strata, the possible samples in stratum j will be the same and have the same probabilities, whatever sample has been drawn in stratum h. But since $\bar{y}_j$ is assumed unbiased, the average of $(\bar{y}_j - \bar{Y}_j)$ is zero. Hence all cross-product terms vanish.

The squared terms give

$$V(\bar{y}_{st}) = \frac{\sum N_h^2 E(\bar{y}_h - \bar{Y}_h)^2}{N^2} = \frac{\sum N_h^2 V(\bar{y}_h)}{N^2}$$

The important point about this result is that the variance of $\bar{y}_{st}$ depends only on the variances of the estimates of the individual stratum means $\bar{Y}_h$. If it were possible to divide a highly variable population into strata such that all items had the same value within a stratum, we could estimate $\bar{Y}$

without any error. Equation (5.4) shows that it is the use of the correct stratum weights N_h/N in making the estimate $\bar{y}_{st}$ that leads to this result.

Theorem 5.3. For stratified random sampling, the variance of the estimate $\bar{y}_{st}$ is

$$V(\bar{y}_{st}) = \frac{1}{N^2} \sum_{h=1}^{L} N_h(N_h - n_h) \frac{S_h^2}{n_h} = \sum_{h=1}^{L} W_h^2 \frac{S_h^2}{n_h} (1 - f_h) \qquad (5.5)$$

Proof. Since $\bar{y}_h$ is an unbiased estimate of $\overline{Y}_h$, theorem 5.2 can be applied. Further, by theorem 2.2, applied to an individual stratum,

$$V(\bar{y}_h) = \frac{S_h^2}{n_h} \frac{N_h - n_h}{N_h}$$

By substitution into the result of theorem 5.2, we obtain

$$V(\bar{y}_{st}) = \frac{1}{N^2} \sum_{h=1}^{L} N_h^2 V(\bar{y}_h) = \frac{1}{N^2} \sum_{h=1}^{L} N_h(N_h - n_h) \frac{S_h^2}{n_h} = \sum W_h^2 \frac{S_h^2}{n_h} (1 - f_h)$$

Some particular cases of this formula are given in the following corollaries.

Corollary 1. If the sampling fractions n_h/N_h are negligible in all strata,

$$V(\bar{y}_{st}) = \frac{1}{N^2} \sum \frac{N_h^2 S_h^2}{n_h} = \sum \frac{W_h^2 S_h^2}{n_h} \qquad (5.6)$$

This is the appropriate formula when finite population corrections can be ignored.

Corollary 2. With proportional allocation, we substitute

$$n_h = \frac{n N_h}{N}$$

in (5.5). The variance reduces to

$$V(\bar{y}_{st}) = \sum \frac{N_h}{N} \frac{S_h^2}{n} \left(\frac{N - n}{N}\right) = \frac{1 - f}{n} \sum W_h S_h^2 \qquad (5.7)$$

Corollary 3. If sampling is proportional and the variances in all strata have the same value, S_w^2, we obtain the simple result

$$V(\bar{y}_{st}) = \frac{S_w^2}{n} \left(\frac{N - n}{N}\right) \qquad (5.8)$$

Theorem 5.4. If $\hat{Y}_{st} = N\bar{y}_{st}$ is the estimate of the population total Y, then

$$V(\hat{Y}_{st}) = \sum N_h(N_h - n_h) \frac{S_h^2}{n_h} \qquad (5.9)$$

This follows at once from theorem 5.3.

TABLE 5.1
SIZES OF 64 CITIES (IN 1000's) IN 1920 AND 1930
1920 Size (x_{hi}) 1930 Size (y_{hi})

Stratum				Stratum			
$h = 1$	2			1	2		
797	314	172	121	900	364	209	113
773	298	172	120	822	317	183	115
748	296	163	119	781	328	163	123
734	258	162	118	805	302	253	154
588	256	161	118	670	288	232	140
577	243	159	116	1238	291	260	119
507	238	153	116	573	253	201	130
507	237	144	113	634	291	147	127
457	235	138	113	578	308	292	100
438	235	138	110	487	272	164	107
415	216	138	110	442	284	143	114
401	208	138	108	451	255	169	111
387	201	136	106	459	270	139	163
381	192	132	104	464	214	170	116
324	180	130	101	400	195	150	122
315	179	126	100	366	260	143	134

Note. Cities are arranged in the same order in both years.

Totals and sums of squares

	1920		1930	
Stratum	$\sum (x_{hi})$	$\sum (x_{hi}^2)$	$\sum (y_{hi})$	$\sum (y_{hi}^2)$
1	8,349	4,756,619	10,070	7,145,450
2	7,941	1,474,871	9,498	2,141,720

Example. Table 5.1 shows the 1920 and 1930 numbers of inhabitants, in thousands, of 64 large cities in the United States. The data were obtained by taking the cities which ranked fifth to sixty-eighth in the United States in total number of inhabitants in 1920. The cities are arranged in two strata, the first containing the 16 largest cities and the second the remaining 48 cities.

The total number of inhabitants in all 64 cities in 1930 is to be estimated from a sample of size 24. Find the standard error of the estimated total for (1) a simple random sample, (2) a stratified random sample with proportional allocation, (3) a stratified random sample with 12 units drawn from each stratum.

This population resembles the populations of many types of business enterprise in that some units—the large cities—contribute very substantially to the total and display much greater variability than the remainder.

The stratum totals and sums of squares are given under Table 5.1. Only the 1930 data are used in this example: the 1920 data appear in a later example. For the complete population in 1930, we find

$$Y = 19,568, \qquad S^2 = 52,448$$

The three estimates of Y are denoted by $\hat{Y}_{ran}$, $\hat{Y}_{prop}$, and $\hat{Y}_{equal}$.

1. For simple random sampling,

$$V(\hat{Y}_{ran}) = \frac{N^2 S^2}{n} \frac{N-n}{N} = \frac{(64)^2(52,448)}{24}\left(\frac{40}{64}\right) = 5,594,453$$

from theorem 2.2, corollary 2. The standard error is

$$\sigma(\hat{Y}_{ran}) = 2365$$

2. For the individual strata the variances are

$$S_1{}^2 = 53,843, \qquad S_2{}^2 = 5581$$

Note that the stratum with the largest cities has a variance nearly 10 times that of the other stratum.

In proportional allocation, we have $n_1 = 6$, $n_2 = 18$. From (5.7), multiplying by N^2, we have

$$V(\hat{Y}_{prop}) = \frac{N-n}{n} \sum N_h S_h{}^2$$

$$= \tfrac{40}{24}[(16)(53,843) + (48)(5581)] = 1,882,293$$

$$\sigma(\hat{Y}_{prop}) = 1372$$

3. For $n_1 = n_2 = 12$ we use the general formula (5.9):

$$V(\hat{Y}_{equal}) = \sum N_h(N_h - n_h)\frac{S_h{}^2}{n_h}$$

$$= \frac{(16)(4)(53,843)}{12} + \frac{(48)(36)(5581)}{12} = 1,090,827$$

$$\sigma(\hat{Y}_{equal}) = 1044$$

In this example equal sample sizes in the two strata are more precise than proportional allocation. Both are greatly superior to simple random sampling.

5.4 THE ESTIMATED VARIANCE AND CONFIDENCE LIMITS

If a simple random sample is taken within each stratum, an unbiased estimate of $S_h{}^2$ (from theorem 2.4) is

$$s_h{}^2 = \frac{1}{n_h - 1} \sum_{i=1}^{n_h}(y_{hi} - \bar{y}_h)^2 \tag{5.10}$$

Hence we obtain the following:

Theorem 5.5. With stratified random sampling, an unbiased estimate of the variance of $\bar{y}_{st}$ is

$$v(\bar{y}_{st}) = s^2(\bar{y}_{st}) = \frac{1}{N^2}\sum_{h=1}^{L} N_h(N_h - n_h)\frac{s_h{}^2}{n_h} \tag{5.11}$$

An alternative form for computing purposes is

$$s^2(\bar{y}_{st}) = \sum_{h=1}^{L} \frac{W_h^2 s_h^2}{n_h} - \sum_{h=1}^{L} \frac{W_h s_h^2}{N} \tag{5.12}$$

The second term on the right represents the reduction due to the fpc.

In order to compute this estimate, there must be at least two units drawn from every stratum. Estimation of the variance when stratification is carried to the point at which only one unit is chosen per stratum is discussed in section 5A.11.

Corollary. In certain applications it is reasonable to suppose that S_h^2 has the same value in all strata. From the analysis of variance of the sample, a pooled estimate of this common variance is

$$s_w^2 = \frac{\sum_{h=1}^{L} \sum_{i=1}^{n_h} (y_{hi} - \bar{y}_h)^2}{n - L}$$

Since sampling is usually proportional in this situation, the estimated variance of $\bar{y}_{st}$ takes the simple form (from theorem 5.3, corollary 3)

$$v(\bar{y}_{st}) = \frac{s_w^2}{n} \frac{N - n}{N}$$

with $n - L$ degrees of freedom.

The formulas for confidence limits are as follows:

Population mean: $\qquad\qquad \bar{y}_{st} \pm ts(\bar{y}_{st}) \qquad\qquad\qquad\qquad$ (5.13)

Population total: $\qquad\qquad N\bar{y}_{st} \pm tNs(\bar{y}_{st}) \qquad\qquad\qquad$ (5.14)

These formulas assume that $\bar{y}_{st}$ is normally distributed and that $s(\bar{y}_{st})$ is well determined, so that the multiplier t can be read from tables of the normal distribution.

If only a few degrees of freedom are provided by each stratum, the usual procedure for taking account of the sampling error attached to a quantity like $s(\bar{y}_{st})$ is to read the t-value from the tables of Student's t instead of from the normal table. The distribution of $s(\bar{y}_{st})$ is in general too complex to allow a strict application of this method. An approximate method of assigning an effective number of degrees of freedom to $s(\bar{y}_{st})$ is as follows (Satterthwaite, 1946):

We may write

$$s^2(\bar{y}_{st}) = \frac{1}{N^2} \sum_{h=1}^{L} g_h s_h^2, \quad \text{where } g_h = \frac{N_h(N_h - n_h)}{n_h}$$

The effective number of degrees of freedom n_e is

$$n_e = \frac{(\sum g_h s_h^2)^2}{\sum \dfrac{g_h^2 s_h^4}{n_h - 1}} \tag{5.15}$$

The value of n_e always lies between the smallest of the values $(n_h - 1)$ and their sum. The approximation takes account of the fact that S_h^2 may vary from stratum to stratum. It requires the assumption that the y_{hi} are normal, since it depends on the result that the variance of s_h^2 is $2\sigma_h^4/(n_h - 1)$. As shown in formula 2.51, page 43, the variance of s_h^2 will be larger than this if the distribution of y_{hi} has positive kurtosis. In this event, formula 5.15 overestimates the effective degrees of freedom.

5.5 OPTIMUM ALLOCATION

In stratified sampling the values of the sample sizes n_h in the respective strata are chosen by the sampler. They may be selected to minimize $V(\bar{y}_{st})$ for a specified cost of taking the sample or to minimize the cost for a specified value of $V(\bar{y}_{st})$.

The simplest cost function is of the form

$$\text{cost} = C = c_0 + \sum c_h n_h \tag{5.16}$$

Within any stratum the cost is proportional to the size of sample, but the cost per unit c_h may vary from stratum to stratum. The term c_0 represents an overhead cost. This cost function is appropriate when the major item of cost is that of taking the measurements on each unit. If travel costs between units are substantial, empirical and mathematical studies suggest that travel costs are better represented by the expression $\sum t_h \sqrt{n_h}$ where t_h is the travel cost per unit [Beardwood et al. (1959)]. Only the linear cost function (5.16) is considered here.

Theorem 5.6. In stratified random sampling with a cost function of the form (5.16) the variance of the estimated mean $\bar{y}_{st}$ is a minimum when n_h is proportional to $N_h S_h / \sqrt{c_h}$.

Proof. The problem is to minimize

$$V(\bar{y}_{st}) = \sum_{h=1}^{L} \frac{W_h^2 S_h^2}{n_h} (1 - f_h) = \sum_{h=1}^{L} \frac{W_h^2 S_h^2}{n_h} - \sum_{h=1}^{L} \frac{W_h^2 S_h^2}{N_h}$$

subject to the restriction

$$c_1 n_1 + c_2 n_2 + \cdots + c_L n_L = C - c_0$$

Using the calculus method of Lagrange multipliers, we select the n_h and the multiplier λ to minimize

$$V(\bar{y}_{st}) + \lambda(\sum c_h n_h - C + c_0)$$
$$= \sum \frac{W_h^2 S_h^2}{n_h} - \sum \frac{W_h^2 S_h^2}{N_h} + \lambda(c_1 n_1 + c_2 n_2 + \cdots + c_L n_L - C + c_0)$$

Differentiation with respect to n_h gives the equations

$$-\frac{W_h^2 S_h^2}{n_h^2} + \lambda c_h = 0 \qquad (h = 1, 2, \cdots, L)$$

that is,

$$n_h \sqrt{\lambda} = \frac{W_h S_h}{\sqrt{c_h}} \tag{5.17}$$

Summing over all strata, we obtain

$$n\sqrt{\lambda} = \sum \frac{W_h S_h}{\sqrt{c_h}} \tag{5.18}$$

Finally, the ratio of (5.17) to (5.18) gives

$$\frac{n_h}{n} = \frac{W_h S_h / \sqrt{c_h}}{\sum (W_h S_h / \sqrt{c_h})} = \frac{N_h S_h / \sqrt{c_h}}{\sum (N_h S_h / \sqrt{c_h})} \tag{5.19}$$

This theorem leads to the following rules of conduct. In a given stratum, take a larger sample if

1. the stratum is larger,
2. the stratum is more variable internally,
3. sampling is cheaper in the stratum.

One further step is needed to complete the allocation. Equation (5.19) gives the n_h in terms of n, but we do not yet know what value n has. The solution depends on whether the sample is chosen to meet a specified total cost C or to give a specified variance V for $\bar{y}_{st}$. If *cost* is fixed, substitute the optimum values of n_h in the cost function (5.16) and solve for n. This gives

$$n = \frac{(C - c_0)\sum(N_h S_h / \sqrt{c_h})}{\sum(N_h S_h \sqrt{c_h})}$$

If V is fixed, substitute the optimum n_h in the formula for $V(\bar{y}_{st})$. We find

$$n = \frac{(\sum W_h S_h \sqrt{c_h}) \sum W_h S_h / \sqrt{c_h}}{V + (1/N) \sum W_h S_h^2}$$

where $W_h = N_h / N$.

An important special case arises if $c_h = c$, that is, if the cost per unit is the same in all strata. The cost becomes $C = c_0 + cn$, and optimum allocation for fixed cost reduces to optimum allocation for fixed sample size. The result in this special case is as follows:

Theorem 5.7. In stratified random sampling $V(\bar{y}_{st})$ is minimized for a fixed total size of sample n if

$$n_h = n \frac{W_h S_h}{\sum W_h S_h} = n \frac{N_h S_h}{\sum N_h S_h} \tag{5.20}$$

This allocation is sometimes called the *Neyman allocation*, after Neyman (1934), whose proof gave the result prominence. An earlier proof by Tschuprow (1923) was later discovered.

A formula for the minimum variance with fixed n is obtained by substituting the value of n_h in (5.20) into the general formula for $V(\bar{y}_{st})$. The result is

$$V_{min}(\bar{y}_{st}) = \frac{(\sum W_h S_h)^2}{n} - \frac{\sum W_h S_h^2}{N} \tag{5.21}$$

The second term on the right represents the fpc.

An alternative proof of the allocation results (Stuart, 1954) uses the Cauchy-Schwarz inequality. Minimizing V for fixed C or C for fixed V are both equivalent to minimizing the product

$$V'C' = \left(\sum \frac{W_h^2 S_h^2}{n_h} \right) (\sum c_h n_h)$$

since V' and C' are the parts of V and C that depend on the n_h. The inequality states that if a_h, b_h are two sets of positive numbers, then

$$(\sum a_h^2)(\sum b_h^2) \geq (\sum a_h b_h)^2 \tag{5.22}$$

the equality occurring only if b_h/a_h is constant for all h. Take

$$a_h = \frac{W_h S_h}{\sqrt{n_h}}, \qquad b_h = \sqrt{c_h n_h}$$

The inequality (5.22) gives

$$V'C' = \left(\sum \frac{W_h^2 S_h^2}{n_h} \right) (\sum c_h n_h) = (\sum a_h^2)(\sum b_h^2) \geq (\sum W_h S_h \sqrt{c_h})^2$$

The minimum value occurs when

$$\frac{b_h}{a_h} = \frac{n_h \sqrt{c_h}}{W_h S_h} = \text{constant}$$

in agreement with theorem 5.6.

5.6 RELATIVE PRECISION OF STRATIFIED RANDOM AND SIMPLE RANDOM SAMPLING

If intelligently used, stratification nearly always results in a smaller variance for the estimated mean or total than is given by a comparable simple random sample. It is not true, however, that *any* stratified random sample gives a smaller variance than a simple random sample. If the values of the n_h are far from optimum, stratified sampling may have a higher variance. In fact, even stratification with optimum allocation for fixed total sample size may give a higher variance, though this result is an academic curiosity rather than something likely to happen in practice.

In this section a comparison is made between simple random sampling and stratified random sampling with proportional and optimum allocation.* This comparison shows how the gain due to stratification is achieved. The fpc is ignored.

The variances of the estimated *means* are denoted by V_{ran}, V_{prop}, and V_{opt}, respectively.

Theorem 5.8.   If terms in n_h/N_h are ignored,

$$V_{opt} \leq V_{prop} \leq V_{ran} \tag{5.23}$$

where the optimum allocation is for fixed n, that is, with $n_h \propto N_h S_h$.
Proof.   If the fpc is ignored,

$$V_{ran} = \frac{S^2}{n} \tag{5.24}$$

$$V_{prop} = \frac{\sum N_h S_h^2}{nN} \qquad \text{[from equation (5.7), section 5.3]} \tag{5.25}$$

$$V_{opt} = \frac{(\sum N_h S_h)^2}{nN^2} \qquad \text{[from equation (5.21), section 5.5]} \tag{5.26}$$

From the standard algebraic identity for the analysis of variance of the stratified population, we have

$$(N - 1)S^2 = \sum_h \sum_i (y_{hi} - \bar{Y})^2$$

$$= \sum_h \sum_i (y_{hi} - \bar{Y}_h)^2 + \sum_h N_h(\bar{Y}_h - \bar{Y})^2$$

$$= \sum_h (N_h - 1)S_h^2 + \sum_h N_h(\bar{Y}_h - \bar{Y})^2 \tag{5.27}$$

* Interesting discussions of this question are given by Armitage (1947) and Evans (1951).

Since terms in $1/N_h$ are negligible, this may be written

$$NS^2 = \sum_h N_h S_h^2 + \sum_h N_h(\overline{Y}_h - \overline{Y})^2$$

Hence

$$V_{ran} = \frac{S^2}{n} = \frac{\sum N_h S_h^2}{nN} + \frac{\sum N_h(\overline{Y}_h - \overline{Y})^2}{nN}$$

$$= V_{prop} + \frac{\sum N_h(\overline{Y}_h - \overline{Y})^2}{nN} \tag{5.28}$$

By the definition of V_{opt}, we must have $V_{prop} \geq V_{opt}$. Their difference is

$$V_{prop} - V_{opt} = \frac{1}{nN}\left[\sum N_h S_h^2 - \frac{(\sum N_h S_h)^2}{N}\right]$$

$$= \frac{1}{nN}\sum N_h(S_h - \bar{S})^2 \tag{5.29}$$

where $\bar{S} = \sum N_h S_h / N$. From (5.29) and (5.28)

$$V_{ran} = V_{opt} + \frac{\sum N_h(S_h - \bar{S})^2}{nN} + \frac{\sum N_h(\overline{Y}_h - \overline{Y})^2}{nN} \tag{5.30}$$

To summarize, there are two components to the decrease in variance as we change from simple random sampling to optimum allocation. The first component (term on the extreme right) comes from the elimination of differences among the stratum means; the second (middle term on the right) from elimination of the effect of differences among the stratum standard deviations. The second component represents the difference in variance between optimum and proportional allocation.

If the fpc cannot be neglected, the same type of analysis leads to the result

$$V_{ran} = V_{prop} + \frac{N-n}{nN(N-1)}\left[\sum N_h(\overline{Y}_h - \overline{Y})^2 - \frac{1}{N}\sum(N - N_h)S_h^2\right] \tag{5.31}$$

It follows that proportional stratification gives a higher variance than simple random sampling if

$$\sum N_h(\overline{Y}_h - \overline{Y})^2 < \frac{1}{N}\sum(N - N_h)S_h^2 \tag{5.32}$$

Mathematically, this can happen. Suppose that the S_h^2 are all equal to S_w^2, so that proportional allocation is optimum in the sense of Neyman. Then (5.32) becomes

$$\sum N_h(\overline{Y}_h - \overline{Y})^2 < (L - 1)S_w^2$$

or

$$\frac{\sum N_h(\overline{Y}_h - \overline{Y})^2}{L - 1} < S_w^{\ 2}$$

Those familiar with the analysis of variance will recognize this relation as implying that the mean square among strata is smaller than the mean square within strata, that is, that the F-ratio is less than 1.

5.7 WHEN DOES STRATIFICATION PRODUCE LARGE GAINS IN PRECISION?

The ideal variate for stratification is the value of y itself—the quantity to be measured in the survey. If we could stratify by the values of y, there would be no overlap between strata, and the variance within strata would be much smaller than the over-all variance, particularly if there were many strata. This situation is illustrated by the example in section 5.3, page 92. The population consisted of the sizes (numbers of inhabitants) of 64 cities in 1930, stratified by size. Although there were only two strata, proportional stratification reduced the s.e. ($\hat{Y}$) from 2365 to 1372. Stratification with $n_1 = n_2 = 12$, which is optimum under Neyman allocation, produced a further reduction to 1044.

In practice, of course, we cannot stratify by the values of y. But some important applications come close to this situation, and therefore give large gains in precision, by satisfying the following three conditions.

1. The population is composed of institutions varying widely in size.
2. The principal variables to be measured are closely related to the sizes of the institutions.
3. A good measure of size is available for setting up the strata.

Examples are businesses of a specific kind, for example, groceries (in surveys dealing with the volume of business or number of employees), schools (in surveys related to numbers of pupils), hospitals (in studies of patient load), and income tax returns (for items highly correlated with taxable income). In the United States farms also vary greatly in size as measured by total acreage or gross income, but common farm items, such as the production of particular crops or types of livestock, often exhibit only a moderate correlation with farm size, so that the gains from stratification by farm size are not huge.

If the size of the institution remains stable through time, at least for short periods, then its best practical measure is usually the size of the institution on some recent occasion when a census was taken. The example in section 5.3 illustrates the situation in which good previous data are available. Table 5.2 shows the S_h and the resulting optimum $n_h \propto N_h S_h$, when the allocation is made from 1920 and 1930 data, respectively.

The 1920 data indicate an n_1 of 11.56, as against a "true" optimum of 12.21 for the 1930 data. When rounded to integers, both sets of data give the same allocation—a sample size of 12 from each stratum.

Note that the optimum sampling fraction is 75% in stratum 1 but only 25% in stratum 2. It is often found that because of the high variability of the stratum consisting of the largest institutions the formula calls for 100% sampling in this stratum. Indeed, the allocation may call for more than

TABLE 5.2

CALCULATION OF THE OPTIMUM ALLOCATION

Stratum	N_h	1920 Data			1930 Data		
		S_h	$N_h S_h$	n_h	S_h	$N_h S_h$	n_h
1	16	163.30	2612.80	11.56	232.04	3712.64	12.21
2	48	58.55	2810.40	12.44	74.71	3586.08	11.79
Totals	64		5423.20	24.00		7298.72	24.00

100% sampling (see section 5.8). Note also that the S_h are smaller in 1920 than in 1930. The 1920 data give an overoptimistic impression of the precision to be obtained in a 1930 survey. As mentioned in section 4.6, the possibility of a change in the levels of the S_h should always be considered when using past data, even though an allowance for change may have to be something of a guess.

Geographic stratification, in which the strata are compact areas such as counties or neighborhoods in a city, is common—often for administrative convenience or because separate data are wanted for each stratum. It is usually accompanied by some increase in precision because many factors operate to make people living or crops growing in the same area show similarities in their principal characteristics. The gains from geographic stratification, however, are generally modest. For example, Table 5.3 shows data published by Jessen (1942) and Jessen and Houseman (1944) on the effectiveness of geographic stratification for a number of typical farm economic items.

Four sizes of stratum are represented—the township, the county, the "type of farming" area, and the state. To give some idea of the relative sizes of the strata, there are about 1600 townships, 100 counties, and 5 areas in Iowa.

In the table the precision of a method of stratification is taken as inversely proportional to the value of $V(\bar{y}_{st})$ given by the method. Thus the relative precision of method 1 to method 2 is the ratio $V_2(\bar{y}_{st})/V_1(\bar{y}_{st})$, expressed as a percentage. The data shown are averages over the numbers of items given in the second column. The county is taken as a standard in each case. As indicated, the gains in precision are moderate. In Iowa the use of 1600 strata (townships) compared with no stratification (state) increases the precision by about 30%; that is, it reduces the variance by about 25%.

TABLE 5.3

RELATIVE PRECISION OF DIFFERENT KINDS OF GEOGRAPHIC
STRATIFICATION (IN PER CENT)

		Stratum			
State	No. of Items	Township	County	Type of Farming Area	State
Iowa, 1938	18	115	100	96	91
Iowa, 1939	19	121	100	97	91
Florida, 1942					
Citrus fruit area	14	144	100	..	
Truck farming area	15	111	100	..	
California, 1942	17	113	100	97	

As regards proportional versus optimum stratification, there are two situations in which optimum stratification wins handsomely. The first is the case, already discussed, in which the population consists of large and small institutions, stratified by some measure of size. The variances S_h^2 are usually much greater for the large institutions than for the small, making proportional stratification inefficient. The second situation is found in surveys in which some strata are much more expensive to sample than others. The influence of the factor $\sqrt{c_h}$ may make proportional allocation poor.

When planning an allocation in which the estimated n_h do not differ greatly from proportionality, it is worthwhile to estimate how much larger $V(\bar{y}_{st})$ or $V(\hat{Y}_{st})$ become if proportional allocation is used. The optima in the allocation problem are rather flat (see section 5A.2) and the increase in variance may turn out surprisingly small. Moreover, the superiority of the optimum, as computed from estimated values of the S_h, is always exaggerated because of the errors in the estimated S_h. The simplicity and the self-weighting feature of proportional allocation are probably worth a 10-to-20% increase in variance.

5.8 ALLOCATION REQUIRING MORE THAN 100 PER CENT SAMPLING

As mentioned in section 5.7, the formula for the optimum may produce an n_h in some stratum that is larger than the corresponding N_h. Consider the example on city sizes in section 5.3. A sample of 24 cities, distributed between two strata, called for 12 cities out of 16 in the first stratum and 12 out of 48 in the second. Had the sample size been 48, the allocation would demand 24 cities out of 16 in the first stratum. The best that can be done is to take all cities in the stratum, leaving 32 cities for the second stratum instead of the 24 postulated by the formula. This problem arises only when the over-all sampling fraction is substantial and one stratum is much more variable than the others. It has occurred in practice on several occasions.

Care must be taken to use the correct formula in predicting the expected variance from this allocation or in comparing the allocation with others. Formula 5.5 in section 5.3 is appropriate if the n_h given by the *revised* optimum allocation are substituted. Formula 5.21 for the minimum variance for fixed n

$$V_{min}(\bar{y}_{st}) = \frac{(\sum W_h S_h)^2}{n} - \frac{\sum W_h S_h^2}{N}$$

is no longer correct. If stratum 1 is the only stratum in which oversampling is indicated, the correct formula for V_{min} becomes

$$V_{min}(\bar{y}_{st}) = \frac{1}{N^2} \frac{(\sum' N_h S_h)^2}{n - N_1} - \frac{1}{N^2} \sum' N_h S_h^2$$

where $\sum'$ denotes summation over all strata except stratum 1.

5.9 ESTIMATION OF SAMPLE SIZE WITH CONTINUOUS DATA

Formulas for the determination of n under an estimated optimum allocation were given in section 5.5. The present section presents formulas for any allocation, with some useful special cases. It is assumed that the estimate has a specified variance V. If, instead, the margin of error d (section 4.4) has been specified, $V = (d/t)^2$, where t is the normal deviate corresponding to the allowable probability that the error will exceed the desired margin.

Estimation of the Population Mean $\bar{Y}$

Let s_h be the estimate of S_h and let $n_h = w_h n$, where the w_h have been chosen. In these terms the anticipated $V(\bar{y}_{st})$ (from theorem 5.3, section 5.3) is

$$V = \frac{1}{n} \sum \frac{W_h^2 s_h^2}{w_h} - \frac{1}{N} \sum W_h s_h^2 \qquad (5.33)$$

with $W_h = N_h/N$. This gives, as a general formula for n,

$$n = \frac{\sum \dfrac{W_h^2 s_h^2}{w_h}}{V + \dfrac{1}{N} \sum W_h s_h^2} \qquad (5.34)$$

If the fpc is ignored, we have, as a first approximation,

$$n_0 = \frac{1}{V} \sum \frac{W_h^2 s_h^2}{w_h} \qquad (5.35)$$

If n_0/N is not negligible, we may calculate n as

$$n = \frac{n_0}{1 + \dfrac{1}{NV} \sum W_h s_h^2} \qquad (5.36)$$

In particular cases the formulas take various forms that may be more convenient for computation. A few are given.

Presumed optimum allocation (for fixed n): $w_h \propto W_h s_h$.

$$n = \frac{\left(\sum W_h s_h \right)^2}{V + \dfrac{1}{N} \sum W_h s_h^2} \qquad (5.37)$$

Proportional allocation: $w_h = W_h = N_h/N$.

$$n_0 = \frac{\sum W_h s_h^2}{V}, \qquad n = \frac{n_0}{1 + \dfrac{n_0}{N}} \qquad (5.38)$$

Estimation of the Population Total

If V is the desired $V(\hat{Y}_{st})$, the principal formulas are as follows:

General:

$$n = \frac{\sum \dfrac{N_h^2 s_h^2}{w_h}}{V + \sum N_h s_h^2} \qquad (5.39)$$

Presumed optimum (for fixed *n*):

$$n = \frac{(\sum N_h s_h)^2}{V + \sum N_h s_h^2} \tag{5.40}$$

Proportional:

$$n_0 = \frac{N}{V} \sum N_h s_h^2, \qquad n = \frac{n_0}{1 + \dfrac{n_0}{N}} \tag{5.41}$$

Example. This example comes from a paper by Cornell (1947), which describes a sample of United States colleges and universities drawn in 1946 by the U.S. Office of Education in order to estimate enrollments for the 1946–1947 academic year. The illustration is for the population of 196 teachers' colleges and normal schools. These were arranged in seven strata, of which one small stratum will be ignored. The first five strata were constructed by size of institution; the sixth contained colleges for women only. Estimates s_h of the S_h were computed from results for the 1943–1944 academic year. An "optimum" stratification based on these s_h was employed.

The objective was a coefficient of variation of 5% in the estimated total enrollment. In 1943 the total enrollment for this group of colleges was 56,472. Thus the desired standard error is

$$(0.05)(56{,}472) = 2824$$

so that the desired variance is

$$V = (2824)^2 = 7{,}974{,}976$$

It may be objected that enrollments will be greater in 1946 than in 1943 and that allowance should be made for this increase. Actually, the calculation assumes only that the cv per college remains the same in 1943 and 1946—an assumption that may not be unreasonable.

Table 5.4 shows the values of N_h, s_h, and $N_h s_h$, which were known before determining *n*.

The appropriate formula for *n* is (5.40), which applies to an "optimum" allocation for estimating a total. With only 196 units in this population, it is

TABLE 5.4

DATA FOR ESTIMATING SAMPLE SIZE

Stratum	N_h	s_h	$N_h s_h$	n_h
1	13	325	4,225	9
2	18	190	3,420	7
3	26	189	4,914	10
4	42	82	3,444	7
5	73	86	6,278	13
6	24	190	4,560	10
Totals	196		26,841	56

improbable that the fpc will be negligible. However, for purposes of illustration, a first approximation ignoring the fpc will be sought. This is

$$n_0 = \frac{(\sum N_h s_h)^2}{V} = \frac{(26,841)^2}{7,974,976} = 90.34$$

Adjustment is obviously needed. For the correct n in (5.40), we have

$$n = \frac{n_0}{1 + \dfrac{1}{V} \sum N_h s_h^2} = \frac{90.34}{1 + \dfrac{4,640,387}{7,974,976}} = 57.1$$

A sample size of 56 was chosen.* The n_h for individual strata appear in the right-hand column of Table 5.4.

5.10 STRATIFIED SAMPLING FOR PROPORTIONS

If we wish to estimate the proportion of units in the population that fall into some defined class C, the ideal stratification is attained if we can place in the first stratum every unit that falls in C, and in the second every unit that does not. Failing this, we try to construct strata such that the proportion in class C varies as much as possible from stratum to stratum.

Let

$$P_h = \frac{A_h}{N_h}, \qquad p_h = \frac{a_h}{n_h}$$

be the proportions of units in C in the hth stratum and in the sample from that stratum, respectively. For the proportion in the whole population, the estimate appropriate to stratified random sampling is

$$p_{st} = \sum \frac{N_h p_h}{N} \qquad (5.42)$$

Theorem 5.9. With stratified random sampling, the variance of p_{st} is

$$V(p_{st}) = \frac{1}{N^2} \sum \frac{N_h^2 (N_h - n_h)}{N_h - 1} \frac{P_h Q_h}{n_h} \qquad (5.43)$$

Proof. This is a particular case of the general theorem for the variance of the estimated mean. From theorem 5.3

$$V(\bar{y}_{st}) = \frac{1}{N^2} \sum N_h (N_h - n_h) \frac{S_h^2}{n_h}$$

Let y_{hi} be a variate which has the value 1 when the unit is in C, and zero

---

* The arithmetical results differ slightly from those given by Cornell (1947).

otherwise. In section 3.2, equation 3.4, it was shown that for this variate

$$S_h^2 = \frac{N_h}{N_h - 1} P_h Q_h$$

This gives the result.

Note. In nearly all applications, even if the fpc is not negligible, terms in $1/N_h$ will be negligible, and the slightly simpler formula

$$V(p_{st}) = \frac{1}{N^2} \sum N_h(N_h - n_h) \frac{P_h Q_h}{n_h} = \sum \frac{W_h^2 P_h Q_h}{n_h} (1 - f_h) \quad (5.44)$$

can be used.

Corollary 1. When the fpc can be ignored,

$$V(p_{st}) = \sum W_h^2 \frac{P_h Q_h}{n_h} \quad (5.45)$$

Corollary 2. With proportional allocation,

$$V(p_{st}) = \frac{N - n}{N} \frac{1}{nN} \sum \frac{N_h^2 P_h Q_h}{N_h - 1} \quad (5.46)$$

$$\doteq \frac{1 - f}{n} \sum W_h P_h Q_h \quad (5.47)$$

For a sample estimate of the variance, substitute $p_h q_h/(n_h - 1)$ for the unknown $P_h Q_h/n_h$ in any of the formulas above.

The best choice of the n_h in order to minimize $V(p_{st})$ follows from the general theory in section 5.5.

Minimum Variance for Fixed Total Sample Size.

$$n_h \propto N_h \sqrt{N_h/(N_h - 1)} \sqrt{P_h Q_h} \doteq N_h \sqrt{P_h Q_h}$$

Thus

$$n_h \doteq n \frac{N_h \sqrt{P_h Q_h}}{\sum N_h \sqrt{P_h Q_h}} \quad (5.48)$$

Minimum Variance for Fixed Cost, where Cost $= c_0 + \sum c_h n_h$.

$$n_h \doteq n \frac{N_h \sqrt{P_h Q_h/c_h}}{\sum N_h \sqrt{P_h Q_h/c_h}} \quad (5.49)$$

The value of n is found as in section 5.5.

5.11 GAINS IN PRECISION IN STRATIFIED SAMPLING FOR PROPORTIONS

If the costs per unit are the same in all strata, two useful working rules are that (*a*) the gain in precision from stratified random over simple random sampling is small or modest unless the P_h vary greatly from stratum to stratum; (b) optimum allocation for fixed n gains little over proportional allocation if all P_h lie between 0.1 and 0.9.

To illustrate the first result, Table 5.5 compares stratified random sampling (proportional allocation) with simple random sampling for three strata of equal sizes ($W_h = \frac{1}{3}$). Four cases are included, the first having $P_h = 0.4, 0.5,$ and 0.6 in the three strata and the last (and most extreme) having $P_h = 0.1, 0.5,$ and 0.9. The first two columns show the variances of the estimated proportion, multiplied by $n/(1 - f)$, and the last gives the

TABLE 5.5

RELATIVE PRECISION OF STRATIFIED AND SIMPLE RANDOM SAMPLING

	Simple	Stratified	
P_h	$nV(p)/(1 - f)$ $= PQ$	$nV(p_{st})/(1 - f)$ $= \frac{1}{3}\sum P_h Q_h$	Relative Precision (%)
0.4, 0.5, 0.6	2500	2433	103
0.3, 0.5, 0.7	2500	2233	112
0.2, 0.5, 0.8	2500	1900	132
0.1, 0.5, 0.9	2500	1433	174

relative precisions of stratified to simple random sampling. The gain in precision is large only in the last two cases.

To compare proportional with optimum allocation for fixed n, it will be found that if the fpc is ignored

$$V_{opt} = \frac{(\sum W_h\sqrt{P_h Q_h})^2}{n}, \qquad V_{prop} = \frac{\sum W_h P_h Q_h}{n}$$

The relative precision of proportional to optimum allocation is therefore

$$\frac{V_{opt}}{V_{prop}} = \frac{(\sum W_h\sqrt{P_h Q_h})^2}{\sum W_h P_h Q_h}$$

If all P_h lie between the two values P_0 and $(1 - P_0)$, we are interested in the smallest value the relative precision will take. For simplicity, we consider two strata of equal size ($W_1 = W_2$). The minimum relative precision is attained when $P_1 = \frac{1}{2}$ and $P_2 = P_0$. The relative precision then becomes

$$\frac{V_{opt}}{V_{prop}} = \frac{(0.5 + \sqrt{P_0 Q_0})^2}{2(0.25 + P_0 Q_0)}$$

Some values of this function are given in Table 5.6. Even with P_0 equal to 0.1, or as high as 0.9, the relative precision is 94%. In most cases the simplicity and the self-weighting feature of proportional stratification more than compensate for this slight loss in precision.

The limitations of the example should be noted. It does not take account of differential costs of sampling in different strata. In some surveys the P_h are very small, but they range from, say, 0.001 to 0.05 in different

TABLE 5.6

RELATIVE PRECISION OF PROPORTIONAL TO OPTIMUM ALLOCATION

P_0	0.4 or 0.6	0.3 or 0.7	0.2 or 0.8	0.1 or 0.9	0.05 or 0.95
RP(%)	100.0	99.8	98.8	94.1	86.6

strata. Here there would be a more substantial gain from optimum stratification.

5.12 ESTIMATION OF SAMPLE SIZE WITH PROPORTIONS

Formulas can be deduced from the more general formulas in section 5.9. Let V be the desired variance in the estimate of the proportion P for the whole population. The formulas for the two principal types of allocation are as follows:

Proportional:

$$n_0 = \frac{\sum W_h p_h q_h}{V}, \qquad n = \frac{n_0}{1 + \dfrac{n_0}{N}} \tag{5.50}$$

Presumed optimum:

$$n_0 = \frac{(\sum W_h \sqrt{p_h q_h})^2}{V}, \qquad n = \frac{n_0}{1 + \dfrac{1}{NV} \sum W_h p_h q_h} \tag{5.51}$$

where n_0 is the first approximation, which ignores the fpc, and n is the corrected value taking account of the fpc. In the development of these formulas, the factors $N_h/(N_h - 1)$ have been taken as unity.

These results apply to the estimate of a *proportion*. If it is preferable to think in terms of percentages, the same formulas apply if P_h, Q_h, V, etc., are expressed as percentages. For the estimation of the total number in the population in class C, that is, of NP, all variances are multiplied by N^2.

EXERCISES

• 5.1   In a population with $N = 6$ and $L = 2$ the values of y_{hi} are 0, 1, 2 in stratum 1 and 4, 6, 11 in stratum 2. A sample with $n = 4$ is to be taken. (a) Show that the optimum n_h under Neyman allocation, when rounded to integers, are $n_h = 1$ in stratum 1 and $n_h = 3$ in stratum 2. (b) Compute the estimate $\bar{y}_{st}$ for every possible sample that can be drawn under optimum allocation and under proportional allocation. Verify that the estimates are unbiased. Hence find $V_{opt}(\bar{y}_{st})$ and $V_{prop}(\bar{y}_{st})$ directly. (c) Verify that $V_{opt}(\bar{y}_{st})$ agrees with the formula given in equation 5.5 and that $V_{prop}(\bar{y}_{st})$ agrees with the formula given in equation 5.7, page 91. (d) Use of formula 5.21, page 97, to compute $V_{opt}(\bar{y}_{st})$ is slightly incorrect because it does not allow for the fact that the n_h were rounded to integers. How well does it agree with the correct value?

- 5.2   The households in a town are to be sampled in order to estimate the average amount of assets per household that are readily convertible into cash. The households are stratified into a high-rent and a low-rent stratum. A house in the high-rent stratum is thought to have about nine times as much assets as one in the low-rent stratum, and S_h is expected to be proportional to the square root of the stratum mean.

There are 4000 households in the high-rent stratum and 20,000 in the low-rent stratum. (a) How would you distribute a sample of 1000 households between the two strata? (b) If the object is to estimate the difference between assets per household in the two strata, how should the sample be distributed?

• 5.3   The following data show the stratification of all the farms in a county by farm size and the average acres of corn (maize) per farm in each stratum.

Farm Size (acres)	Number of Farms N_h	Average Corn Acres $\bar{Y}_h$	Standard Deviation S_h
0–40	394	5.4	8.3
41–80	461	16.3	13.3
81–120	391	24.3	15.1
121–160	334	34.5	19.8
161–200	169	42.1	24.5
201–240	113	50.1	26.0
241–	148	63.8	35.2
Total or mean	2010	26.3	

For a sample of 100 farms, compute the sample sizes in each stratum under (a) proportional allocation, (b) optimum allocation. Compare the precisions of these methods with that of simple random sampling.

• 5.4   Prove the result stated in formula 5.31, section 5.6:

$$V_{ran} = V_{prop} + \frac{(N-n)}{nN(N-1)}\left[\sum N_h(\bar{Y}_h - \bar{Y})^2 - \frac{1}{N}\sum (N - N_h)S_h^2\right]$$

• 5.5 A sampler has two strata with relative sizes W_1, W_2. He believes that S_1, S_2 can be taken as equal but thinks that c_2 may be between $2c_1$ and $4c_1$. He would prefer to use proportional allocation but does not wish to incur a substantial increase in variance compared with optimum allocation. For a given cost $C = c_1 n_1 + c_2 n_2$, ignoring the fpc, show that

$$\frac{V_{prop}(\bar{y}_{st})}{V_{opt}(\bar{y}_{st})} = \frac{W_1 c_1 + W_2 c_2}{(W_1 \sqrt{c_1} + W_2 \sqrt{c_2})^2}$$

If $W_1 = W_2$, compute the relative increases in variance from using proportional allocation when $c_2/c_1 = 2, 4$.

• 5.6 A sampler proposes to take a stratified random sample. He expects that his field costs will be of the form $\sum c_h n_h$. His advance estimates of relevant quantities for the two strata are as follows:

Stratum	W_h	S_h	C_h
1	0.4	10	\$4
2	0.6	20	\$9

(a) Find the values of n_1/n and n_2/n that minimize the total field cost for a given value of $V(\bar{y}_{st})$. (b) Find the sample size required, under this optimum allocation, to make $V(\bar{y}_{st}) = 1$. Ignore the fpc. (c) How much will the total field cost be?

• 5.7 After the sample in exercise 5.6 is taken, the sampler finds that his field costs were actually \$2 per unit in stratum 1 and \$12 in stratum 2. (a) How much greater is the field cost than anticipated? (b) If he had known the correct field costs in advance, could he have attained $V(\bar{y}_{st}) = 1$ for the original estimated field cost in exercise 5.6? (Hint. The Cauchy-Schwarz inequality, page 97, with $V = 1$, gives the answer to this question without finding the new allocation.)

• 5.8 In a stratification with two strata, the values of the W_h and S_h are as follows:

Stratum	W_h	S_h
1	0.8	2
2	0.2	4

Compute the sample sizes n_1, n_2 in the two strata needed to satisfy the following conditions. Each case requires a separate computation. (Ignore the fpc.) (a) The standard error of the estimated population mean $\bar{y}_{st}$ is to be 0.1 and the total sample size $n = n_1 + n_2$ is to be minimized. (b) The standard error of the estimated mean of each stratum is to be 0.1. (c) The standard error of the difference between the two estimated stratum means is to be 0.1, again minimizing the total size of sample.

• 5.9 With two strata, a sampler would like to have $n_1 = n_2$ for administrative convenience, instead of using the values given by the Neyman allocation. If $V(\bar{y}_{st})$, $V_{opt}(\bar{y}_{st})$ denote the variances given by the $n_1 = n_2$ and the Neyman allocations, respectively, show that the fractional increase in variance

$$\frac{V(\bar{y}_{st}) - V_{opt}(\bar{y}_{st})}{V_{opt}(\bar{y}_{st})} = \left(\frac{r - 1}{r + 1}\right)^2$$

where $r = n_1/n_2$ as given by Neyman allocation. For the strata in exercise 5.8, case a, what would the fractional increase in variance be by using $n_1 = n_2$ instead of the optimum?

• 5.10   If the cost function is of the form $C = c_0 + \sum t_h \sqrt{n_h}$, where c_0 and the t_h are known numbers, show that in order to minimize $V(\bar{y}_{st})$ for fixed total cost n_h must be proportional to

$$\left(\frac{W_h^2 S_h^2}{t_h}\right)^{2/3}$$

Find the n_h for a sample of size 1000 under the following conditions:

Stratum	W_h	S_h	t_h
1	0.4	4	1
2	0.3	5	2
3	0.2	6	4

5.11   If $V_{prop}(\bar{y}_{st})$ is the variance of the estimated mean from a stratified random sample of size n with proportional allocation and $V(\bar{y})$ is the variance of the mean of a simple random sample of size n, show that the ratio

$$\frac{V_{prop}(\bar{y}_{st})}{V(\bar{y})}$$

does not depend on the size of sample but that the ratio

$$\frac{V_{min}(\bar{y}_{st})}{V_{prop}(\bar{y}_{st})}$$

decreases as n increases. (This implies that optimum allocation for fixed n becomes more effective in relation to proportional allocation as n increases.) (Use formulas 5.7 and 5.21.)

• 5.12   Compare the values obtained for $V(p_{st})$ under proportional allocation and optimum allocation for fixed sample size in the following two populations. Each stratum is of equal size. The fpc may be ignored.

	Population 1		Population 2
Stratum	P_h	Stratum	P_h
1	0.1	1	0.01
2	0.5	2	0.05
3	0.9	3	0.10

What general result is illustrated by these two populations?

5.13   Show that in the estimation of proportions the results corresponding to theorem 5.8 are as follows:

$$V_{ran} = V_{prop} + \frac{\sum W_h(P_h - P)^2}{n}$$

$$V_{prop} = V_{opt} + \frac{\sum W_h\left(\sqrt{P_h Q_h} - \overline{\sqrt{P_h Q_h}}\right)^2}{n}$$

where $$\sqrt{\overline{P_h Q_h}} = \sum W_h \sqrt{P_h Q_h}.$$

• 5.14 In a firm, 62% of the employees are skilled or unskilled males, 31% are clerical females, and 7% are supervisory. From a sample of 400 employees the firm wishes to estimate the proportion that uses certain recreational facilities. Rough guesses are that the facilities are used by 40 to 50% of the males, 20 to 30% of the females, and 5 to 10% of the supervisors. (a) How would you allocate the sample among the three groups? (b) If the true proportions of users were 48, 21, and 4%, respectively, what would the s.e. of the estimated proportion p_{st} be? (c) What would the s.e. of p be from a simple random sample with $n = 400$?

REFERENCES

Armitage, P. (1947). A comparison of stratified with unrestricted random sampling from a finite population. *Biometrika*, **34**, 273–280.

Beardwood, J., Halton, J. H., and Hammersley, J. M. (1959). The shortest path through many points. *Proc. Cambridge Phil. Soc.*, **55**, 299–327.

Cornell, F. G. (1947). A stratified random sample of a small finite population. *Jour. Amer. Stat. Assoc.*, **42**, 523–532.

Evans, W. D. (1951). On stratification and optimum allocations. *Jour. Amer. Stat. Assoc.*, **46**, 95–104.

Jessen, R. J. (1942). Statistical investigation of a sample survey for obtaining farm facts. *Iowa Agr. Exp. Sta. Res. Bull.* 304.

Jessen, R. J., and Houseman, E. E. (1944). Statistical investigations of farm sample surveys taken in Iowa, Florida and California. *Iowa Agr. Exp. Sta. Res. Bull.* 329.

Neyman, J. (1934). On the two different aspects of the representative method: the method of stratified sampling and the method of purposive selection. *Jour. Roy. Stat. Soc.*, **97**, 558–606.

Stuart, A. (1954). A simple presentation of optimum sampling results. *Jour. Roy. Stat. Soc. B*, **16**, 239–241.

Satterthwaite, F. E. (1946). An approximate distribution of estimates of variance components. *Biometrics*, **2**, 110–114.

Tschuprow, A. A. (1923). On the mathematical expectation of the moments of frequency distributions in the case of correlated observations. *Metron*, **2**, 461–493, 646–683.

Further Aspects
of Stratified Sampling

5A.1 EFFECTS OF DEVIATIONS FROM THE OPTIMUM ALLOCATION

The following sections discuss a number of special topics in the practical use of stratified sampling. Sections 5A.1 to 5A.7 deal with problems that may come up in the planning of the sample, and sections 5A.8 to 5A.12 with techniques of analysis of results, including short cuts in the computation of standard errors. Finally, an introductory account is given of some useful results when the data are taken for analytical purposes (section 5A.13). The present section considers the loss in precision by failure to achieve an optimum allocation of the sample.

Suppose that it is intended to use optimum allocation for given n. The sample size n_h' in stratum h should be

$$n_h' = \frac{n(W_h S_h)}{\sum W_h S_h} \qquad (5A.1)$$

From equation 5.21, page 97, the resulting minimum variance is

$$V_{min}(\bar{y}_{st}) = \frac{1}{n}\left(\sum W_h S_h\right)^2 - \frac{1}{N}\sum W_h S_h^2 \qquad (5A.2)$$

In practice, since the S_h are not known, we can only approximate this allocation. If $\hat{n}_h$ is the sample size used in stratum h, the variance actually attained, from equation 5.5, page 91 is

$$V(\bar{y}_{st}) = \sum \frac{W_h^2 S_h^2}{\hat{n}_h} - \frac{1}{N}\sum W_h S_h^2 \qquad (5A.3)$$

The increase in variance caused by the imperfect allocation is

$$V(\bar{y}_{st}) - V_{min}(\bar{y}_{st}) = \sum \frac{W_h^2 S_h^2}{\hat{n}_h} - \frac{1}{n}\left(\sum W_h S_h\right)^2$$

In the first term on the right substitute for $W_h S_h$ in terms of $n_h{}'$ from (5A.1). This gives the interesting result

$$V(\bar{y}_{st}) - V_{min}(\bar{y}_{st}) = \frac{(\sum W_h S_h)^2}{n^2}\left(\sum \frac{n_h'^2}{\hat{n}_h} - n\right)$$

$$= \frac{(\sum W_h S_h)^2}{n^2}\sum \frac{(\hat{n}_h - n_h')^2}{\hat{n}_h} \qquad (5A.4)$$

Reverting to equation 5A.2, if the fpc (last term on the right) is negligible, we see that

$$\frac{V_{min}(\bar{y}_{st})}{n} = \frac{(\sum W_h S_h)^2}{n^2}$$

Hence the proportional increase in variance resulting from deviations from the optimum allocation is

$$\frac{V(\bar{y}_{st}) - V_{min}(\bar{y}_{st})}{V_{min}(\bar{y}_{st})} = \frac{1}{n}\sum_{h=1}^{L} \frac{(\hat{n}_h - n_h')^2}{\hat{n}_h} \qquad (5A.5)$$

where $\hat{n}_h$ is the actual and n_h' the optimum sample size in stratum h. If the fpc is not negligible, the $=$ sign in (5A.5) becomes $\geq$.

It is difficult to visualize the practical implications of this result without working out numerical examples. One general consequence, though somewhat conservative, is helpful. Let g be the greatest of the values $|\hat{n}_h - n_h'|/\hat{n}_h$ found in any of the strata. Then from (5A.5)

$$\frac{V - V_{min}}{V_{min}} \leq \frac{1}{n}\sum \frac{\hat{n}_h^2 g^2}{\hat{n}_h} = g^2$$

For instance, if the maximum deviation $|\hat{n}_h - n_h'|$, expressed as a fraction of $\hat{n}_h$, is 0.2, or 20%, the proportional increase in variance cannot exceed $(0.2)^2 = 0.04$, or 4%. If $g = 30\%$, the proportional increase is at most 9%. In this sense the optimum can be described as flat.

This rough rule usually overestimates the actual increase in variance by a substantial amount. Table 5A.1 gives an example with three strata for

TABLE 5A.1

EFFECTS OF DEVIATIONS FROM OPTIMUM ALLOCATION

Stratum	n_h' (opt)	$\hat{n}_h$ (act)	$\dfrac{|\hat{n}_h - n_h'|}{\hat{n}_h}$	$\dfrac{(\hat{n}_h - n_h')^2}{\hat{n}_h}$
1	200	150	0.33	16.7
2	100	120	0.17	3.3
3	40	70	0.43	12.9
Total	340	340	—	32.9

$n = 340$. Optimum allocation requires sample sizes of 200, 100, and 40, whereas the sizes actually used are 150, 120, and 70.

Since the value of g is 0.43 (stratum 3), the rough rule gives 18% as the proportional increase in variance. From the column on the right, the actual increase is seen to be $32.9/340 = 9.7\%$.

Evans (1951) examined the same question in terms of the effects of errors in the estimated S_h and developed an approximate rule showing whether an estimated optimum is likely to be more precise than proportional allocation. He supposes that the coefficient of variation of the estimated S_h is the same in all strata. This assumption is appropriate when the S_h have been estimated from a preliminary sample of the same size in each stratum. He shows how to compute the size of a preliminary sample needed to make an "optimum" allocation better, on the average, than proportional allocation. Previously, Sukhatme (1935) showed that a small initial sample usually gives a high probability that "optimum" allocation will be superior to simple random sampling.

5A.2 EFFECTS OF ERRORS IN THE STRATUM SIZES

For a desirable type of stratification, the stratum totals N_h may not be known exactly, being derived from census data that are out of date. Instead of the true stratum proportions W_h, we have estimates w_h. The sample estimate of $\bar{Y}$ is $\sum w_h \bar{y}_h$.

In general terms, the consequences of using weights that are in error are as follows:

1. The sample estimate is *biased*. Because of the bias, we measure the precision of the estimate by its mean square error about $\bar{Y}$ rather than by its variance about its own mean (see section 1.8).
2. The bias remains constant as the sample size increases. Consequently, a size of sample is always reached for which the estimate is less precise than simple random sampling, and all the gain in precision from stratification is lost.
3. The usual estimate $s(\bar{y}_{st})$ underestimates the true error of $\bar{y}_{st}$, since it does not contain the contribution of the bias to the error.

To justify these statements, note that in repeated sampling the mean value of the estimate is $\sum w_h \bar{Y}_h$. The bias therefore amounts to

$$\sum (w_h - W_h) \bar{Y}_h$$

It is independent of the size of the sample. In finding the mean square error (MSE) of the estimate, it is easy to verify that the variance term is given by the usual formula, with w_h in place of W_h. Hence

$$\text{MSE}\,(\bar{y}_{st}) = \sum \frac{w_h{}^2 S_h{}^2}{n_h}(1 - f_h) + [\sum (w_h - W_h)\bar{Y}_h]^2 \qquad (5A.6)$$

This expression was given by Stephan (1941). Finally, the usual formula for $s^2(\bar{y}_{st})$ is clearly an unbiased estimate of the first term in (5A.6) but takes no account of the second term.

Example. This illustrates the loss of precision from incorrect weights when stratification is (a) slightly effective, (b) highly effective. Consider a large population with $S^2 = 1$, divisible into two strata with $W_1 = 0.9$, $W_2 = 0.1$. We shall assume $S_1 = S_2 = S_h$. Then, neglecting terms in $1/N_h$,

$$S^2 \doteq \sum W_h S_h{}^2 + \sum W_h(\bar{Y}_h - \bar{Y})^2 \qquad (5A.7)$$
$$= S_h{}^2 + W_1 W_2(\bar{Y}_1 - \bar{Y}_2)^2$$

that is, $\qquad 1 = S_h{}^2 + 0.09(\bar{Y}_1 - \bar{Y}_2)^2$

In (a) take $\bar{Y}_1 - \bar{Y}_2 = 1$. Then $S_h{}^2 = 0.91$, and proportional stratification reduces the variance by 9%, compared with simple random sampling.

In (b) take $\bar{Y}_1 - \bar{Y}_2 = 3$, giving $S_h{}^2 = 0.19$, a reduction in variance of more than 80%.

With two strata, the bias may be written

$$(w_1 - W_1)(\bar{Y}_1 - \bar{Y}_2)$$

since $(w_1 - W_1) = -(w_2 - W_2)$. Suppose that the estimated weights are $w_1 = 0.92$ and $w_2 = 0.08$. The bias amounts to $(0.02)(1) = 0.02$ in (a) and to 0.06 in (b). Hence we have the following comparable variances for a sample of size n:

Simple random sampling: $V(\bar{y}) = \dfrac{1}{n}$

Stratified random sampling:

$$(a):\quad V(\bar{y}_{st}) = \frac{0.91}{n} + 0.0004$$

$$(b):\quad V(\bar{y}_{st}) = \frac{0.19}{n} + 0.0036$$

TABLE 5A.2

COMPARABLE VALUES OF $V(\bar{y})$

n	Simple Random	Stratified Random (a)	(b)
50	0.0200	0.0186	0.0074
100	0.0100	0.0095	0.0055
200	0.0050	0.0049	0.0045
300	0.0033	0.0034	0.0042
400	0.0025	0.0027	0.0041
1000	0.0010	0.0013	0.0038

Relative to (*a*), simple random sampling begins to win at $n = 300$. There is little to choose between the two methods, however, up to $n = 1000$.

In (*b*), with more at stake, stratification is superior up to $n = 200$, although most of the potential gain has already been lost at this sample size. Beyond $n = 300$ stratification becomes markedly inferior to simple random sampling. Accurate estimation of the W_h is particularly important when stratification is highly effective or when the sample size is large.

In some surveys a large preliminary sample of size n' can be taken in order to estimate the W_h. This technique, known as *double sampling* or *two-phase sampling*, has numerous applications and is discussed in Chapter 12. It will be shown that with double sampling the mean square error of $\bar{y}_{st}$ is approximately

$$\frac{\sum W_h S_h^2}{n} + \frac{\sum W_h (\bar{Y}_h - \bar{Y})^2}{n'}$$

By comparing this MSE with S^2/n, as given by equation 5A.7, we see that most of the gain from stratification is retained provided that n' is much greater than n. To put it more generally, a set of estimated weights preserves most of the potential gain from stratification if the weights are much more accurately estimated than they would be from a simple random sample of size n.

5A.3 THE PROBLEM OF ALLOCATION WITH MORE THAN ONE ITEM

Since the best allocation for one item will not in general be best for another, some compromise must be reached in a survey with numerous items. The first step is to reduce the items considered in the allocation to a relatively small number thought to be most important. If good previous data are available, we can then compute the optimum allocation for each item separately and see to what extent there is disagreement. In a survey of a specialized type the correlations among the items may be high and the allocations may differ relatively little.

Example. Data given by Jessen (1942) illustrate a farm survey of this kind. The state of Iowa was divided into five geographic regions, each denoted by its major agricultural enterprise. Suppose that these regions are to be used as strata in a survey on dairy farming. The three items of most interest are the number of cows milked per day, the number of gallons of milk per day, and the total annual cash receipts from dairy products. From a survey made in 1938, the estimated standard deviations s_h within strata are shown in Table 5A.3. In Table 5A.4 the optimum Neyman allocations based on these s_h are given for the individual items in a sample of 1000 farms.

TABLE 5A.3

STANDARD DEVIATIONS WITHIN STRATA

Stratum	$W_h = \dfrac{N_h}{N}$	s_h Cows Milked	s_h Gallons of Milk	s_h Receipts for Dairy Products ($)
Northeast dairy	0.197	4.6	11.7	332
Cash grain	0.191	3.4	9.8	357
Western livestock	0.219	3.3	7.0	246
Southern pasture	0.184	2.8	6.5	173
Eastern livestock	0.208	3.7	9.8	279

TABLE 5A.4

SAMPLE SIZES WITHIN STRATA ($n = 1000$)

Allocation

Stratum	Proportional	Optimum for Cows	Optimum for Gallons	Optimum for Receipts	Average m_h
Northeast dairy	197	254	258	236	250
Cash grain	191	182	209	246	212
Western livestock	219	203	171	194	189
Southern pasture	184	145	134	115	131
Eastern livestock	208	216	228	209	218

TABLE 5A.5

EXPECTED VARIANCES OF THE ESTIMATED MEAN

Type of allocation	Cows	Gallons	Receipts
Optimum	0.0127	0.0800	76.9
Compromise	0.0128	0.0802	77.6
Proportional	0.0131	0.0837	80.9

The individual optimum allocations differ only moderately from each other. With one exception, all three deviate in the same direction from a proportional allocation. Thus, in the first stratum, proportional allocation suggests 197 farms, and the individual allocations lead to numbers between 236 and 258. The average of the optimum sample sizes for the three items, shown in the right-hand column, provides a satisfactory compromise allocation.

Table 5A.5 shows the expected sampling variances of $\bar{y}_{st}$, as given by the individual optima, the compromise, and the proportional allocations. The formulas are as follows:

$$v_{opt} = \frac{(\sum W_h s_h)^2}{n}, \qquad v_{comp} = \sum \frac{(W_h s_h)^2}{m_h}, \qquad v_{prop} = \frac{\sum W_h s_h^2}{n}$$

The compromise allocation gives results almost as precise as if it were possible to use separate optimum allocations for each item. What is more noteworthy is that proportional allocation is only slightly less precise than the compromise or the individual optima. Further, Table 5A.5 overestimates the precision of the optima and of the compromise, since these allocations were made from estimated variances. This result is another illustration of the flatness of the optimum mentioned in section 5A.1.

5A.4 OTHER METHODS WITH MORE THAN ONE ITEM

In some surveys the optimum allocations for individual variates differ so much that there is no obvious compromise. Some principle is needed that will determine the allocation to be used, although none seems best for all applications. Two useful ones suggested by Yates (1960) are presented.

The first applies to surveys taken for a specialized objective, in which the loss due to an error of a given size in an estimate can be measured in terms of money or utility, as discussed in section 4.9. With v variates and quadratic loss functions, it may be reasonable to express the total expected loss as a linear function

$$L(n_h) = a_1 V_1 + a_2 V_2 + \cdots + a_v V_v \qquad (5A.8)$$

where the a's are known numbers, and $V_j = V(\bar{y}_{st})$ for the jth variate. With a linear function for the costs of sampling, we have

$$C = c_0 + \sum c_h n_h \qquad (5A.9)$$

The n_h are determined to minimize $(C + L)$. By ordinary calculus methods we find

$$n_h = \frac{W_h}{\sqrt{c_h}} \sqrt{\sum_{j=1}^{v} a_j S_{jh}^2} \qquad (5A.10)$$

where S_{jh}^2 is the variance of the jth variate in stratum h.

In the second approach we specify the desired standard error or variance V_j ($j = 1, 2, \cdots, v$) for each variate. If population means are being estimated, this implies that

$$\sum_{h=1}^{L} \frac{W_h^2 S_{jh}^2}{n_h} - \sum_{h=1}^{L} \frac{W_h S_{jh}^2}{N} \le V_j \qquad (j = 1, 2, \cdots, v) \qquad (5A.11)$$

Inequality signs are used because the most economical allocation may supply variances smaller than the desired V_j for some of the items.

In this approach the cost (equation 5A.9) is minimized subject to the tolerances V_j.

The first step is to work out the optimum allocation for each variate separately and to find the cost of satisfying its tolerance. Take the variate, say y_1, for which the cost C_1 is highest and examine whether the optimum allocation for y_1 satisfies all the other $(v - 1)$ tolerances. If so, we use this allocation and the problem is solved, because no other allocation will satisfy the tolerance V_1 for y_1 at a cost as low as C_1.

If some of the tolerances are not met, the problem is more difficult. Dalenius (1957) gives an ingenious graphical solution usable when there are only two strata, and Yates (1960) gives a more general mathematical approach. These methods are illustrated by the following examples.

Example 1 (Two Strata, Three Variates). The W_h, S_{jh} appear in columns 1 to 4 of Table 5A.6. It is assumed that the fpc is negligible and that c_h = constant.

TABLE 5A.6

ARTIFICIAL DATA FOR TWO STRATA, THREE VARIATES

Column	(1)	(2)	(3)	(4)	(5)	(6)	(7)	(8)	(9)
Stratum	W_h	S_{1h}	S_{2h}	S_{3h}	W_hS_{1h}	W_hS_{2h}	W_hS_{3h}	$(6)^2/(5)$	$(7)^2/(5)$
1	0.8	4	2	1	3.2	1.6	0.8	0.8	0.2
2	0.2	4	6	8	0.8	1.2	1.6	1.8	3.2
			Totals		4.0	2.8	2.4	2.6	3.4

The extra computation required when these assumptions do not hold is minor. Under optimum allocation for the jth variate,

$$V(\bar{y}_{j\,st}) = \frac{(\sum W_hS_{jh})^2}{n}$$

Columns 5 through 7 give the material for computing the individual optimum variances.

Case 1. This illustrates a situation with an easy solution. Suppose that the desired s.e. for each estimate is 0.1, so that each $V_j = 0.01$. From columns 5 through 7 it is clear that the first variate requires the largest sample: $(4.0)^2/0.01$ = 1600. From column 5, its allocation is $_1n_1 = 1280$, $_1n_2 = 320$, where the *first* subscript signifies that the allocation is the optimum for y_1.

We now determine whether this solution supplies the two other desired tolerances. A useful general result for this purpose is as follows. If the optimum allocation for the jth variate is used, the variance obtained for the kth variate is

$$_jV(\bar{y}_{kst}) = \sum_{h=1}^{L} \frac{W_h^2 S_{kh}^2}{_jn_h} = \frac{\sum W_hS_{jh}}{n}\left(\sum \frac{W_h^2 S_{kh}^2}{W_hS_{jh}}\right) \qquad (5A.12)$$

since $_jn_h = nW_hS_{jh}/\sum W_hS_{jh}$. We require this result for $j = 1$, $k = 2,3$. In columns 8 and 9 the terms inside the parentheses are computed from columns 5 through 7. These results give

$$_1V(\bar{y}_{2\ st}) = \frac{(4.0)(2.6)}{1600} = 0.0065, \qquad _1V(\bar{y}_{3\ st}) = \frac{(4.0)(3.4)}{1600} = 0.0085$$

Both tolerances are more than satisfied.

Case 2. With the same data, the desired s.e.'s are 0.1 for y_1 and y_2, but 0.08 for y_3, so that $V_3 = 0.0064$. The foregoing solution no longer holds, since it gives $V_3 = 0.0085$. The graphical method of Dalenius may be used. Equation 5A.11 shows that for any specified variate the values of n_1, n_2 which satisfy the tolerance exactly lie on a hyperbola in n_1 and n_2. Figure 5A.1 shows the three hyperbolas for this problem. With y_1, for instance, the equation of the hyperbola is

$$\frac{(W_1S_{11})^2}{n_1} + \frac{(W_2S_{12})^2}{n_2} = \frac{10.24}{n_1} + \frac{0.64}{n_2} = 0.01$$

The region in which all these requirements are met is the area above and to the right of the dotted lines AB, BC. We seek the point in this region at which $n_1 + n_2$ is a minimum. This is clearly the point B. Hence the graph gives the solution $n_1 = 1200$, $n_2 = 430$, $n = 1630$. This solution can be found arithmetically, since it is the point at which both variates y_1 and y_3 meet their tolerances exactly. The reader may verify that the arithmetical method gives $n_1 = 1200$, $n_2 = 437$.

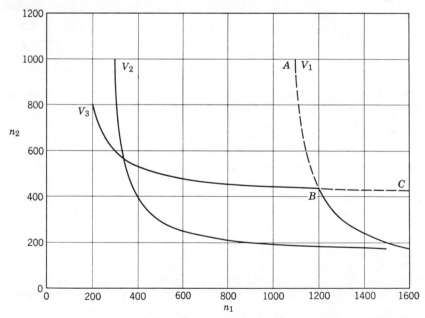

Fig. 5A   Graphical solution of allocation problem (three variables, two strata).

With two strata, the graphical method works for any number of variates. The situation with more than two strata, which is more complex, is illustrated by example 2.

Example 2. (Four Strata, Two Variates) The data are shown in columns 1

TABLE 5A.7

ARTIFICIAL DATA FOR FOUR STRATA, TWO VARIATES

Column	(1)	(2)	(3)	(4)	(5)	(6)	(7)
Stratum	W_h	S_{1h}	S_{2h}	W_hS_{1h}	W_hS_{2h}	$(5)^2/(4)$	$(4)^2/(5)$
1	0.4	5	1	2.0	0.4	0.08	10.00
2	0.3	5	2	1.5	0.6	0.24	3.75
3	0.2	5	4	1.0	0.8	0.64	1.25
4	0.1	5	8	0.5	0.8	1.28	0.31
			Totals	5.0	2.6	2.24	15.31

through 3 of Table 5A.7. The problem is to find the smallest sample size for which
$$V_1 \le 0.04, \qquad V_2 \le 0.01$$
As before, we first work out the optimum allocation and resulting sample size for each variate. From columns 4 and 5,

$$_1V(\bar{y}_{1\,st}) = \frac{25}{n}, \qquad _1n = \frac{25}{0.04} = 625$$

$$_2V(\bar{y}_{2\,st}) = \frac{6.76}{n}, \qquad _2n = \frac{6.76}{0.01} = 676$$

From equation 5A.12 and column 7, the variance obtained for y_1 if allocation 2 is used with $n = 676$ is

$$_2V(\bar{y}_{1\,st}) = \frac{(2.6)(15.31)}{676} = \frac{39.81}{676} = 0.0589$$

This is larger than the value 0.04 specified for V_1.

We must seek a compromise allocation that satisfies both tolerances exactly. Using Lagrange multipliers λ_1 and λ_2, we find the values of n_h that minimize

$$\sum_{h=1}^{L} c_h n_h + \lambda_1 \sum_{h=1}^{L} \frac{W_h^2 S_{1h}^2}{n_h} + \lambda_2 \sum_{h=1}^{L} \frac{W_h^2 S_{2h}^2}{n_h}$$

In this example $c_h = 1$, but the general method is given. Differentiation with respect to n_h leads to

$$n_h = \frac{n\sqrt{\lambda_1 \dfrac{W_h^2 S_{1h}^2}{c_h} + \lambda_2 \dfrac{W_h^2 S_{2h}^2}{c_h}}}{\sum \sqrt{\lambda_1 \dfrac{W_h^2 S_{1h}^2}{c_h} + \lambda_2 \dfrac{W_h^2 S_{2h}^2}{c_h}}} \qquad (5A.13)$$

To obtain a solution, the values of λ_1, λ_2, and n that satisfy the two variance conditions and the cost condition must be found. Since there is no simple explicit solution, some method of successive approximation must be selected. An approach is used in which the n_h are determined first.

From (5A.13), the optimum n_h is a kind of weighted combination of S_{1h}^2 and S_{2h}^2. Clearly, λ_1 and λ_2 enter (5A.13) only in their ratio λ_1/λ_2. Since S_{1h}^2 and S_{2h}^2 may have widely different values, it is hard to guess a good first approximation to λ_1/λ_2. A change of scale that gives a better initial approximation is introduced.

If λ_1/λ_2 tends to infinity, n_h in (5A.13) becomes $_1n_h$, the optimum under allocation 1. Similarly, if $\lambda_1/\lambda_2 = 0$, $n_h \to {}_2n_h$. It follows that with the correct value of $\lambda = \lambda_1/(\lambda_1 + \lambda_2)$, (5A.13) is equivalent to

$$n_h = \frac{n\sqrt{\lambda(_1n_h)^2 + (1 - \lambda)(_2n_h)^2}}{\sum \sqrt{\lambda(_1n_h)^2 + (1 - \lambda)(_2n_h)^2}} \qquad (5A.14)$$

For any value of λ, write

$$V(\bar{y}_{1\,st}) = \frac{\phi_1(\lambda)}{n}, \quad : \quad V(\bar{y}_{2\,st}) = \frac{\phi_2(\lambda)}{n}$$

We want to find λ and n such that

$$\frac{\phi_1(\lambda)}{n} = V_1 = 0.04, \quad : \quad \frac{\phi_2(\lambda)}{n} = V_2 = 0.01 \qquad (5A.15)$$

From the initial calculations, we know that when $\lambda = 1$, $\phi_1(\lambda) = 25$, this being its minimum value, and that when $\lambda = 0$, $\phi_1(\lambda) = 39.81$. As an approximation, assume that $\phi_1(\lambda)$ is a parabola in λ, with its vertex at $\lambda = 1$. This gives

$$\frac{\phi_1(\lambda)}{n} \doteq \frac{25 + 14.81(1 - \lambda)^2}{n} = 0.04 \qquad (5A.16)$$

For $\phi_2(\lambda)$, the minimum is 6.76, at $\lambda = 0$. Its value at $\lambda = 1$ is found by computing $V(\bar{y}_{2\,st})$ under allocation 1. From columns 4 and 6 of Table 5A.7, we obtain $\phi_2(1) = (5.0)(2.24) = 11.20$. The parabolic approximation gives

$$\frac{\phi_2(\lambda)}{n} = \frac{6.76 + 4.44\lambda^2}{n} = 0.01 \qquad (5A.17)$$

Equations 5A.16 and 5A.17 are easily solved to give $\lambda = 0.41$, $n = 751$ as first approximations.

The next step is to compute the n_h, say $_\lambda n_h$, given by this allocation.· Then we find the sample sizes needed for each variate in order to meet its tolerance. If this allocation is near the optimum, these two sample sizes should be almost equal (and, we expect, not far from $n = 751$).

Equation 5A.14 gives the $_\lambda n_h$. If

$$r_h = \sqrt{\lambda(_1n_h/n)^2 + (1 - \lambda)(_2n_h/n)^2}$$

then (5A.14) may be expressed in the form

$$\frac{n_h}{n} = \frac{r_h}{\sum r_h}$$

This form is convenient because from the Neyman allocation rule

$$\frac{_1n_h}{n} = \frac{W_h S_{1h}}{\sum W_h S_{1h}}, \qquad \frac{_2n_h}{n} = \frac{W_h S_{2h}}{\sum W_h S_{1h}}$$

and the quantities $W_h S_{1h}$, $W_h S_{2h}$ have already been computed in columns 4 and 5 of Table 5A.7.

TABLE 5A.8

CHECK ON FIRST APPROXIMATION TO THE ALLOCATION

Column	(1)	(2)	(3)	(4)	(5)	(6)	(7)
Stratum	$\left(\dfrac{_1n_h}{n}\right)^2$	$\left(\dfrac{_2n_h}{n}\right)^2$	r_h	$\dfrac{r_h}{\sum r_h} = \dfrac{n_h}{n}$	$\dfrac{W_h^2 S_{1h}^2}{n_h/n}$	$\dfrac{W_h^2 S_{2h}^2}{n_h/n}$	n_h
1	0.16	0.0225	0.2808	0.2652	15.08	0.60	194
2	0.09	0.0529	0.2610	0.2465	9.13	1.46	180
3	0.04	0.0961	0.2704	0.2554	3.92	2.51	187
4	0.01	0.0961	0.2466	0.2329	1.07	2.75	171
Totals			1.0588	1.0000	29.20	7.32	732

Table 5A.8 shows the rest of the calculations, column 4 giving the n_h/n. To find the resulting variances for a sample of size n, we use the result

$$_\lambda V(\bar{y}_{1\,st}) = \sum \frac{W_h^2 S_{1h}^2}{n_h} = \frac{1}{n} \sum \frac{W_h^2 S_{1h}^2}{n_h/n}$$

The quantities $W_h^2 S_{1h}^2/n_h/n$ are given in columns 5 and 6. From the column totals,

$$_\lambda V(\bar{y}_{1\,st}) = \frac{29.20}{n} = 0.04, \qquad n = 730$$

$$_\lambda V(\bar{y}_{2\,st}) = \frac{7.32}{n} = 0.01 \qquad n = 732$$

The two n's are so close that we accept this allocation and take $n = 732$. The values of the n_h, shown in column 7, are found by multiplying column 4 by 732.

If the two values of n given by the first approximation differ materially, a second approximation to λ and n is computed, either graphically or by the parabolic functions, using the already computed values of $\phi_1(\lambda)$ and $\phi_2(\lambda)$. With two variates, the same method applies to any number of strata.

With more than two strata and more than two variates, the best computing method is not clear. Some results obtained in the mathematical study of programming may be useful. More complicated problems can also arise; we might wish to specify upper limits to the variances for certain subdivisions of the population as well as over-all variances.

5A.5   TWO-WAY STRATIFICATION WITH SMALL SAMPLES

Suppose that there are two criteria of stratification, say by R rows and C columns, making RC cells. If $n \geq RC$, every cell can be represented in the sample. A problem arises when $n < RC$, and we would like the sample to give proportional representation to each criterion of stratification.

TABLE 5A.9

NUMBER AND PROPORTION OF SCHOOLS IN EACH CELL

Size of City		A	B	C	D	Totals		$n_{i.}$
			Expenditure per Pupil					
I	m_{1j}	15	21	17	9	$m_{1.}$	62	
	P_{1j}	0.091	0.127	0.103	0.055	$P_{1.}$	0.376	4
II	m_{2j}	10	8	13	7	$m_{2.}$	38	
	P_{2j}	0.061	0.049	0.079	0.042	$P_{2.}$	0.231	2
III	m_{3j}	6	9	5	8	$m_{3.}$	28	
	P_{3j}	0.036	0.055	0.030	0.049	$P_{3.}$	0.170	2
IV	m_{4j}	4	3	6	6	$m_{4.}$	19	
	P_{4j}	0.024	0.018	0.036	0.036	$P_{4.}$	0.114	1
V	m_{5j}	3	2	5	8	$m_{5.}$	18	
	P_{5j}	0.018	0.012	0.030	0.049	$P_{5.}$	0.109	1
Totals	$m_{.j}$	38	43	46	38		165	
	$P_{.j}$	0.230	0.261	0.278	0.231		1.000	
	$n_{.j}$	2	3	3	2			

In a simple method developed by Bryant, Hartley, and Jessen (1960) the technique requires only that n exceed the greater of R and C.

To illustrate this method, suppose that a small population of 165 schools has been stratified by size of city into five classes and by average expenditure per pupil into four classes. The numbers of schools m_{ij} and the proportions of schools $P_{ij} = m_{ij}/165$ in each of the 20 cells are shown in Table 5A.9.

The objective is to give each school an approximately equal chance of selection while giving each marginal class its proportional representation. In this illustration $n = 10$. Compute the numbers $n_{i.} = nP_{i.}$ and $n_{.j} = nP_{.j}$, where these products are rounded to the nearest integers (with a further minor adjustment, if needed, so that the $n_{i.}$ and the $n_{.j}$ both add to n). These numbers are shown in Table 5A.9.

The next step is to draw $n = 10$ cells with probability $n_{i.}n_{.j}/n^2$ for the ijth cell. This is done by constructing an $n \times n$ square (Table 5A.10). In row 1 one column is drawn at random. In row 2 one of the remaining columns is drawn at random, and so on. At the end, each row and column

TABLE 5A.10

10 × 10 SQUARE FOR DRAWING THE SAMPLE

			Column								
Row		1 *A*	2	3 *B*	4	5	6 *C*	7	8	9 *D*	10
1	I	×									
2					×						
3			×								
4								×			
5	II						×				
6									×		
7	III			×							
8										×	
9	IV					×					
10	V										×

contains one unit. (This draw is most quickly made by a random permutation of the numbers 1 to 10.) The results of one draw are indicated by ×'s in Table 5A.10.

Note that columns 1 and 2 are assigned to marginal stratum A, since $n_{.1} = 2$. Similarly, rows 1 through 4 are assigned to marginal stratum I, since $n_{1.} = 4$, and so on. This completes the allocation of the sample to the 20 cells. The allocation appears in more compact form in Table 5A.11. Two schools are drawn at random from the 15 schools in cell IA, and so on. The probability that a school in row i, column j is drawn is proportional to $n_{i.}n_{.j}/P_{ij}$. Thus the probabilities are not equal, though they will be approximately so if $P_{ij} \doteq n_{i.}n_{.j}/n^2$.

An unbiased estimate of the mean per school is

$$\bar{y}_U = \frac{1}{n} \sum \frac{n^2 P_{ij}}{n_{i.}n_{.j}} y_{ij}$$

where y_{ij} is the sample *total* in the ijth cell. If, however, $P_{ij} \doteq n_{i.}n_{.j}/n^2$, the sample mean $\bar{y}$ is probably preferable, since its bias should be negligible. A sample estimate of variance is available for both the unbiased and biased estimates, provided that n is at least twice the greater of R and C and that at least two units are drawn in every row and column.

If P_{ij} differs markedly from $n_{i.}n_{.j}/n^2$ in some cells, an extra step keeps the probabilities of selection of schools more nearly constant. After computing the $n_{i.}$ and $n_{.j}$, examine the quantities $D_{ij} = nP_{ij} - n_{i.}n_{.j}/n$,

TABLE 5A.11

ALLOCATION OF THE SAMPLE TO THE 20 CELLS

	A	B	C	D	Total
I	2	1	1	0	4
II	0	0	2	0	2
III	0	1	0	1	2
IV	0	1	0	0	1
V	0	0	0	1	1
Total	2	3	3	2	10

after rounding them to integers. If, in any cell, D_{ij} is a positive integer, automatically assign D_{ij} units to this cell. Reduce n, the $n_{i.}$, and the $n_{.j}$ 'by the amounts required by this fixed allocation and carry out the remaining allocation as before.

An earlier technique for this problem, including the situation in which a substantial number of cells are empty, was named *controlled selection* by Goodman and Kish (1950). In their applications rows represent the principal stratification, one unit being drawn from each row. They show how to find a limited number of acceptable allocations, each with its appropriate probability, such that cells are selected with probabilities P_{ij}.

5A.6 THE CONSTRUCTION OF STRATA

This topic raises several questions. What is the best characteristic for the construction of strata? How should the boundaries between the strata be determined? How many strata should there be? For a single item or variable y the best characteristic is clearly the frequency distribution of y itself. The next best is presumably the frequency distribution of some other quantity highly correlated with y. Given the number of strata, the equations for determining the best stratum boundaries under proportional and Neyman allocation have been worked out by Dalenius (1957), and quicker approximate methods by several workers. We shall consider Neyman allocation, since it is usually superior to proportional allocation in populations in which gains from stratification are greatest. It is assumed at first that the strata are set up by using the value of y itself.

Let y_0, y_L be the smallest and largest values of y in the population. The problem is to find intermediate stratum boundaries $y_1, y_2, \cdots, y_{L-1}$ such that

$$V(\bar{y}_{st}) = \frac{1}{n}\left(\sum_{h=1}^{L} W_h S_h\right)^2 - \frac{1}{N}\sum_{h=1}^{L} W_h S_h^2 \tag{5A.18}$$

is a minimum. If the fpc is ignored, it is sufficient to minimize $\sum W_h S_h$. Since y_h appears in this sum only in the terms $W_h S_h$ and $W_{h+1}S_{h+1}$, we have

$$\frac{\partial}{\partial y_h}\left(\sum W_h S_h\right) = \frac{\partial}{\partial y_h}(W_h S_h) + \frac{\partial}{\partial y_h}(W_{h+1}S_{h+1})$$

Now if $f(y)$ is the frequency function of y,

$$W_h = \int_{y_{h-1}}^{y_h} f(t)\, dt, \qquad \frac{\partial W_h}{\partial y_h} = f(y_h) \tag{5A.19}$$

Further,

$$W_h S_h^2 = \int_{y_{h-1}}^{y_h} t^2 f(t)\, dt - \frac{\left[\displaystyle\int_{y_{h-1}}^{y_h} t f(t)\, dt\right]^2}{\displaystyle\int_{y_{h-1}}^{y_h} f(t)\, dt} \tag{5A.20}$$

Differentiation of (5A.20) gives

$$S_h^2 \frac{\partial W_h}{\partial y_h} + 2W_h S_h \frac{\partial S_h}{\partial y_h} = y_h^2 f(y_h) - 2y_h \mu_h f(y_h) + \mu_h^2 f(y_h)$$

where μ_h is the mean of y in stratum h. Add $S_h^2\, \partial W_h/\partial y_h$ to the left side, and the equal quantity $S_h^2 f(y_h)$ to the right side. This gives, on dividing by $2S_h$,

$$\frac{\partial(W_h S_h)}{\partial y_h} = S_h \frac{\partial W_h}{\partial y_h} + W_h \frac{\partial S_h}{\partial y_h} = \frac{1}{2}f(y_h)\frac{(y_h - \mu_h)^2 + S_h^2}{S_h}$$

Similarly we find

$$\frac{\partial(W_{h+1}S_{h+1})}{\partial y_h} = -\frac{1}{2}f(y_h)\frac{(y_h - \mu_{h+1})^2 + S_{h+1}^2}{S_{h+1}}$$

Hence the calculus equations for y_h are

$$\frac{(y_h - \mu_h)^2 + S_h^2}{S_h} = \frac{(y_h - \mu_{h+1})^2 + S_{h+1}^2}{S_{h+1}} \quad (h = 1, 2, \cdots, L-1) \tag{5A.21}$$

Unfortunately, these equations are ill adapted to practical computation, since both μ_h and S_h depend on y_h. A quick approximate method, due to Dalenius and Hodges (1959), is presented. Let

$$Z(y) = \int_{y_0}^{y} \sqrt{f(t)}\, dt$$

If the strata are numerous and narrow, $f(y)$ should be approximately constant (rectangular) within a given stratum. Hence.

$$W_h = \int_{y_{h-1}}^{y_h} f(t)\, dt \doteq f_h(y_h - y_{h-1})$$

$$S_h \doteq \frac{1}{\sqrt{12}} (y_h - y_{h-1})$$

$$Z_h - Z_{h-1} = \int_{y_{h-1}}^{y_h} \sqrt{f(t)}\, dt \doteq \sqrt{f_h}(y_h - y_{h-1})$$

where f_h is the "constant" value of $f(y)$ in stratum h. By substituting these approximations, we find

$$\sqrt{12} \sum_{h=1}^{L} W_h S_h \doteq \sum_{h=1}^{L} f_h(y_h - y_{h-1})^2 \doteq \sum_{h=1}^{L} (Z_h - Z_{h-1})^2 \qquad (5A.22)$$

Since $(Z_L - Z_0)$ is fixed, it is easy to verify that the sum on the right is minimized by making $(Z_h - Z_{h-1})$ constant.

Given $f(y)$, the rule is to form the cumulative of $\sqrt{f(y)}$ and choose the y_h so that they create equal intervals on the cum $\sqrt{f(y)}$ scale. Table 5A.12 illustrates the use of the rule.

TABLE 5A.12

CALCULATION OF STRATUM BOUNDARIES BY THE CUM $\sqrt{f(y)}$ RULE

$\dfrac{\text{Industrial Loans}}{\text{Total Loans}}\%$	$f(y)$	Cum $\sqrt{f(y)}$	$\dfrac{\text{Industrial Loans}}{\text{Total Loans}}\%$	$f(y)$	Cum $\sqrt{f(y)}$
0–5	3464	58.9	50–55	126	340.3
5–10	2516	109.1	55–60	107	350.6
10–15	2157	155.5	60–65	82	359.7
15–20	1581	195.3	65–70	50	366.8
20–25	1142	229.1	70–75	39	373.0
25–30	746	256.4	75–80	25	378.0
30–35	512	279.0	80–85	16	382.0
35–40	376	298.4	85–90	19	386.4
40–45	265	314.7	90–95	2	387.8
45–50	207	329.1	95–100	3	389.5

Example. The data show the frequency distribution of the percentage of bank loans devoted to industrial loans in a population of 13,435 banks of the United States (McEvoy, 1956). The distribution is skew, with its mode at the lower end. In the cum $\sqrt{f}$ column, $58.9 = \sqrt{3464}$, $109.1 = \sqrt{3464} + \sqrt{2516}$, and so on.

Suppose that we want five strata. Since the total of cum $\sqrt{f}$ is 389.5, the division points should be at 77.9, 155.8, 233.7, and 311.6 on this scale. The nearest available points are as follows:

	Stratum				
	1	2	3	4	5
Boundaries	0–5%	5–15%	15–25%	25–45%	45–100%
Interval on cum $\sqrt{f}$	58.9	96.6	73.6	85.6	74.8

The first two intervals, 58.9 and 96.6, are rather unequal, but cannot be improved upon without a finer subdivision of the original classes.

If the class intervals in the original distribution of y are of unequal length, a slight change is needed. When the interval changes from one of length d to one of length ud, the value of $\sqrt{f}$ for the second interval is multiplied by $\sqrt{u}$ when forming cum $\sqrt{f}$.

Although the mathematics behind the rule is crude, the rule has worked well in both theoretical and actual distributions [Cochran (1961)]. In another rule that does well, Ekman (1959), the boundaries are constructed so that $W_h(y_h - y_{h-1})$ is constant.

The approximate rule has an interesting consequence. From equation 5A.22, the rule is equivalent to making $W_h S_h$ approximately constant, as conjectured by Dalenius and Gurney (1951). But with $W_h S_h$ constant, Neyman allocation gives a *constant* sample size $n_h = n/L$ in all strata. Since the optimum is flat with respect to variations in the n_h (section 5A.1), use of the cum $\sqrt{f}$ rule, taking equal sample sizes in the resulting strata, is highly efficient.

Thus far we have made the unrealistic assumption that stratification can be based on the values of y itself. In practice, some other variable x is used (perhaps the value of y at a recent census). Dalenius (1957) develops equations for the boundaries of x that minimize $\sum W_h S_{yh}$, given a knowledge of the regression of y on x. If this regression is nonlinear, these boundaries may differ considerably from those that are optimum when x itself is the variable to be measured. The equations indicate, however, that if the regression of y on x is linear and the correlation between y and x is high within all strata the two sets of boundaries should be nearly the same. Let

$$y = \alpha + \beta x + e$$

where $E(e) = 0$ for all x and e, x are uncorrelated. The variance of e within stratum h is S_{eh}^2. Then the x-boundaries which make $V(\bar{y}_{st})$ a minimum satisfy the equations [Dalenius (1957)].

$$\frac{\beta^2[(x_h - \mu_{xh})^2 + S_{xh}^2] + 2S_{eh}^2}{\beta S_{xh}\sqrt{1 + S_{eh}^2/\beta^2 S_{xh}^2}} = \frac{\beta^2[(x_h - \mu_{x,h+1})^2 + S_{x,h+1}^2] + 2S_{e,h+1}^2}{\beta S_{x,h+1}\sqrt{1 + S_{e,h+1}^2/\beta^2 S_{x,h+1}^2}}$$

If $S_{eh}^2/\beta^2 S_{xh}^2$ is small for all h, these equations reduce to the form (5A.21) that gives optimum boundaries for x. But $S_{eh}^2/\beta^2 S_{xh}^2 = (1 - \rho_h^2)/\rho_h^2$ where ρ_h is the correlation between y and x within stratum h.

Although more investigation is needed, this result suggests that the cum $\sqrt{f}$ rule applied to x should give an efficient stratification for another variable y that has a linear regression on x with high correlation. Some numerical results by Cochran (1961) support this conjecture. Moreover, if the ρ_h are only moderate, as will happen when the number of strata is increased, failure to use the optimum x-boundaries should have a less deleterious effect on y.

The preceding discussion is, of course, mainly relevant to the sampling of institutions stratified by some measure of size. The results are also applicable when the survey contains several variables of major interest, provided that all are related more or less to the *same* measure of size. For instance, suppose that some variables are roughly proportional to the measure of size, others to its square root, and others are almost independent of size. Selection of boundaries by the cum $\sqrt{f}$ rule should be roughly optimum for the first set of variables and fairly good for the second set (where the gains from stratification are smaller in any event). The third set may suffer some loss of precision from the use of unequal sampling fractions.

The situation is different when one set of variables is closely related to one measure of size, and another set is closely related to a second measure with a markedly different frequency distribution. The general approach given in section 5A.4 is applicable, but the best computational methods for obtaining the boundaries that meet the desired tolerances for the variances have not been worked out.

In geographical stratification the problem is less amenable to a mathematical approach, since there are so many different ways in which stratum boundaries may be formed. The usual procedure is to select a few variables that have high correlations with the principal items in the survey and to use a combination of judgment and trial and error to construct boundaries that are good for these selected variables. Since the gains in precision from stratification are likely to be modest, it is not worthwhile to expend a great deal of effort in improving boundaries. Bases of stratification for economic items have been discussed by Stephan (1941) and

Hagood and Bernert (1945) and for farm items by King and McCarty (1941).

5A.7 NUMBER OF STRATA

The two questions relevant to a decision about the number of strata L are (a) at what rate does the variance decrease as L is increased? (b) How is the cost of the survey affected by an increase in L?

As regards (a), suppose first that strata are constructed by the values of y. To take the simplest case, let the distribution of y be rectangular in the interval $(a, a + d)$. Then S_y^2, before stratification, is $d^2/12$, so that with a simple random sample of size n, $V(\bar{y}) = d^2/12n$. If L strata of equal size are created, the variance within any stratum is $S_{yh}^2 = d^2/12L^2$. Hence, for a stratified sample, with $W_h = 1/L$ and $n_h = n/L$,

$$V(\bar{y}_{st}) = \frac{1}{n}\left(\sum_{h=1}^{L} W_h S_{yh}\right)^2 = \frac{1}{n}\left(\sum_{h=1}^{L} \frac{1}{L} \cdot \frac{d}{\sqrt{12L}}\right)^2 = \frac{d^2}{12nL^2} = \frac{V(\bar{y})}{L^2}$$

Thus with a rectangular distribution the variance of $\bar{y}_{st}$ decreases inversely as the *square* of the number of strata. Rather remarkably, this relation continues to hold, roughly, when actual skew distributions with finite range are stratified with the optimum choice of boundaries for Neyman allocation. In eight distributions of data of the type likely to occur in practice, Cochran (1961) found that the average values of $V(\bar{y}_{st})/V(\bar{y})$ were 0.232, 0.098, and 0.053 for $L = 2, 3, 4$, as compared with 0.250, 0.111, and 0.062 for the rectangular distribution.

These results, which suggest that multiplication of strata is profitable, give a misleading picture of what happens when some other variable x is used to construct the strata. If $\phi(x) = E(y \mid x)$ is the regression of y on x, we may write

$$y = \phi(x) + e$$

where ϕ and e are uncorrelated. Hence

$$S_y^2 = S_\phi^2 + S_e^2$$

By the preceding results, creation of L optimal strata for x may reduce S_ϕ^2 to S_ϕ^2/L^2 if $\phi(x)$ is linear or at a smaller rate if $\phi(x)$ is nonlinear. But the term S_e^2 is not reduced by stratification on x. As L increases, a value is reached sooner or later at which the term S_e^2 dominates. Further increases in L will produce only a trivial proportional reduction in $V(\bar{y}_{st})$.

How quickly the point of diminishing returns is reached depends on a number of factors—particularly the relative sizes of S_e^2 and S_ϕ^2 and the nature of $\phi(x)$. Only a few examples from actual data are available in the literature. To supplement them, a simple theoretical approach is used. Suppose that the optimum choice of stratum boundaries by means of x, with samples of equal size n/L in each stratum, reduces $V(\bar{x}_{st})$ at a rate proportional to $1/L^2$. Thus

$$V(\bar{x}_{st}) = \frac{L}{n} \sum_{h=1}^{L} W_h^2 S_{xh}^2 = \frac{S_x^2}{nL^2} \tag{5A.23}$$

Suppose also that the regression of y on x is linear, that is,

$$y = \alpha + \beta x + e$$

where S_e^2 is constant. Then,

$$V(\bar{y}_{st}) = \frac{L}{n} \sum_{h=1}^{L} W_h^2 S_{yh}^2 = \frac{L\beta^2}{n} \sum_{h=1}^{L} W_h^2 S_{xh}^2 + \frac{LS_e^2}{n} \sum_{h=1}^{L} W_h^2$$

For any set of L strata, $\sum W_h^2 \geq \dfrac{1}{L}$. Using (5A.23), we have

$$V(\bar{y}_{st}) \geq \frac{1}{n}\left(\frac{\beta^2 S_x^2}{L^2} + S_e^2\right) = \frac{S_y^2}{n}\left[\frac{\rho^2}{L^2} + (1 - \rho^2)\right] \tag{5A.24}$$

where ρ is the correlation between y and x in the unstratified population.

With this model, Table 5A.13 shows $V(\bar{y}_{st})/V(\bar{y})$ for $\rho = 0.99, 0.95, 0.90$, and 0.85 and $L = 2$ to 6, assuming that relation (5A.24) is an equality. The right-hand columns of the table give $V(\bar{y}_{st})/V(\bar{y})$ for three sets of actual data, described under the table, in which x is the value of y at some earlier time.

The results for the regression model indicate that unless ρ exceeds 0.95, little reduction in variance is to be expected beyond $L = 6$. Data sets 2 and 3 support this conclusion, although some further increase in L might be profitable with the college enrollment data (set 1).

To complete this analysis, we require a cost function that shows how the cost depends on L. Dalenius (1957) suggests the relation $C = LC_s + nC_n$. The cost ratio C_s/C_n will vary with the type of survey. An increase in the number of strata involves extra work in planning and drawing the sample and increases the number of weights used in computing the estimates, unless they are self-weighting. In some surveys almost no change is required in the organization of the field work; in others a separate field unit is set up in each stratum. Whatever the form of the cost function, the results in Table 5A.13 suggest that if an increase in L beyond 6 necessitates any substantial decrease in n in order to keep the cost constant the increase will seldom be profitable.

The discussion in this section is confined to surveys in which only over-all estimates are to be made. If estimates are wanted also for geographic

TABLE 5A.13

$V(\bar{y}_{st})/V(\bar{y})$ AS A FUNCTION OF L FOR THE LINEAR REGRESSION MODEL AND FOR SOME ACTUAL DATA

	Linear Regression Model				Data, Set		
	$\rho =$						
L	0.99	0.95	0.90	0.85	1	2	3
2	0.265	0.323	0.392	0.458	0.197	0.295	0.500
3	0.129	0.198	0.280	0.358	0.108	0.178	0.375
4	0.081	0.154	0.241	0.323	0.075	0.142	0.244
5	0.059	0.134	0.222	0.306	0.065	0.105	0.241
6	0.047	0.123	0.212	0.298	0.050	0.104	0.212
∞	0.020	0.098	0.190	0.277	—	—	—

		Type of Data			
Set	Data	x	y	Source	
1	College enrollments	1952	1958	Cochran (1961)	
2	City sizes	1940	1950	Cochran (1961)	
3	Family incomes	1929	1933	Dalenius and Gurney (1951)	

subdivisions of the population, the argument for a larger number of strata is stronger.

5A.8   STRATIFICATION AFTER SELECTION OF THE SAMPLE

With some variables that are suitable for stratification, the stratum to which a unit belongs is not known until the data have been collected. Personal characteristics such as age, sex, race, and educational level are common examples. The stratum sizes N_h may be obtainable fairly accurately from official statistics, but the units can be classified into the strata only after the sample data are known.

One procedure is to take a simple random sample of size n and classify the units. Instead of the sample mean $\bar{y}$, we use the estimate $\bar{y}_W = \sum W_h \bar{y}_h$, where $\bar{y}_h$ is the mean of the sample units that fall in stratum h, and $W_h = N_h/N$. This method is almost as precise as *proportional* stratified sampling, provided that (a) the sample is reasonably large, say >20, in every stratum, and (b) the effects of errors in the weights W_h can be ignored (see section 5A.2).

To show this, let m_h be the number of units in the sample that fall in stratum h, where m_h will vary from sample to sample. For samples in which the m_h are fixed,

$$V(\bar{y}_W) = \sum \frac{W_h^2 S_h^2}{m_h} - \frac{1}{N} \sum W_h S_h^2$$

The average value of this quantity in repeated samples of size n must now be calculated. This requires a little care, since one or more of the m_h could be zero. If this happened, two or more strata would have to be combined before making the estimate, and a less precise estimate would be produced. With increasing n, the probability that any m_h is zero becomes so small that the contribution to the variance from this source is negligible.

If the case in which m_h is zero is ignored, Stephan (1945) has shown that to terms of order n^{-2}

$$E\left(\frac{1}{m_h}\right) = \frac{1}{nW_h} + \frac{1 - W_h}{n^2 W_h^2}$$

Hence

$$E[V(\bar{y}_W)] = \frac{1 - f}{n} \sum W_h S_h^2 + \frac{1}{n^2} \sum (1 - W_h) S_h^2$$

The first term is the value of $V(\bar{y}_{st})$ for proportional stratification. The second represents the increase in variance that arises because the m_h do not distribute themselves proportionally. But

$$\frac{1}{n^2} \sum (1 - W_h) S_h^2 = \frac{1}{n}\left(\frac{L}{n}\right) \bar{S}_h^2 - \frac{1}{n^2} \sum W_h S_h^2 = \frac{1}{n\bar{n}_h} \bar{S}_h^2 - \frac{1}{n^2} \sum W_h S_h^2$$

where $\bar{S}_h^2$ is the average of the S_h^2 and $\bar{n}_h = n/L$ is the average number of units per stratum. Thus, if the S_h^2 do not differ greatly, the "increase" term is about $1/\bar{n}_h$ times the variance for proportional stratification. The increase will be small if $\bar{n}_h$ is reasonably large.

This method can also be applied to a sample that is already stratified by another factor, for example, into five geographic regions, provided that the W_h are known separately within each region.

5A.9   QUOTA SAMPLING

In another method that has been widely used in opinion and market research surveys the n_h required in each stratum is computed in advance so that stratification is proportional. The enumerator is instructed to continue sampling until the necessary "quota" has been obtained in each stratum. The most common variables for stratification are geographic area, age, sex, race, and some measure of economic level. If the enumerator were to choose persons at random within the geographic areas and assign each to his appropriate stratum, the method would be identical with stratified random sampling. A considerable amount of field work would be required to fill all quotas, however, since in the later stages most of the persons approached would fall in quotas already filled.

To expedite the filling of quotas, some latitude is allowed to the enumerator regarding the persons or households to be included. The amount of latitude varies with the agency, but, in general, quota sampling may be described as stratified sampling with a more or less nonrandom selection of units within strata. For this reason, sampling-error formulas cannot be applied with confidence to the results of quota samples. A number of comparisons between the results of quota and probability samples are summarized by Stephan and McCarthy (1958), who give an excellent critique of the performance of both types of survey. The quota method seems likely to produce samples that are biased on characteristics such as income, education and occupation, although it often agrees well with the probability samples on questions of opinion and attitude.

5A.10 ESTIMATION FROM A SAMPLE OF THE GAIN DUE TO STRATIFICATION

When a stratified random sample has been taken, it may be of interest, as a guide to the conduct of future surveys, to appraise the gain in precision relative to simple random sampling.

The data available from the sample are the values of N_h, n_h, $\bar{y}_h$, and s_h^2. From section 5.4, the estimated variance of the weighted mean from the stratified sample is

$$v(\bar{y}_{st}) = \sum \frac{W_h^2 s_h^2}{n_h} - \sum \frac{W_h s_h^2}{N}$$

The problem is to compare this variance with an estimate of the variance of the mean that would have been obtained from a simple random sample. One procedure sometimes used calculates the familiar mean square deviation from the sample mean,

$$s^2 = \frac{\sum (y_{hi} - \bar{y})^2}{n - 1}$$

where the strata are ignored. This is taken as an estimate of the variance per unit for a simple random sample. This method works well enough if the allocation is proportional, since a simple random sample distributes itself approximately proportionally among strata. But, if an allocation far from proportional has been adopted, the sample actually taken does not resemble a simple random sample, and this s^2 may be a poor estimate. A general procedure is given.

The true variance of the mean of a simple random sample is

$$V_{ran} = \frac{(N-n)}{nN} S^2 = \frac{(N-n)}{nN} \left[\frac{\sum (N_h - 1)S_h^2 + \sum N_h(\bar{Y}_h - \bar{Y})^2}{(N-1)} \right]$$

(5A.25)

by an algebraic identity for S^2.

In the first term inside the bracket, we need only put s_h^2 for S_h^2. The second term requires investigation. For estimating $\sum N_h(\bar{Y}_h - \bar{Y})^2$ it is natural to try $\sum N_h(\bar{y}_h - \bar{y}_{st})^2$. This quantity turns out to be an overestimate that needs adjustment. The relevant result is stated as a theorem, since it will be useful later.

Theorem 5A.1. In stratified random sampling,

$$E[\sum N_h(\bar{y}_h - \bar{y}_{st})^2] = \sum N_h(\bar{Y}_h - \bar{Y})^2 + \sum \frac{S_h^2(N_h - n_h)}{n_h} \left(1 - \frac{N_h}{N}\right)$$

$$= \sum N_h(\bar{Y}_h - \bar{Y})^2 + \sum \frac{N_h S_h^2}{n_h} (1 - f_h)(1 - W_h)$$

Proof.
We may write

$$\sum N_h(\bar{y}_h - \bar{y}_{st})^2 = \sum N_h[(\bar{Y}_h - \bar{Y}) + (\bar{y}_h - \bar{Y}_h) - (\bar{y}_{st} - \bar{Y})]^2$$

We now expand and take the average over all possible samples. It may be verified that the average of each of the two cross-product terms involving $(\bar{Y}_h - \bar{Y})$ vanishes. This gives

$$E \sum N_h(\bar{y}_h - \bar{y}_{st})^2 = \sum N_h(\bar{Y}_h - \bar{Y})^2 + E \sum N_h(\bar{y}_h - \bar{Y}_h)^2$$

$$+ E \sum N_h(\bar{y}_{st} - \bar{Y})^2 - 2E \sum N_h(\bar{y}_h - \bar{Y}_h)(\bar{y}_{st} - \bar{Y}) \quad (5A.26)$$

But

$$\sum N_h(\bar{y}_h - \bar{Y}_h)(\bar{y}_{st} - \bar{Y}) = N(\bar{y}_{st} - \bar{Y})^2$$

by the definitions of $\bar{y}_{st}$ and $\bar{Y}$. Thus the last two terms in (5A.26) coalesce to give

$$-EN(\bar{y}_{st} - \bar{Y})^2 = -\sum \frac{N_h(N_h - n_h)}{N} \frac{S_h^2}{n_h}$$

since this expression is N times the variance of $\bar{y}_{st}$. For the second term on the right in (5A.26),

$$E \sum N_h(\bar{y}_h - \bar{Y}_h)^2 = \sum \frac{N_h(N_h - n_h)}{N_h} \frac{S_h^2}{n_h} = \sum (N_h - n_h) \frac{S_h^2}{n_h}$$

because within each stratum $\bar{y}_h$ is the mean of a simple random sample. Hence

$$E \sum N_h(\bar{y}_h - \bar{y}_{st})^2 = \sum N_h(\bar{Y}_h - \bar{Y})^2$$

$$+ \sum (N_h - n_h) \frac{S_h^2}{n_h} - \frac{\sum N_h(N_h - n_h)}{N} \frac{S_h^2}{n_h}$$

$$= \sum N_h(\bar{Y}_h - \bar{Y})^2 + \sum \frac{S_h^2(N_h - n_h)}{n_h}\left(1 - \frac{N_h}{N}\right)$$

$$= \sum N_h(\bar{Y}_h - \bar{Y})^2 + \sum \frac{N_h S_h^2}{n_h}(1 - f_h)(1 - W_h)$$

Corollary. An unbiased estimate of $\sum N_h(\bar{Y}_h - \bar{Y})^2$ is

$$\sum N_h(\bar{y}_h - \bar{y}_{st})^2 - \sum \frac{N_h S_h^2}{n_h}(1 - f_h)(1 - W_h)$$

When this expression is substituted in (5A.25), we find that an unbiased estimate of V_{ran} is

$$v_{ran} = \frac{N - n}{n(N - 1)}\left[\sum W_h s_h^2 - \sum \frac{W_h s_h^2}{n_h}\right.$$

$$\left. + \sum \frac{W_h^2 s_h^2}{n_h} - \frac{\sum W_h s_h^2}{N} + \sum W_h \bar{y}_h^2 - (\sum W_h \bar{y}_h)^2\right]$$

This expression is unattractive to compute. In nearly all applications simplifications can be utilized. Two are given.

$N > 50$. This will hold for almost all populations. The fourth term inside the bracket may be omitted, since it equals the first term divided by N. We obtain

$$v_{ran} = \frac{N - n}{nN}\left[\sum W_h s_h^2 - \sum \frac{W_h s_h^2}{n_h}\right.$$

$$\left. + \sum \frac{W_h^2 s_h^2}{n_h} + \sum W_h \bar{y}_h^2 - (\sum W_h \bar{y}_h)^2\right] \quad (5A.27)$$

All $n_h > 50$. The second and third terms inside the bracket may be dropped to give

$$v_{ran} = \frac{N - n}{nN}[\sum W_h s_h^2 + \sum W_h \bar{y}_h^2 - (\sum W_h \bar{y}_h)^2] \quad (5A.28)$$

Example. The calculations are illustrated from the first three strata in the sample of teachers' colleges (section 5.9). Data from the 1946 sample appear in Table 5A.14. The means represent enrollment per college, in thousands.

TABLE 5A.14

BASIC DATA FROM A STRATIFIED SAMPLE

Stratum	N_h	n_h	$\bar{y}_h$	$s_h{}^2$
1	13	9	2.200	1.615
2	18	7	1.638	0.063
3	26	10	0.992	0.077
Totals	57	26		

The sample is so small that expression (5A.27) for v_{ran} will be used. The supplementary calculations are given in Table 5A.15.

TABLE 5A.15

ARRANGEMENT OF CALCULATIONS

Stratum	W_h	$W_h s_h{}^2$	$W_h s_h{}^2/n_h$	$W_h{}^2 s_h{}^2/n_h$	$W_h \bar{y}_h$
1	0.228	0.36822	0.04091	0.00933	0.50160
2	0.316	0.01991	0.00284	0.00090	0.51761
3	0.456	0.03511	0.00351	0.00160	0.45235
Totals	1.000	0.42324	0.04726	0.01183	1.47156

The formulas work out as follows:

$$v_{st} = \sum \frac{W_h{}^2 s_h{}^2}{n_h} - \sum \frac{W_h s_h{}^2}{N} = 0.01183 - 0.00743 = 0.0044$$

$$v_{ran} = \frac{31}{(57)(26)} [0.4232 - 0.0473 + 0.0118 + 2.4000 - 2.1655] = 0.0130$$

Stratification appears to have reduced the variance to about one-third of the value for a simple random sample.

Proportional Allocation. An estimate v_{ran} that is usually adequate is obtained from the sum of squares of deviations of the sample values from their mean, for

$$s^2 = \frac{\sum (y_{hi} - \bar{y})^2}{n - 1}$$

$$= \frac{1}{n - 1} \left[\sum (n_h - 1)s_h{}^2 + \sum n_h \bar{y}_h{}^2 - \frac{(\sum n_h \bar{y}_h)^2}{n} \right]$$

by the usual identity in the analysis of variance. If terms in $1/n_h$ are negligible, this is equivalent to

$$\sum W_h s_h{}^2 + \sum W_h \bar{y}_h{}^2 - (\sum W_h \bar{y}_h)^2$$

since $W_h = n_h/n$. This in turn equals the quantity inside the bracket in

5A.28. Thus the expression

$$v_{ran} = \frac{(N - n)}{N} \frac{s^2}{n}$$

is satisfactory if allocation is proportional and terms in $1/n_h$ are negligible.

5A.11 ESTIMATION OF VARIANCE WITH ONE UNIT PER STRATUM

If the population is highly variable and many effective criteria for stratification are known, stratification may be carried to the point at which the sample contains only one unit in each stratum. In this event the formula previously given for estimating $V(\bar{y}_{st})$ cannot be used. An estimate may be attempted by grouping the strata in pairs. In the two strata that form a pair we shall assume that the sizes N_h are equal. Slight deviations from equality do not vitiate the method. The population means $\bar{Y}_h$ for the two members of a pair should not differ greatly, but the allocation into pairs should be made before seeing the sample results, for reasons that will become evident. The number of strata should be at least 20, to allow a minimum of 10 df in the estimated variance.

Let the observations in a typical pair be y_{j1}, y_{j2}, where j goes from 1 to $L/2$. Then, averaging over all samples from this pair,

$$E(y_{j1} - y_{j2})^2 = (\bar{Y}_{j1} - \bar{Y}_{j2})^2 + \frac{N_j - 1}{N_j}(S_{j1}^2 + S_{j2}^2) \qquad (5A.29)$$

where $N_j = N_h$ is the size of each stratum in the pair. Consider the estimate

$$v(\bar{y}_{st}) = \frac{1}{N^2} \sum_{j=1}^{L/2} N_j^2 (y_{j1} - y_{j2})^2 \qquad (5A.30)$$

By (5A.29) the expected value of this quantity is

$$Ev(\bar{y}_{st}) = \frac{1}{N^2}\left[\sum_{h=1}^{L} N_h(N_h - 1)S_h^2 + \sum_{j=1}^{L/2} N_j^2(\bar{Y}_{j1} - \bar{Y}_{j2})^2 \right] \qquad (5A.31)$$

The first term on the right is the correct variance (by theorem 5.3 with $n_h = 1$): the second represents a positive bias. The size of the bias depends on the success attained in the formation of pairs of strata whose true means differ little. The form of estimate (5A.30) warns us not to construct pairs by making the *sample* values differ as little as possible, since this gives a serious underestimate. The technique is sometimes called the method of "collapsed strata."

142

In an alternative method of sampling each pair is used as a single stratum, with $L/2$ strata and two units chosen at random per stratum. An unbiased estimate of $V(\bar{y}_{st})$ for this kind of sampling is obtainable from the usual formula. The reader may verify that

$$V(\bar{y}_{st}) = \frac{1}{N^2}\left[\sum_{h=1}^{L} N_h(N_h - 1)\frac{2N_h - 2}{2N_h - 1}S_h^2 + \sum_{j=1}^{L/2}N_j^2\frac{N_j - 1}{2N_j - 1}(\bar{Y}_{j1} - \bar{Y}_{j2})^2\right]$$

(5A.32)

By comparison with (5A.31), it appears that formula (5A.30) overestimates not only the true variance with one unit per stratum but also the variance that would apply if strata twice as large were used.

Whether the smaller strata are preferable, in the light of this result, is debatable. Unfortunately, if there is a large gain in precision from one unit per stratum, compared with two units per pair, there is also a large overestimation of the variance.

5A.12 SHORT-CUTS IN THE COMPUTATION OF STANDARD ERRORS

One of the merits of probability sampling is that a standard error can be computed for any estimate made from the sample. Unfortunately, the computation of standard errors is more laborious than the computation of the estimates themselves. In complex national surveys containing hundreds or thousands of items, calculation and presentation of standard errors is a major problem. A number of devices have been proposed to cut down the labor and expense. The extent to which any device is helpful will of course depend on the computing machines and methods that are being used.

As a reminder, the formulas for the estimated population mean and total are as follows:

$$V(\bar{y}_{st}) = \sum_{h=1}^{L}\frac{W_h^2 S_h^2}{n_h}(1 - f_h)$$

(5A.33)

$$V(\hat{Y}_{st}) = \sum_{h=1}^{L}\frac{N_h^2 S_h^2}{n_h}(1 - f_h)$$

(5A.34)

Consider first a survey in which the number of strata is small, say ≤ 10, and the sample is relatively large. In such surveys S_h^2 and f_h may vary markedly from stratum to stratum. One device is to compute S_h^2 from a subsample of the n_h units in stratum h. A subsample of size 20 should be adequate for most purposes. The subsample should be drawn at random. A *systematic* subsample (e.g., of every sixth unit in the sample record book if n_h is about 120) is quicker to draw, but it is likely to give an overestimate of $S_h{}^2$ if there is some systematic pattern in the order in which units are listed in the record book (see section 8.3).

If the units are listed in an essentially random order, a second possibility is to record subtotals as the units are being added to compute the sample total in the stratum. For instance, if $n_h = 123$, we might subtotal after every 10 units, giving 12 subtotals $T_1, T_2, \cdots, T_{12}$. The last three units are ignored in the subtotals, though they are included in the sample total. Then $\sum(T_i - \bar{T})^2/110$ provides an estimate of $S_h{}^2$, with 11 d.f. If the distribution of y is non-normal, this estimate is likely to be more precise than an estimate computed from 12 random units because the use of subtotals diminishes the effect of kurtosis (section 2.14) on $V(s^2)$.

Suppose now that the strata are numerous and the sample sizes are small within strata, as, for instance, in geographic stratification covering a wide area. For a large group of strata it may be reasonable to assume that $S_h{}^2$ varies little from stratum to stratum. We might then draw a random sub-sample (e.g., of eight strata out of 40 to 50), compute $s_h{}^2$ in each of the eight strata, and form a pooled $s_h{}^2$ to be used for all the 40 to 50 strata. This method is riskier than that of estimating $S_h{}^2$ in every stratum by means of a random subsample of two or three units and is preferable only if it is time saving.

Other methods are possible when n_h is constant in all strata or in a large group of strata. Suppose that $n_h = 2$ and N_h is constant. Let y_{h1}, y_{h2} be the measurements on the two units, and let $d_h = y_{h1} - y_{h2}$. Then

$$E(d_h{}^2) = 2S_h{}^2$$

Hence an unbiased estimate of $V(\hat{Y}_{st})$ over this group of strata is

$$v(\hat{Y}_{st}) = N_h{}^2(1 - f_h)\sum_{h=1}^{L}\frac{d_h{}^2}{4}$$

This result may be verified by comparison with (5A.34).

This estimate contains L df—more than is needed if L is large. The strata can be grouped to form k groups, which may contain different numbers of strata. Let $D_j = \sum d_h$, taken over the strata in the jth group. Then it is easily shown that an unbiased estimate of $V(\hat{Y}_{st})$, with k df, is

$$v(\hat{Y}_{st}) = N_h{}^2(1 - f_h)\sum_{j=1}^{k}\frac{D_j{}^2}{4}$$

Similar methods apply when n_h is constant and greater than 2. Suppose that $n_h = 4$ and that 18 df are desired for the estimate $v(\hat{Y}_{st})$. Divide the strata into six groups. In each stratum identify the four units in any convenient way as the first, second, third, and fourth units, respectively. In group j let T_{j1}, T_{j2}, T_{j3}, T_{j4} be the totals over the first, second, third, and fourth units, with mean $\bar{T}_j$. Then

$$v(\hat{Y}_{st}) = N_h^2(1 - f_h) \sum_{j=1}^{6} \sum_{u=1}^{4} \frac{(T_{ju} - \bar{T}_j)^2}{12}$$

The general divisor in place of 12 is $n_h(n_h - 1)$.

If n_h is constant but N_h is not, the grouping method becomes more laborious. Instead of the totals T_{ju}, we form totals

$$\hat{Y}_{ju} = \sum N_h y_{hu} \qquad (u = 1, 2, \cdots, n_h)$$

where y_{hu} denotes the unit identified as the "uth" in the stratum and the sum is over the jth group of strata. With k groups, it can be shown that

$$E\left[\sum_{j=1}^{k} \sum_{u=1}^{n_h} \frac{(\hat{Y}_{ju} - \hat{\bar{Y}}_j)^2}{n_h(n_h - 1)}\right] = \sum_{h=1}^{L} \frac{N_h^2 S_h^2}{n_h}$$

the df being $k(n_h - 1)$. The quantity on the left is an overestimate of $V(\hat{Y}_{st})$, since its expectation does not contain the correct fpc term $1 - f_h$. If necessary, the estimate may be multiplied by $1 - n/N$ as a rough correction.

If $k = 1$, the n_h quantities $\hat{Y}_{ju}$ are all unbiased estimates of the population total Y and the method provides an estimate of $V(\hat{Y}_{st})$ based on $n_h - 1$ df.

In surveys containing many items the relation between s($\hat{Y}$) and $\hat{Y}$ may be substantially the same over a large class of items. This can be investigated by plotting s($\hat{Y}$) against $\hat{Y}$ for different items and seeking scales on which a simple relation gives a good fit. An "error graph" of this kind, as Yates (1960) has called it, is extremely helpful. If a good one exists, there is less danger in computing s.e.'s from small numbers of df. For less important items, the computation of the s.e. may be omitted and the graph relied on to give an estimated s.e. Use of the graph or a table derived from it in presenting s.e.'s may avoid the printing of hundreds of individual figures. Examples of error graphs have been given by Yates (1960) and Hansen et al. (1953).

In repetitive studies the relation between s($\hat{Y}$) and $\hat{Y}$ may remain stable or change only slowly over time. This provides an opportunity for further savings. When an error graph has been constructed, computation of s.e.'s in the future need be made only at certain time intervals, with only the amount of detail required to detect an important change in the shape or position of the error graph.

Zarkovic (1960) gives a review of short-cut computing methods and Keyfitz (1957) presents ingenious methods usable when $n_h = 2$.

5A.13   STRATA AS DOMAINS OF STUDY

This section deals with surveys in which the primary purpose is to make comparisons between different strata, assumed to be identifiable in advance. The rules for allocating the sample sizes to the strata are different from those that apply when the objective is to make over-all population estimates. If there are only two strata, we might choose n_1, n_2 to minimize the variance of the difference $(\bar{y}_1 - \bar{y}_2)$ between the estimated strata means. Omitting the fpc's for reasons given in section 2.12, we have

$$V(\bar{y}_1 - \bar{y}_2) = \frac{S_1^2}{n_1} + \frac{S_2^2}{n_2}$$

With a linear cost function

$$C = c_0 + c_1 n_1 + c_2 n_2$$

V is minimized when

$$n_1 = \frac{\frac{nS_1}{\sqrt{c_1}}}{S_1/\sqrt{c_1} + S_2/\sqrt{c_2}}, \qquad n_2 = \frac{\frac{nS_2}{\sqrt{c_2}}}{S_1/\sqrt{c_1} + S_2/\sqrt{c_2}} \qquad (5A.35)$$

With L strata, $L > 2$, the optimum allocation depends on the amounts of precision desired for different comparisons. For instance, the cost might be minimized subject to the set of $L(L - 1)/2$ conditions that $V(\bar{y}_h - \bar{y}_i) \leq V_{hi}$, where the values of V_{hi} are chosen according to the precision considered necessary for a satisfactory comparison of strata h and i.

Frequently a simpler method of allocation is adequate, especially if the S_h and c_h do not differ greatly. One approach is to minimize the *average* variance of the difference between all $L(L - 1)/2$ pairs of strata, that is, to minimize

$$\bar{V} = \frac{2}{L}\left(\frac{S_1^2}{n_1} + \frac{S_2^2}{n_2} + \cdots + \frac{S_L^2}{n_L}\right)$$

V is minimized, for fixed C, by the rule in (5A.35),

$$n_h \propto \frac{S_h}{\sqrt{c_h}}$$

This rule may result in certain pairs of strata being more precisely compared and others less precisely than is felt appropriate. An alternative is to select the n_h so that the s.e. of the difference is the same, say $\sqrt{V}$, for every pair of strata. This amounts to making $S_h^2/n_h = V/2$ for every stratum.

For a fixed cost this method gives less over-all precision than the first method. The reader may verify that the two optimum allocations give

$$\bar{V} = \frac{2(\sum S_h \sqrt{c_h})^2}{L(C - c_0)}, \qquad V = \frac{2(\sum S_h^2 c_h)}{(C - c_0')}$$

It follows from the Cauchy–Schwarz inequality that V is always greater than $\bar{V}$ unless $S_h \sqrt{c_h} = $ constant. If V is substantially greater than $\bar{V}$, a compromise allocation can sometimes be found, after a little trial and error, that will give an average variance close to $\bar{V}$ and also keep $V(\bar{y}_h - \bar{y}_i)$ reasonably constant.

Sometimes the objective is to obtain estimates for each stratum as well as over-all estimates for the whole population. In planning the survey, we might specify the following conditions:

$$V(\bar{y}_h) = \frac{S_h^2}{n_h}(1 - f_h) \leq V_h, \qquad V(\bar{y}_{st}) = \sum \frac{N_h^2 S_h^2}{n_h}(1 - f_h) \leq V$$

The fpc terms are now included, since the purpose is to specify the precision with which the means in the finite population are to be estimated. The conditions on the $V(\bar{y}_h)$ determine lower limits to the values of the n_h. If these lower limits are found to satisfy the condition on $V(\bar{y}_{st})$, the allocation problem is solved. When the condition on $V(\bar{y}_{st})$ is not satisfied, Dalenius (1957) has indicated a graphical approach.

5A.14 ESTIMATING TOTALS AND MEANS
OVER SUBPOPULATIONS

Frequently the subpopulations or domains of study are represented in all strata. If stratification is geographic, for example, separate estimates may be wanted, over the whole population, for males and females, for different age groups, for users and nonusers of Blank's toothpaste, etc. The problem presents some complications. The basic formulas were given by Yates (1953) with further discussion and proofs by Durbin (1958) and Hartley (1959). Methods applicable to a single stratum are discussed in sections 2.10 and 2.11.

The following notation applies to the units in stratum h which lie in domain j.

Notation.

Number of units: N_{hj}, $\quad \sum_j N_{hj} = N_h$

Number in sample: n_{hj}, $\quad \sum_j n_{hj} = n_h$

Measurement on individual unit: y_{hij}

Sample mean: $\bar{y}_{hj} = \sum\limits_{i=1}^{n_{hj}} \dfrac{y_{hij}}{n_{hj}}$

Domain mean: $\bar{Y}_{hj} = \sum\limits_{i=1}^{N_{hj}} \dfrac{y_{hij}}{N_{hj}}$

The population total and mean for domain j over all strata are, respectively,

$$Y_j = \sum_h N_{hj}\,\bar{Y}_{hj}, \qquad \bar{Y}_j = \frac{Y_j}{N_j}$$

where $N_j = \sum\limits_h N_{hj}$

The complication arises because the n_{hj} are random variables. If the N_{hj} were known, the problem would be simple. As estimates of Y_j and $\bar{Y}_j$, we could use

$$\hat{Y}_j{}' = \sum_h N_{hj}\bar{y}_{hj}, \qquad \hat{\bar{Y}}_j{}' = \frac{\hat{Y}_j{}'}{N_j}$$

As shown in section 2.10, the ordinary formula for $V(\bar{y}_{hj})$ is still valid. Thus

$$V(\hat{Y}_j{}') = \sum_h \frac{N_{hj}^2 S_{hj}^2}{n_{hj}}\left(1 - \frac{n_{hj}}{N_{hj}}\right)$$

where S_{hj}^2 is the variance among units in domain j within stratum h. In applications, however, the N_{hj} are rarely known.

Estimating Domain Totals

In default of the N_{hj}, each stratum total of the domain is estimated as in section 2.11. These totals are added to obtain an estimated domain total, that is,

$$\hat{Y}_j = \sum_h \frac{N_h}{n_h} \sum_i^{n_{hj}} y_{hij}$$

The true and estimated variance of $\hat{Y}_j$ are found by the device used in section 2.11. A variate $y_{hi}{}'$ is introduced which equals y_{hij} for all units in domain j and equals zero for all other units in the population. As shown in section 2.11, this gives for the estimated variance

$$v(\hat{Y}_j) = \sum_h \frac{N_h^2}{n_h(n_h - 1)}(1 - f_h)\left[\sum_i^{n_{hj}} y_{hij}^2 - \frac{(\sum y_{hij})^2}{n_h}\right]$$

Estimating Domain Means

In order to estimate the domain mean Y_j/N_j, a sample estimate of N_j is required. An unbiased estimate is

$$\hat{N}_j = \sum_h \frac{N_h}{n_h} n_{hj}$$

Hence we take

$$\hat{\bar{Y}}_j = \frac{\hat{Y}_j}{\hat{N}_j} = \frac{\sum_h \dfrac{N_h}{n_h} \sum_i y_{hij}}{\sum_h \dfrac{N_h}{n_h} n_{hj}}$$

With proportional stratification, $\hat{\bar{Y}}_j$ reduces to the ordinary sample mean of the units that fall in domain j. In the general case, this estimate is known as a *combined ratio estimate*, discussed later in section 6.11. To show it, introduce another dummy variate x_{hi}' which equals 1 for every unit in domain j and 0 for all other units, where i now goes from 1 to N_h. Clearly,

$$\bar{x}_h' = \frac{\sum_i^{n_h} x_{hi}'}{n_h} = \frac{n_{hj}}{n_h}, \qquad \bar{y}_h' = \frac{\sum_i^{n_h} y_{hi}}{n_h} = \frac{\sum_i^{n_{hj}} y_{hij}}{n_h} = \frac{n_{hj}}{n_h} \bar{y}_{hj} \qquad (5\text{A}.36)$$

so that the estimated domain mean may be written

$$\hat{\bar{Y}}_j = \frac{\sum_h \dfrac{N_h}{n_h} \sum_i y_{hij}}{\sum_h \dfrac{N_h}{n_h} n_{hj}} = \frac{\sum_h N_h \bar{y}_h'}{\sum_h N_h \bar{x}_h'} = \frac{\bar{y}_{st}'}{\bar{x}_{st}'}$$

This is the formula for the combined ratio estimate for the two variables y_{hi}' and x_{hi}'. From section 6.11, the estimated variance may be expressed approximately as

$$v(\hat{\bar{Y}}_j) \doteq \frac{1}{\hat{N}_j^2} \sum_h \frac{N_h^2(1-f_h)}{n_h(n_h-1)} \sum_i^{n_h} [y_{hi}' - \hat{\bar{Y}}_j x_{hi}' - (\bar{y}_h' - \hat{\bar{Y}}_j \bar{x}_h')]^2 \qquad (5\text{A}.37)$$

The second summation may be written

$$\sum_i^{n_h} (y_{hi}' - \hat{\bar{Y}}_j x_{hi}')^2 - n_h(\bar{y}_h' - \hat{\bar{Y}}_j \bar{x}_h')^2 = \sum_i^{n_{hj}} (y_{hij} - \hat{\bar{Y}}_j)^2 - \frac{n_{hj}^2}{n_h}(\bar{y}_{hj} - \hat{\bar{Y}}_j)^2$$

$$(5\text{A}.38)$$

using (5A.36). Further, the first term in (5A.38) can be expressed alternatively as

$$\sum_i^{n_{hj}} (y_{hij} - \bar{y}_{hj})^2 + n_{hj}(\bar{y}_{hj} - \hat{\bar{Y}}_j)^2$$

Inserting these results in (5A.37) gives, finally, for the estimated variance,

$$v(\hat{\bar{Y}}_j) \doteq \frac{1}{\hat{N}_j^2} \sum_h \frac{N_h^2(1 - f_h)}{n_h(n_h - 1)} \left[\sum_i (y_{hij} - \bar{y}_{hj})^2 + n_{hj}\left(1 - \frac{n_{hj}}{n_h}\right)(\bar{y}_{hj} - \hat{\bar{Y}}_j)^2 \right]$$

(5A.39)

The term on the right represents a between-stratum contribution to the variance. Differences among strata means are not entirely eliminated from the variance of the estimated mean of any subpopulation. The between-stratum contribution is small if the terms $1 - n_{hj}/n_h$ are small, that is, if the subpopulation is almost as large as the complete population.

As Durbin (1958) has pointed out, (5A.39) applies also to means estimated for the whole population, if the sample is incomplete for any reason such as nonresponse, provided, of course, that $\hat{\bar{Y}}_j$ is the estimate used. In this event $\hat{\bar{Y}}_j$ is interpreted as the estimated mean for the part of the population that would give a response under the methods of data collection employed. There is, however, an additional complication, in that the "nonresponse" part of the population often has a different mean from the "response" part. Thus $\hat{\bar{Y}}_j$ is a biased estimate of the mean of the whole population, and this bias contribution is not included in (5A.39).

EXERCISES

' 5A.1   In planning a survey of sales in a certain type of store, with $n = 550$, good estimates of S_h are available from a previous survey in two of the three strata. The third stratum consists of new stores and stores that had no sales in the previous survey, so that a value for S_3 has to be guessed. If S_3 is actually 10, compute $V(\bar{y}_{st})$ as given by an estimated Neyman allocation when S_3 is guessed as (a) 5, (b) 20. Show that in both cases the proportional increase in variance over the true optimum is slightly over 2%.

Stratum	W_h	True S_h	Estimated S_h (a)	(b)
1	0.3	30	30	30
2	0.6	20	20	20
3	0.1	10	5	20

5A.2   Show that if all S_h, except S_L, are correctly estimated and S_L is estimated as $\hat{S}_L = S_L(1 + \lambda)$, the proportional increase in $V_{opt}(\bar{y}_{st})$, using $\hat{S}_L$ instead of the true S_L for Neyman allocation, is

$$\frac{\lambda^2 n_L'(n - n_L')}{(1 + \lambda)n^2}$$

where n_L' is the sample size in stratum L under true Neyman allocation. Verify that this formula agrees with the results in exercise 5A.1. (The agreement is not exact because of the rounding of the n_h to integers.) Hence show that a 50% underestimation of S_L has the same effect as a 100% overestimation.

5A.3 If there are two strata and if ϕ is the ratio of the actual n_1/n_2 to the Neyman optimum n_1/n_2, show that whatever the values of N_1, N_2, S_1, and S_2, the ratio $V_{min}(\bar{y}_{st})/V(\bar{y}_{st})$ is never less than $4\phi/(1 + \phi)^2$.

• 5A.4 The results of a simple random sample with $n = 1000$ can be classified into three "strata," with $\bar{y}_h = 10.2$, 12.6, and 17.1, $s_h^2 = 10.82$ (the same in each stratum), and $s^2 = 17.66$. The estimated stratum weights are $w_h = 0.5, 0.3, 0.2$, respectively. These weights are known to be inexact, but it is thought that all are correct within 5%, so that the worst cases are either $W_h = 0.525, 0.285$, and 0.190 or $W_h = 0.475, 0.315$, and 0.210. By the methods of section 5A.2, would you recommend stratification? (Where needed, assume that $\bar{y}_h = \bar{Y}_h$ and $s_h^2 = S_h^2$.)

• 5A.5 A survey with three strata is planned to estimate the percentage of families who have accounts in savings banks and the average amount invested per family. Advance estimates of the percentages P_h and the within-stratum S_h of the amount invested are as follows.

Stratum	W_h	$P_h(\%)$	$S_h(\$)$
1	0.6	20	90
2	0.3	40	180
3	0.1	70	520

Compute the smallest sample sizes n and the n_h that satisfy the following requirements: (a) The percentage of families is to be estimated with s.e. = 2 and the average amount invested with s.e. = \$5. (b) The percentage of families is to be estimated with s.e. = 1.5 and the average amount invested with s.e. = \$5.

• 5A.6 The table at top of p. 151 shows the frequency distribution of a population of 911 city sizes for cities from 10,000 to 60,000, arranged in classes of 2000. To shorten the calculations, a coded y' and values of $\sqrt{f}$, cum. $\sqrt{f}$, cum.f, fy', and $\Sigma fy'^2$ are given. Apply the Dalenius-Hodges rule to create two strata for optimum allocation in the sense of Neyman. Find the values of W_h and S_h for each of your strata. Verify (a) that the optimum sample sizes are almost the same in the two strata and (b) by finding S^2 for the whole population, that

$$\frac{V(\bar{y})}{V_{opt}(\bar{y}_{st})} \doteq 4.8$$

• 5A.7 The right triangular distribution $f(y) = 2(1 - y)$, $0 < y < 1$, is divided into two strata at the point a. (a) Show that

$$W_1 = a(2 - a), \qquad W_2 = (1 - a)^2$$

$$S_1^2 = \frac{a^2(6 - 6a + a^2)}{18(2 - a)^2}, \qquad S_2^2 = \frac{(1 - a)^2}{18}$$

(b) Show that under the cum. $\sqrt{f}$ rule the best choice of a is $1 - 1/\sqrt[3]{4} = 0.37$ and that with this boundary the optimum n_1/n_2 is about $\frac{27}{25}$ and $V(\bar{y}_{st})$ is about 27% of the value given by simple random sampling.

	f	y'	$\sqrt{f}$	Cum f	Cum $\sqrt{f}$	fy'
10 –	205	0	14.3	205	14.3	0
12 –	135	1	11.6	340	25.9	135
14 –	106	2	10.3	446	36.2	212
16 –	82	3	9.1	528	45.3	246
18 –	61	4	7.8	589	53.1	244
20 –	42	5	6.5	631	59.6	210
22 –	32	6	5.7	663	65.3	192
24 –	30	7	5.5	693	70.8	210
26 –	27	8	5.2	720	76.0	216
28 –	18	9	4.2	738	80.2	162
30 –	22	10	4.7	760	84.9	220
32 –	21	11	4.6	781	89.5	231
34 –	19	12	4.4	800	93.9	228
36 –	16	13	4.0	816	97.9	208
38 –	14	14	3.7	830	101.6	196
40 –	17	15	4.1	847	105.7	255
42 –	9	16	3.0	856	108.7	144
44 –	8	17	2.8	864	111.5	136
46 –	11	18	3.3	875	114.8	198
48 –	9	19	3.0	884	117.8	171
50 –	7	20	2.6	891	120.4	140
52 –	4	21	2.0	895	122.4	84
54 –	5	22	2.2	900	124.6	110
56 –	5	23	2.2	905	126.8	115
58 –	6	24	2.4	911	129.2	144

| Totals | 911 | | 129.2 | | | 4407 |

$$\sum fy'^2 = 50,395$$

⋆ 5A.8 A sum of \$5000 is available for a stratified sample. In the notation of section 5A.7 the cost function is thought to be, roughly, $C = 200L + 10n$ and

$$V(\bar{y}_{st}) \doteq \frac{S^2}{n}\left[\frac{\rho^2}{L^2} + (1 - \rho^2)\right]$$

where ρ is the correlation between the variate used to construct the strata and the variate to be measured in the survey. Compute the optimum L for $\rho = 0.95$, 0.9, and 0.8. What is a good compromise number of strata to use for all three values of ρ?

⋆ 5A.9 The following data are derived from a stratified sample of tire dealers taken in March 1945 (Deming and Simmons, 1946). The dealers were assigned to strata according to the number of new tires held at a previous census. The sample means $\bar{y}_h$ are the mean numbers of new tires per dealer. (a) Estimate the gain in precision due to the stratification. (b) Compare this result with the gain that would have been attained from proportional allocation.

Stratum Boundaries	N_h	W_h	$\bar{y}_h$	s_h^2	n_h
1–9	19,850	0.8032	4.1	34.8	3000
10–19	3,250	0.1315	13.0	92.2	600
20–29	1,007	0.0407	25.0	174.2	340
30–39	606	0.0245	38.2	320.4	230
Totals	24,713	0.9999			4170

• 5A.10 For a population with $N = 6$, $L = 2$, the values of y_{hi} are 0, 1, 3 in the first stratum and 5, 6, 9 in the second stratum. Compute (a) $V(\bar{y})$ for a simple random sample with $n = 2$, (b) $V(\bar{y}_{st})$ for a stratified random sample with one unit per stratum, (c) the average value $\bar{v}(\bar{y}_{st})$ as estimated by the method of collapsed strata. Verify that $\bar{v}(\bar{y}_{st}) > V(\bar{y})$.

REFERENCES

Bryant, E. C., Hartley, H. O., and Jessen, R. J. (1960). Design and estimation in two-way stratification. *Jour. Amer. Stat. Assoc.*, **55**, 105–124.

Cochran, W. G. (1961). Comparison of methods for determining stratum boundaries. *Bull. Int. Stat. Inst.*, **38**, 2, 345–358.

Dalenius, T. (1957). *Sampling in Sweden.* Contributions to the methods and theories of sample survey practice. Almqvist and Wicksell, Stockholm.

Dalenius, T., and Gurney, M. (1951). The problem of optimum stratification. II. *Skand. Akt.*, **34**, 133–148.

Dalenius, T., and Hodges, J. L., Jr. (1959). Minimum variance stratification. *Jour. Amer. Strat. Assoc.*, **54**, 88–101.

Deming, W. E., and Simmons, W. R. (1946). On the design of a sample for dealer inventories. *Jour. Amer. Stat. Assoc.*, **41**, 16–33.

Durbin, J. (1958). Sampling theory for estimates based on fewer individuals than the number selected. *Bull. Int. Stat. Inst.*, **36**, 3, 113–119.

Ekman, G. (1959). An approximation useful in univariate stratification. *Ann. Math. Stat.*, **30**, 219–229.

Evans, W. D. (1951). On stratification and optimum allocations. *Jour. Amer. Stat. Assoc.*, **46**, 95–104.

Goodman, R., and Kish, L. (1950). Controlled selection—a technique in probability sampling. *Jour. Amer. Stat. Assoc.*, **45**, 350–372.

Hagood, M. J., and Bernert, E. H. (1945). Component indexes as a basis for stratification. *Jour. Amer. Stat. Assoc.*, **40**, 330–341.

Hartley, H. O. (1959). *Analytic studies of survey data.* Istituto di Statistica, Rome, volume in onora di Corrado Gini.

Jessen, R. J. (1942). Statistical investigation of a sample survey for obtaining farm facts. *Iowa Agr. Exp. Sta. Res. Bull.* 304.

Keyfitz, N. (1957). Estimates of sampling variance where two units are selected from each stratum. *Jour. Amer. Stat. Assoc.*, **52**, 503–510.

King, A. J., and McCarty, D. E. (1941). Application of sampling to agricultural statistics with emphasis on stratified sampling. *Jour. Marketing*, **5**, 462–474.

McEvoy, R. H. (1956). Variation in bank asset portfolios. *Jour. Finance*, **11**, 463–473.

Stephan, F. F. (1941). Stratification in representative sampling. *Jour. Marketing*, **6**, 38–46.

Stephan, F. F. (1945). The expected value and variance of the reciprocal and other negative powers of a positive Bernoullian variate. *Ann. Math. Stat.*, **16**, 50–61.

Stephan, F. F., and McCarthy, P. J. (1958). *Sampling opinions*. John Wiley & Sons, New York.

Sukhatme, P. V. (1935). Contribution to the theory of the representative method. *Supp. Jour. Roy. Stat. Soc.*, **2**, 253–268.

Yates, F. (1953). *Sampling methods for censuses and surveys*. Hafner, New York, Second edition.

Zarkovic, S. S. (1960). Computation of errors for sample estimates. *Monthly Bull. Agr. Econ. and Stat.* F.A.O. Rome, **9**, No. 4, 1–9.

CHAPTER 6

Ratio Estimates

6.1 METHODS OF ESTIMATION

One feature of the growth of theoretical statistics is the emergence of a large body of theory which discusses how to make good estimates from data. In the development of theory specifically for sample surveys, little use has been made of this knowledge. I think there are two principal reasons. First, in routine surveys that contain a large number of items there is a great advantage in an estimation procedure that requires little more than simple addition, whereas the superior methods of estimation in statistical theory, such as maximum likelihood, may necessitate a series of successive approximations before the estimate can be found. Second, there has been a difference in attitude in the two lines of research. Most of the estimation methods in theoretical statistics take it for granted that we know the functional form of the frequency distribution followed by the data in the sample, and the method of estimation is carefully geared to this type of distribution. The preference in sample survey theory has been to make only limited assumptions about this frequency distribution (that it is very skew or rather symmetrical) and to leave its specific functional form out of the discussion. This attitude is a reasonable one for handling surveys in which the type of distribution may change from one item to another and when we do not wish to stop and examine all of them before deciding how to make each estimate.

Consequently, estimation techniques for sample survey work are at present restricted in scope. Two techniques are considered—the ratio method in this chapter and the linear regression method in Chapter 7. The use of more complex methods may increase, at least in small, specialized surveys, because the gain in precision from a superior method of estimation can often be secured cheaply, since only the final computations are affected.

154

6.2 THE RATIO ESTIMATE

In the ratio method an auxiliary variate x_i, correlated with y_i, is obtained for each unit in the sample. The population total X of the x_i must be known. In practice, x_i is often the value of y_i at some previous time when a complete census was taken. The aim in this method is to obtain increased precision by taking advantage of the correlation between y_i and x_i. At present we assume simple random sampling.

The ratio estimate of Y, the population total of the y_i, is

$$\hat{Y}_R = \frac{y}{x} X = \frac{\bar{y}}{\bar{x}} X \tag{6.1}$$

where y, x are the sample totals of the y_i and x_i, respectively.

If x_i is the value of y_i at some previous time, the ratio method uses the sample to estimate the relative change Y/X that has occurred since that time. The estimated relative change y/x is multiplied by the known population total X on the previous occasion to provide an estimate of the current population total. If the ratio y_i/x_i is nearly the same on all sampling units, the values of y/x vary little from one sample to another, and the ratio estimate is of high precision. In another application x_i may be the total acreage of a farm and y_i the number of acres sown to some crop. The ratio estimate will be successful in this case if all farmers devote about the same percentage of their total acreage to this crop.

If the quantity to be estimated is $\bar{Y}$, the population mean value of y_i, the ratio estimate is

$$\hat{\bar{Y}}_R = \frac{y}{x} \bar{X}$$

Frequently we wish to estimate a ratio rather than a total or mean, for example, the ratio of corn acres to wheat acres, the ratio of expenditures on labor to total expenditures, or the ratio of liquid assets to total assets. The sample estimate is $\hat{R} = y/x$. In this case X need not be known. The use of ratio estimates for this purpose has already been discussed in sections 2.9 and (with cluster sampling for proportions) 3.12.

Example. Table 6.1 shows the number of inhabitants (in 1000's) in each of a simple random sample of 49 cities drawn from the population of 196 large cities discussed in section 2.13. The problem is to estimate the total number of inhabitants in the 196 cities in 1930. The true 1920 total, X, is assumed to be known. Its value is 22,919.

The example is a suitable one for the ratio estimate. The majority of the cities in the sample show an increase in size from 1920 to 1930 of the order of 20%. From the sample data we have

$$y = \sum y_i = 6262, \qquad x = \sum x_i = 5054$$

TABLE 6.1

SIZES OF 49 LARGE UNITED STATES CITIES (in 1000's) IN 1920 (x_i) AND 1930 (y_i)

x_i	y_i	x_i	y_i	x_i	y_i
76	80	2	50	243	291
138	143	507	634	87	105
67	67	179	260	30	111
29	50	121	113	71	79
381	464	50	64	256	288
23	48	44	58	43	61
37	63	77	89	25	57
120	115	64	63	94	85
61	69	64	77	43	50
387	459	56	142	298	317
93	104	40	60	36	46
172	183	40	64	161	232
78	106	38	52	74	93
66	86	136	139	45	53
60	57	116	130	36	54
46	65	46	53	50	58
				48	75

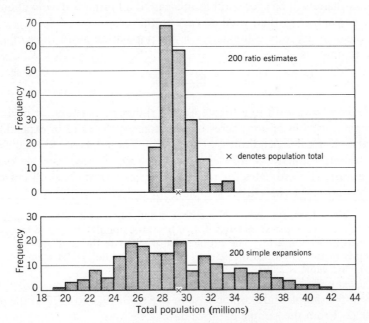

Fig. 6.1 Experimental comparison of the ratio estimate with the estimate based on the sample pages.

Consequently the ratio estimate of the 1930 total for all 196 cities is

$$\hat{Y}_R = \frac{y}{x} X = \frac{6262}{5054} (22,919) = 28,397$$

The corresponding estimate based on the sample mean per city is

$$\hat{Y} = N\bar{y} = \frac{(196)(6262)}{49} = 25,048$$

The correct total in 1930 is 29,351.

Figure 6.1 shows the ratio estimate and the estimate based on the sample mean per city for each of 200 simple random samples of size 49 drawn from this population. A substantial improvement in precision from the ratio method is apparent.

6.3 APPROXIMATE VARIANCE OF THE RATIO ESTIMATE

The distribution of the ratio estimate has proved annoyingly intractable because both y and x vary from sample to sample. The known theoretical results fall short of what we would like to know for practical applications. The principal results are stated first without proof.

The ratio estimate is consistent (this is obvious). It is biased, except for some special types of population, although the bias is negligible in large samples. The limiting distribution of the ratio estimate, as n becomes very large, is normal, subject to some mild restrictions on the type of population from which we are sampling. In samples of moderate size the distribution shows a tendency to positive skewness in the kinds of populations for which the method is most often used. We do not possess exact formulas for the bias and the sampling variance of the estimate but only approximations that are valid in large samples.

These results amount to saying that there is no difficulty if the sample is large enough so that (a) the ratio is nearly normally distributed and (b) the large-sample formula for its variance is valid. As a working rule, the large-sample results may be used if the sample size exceeds 30 and is also large enough so that the coefficients of variation of $\bar{x}$ and $\bar{y}$ are both less than 10%.

Theorem 6.1. The ratio estimates of the population total Y, the population mean $\bar{Y}$, and the population ratio Y/X are, respectively,

$$\hat{Y}_R = \frac{\bar{y}}{\bar{x}} X, \qquad \hat{\bar{Y}}_R = \frac{\bar{y}}{\bar{x}} \bar{X}, \qquad \hat{R} = \frac{\bar{y}}{\bar{x}}$$

In a simple random sample of size n (n large)

$$V(\hat{Y}_R) \doteq \frac{N^2(1-f)}{n} \left[\frac{\sum\limits_{i=1}^{N} (y_i - Rx_i)^2}{N-1} \right].$$ (6.2)

$$V(\hat{\bar{Y}}_R) \doteq \frac{1-f}{n} \left[\frac{\sum\limits_{i=1}^{N} (y_i - Rx_i)^2}{N-1} \right]$$ (6.3)

$$V(\hat{R}) \doteq \frac{1-f}{n\bar{X}^2} \left[\frac{\sum\limits_{i=1}^{N} (y_i - Rx_i)^2}{N-1} \right]$$ (6.4)

where $f = n/N$ is the sampling fraction.

The argument leading to the approximate result (6.4) was given in theorem 2.5. Since $\hat{\bar{Y}}_R = \bar{X}\hat{R}$, $\hat{Y}_R = N\bar{X}\hat{R}$, the other two results follow immediately.

Corollary 1. There are various alternative forms of the result. Since $\bar{Y} = R\bar{X}$, we may write

$$V(\hat{Y}_R) = \frac{N^2(1-f)}{n(N-1)} \sum_{i=1}^{N} [(y_i - \bar{Y}) - R(x_i - \bar{X})]^2$$

$$= \frac{N^2(1-f)}{n(N-1)} [\sum (y_i - \bar{Y})^2 + R^2 \sum (x_i - \bar{X})^2$$

$$- 2R \sum (y_i - \bar{Y})(x_i - \bar{X})]$$

The correlation coefficient ρ between y_i and x_i in the finite population is defined by the equation

$$\rho = \frac{E(y_i - \bar{Y})(x_i - \bar{X})}{\sqrt{E(y_i - \bar{Y})^2 E(x_i - \bar{X})^2}} = \frac{\sum\limits^{N} (y_i - \bar{Y})(x_i - \bar{X})}{(N-1)S_y S_x}$$

This leads to the result

$$V(\hat{Y}_R) = \frac{N^2(1-f)}{n} (S_y^2 + R^2 S_x^2 - 2R\rho S_y S_x)$$ (6.5)

An equivalent form is

$$V(\hat{Y}_R) = (1-f)\frac{Y^2}{n} \left(\frac{S_y^2}{\bar{Y}^2} + \frac{S_x^2}{\bar{X}^2} - \frac{2S_{yx}}{\bar{Y}\bar{X}} \right)$$ (6.6)

where $S_{yx} = \rho S_y S_x$ is the covariance between y_i and x_i. This relation may also be written as

$$V(\hat{Y}_R) = (1-f)\frac{Y^2}{n} (C_{yy} + C_{xx} - 2C_{yx})$$ (6.7)

where C_{yy}, C_{xx} are the squares of the coefficients of variation (cv) of y_i and x_i, respectively, and C_{yx} is the relative covariance.

Corollary 2. Since $\hat{Y}_R$, $\hat{\bar{Y}}_R$, and $\hat{R}$ differ only by known multipliers, the coefficient of variation (i.e., the standard error divided by the quantity being estimated) is the same for all three estimates. From (6.7) the square of this cv is

$$(\text{cv})^2 = \frac{V(\hat{Y}_R)}{Y^2} = \frac{1-f}{n}(C_{yy} + C_{xx} - 2C_{yx}) \tag{6.8}$$

The quantity $(\text{cv})^2$ has been called the *relative variance* by Hansen et al. (1953). Its use avoids repetition of variance formulas for related quantities like the estimated population total and mean.

6.4 ACCURACY OF THE APPROXIMATE VARIANCE

Sukhatme (1954) has investigated the error involved in the approximate formula for $V(\hat{R})$. It will be recalled (theorem 2.5) that the approximate formula was obtained by writing

$$\hat{R} - R = \frac{\bar{y}}{\bar{x}} - R = \frac{\bar{y} - R\bar{x}}{\bar{x}}$$

and then replacing $\bar{x}$ by $\bar{X}$ in the denominator. Instead, we write

$$\frac{1}{\bar{x}} = \frac{1}{\bar{X} + (\bar{x} - \bar{X})} = \frac{1}{\bar{X}}\left(1 + \frac{\bar{x} - \bar{X}}{\bar{X}}\right)^{-1}$$

and expand the right-hand term in parentheses by a Taylor's series. This gives

$$\hat{R} - R = \frac{\bar{y} - R\bar{x}}{\bar{X}}\left[1 - \frac{\bar{x} - \bar{X}}{\bar{X}} + \frac{(\bar{x} - \bar{X})^2}{\bar{X}^2} - \cdots\right] \tag{6.9}$$

By squaring this expression, we can express $E(\hat{R} - R)^2$ in terms of the moments of the joint distribution of y and x. Unfortunately, the result is too complicated to lead to a useful guide for practical applications and will not be given here.

If y and x follow a bivariate normal distribution, the result simplifies considerably. Sukhatme (1954) has shown that to terms of order $1/n^2$

$$E\left(\frac{\hat{R} - R}{R}\right)^2 \doteq V_1\left(1 + \frac{3C_{xx}}{n}\right) + \frac{6C_{xx}(\rho^2 C_{yy} + C_{xx} - 2C_{yx})}{n^2} \tag{6.10}$$

where

$$V_1 = \frac{1}{n}(C_{yy} + C_{xx} - 2C_{yx})$$

is the first approximation to the relative variance of $\hat{R}$, as given by (6.8), with the fpc ignored. Taking V_1 as a common factor in (6.10), we have

$$E\left(\frac{\hat{R} - R}{R}\right)^2 \doteq V_1\left(1 + \frac{3C_{xx}}{n} + \frac{6C_{xx}}{n} \cdot \frac{\rho^2 C_{yy} + C_{xx} - 2C_{yx}}{C_{yy} + C_{xx} - 2C_{yx}}\right) \quad (6.11)$$

Since the right-hand term inside the parentheses is less than $6C_{xx}/n$, this gives

$$E\left(\frac{\hat{R} - R}{R}\right)^2 < V_1\left(1 + \frac{9C_{xx}}{n}\right) \quad (6.12)$$

to terms of order $1/n^2$. Now C_{xx}/n is the square of the coefficient of variation of $\bar{x}$. Thus, if n is large enough so that the cv of $\bar{x}$ is less than 0.1, use of V_1 should not underestimate by more than 9%. In practice, the multiplier 9 in (6.12) appears to be unduly high as compared with (6.11). For instance, if $C_{xx} = C_{yy}$, (6.11) reduces to

$$E\left(\frac{\hat{R} - R}{R}\right)^2 \doteq V_1\left[1 + \frac{C_{xx}}{n}(6 - 3\rho)\right]$$

Since ρ is almost always positive in applications of the ratio method, a multiplier between 3 and 6 is more representative. However, the effects of non-normality in y and x also enter into the term of order $1/n^2$.

The expression $E(\hat{R} - R)^2$ is the mean square error of $\hat{R}$ about the true ratio R rather than the variance of $\hat{R}$. Since $\hat{R}$ is, in general, biased, the mean square error is more appropriate than the variance as a measure of its accuracy.

6.5 BIAS OF THE RATIO ESTIMATE

The ratio estimate has a bias of order $1/n$. Since the s.e. of the estimate is of order $1/\sqrt{n}$, the ratio of the bias to the s.e. is also of order $1/\sqrt{n}$ and becomes negligible as n becomes large. In practice, the bias is usually found to be unimportant even in samples of moderate size. Three useful results about the bias are presented.

The first gives the leading term in the bias when it is expanded in a Taylor's series. From (6.9), retaining the first two terms, we have

$$\hat{R} - R \doteq \frac{\bar{y} - R\bar{x}}{\bar{X}}\left(1 - \frac{\bar{x} - \bar{X}}{\bar{X}}\right)$$

Now

$$E(\bar{y} - R\bar{x}) = \bar{Y} - R\bar{X} = 0$$

so that the leading term in the bias comes from the second term inside the brackets. Further,

$$E\bar{y}(\bar{x} - \bar{X}) = E(\bar{y} - \bar{Y})(\bar{x} - \bar{X}) = \frac{1 - f}{n}\rho S_y S_x$$

by theorem 2.3 (p. 24) and the definition of ρ. Also,

$$E\bar{x}(\bar{x} - \bar{X}) = E(\bar{x} - \bar{X})^2 = \frac{1-f}{n} S_x^2$$

Hence the leading term in the bias is

$$E(\hat{R} - R) \doteq \frac{1-f}{n\,\bar{X}^2}(RS_x^2 - \rho S_y S_x) \tag{6.13}$$

The relative bias (i.e., bias/R), which is the same for $\hat{R}$, $\hat{Y}_R$, and $\hat{\bar{Y}}_R$ is

$$\frac{E(\hat{R} - R)}{R} \doteq \frac{1-f}{n\,\bar{X}\bar{Y}}(RS_x^2 - \rho S_y S_x) \tag{6.14}$$

$$\doteq \frac{1-f}{n}(C_{xx} - C_{yx})$$

Since sample estimates of R, S_x, S_y, ρ, $\bar{X}$, and $\bar{Y}$ can be computed, (6.13) and (6.14) are sometimes used as a rough check on the size of the bias in a specific sample.

A second result is that the ratio estimate is unbiased if the regression of y and x is a straight line through the origin. This means that $E(y \mid x) = \beta x$. In a finite population this relation implies that (a) if several units have exactly the same value of x, the mean of their y-values is βx, and (b) if a specific value of x occurs on only one unit in the population the value of y for that unit is βx. These relations are unlikely to be satisfied exactly in a finite population. However, they will frequently be satisfied approximately, since, as mentioned in section 6.2, the ratio estimate is likely to be used when there is reason to think that y/x is approximately constant.

Theorem 6.2. If $E(y \mid x) = \beta x$ for all values of x in a finite population, the estimates $\hat{Y}_R$, $\hat{\bar{Y}}_R$, and $\hat{R}$ are unbiased in simple random samples of size n.

Proof. Write

$$y = \beta x + e$$

Then

$$E(e \mid x) = 0 \tag{6.15}$$

for any value of x. Averaging over the population, we have

$$\bar{Y} = \beta \bar{X}$$

so that $R = \beta$. Further, averaging over a sample,

$$\frac{\bar{y}}{\bar{x}} = \beta + \frac{\bar{e}}{\bar{x}}$$

that is,

$$\hat{R} = R + \frac{\bar{e}}{\bar{x}}$$

Take the average of $\hat{R}$ over all samples of size n that contain the same set of values of x, so that $\bar{x}$ remains constant during this averaging. Suppose that a particular value of x, say x', occurs in m' units in the sample and in M' units in the population. Then in this averaging each of the M' units appears equally often in the sample. But by (6.15)

$$E(e \mid x') = 0$$

Hence $E(\bar{e}) = 0$ over this set of samples. It follows that $E(\hat{R}) = R$ over this set of samples and that $E(\hat{R}) = R$ over all simple random samples of size n.

The third result, due to Hartley and Ross (1954), gives an upper bound to the ratio of the bias to the standard error. Consider the covariance, in simple random samples of size n, of the quantities $\hat{R}$ and $\bar{x}$. We have

$$\text{cov}\,(\hat{R}, \bar{x}) = E\left(\frac{\bar{y}}{\bar{x}} \cdot \bar{x}\right) - E(\hat{R})\,E(\bar{x})$$

$$= \bar{Y} - \bar{X}\,E(\hat{R})$$

Hence

$$E(\hat{R}) = \frac{\bar{Y}}{\bar{X}} - \frac{1}{\bar{X}}\,\text{cov}\,(\hat{R}, \bar{x}) = R - \frac{1}{\bar{X}}\,\text{cov}\,(\hat{R}, \bar{x}) \qquad (6.16)$$

Thus the bias in $\hat{R}$ is $-\text{cov}\,(\hat{R}, \bar{x})/\bar{X}$. Unlike the Taylor approximation (6.13) to the bias, this expression is exact.
Further,

$$|\text{bias in } \hat{R}| = \frac{|\rho_{\hat{R},\bar{x}}\sigma_{\hat{R}}\sigma_{\bar{x}}|}{\bar{X}}$$

$$\leq \frac{\sigma_{\hat{R}}\sigma_{\bar{x}}}{\bar{X}}$$

since $\hat{R}$ and $\bar{x}$ cannot have a correlation > 1. Hence

$$\frac{|\text{bias in } \hat{R}|}{\sigma_{\hat{R}}} \leq \frac{\sigma_{\bar{x}}}{\bar{X}} = \text{cv of } \bar{x} \qquad (6.17)$$

The same bound applies, of course, to the bias in $\hat{Y}_R$ and $\hat{\bar{Y}}_R$. Thus if the cv of $\bar{x}$ is less than 0.1, the bias may safely be regarded as negligible in relation to the s.e.

6.6 ESTIMATION OF THE VARIANCE FROM A SAMPLE

From equation (6.2)

$$V(\hat{Y}_R) \doteq \frac{N^2(1-f)}{n} \frac{\sum\limits_{}^{N}(y_i - Rx_i)^2}{N-1}$$

As already mentioned in section 2.9, we take

$$\frac{\sum\limits_{}^{n}(y_i - \hat{R}x_i)^2}{(n-1)}$$

as a sample estimate of the population variance. This estimate has a bias of order $1/n$.

For the estimated variance, $v(\hat{Y}_R)$, this gives

$$v(\hat{Y}_R) = \frac{N(N-n)}{n(n-1)} \sum_{i=1}^{n}(y_i - \hat{R}x_i)^2$$

$$= \frac{N(N-n)}{n(n-1)} (\sum y_i^2 + \hat{R}^2 \sum x_i^2 - 2\hat{R}\sum y_i x_i) \qquad (6.18)$$

this being the form that is speediest to compute.

Example. This illustrates the calculation of the standard error of a ratio estimate of a population total. The data in Table 6.1 (p. 156) will be used. First calculate

$$y = \sum y_i = 6262 \qquad x = \sum x_i = 5054 \qquad \hat{R} = \frac{y}{x} = 1.239019$$

From (6.18),

$$v(\hat{Y}_R) = \frac{N(N-n)}{n(n-1)} (\sum y_i^2 + \hat{R}^2 \sum x_i^2 - 2\hat{R}\sum y_i x_i)$$

To compute the quadratic term the sums of squares and products are placed on the same row as their multipliers:

		Multiplier
$\sum y_i^2 = 1,527,882$		1
$\sum x_i^2 = 1,044,504$		$1.535168 = \hat{R}^2$
$\sum y_i x_i = 1,251,630$		$2.478038 = 2\hat{R}$

Hence

$$v(\hat{Y}_R) = \frac{(196)(147)}{(49)(48)} (29,784) = 364,854$$

$$s(\hat{Y}_R) = 604$$

6.7 CONFIDENCE LIMITS

If the sample is large enough so that the normal approximation applies, confidence limits for Y and R may be obtained:

$$Y: \quad \hat{Y}_R \pm t\sqrt{v(\hat{Y}_R)} \tag{6.19}$$

$$R: \quad \hat{R} \pm t\sqrt{v(\hat{R})} \tag{6.20}$$

where t is the normal deviate corresponding to the chosen confidence probability.

In section 6.3 it was suggested that the normal approximation applies reasonably well if the sample size is at least 30 and is large enough so that the cv's of $\bar{y}$ and $\bar{x}$ are both less than 0.1. When these conditions do not apply, the formula for $v(\hat{R})$ tends to give values that are too low and the positive skewness in the distribution of $\hat{R}$ may become noticeable.

An alternative method of computing confidence limits has been used in biological assay (Fieller, 1932; Paulson, 1942). This approach requires fewer assumptions than the normal approximation and takes some account of the skewness of the distribution of $\hat{R}$.

The method requires that $\bar{y}$ and $\bar{x}$ follow a bivariate normal distribution, so that $(\bar{y} - R\bar{x})$ is normally distributed. It follows that the quantity

$$\frac{\bar{y} - R\bar{x}}{\sqrt{[(N - n)/Nn]}\sqrt{s_y^2 + R^2 s_x^2 - 2R s_{yx}}} \tag{6.21}$$

is approximately normally distributed with mean zero and unit standard deviation. (We have substituted sample estimates s_y^2, etc., for the corresponding population variances and covariance and are assuming the sample size enough so that this introduces negligible error. In biological assay, in which samples may be quite small, the quantity above would be regarded as following Student's t-distribution.)

The value of R is unknown, but any contemplated value of R which makes this normal deviate large enough may be regarded as rejected by the sample data. Consequently, confidence limits for R are found by setting (6.21) equal to $\pm t$ and solving the resulting quadratic equation for R. The confidence limits are approximate, for, if we try to check them by sampling repeatedly from a fixed population with known R, some values of $\bar{y}$ and $\bar{x}$ turn up for which the two roots of the quadratic are imaginary. Such cases become rare if the cv's of $\bar{y}$ and $\bar{x}$ are less than 0.3.

After some manipulation, the two roots may be expressed as

$$R = \hat{R}\frac{(1 - t^2 c_{\bar{y}\bar{x}}) \pm t\sqrt{(c_{\bar{y}\bar{y}} + c_{\bar{x}\bar{x}} - 2c_{\bar{y}\bar{x}}) - t^2(c_{\bar{y}\bar{y}}c_{\bar{x}\bar{x}} - c_{\bar{y}\bar{x}}^2)}}{1 - t^2 c_{\bar{x}\bar{x}}} \tag{6.22}$$

where

$$c_{\bar{y}\bar{y}} = \frac{N - n}{Nn} \frac{s_y^2}{\bar{y}^2}$$

is the square of the estimated cv of $\bar{y}$, with analogous definitions of $c_{\bar{y}\bar{x}}$ and $c_{\bar{x}\bar{x}}$. If $t^2 c_{\bar{y}\bar{y}}$, $t^2 c_{\bar{x}\bar{x}}$, and $t^2 c_{\bar{y}\bar{x}}$ are all small relative to 1, the limits reduce to

$$R = \hat{R} \pm t\hat{R}\sqrt{c_{\bar{y}\bar{y}} + c_{\bar{x}\bar{x}} - 2c_{\bar{y}\bar{x}}}$$

This expression is the same as the normal approximation (6.20).

Quadratic limits for Y are found by replacing $\hat{R}$ in equation (6.22) by $\hat{Y}_R$.

Although the quadratic limits should in general be more accurate than the normal limits from (6.20), since fewer assumptions are required, Hájek (1958) has shown that if the regression of y on x goes through the origin the normal limits contain R, in large samples, with higher frequency than the quadratic limits.

6.8 COMPARISON OF THE RATIO ESTIMATE WITH THE MEAN PER UNIT

The type of estimate of Y which was studied in preceding chapters is $N\bar{y}$, where $\bar{y}$ is the mean per unit for the sample (in simple random sampling) or a weighted mean per unit (in stratified random sampling). Estimates of this kind are called estimates based on the *mean per unit* or estimates obtained by *simple expansion*.

Theorem 6.3 In large samples, with simple random sampling, the ratio estimate $\hat{Y}_R$ has a smaller variance than the estimate $\hat{Y} = N\bar{y}$ obtained by simple expansion, if

$$\rho > \frac{1}{2}\left(\frac{S_x}{\bar{X}}\right) \bigg/ \left(\frac{S_y}{\bar{Y}}\right) = \frac{\text{coefficient of variation of } x_i}{2(\text{coefficient of variation of } y_i)}$$

Proof. For $\hat{Y}$ we have

$$V(\hat{Y}) = \frac{N^2(1 - f)}{n} S_y^2$$

For the ratio estimate we have from (6.5)

$$V(\hat{Y}_R) = \frac{N^2(1 - f)}{n}(S_y^2 + R^2 S_x^2 - 2R\rho S_y S_x)$$

Hence the ratio estimate has the smaller variance if

$$S_y^2 + R^2 S_x^2 - 2R\rho S_y S_x < S_y^2$$

If $R = \bar{Y}/\bar{X}$ is positive, this condition becomes

$$\rho > \frac{RS_x}{2S_y} = \frac{1}{2}\left(\frac{S_x}{\bar{X}}\right) \bigg/ \left(\frac{S_y}{\bar{Y}}\right)$$

This theorem shows that the ratio estimate may be either more or less precise than a simple expansion. The issue depends on the size of the correlation coefficient between y_i and x_i and on the cv's of these two variates. The variability of the auxiliary variate x_i is an important factor: if its cv is more than twice that of y_i, the ratio estimate is *always* less precise, since ρ cannot exceed 1. When x_i is the value of y_i at some previous time, the two cv's may be about equal. In this event the ratio estimate is superior if ρ exceeds 0.5. If R is negative, the condition is $\rho < RS_x/2S_y$.

Theorem 6.3 applies only for samples large enough so that the approximate formula for $V(\hat{Y}_R)$ is valid. In smaller samples the ratio method probably does not compare so favorably as the theorem suggests, since the approximate formula is usually an underestimate.

6.9 CONDITIONS UNDER WHICH THE RATIO ESTIMATE IS OPTIMUM

A well-known result in the theory of regression indicates the type of population for which the ratio estimate is the best among a wide class of estimates. The theorem applies to infinite populations.

Theorem 6.4. With simple random sampling from an infinite population, the ratio estimate of $\bar{Y}$ is a "best linear unbiased estimate" if two conditions are satisfied:

1. The relation between y_i and x_i is a straight line through the origin.
2. The variance of y_i about this line is proportional to x_i.

A "best linear unbiased estimate" is defined as follows. Consider all estimates that are linear functions of the sample values y_i, that is, that are of the form

$$l_1 y_1 + l_2 y_2 + \cdots + l_n y_n$$

where the l's do not depend on the y_i, although they may be functions of the x_i. The choice of the l's is restricted to those that give unbiased estimates of $\bar{Y}$. The estimate that has the smallest variance is called the "best linear unbiased estimate."

Proof. The mathematical model is

$$y_i = Bx_i + e_i$$

where the e_i are independent of the x_i. In arrays in which x_i is fixed e_i has mean zero and variance λx_i. Hence

$$\bar{Y} = B\bar{X}$$

It was shown by Gauss that the best linear unbiased estimate of $B\bar{X}$ is

$b\bar{X}$, where b is the least squares estimate of B (see, e.g., David and Neyman, 1938). The least squares estimate is

$$b = \frac{\sum w_i y_i x_i}{\sum w_i x_i^2} \quad \text{where } w_i = \frac{1}{\sigma_{e_i}^2} = \frac{1}{\lambda x_i}$$

This gives

$$b = \frac{\sum y_i}{\sum x_i} = \frac{\bar{y}}{\bar{x}}$$

Consequently, the optimum estimate of $\bar{Y}$ is the ratio estimate $(\bar{y}/\bar{x})\bar{X}$.

The practical relevance of this result is that it suggests the conditions under which the ratio estimate is not only superior to the mean per unit but is the best of a whole class of estimates. When we are trying to decide what kind of estimate to use, a graph in which y_i is plotted against x_i is helpful. If this graph shows that the relation is a straight line through the origin and if the variance of the points y_i about the line seems to increase proportionally to x_i, the ratio estimate will be hard to beat.

Sometimes the relation between y_i and x_i is a straight line through the origin, but the variance of y_i in arrays in which x_i is fixed is *not* proportional to x_i. In a population sample of Greece, Jessen et al. (1947) found that the variance increased roughly as x_i^2. This suggests a weighted regression in which $w_i \propto 1/x_i^2$. For the least squares estimate b, this gives

$$b = \frac{\sum w_i y_i x_i}{\sum w_i x_i^2} = \frac{1}{n} \sum \left(\frac{y_i}{x_i}\right)$$

In this situation the best estimate of $\bar{Y}$ is $b\bar{X}$, where b is the mean of the ratios y_i/x_i on the individual sampling units.

6.10 RATIO ESTIMATES IN STRATIFIED RANDOM SAMPLING

There are two ways in which a ratio estimate of the population total Y can be made. One is to make a *separate* ratio estimate of the total of each stratum and add these totals. If y_h, x_h are the sample totals in the hth stratum and X_h is the stratum total of the x_{hi}, this estimate $\hat{Y}_{Rs}$ (s for *separate*) is

$$\hat{Y}_{Rs} = \sum_h \frac{y_h}{x_h} X_h = \sum_h \frac{\bar{y}_h}{\bar{x}_h} X_h \tag{6.23}$$

No assumption is made that the true ratio remains constant from stratum to stratum. The estimate requires a knowledge of the separate totals X_h.

Theorem 6.5.   If the sample sizes n_h are large in all strata,

$$V(\hat{Y}_{Rs}) = \sum_h \frac{N_h^2(1 - f_h)}{n_h} (S_{yh}^2 + R_h^2 S_{xh}^2 - 2R_h\rho_h S_{yh}S_{xh}) \quad (6.24)$$

where $R_h = Y_h/X_h$ is the true ratio in stratum h, and ρ_h is defined as before in each stratum.

Proof.   Write

$$\hat{Y}_{Rh} = \frac{y_h}{x_h} X_h$$

Then

$$\hat{Y}_{Rs} - Y = \sum_h (\hat{Y}_{Rh} - Y_h)$$

Hence

$$V(\hat{Y}_{Rs}) = E(\hat{Y}_{Rs} - Y)^2$$
$$= \sum_h E(\hat{Y}_{Rh} - Y_h)^2 + 2\sum_h \sum_{j>h} E(\hat{Y}_{Rh} - Y_h)(\hat{Y}_{Rj} - Y_j)$$

Since $\hat{Y}_{Rh}$ is the ratio estimate made from a simple random sample within stratum h, we may use (6.5) for the approximate variance of $\hat{Y}_{Rh}$, that is,

$$V(\hat{Y}_{Rh}) = \frac{N_h^2(1 - f_h)}{n_h} (S_{yh}^2 + R_h^2 S_{xh}^2 - 2R_h\rho_h S_{yh}S_{xh})$$

The cross-product terms vanish because the sampling is independent in the different strata and, to the order of approximation used in the variance formula, $\hat{Y}_{Rh}$ is an unbiased estimate of Y_h. Result (6.24) follows.

This formula is valid only if the sample in each stratum is large enough so that the approximate variance formula applies to each stratum. This limitation should be noted in practical applications.

Moreover, when the n_h are small and the number of strata L is large, the bias in $\hat{Y}_{Rs}$ may not be negligible in relation to its standard error, as the following crude argument suggests.

In a single stratum we have seen (section 6.5) that

$$\frac{|\text{bias in } \hat{Y}_{Rh}|}{\sigma(\hat{Y}_{Rh})} \leq \text{cv of } \bar{x}_h$$

If the bias has the same sign in all strata, as may happen, the bias in $\hat{Y}_{Rs}$ will be roughly L times that in $\hat{Y}_{Rh}$. But the standard error of $\hat{Y}_{Rs}$ is only of the order of $\sqrt{L}$ times that of $\hat{Y}_{Rh}$. Hence the ratio

$$\frac{|\text{bias in } \hat{Y}_{Rs}|}{\sigma(\hat{Y}_{Rs})}$$

is of order

$$\sqrt{L}(\text{cv of } \bar{x}_h)$$

For example, with 50 strata and the cv of $\bar{x}_h$ about 0.1 in each stratum, the bias in $\hat{Y}_{Rs}$ might be as large as 0.7 times its standard error. The contribution of the bias to the mean square error of $\hat{Y}_{Rs}$ would then be about one third.

Although in practice the bias is usually much smaller than its upper bound, the danger of bias with the separate ratio estimate should be kept in mind if $\sqrt{L}(\text{cv of } \bar{x}_h)$ exceeds say 0.3.

6.11 THE COMBINED RATIO ESTIMATE

An alternative estimate is derived from a single *combined* ratio (Hansen, Hurwitz, and Gurney, 1946). From the sample data we compute

$$\hat{Y}_{st} = \sum_h N_h \bar{y}_h, \qquad \hat{X}_{st} = \sum_h N_h \bar{x}_h$$

These are the standard estimates of the population totals Y and X, respectively, made from a stratified sample. The combined ratio estimate, $\hat{Y}_{Rc}$ (c for *combined*) is

$$\hat{Y}_{Rc} = \frac{\hat{Y}_{st}}{\hat{X}_{st}} X = \frac{\bar{y}_{st}}{\bar{x}_{st}} X$$

where $\bar{y}_{st} = \hat{Y}_{st}/N$, $\bar{x}_{st} = \hat{X}_{st}/N$ are the estimated population means from a stratified sample.

The estimate $\hat{Y}_{Rc}$ does not require a knowledge of the X_h, but only of X.

The combined estimate is much less subject to the risk of bias than the separate estimate. Using the approach of Hartley and Ross in section 6.5, we have, writing $\hat{R}_c = \bar{y}_{st}/\bar{x}_{st}$,

$$\text{cov}\,(\hat{R}_c, \bar{x}_{st}) = E\left(\frac{\bar{y}_{st}}{\bar{x}_{st}} \cdot \bar{x}_{st}\right) - E(\hat{R}_c)\,E(\bar{x}_{st})$$

$$= \bar{Y} - \bar{X}\,E(\hat{R}_c)$$

Hence

$$E(\hat{R}_c) = R - \frac{1}{\bar{X}}\text{cov}\,(\hat{R}_c, \bar{x}_{st})$$

and

$$\frac{|\text{bias in } \hat{R}_c|}{\sigma_{\hat{R}_c}} = \frac{|\rho_{\hat{R}_c, \bar{x}_{st}} \cdot \sigma_{\bar{x}_{st}}|}{\bar{X}} \leq \text{cv of } \bar{x}_{st}.$$

Thus the biases in $\hat{R}_c$, $\hat{Y}_{Rc}$ are negligible relative to their standard errors, provided only that the cv of $\bar{x}_{st}$ is less than 0.1.

Theorem 6.6.   If the total sample size n is large,

$$V(\hat{Y}_{Rc}) = \sum_h \frac{N_h^2(1 - f_h)}{n_h} (S_{yh}^2 + R^2 S_{xh}^2 - 2R\rho_h S_{yh} S_{xh}) \qquad (6.25)$$

Proof.   This follows the same argument as theorem 2.5. In the present case the key equation is

$$(\hat{Y}_{Rc} - Y) = \frac{N\bar{X}}{\bar{x}_{st}} (\bar{y}_{st} - R\bar{x}_{st}) \doteq N(\bar{y}_{st} - R\bar{x}_{st}) \qquad (6.26)$$

Now consider the variate $u_{hi} = y_{hi} - Rx_{hi}$. The right side of (6.26) is $N\bar{u}_{st}$, where $\bar{u}_{st}$ is the weighted mean of the variate u_{hi} in a stratified sample. Further, the population mean $\bar{U}$ of u_{hi} is zero, since $R = \bar{Y}/\bar{X}$.

Hence we may apply to $\bar{u}_{st}$ theorem 5.3 for the variance of the estimated mean from a stratified random sample. This gives

$$V(\hat{Y}_{Rc}) = N^2 V(\bar{u}_{st}) = \sum_h \frac{N_h(N_h - n_h)}{n_h} S_{uh}^2$$

where

$$S_{uh}^2 = \frac{1}{N_h - 1} \sum_{i=1}^{N_h} (u_{hi} - \bar{U}_h)^2$$

$$= \frac{1}{N_h - 1} \sum_{i=1}^{N_h} [(y_{hi} - \bar{Y}_h) - R(x_{hi} - \bar{X}_h)]^2$$

When the quadratic is expanded, result (6.25) is obtained.

From equations (6.24) and (6.25) it is interesting to note that the approximate variances of $\hat{Y}_{Rs}$ and $\hat{Y}_{Rc}$ assume the same general form, the difference being that the population ratios R_h in the individual strata in (6.24) are all replaced by R in (6.25).

6.12   COMPARISON OF THE COMBINED AND SEPARATE ESTIMATES

We may write

$$V(\hat{Y}_{Rc}) - V(\hat{Y}_{Rs})$$

$$= \sum_h \frac{N_h^2(1 - f_h)}{n_h} [(R^2 - R_h^2)S_{xh}^2 - 2(R - R_h)\rho_h S_{yh} S_{xh}]$$

$$= \sum_h \frac{N_h^2(1 - f_h)}{n_h} [(R - R_h)^2 S_{xh}^2 + 2(R_h - R)(\rho_h S_{yh} S_{xh} - R_h S_{xh}^2)]$$

In situations in which the ratio estimate is appropriate the last term on the right is usually small. (It vanishes if within each stratum the relation between y_{hi} and x_{hi} is a straight line through the origin.) Thus, unless R_h is constant from stratum to stratum, the use of a separate ratio estimate in each stratum is likely to be more precise. This discussion assumes, however, that the sample in each stratum is large enough so that the approximate formula for $V(\hat{Y}_{Rs})$ is valid. With only a small sample in each stratum, the combined estimate is to be recommended unless there is good empirical evidence to the contrary.

For sample estimates of these variances we substitute sample estimates of R_h and R in the appropriate places. The sample mean squares s_{yh}^2 and s_{xh}^2 are substituted for the corresponding variances and the sample covariance for the term $\rho_h S_{yh} S_{xh}$. The sample mean square and covariance must be calculated separately for each stratum.

Example. The data come from a census of all farms in Jefferson County, Iowa. In this example y_{hi} represents acres in corn and x_{hi} acres in the farm. The

TABLE 6.2
DATA FROM JEFFERSON COUNTY, IOWA

Strata	Size (farm acres)	N_h	S_{yh}^2	S_{yxh}	S_{xh}^2	R_h
1	0–160	1580	312	494	2055	0.2350
2	More than 160	430	922	858	7357	0.2109
For complete pop.		2010	620	1453	7619	0.2242

Strata	$\bar{Y}_h$	$\bar{X}_h$	n_h	$Q_h = W_h^2/n_h$	V_h'	V_h''
1	19.40	82.56	70	0.008828	193	194
2	51.63	244.85	30	0.001525	887	907
For complete pop.	26.30	117.28	100			

population is divided into *two* strata, the first stratum containing farms of as many as 160 acres. We assume a sample of 100 farms. When stratified sampling is used, we shall suppose that 70 farms are taken from stratum 1 and 30 from stratum 2, this being roughly the optimum allocation. The data are given in Table 6.2. The last three quantities, Q_h, V_h', and V_h'', are auxiliary quantities to be used in the computations, the last two being defined later.

We consider five methods of estimating the population mean corn acres per farm. The fpc are ignored.

1. Simple random sample: mean per farm estimate.

$$V_1 = \frac{S_y^2}{n} = \frac{620}{100} = 6.20$$

2. Simple random sample: ratio estimate.

$$V_2 = \frac{1}{n}(S_y{}^2 + R^2 S_x{}^2 - 2RS_{yx})$$

$$= \tfrac{1}{100}[620 + (0.2242)^2(7619) - 2(0.2242)(1453)]$$

$$= 3.51$$

3. Stratified random sample: mean per farm estimate.

$$V_3 = \sum \frac{W_h{}^2}{n_h} S_{yh}{}^2 = \sum Q_h S_{yh}{}^2 = 4.16$$

4. Stratified random sample: ratio estimate using a separate ratio in each stratum.

$$V_4 = \sum Q_h(S_{yh}{}^2 + R_h{}^2 S_{xh}{}^2 - 2R_h S_{yxh}) = \sum Q_h V_h{}' = 3.06$$

5. Stratified random sampling: ratio estimate using a combined ratio.

$$V_5 = \sum Q_h(S_{yh}{}^2 + R^2 S_{xh}{}^2 - 2RS_{yxh}) = \sum Q_h V_h{}'' = 3.10$$

The relative precisions of the various methods can be summarized as follows:

Sampling method	Method of Estimation	Relative Precision
1. Simple random	Mean per farm	100
2. Simple random	Ratio	177
3. Stratified random	Mean per farm	149
4. Stratified random	Separate ratio	203
5. Stratified random	Combined ratio	200

The results bring out an interesting point of wide application. Stratification by size of farm accomplishes the same general purpose as a ratio estimate in which the denominator is farm size. Both devices diminish the effect of variations in farm size on the sampling error of the estimated mean corn acres per farm. For instance, the gain in precision from a ratio estimate is 77% when simple random sampling is used, but it is only 36% (203 against 149) when stratified sampling is used.

In the design of surveys there may be a choice between introducing a factor into the stratification or utilizing it in the method of estimation. The best decision depends on the circumstances. Relevant points are: (a) some factors, for example, geographical location, are more easily introduced into the stratification than into the method of estimation; (b) the issue depends on the nature of the relation between y_i and x_i. All simple methods of estimation work most effectively with a linear relation. With a complex or discontinuous relation, stratification may be more effective, since, if there are enough strata, stratification will eliminate the effects of almost any kind of relation between y_i and x_i. (c) If some important variates are roughly proportional to x_i, but others are roughly proportional to another variate z_i, it is better to use x_i and z_i as denominators in ratio estimates than to stratify by one of them.

6.13 SHORT-CUT COMPUTATION OF THE VARIANCE

If $n_h = 2$ in all strata, Keyfitz (1957) has given short-cut methods for computing the relative variance of $\hat{Y}_{Rc}$ or $\hat{R}_c$. From (6.25), substituting the sample estimates,

Let
$$\frac{v(\hat{Y}_{Rc})}{\hat{Y}_{Rc}^2} = \sum_h \frac{N_h^2(1 - f_h)}{2}\left(\frac{s_{yh}^2}{\hat{Y}_{st}^2} + \frac{s_{xh}^2}{\hat{X}_{st}^2} - \frac{2r_h s_{yh} s_{xh}}{\hat{Y}_{st}\hat{X}_{st}}\right)$$

$$y_{h1}' = \frac{N_h y_{h1}}{2}, \qquad y_{h2}' = \frac{N_h y_{h2}}{2}, \qquad dy_h' = y_{h1}' - y_{h2}'$$

with similar definitions for x. Then, with $n_h = 2$, it is easily shown as an algebraic identity that

$$\frac{N_h^2 s_{yh}^2}{2\hat{Y}_{st}^2} = \frac{1}{\hat{Y}_{st}^2}\left(\frac{N_h(y_{h1} - y_{h2})}{2}\right)^2 = \left(\frac{dy_h'}{\hat{Y}_{st}}\right)^2$$

with corresponding expressions for the terms in s_{xh}^2 and $r_h s_{yh} s_{xh}$. Hence the relative variance may be computed as

$$\sum_h \left(\frac{dy_h'}{\hat{Y}_{st}} - \frac{dx_h'}{\hat{X}_{st}}\right)^2$$

In this form the fpc terms have been omitted. If f_h is approximately constant, the multiplier $1 - \bar{f}_h$ may be applied, where $\bar{f}_h = \sum f_h / L$.

6.14 OPTIMUM ALLOCATION WITH A RATIO ESTIMATE

The optimum allocation of the n_h may be different with a ratio estimate than with a mean per unit. Consider first the variate $\hat{Y}_{Rs}$. From theorem 6.5 its variance is

$$V(\hat{Y}_{Rs}) = \sum_h \frac{N_h(N_h - n_h)}{n_h} (S_{yh}^2 + R_h^2 S_{xh}^2 - 2R_h \rho_h S_{yh} S_{xh})$$

$$= \sum_h \frac{N_h(N_h - n_h)}{n_h} S_{dh}^2, \quad \text{with } S_{dh}^2 = \frac{1}{N_h - 1}\sum_{i=1}^{N_h} d_{hi}^2 \quad (6.27)$$

where $d_{hi} = y_{hi} - R_h x_{hi}$ is the deviation of y_{hi} from $R_h x_{hi}$. By the methods given in Chapter 5 for finding optimum allocation, it follows that (6.27) is minimized subject to a total cost of the form $\Sigma c_h n_h$, when

$$n_h \propto \frac{N_h S_{dh}}{\sqrt{c_h}}$$

With a mean per unit it will be recalled that for minimum variance n_h is chosen proportional to $N_h S_{yh}/\sqrt{c_h}$.

In the planning of a sample, the allocation with a ratio estimate may appear a little perplexing, because it seems difficult to speculate about the likely values of S_{dh}. Two rules are helpful. With a population in which the ratio estimate is a best linear unbiased estimate, S_{dh} will be roughly proportional to $\sqrt{\bar{X}_h}$ (by theorem 6.4). In this case the n_h should be proportional to $N_h \sqrt{\bar{X}_h}/\sqrt{c_h}$. Sometimes the variance of d_{hi} may be more nearly proportional to $\bar{X}_h^2$. This leads to the allocation of n_h proportional to $N_h \bar{X}_h/\sqrt{c_h}$, that is, to the stratum total of x_{hi}, divided by the square root of the cost per unit. An example of this type is discussed by Hansen, Hurwitz, and Gurney (1946) for a sample designed to estimate sales of retail stores.

If the estimate $\hat{Y}_{Rc}$ is to be used, the same general argument applies.

Example. The different methods of allocation can be compared from data collected in a complete enumeration of 257 commercial peach orchards in North Carolina in June 1946 (Finkner, 1950). The purpose was to determine the most efficient sampling procedure for estimating commercial peach production in this area. Information was obtained on the number of peach trees and the estimated total peach production in each orchard. The high correlation between these two variables suggested the use of a ratio estimate. One very large orchard was omitted.

For this illustration, the area is divided geographically into three strata. The number of peach trees in an orchard is denoted by x_{hi}, and the estimated production in bushels of peaches by y_{hi}. Only the first ratio estimate $\hat{Y}_{Rs}$ (based on a separate ratio in each stratum) will be considered, since the principle is the same for both types of stratified ratio estimate.

Four methods of allocation are compared: (a) n_h proportional to N_h, (b) n_h proportional to $N_h S_{yh}$, (c) n_h proportional to $N_h \sqrt{\bar{X}_h}$, and (d) n_h proportional to $N_h \bar{X}_h = X_h$. The sample size is 100. The data for these comparisons are summarized in Table 6.3.

The upper part of the table shows the basic data. The method employed to calculate the four variances was first to find the n_h for each type of allocation. These values are shown in the columns headed (a) through (d) in the lower part of the table. Thus, with allocation (a), $n_h = n N_h/N$, so that in the first stratum

$$n_1 = \frac{(100)(47)}{256} = 18$$

TABLE 6.3

DATA FROM THE NORTH CAROLINA PEACH SURVEY

Strata	$S_{xh}{}^2$	S_{yxh}	$S_{yh}{}^2$	S_{xh}	S_{yh}	$\bar{X}_h$	$\bar{Y}_h$	R_h	$S_{dh}{}^2$
1	5186	6462	8699	72.01	93.27	53.80	69.48	1.29133	658
2	2367	3100	4614	48.65	67.93	31.07	43.64	1.40475	573
3	4877	4817	7311	69.83	85.51	56.97	66.39	1.16547	2706
Pop.	3898	4434	6409	62.43	80.06	44.45	56.47	1.27053	1433

Strata	N_h	(a)	$N_h S_{yh}$	(b)	$\sqrt{\bar{X}_h}$	$N_h \sqrt{\bar{X}_h}$	(c)	$N_h \bar{X}_h$	(d)
1	47	18	4384	22	7.33	344.5	20	2529	22
2	118	46	8016	40	5.57	657.3	39	3666	32
3	91	36	7781	38	7.55	687.1	41	5184	46
Pop.	256	100	20181	100	20.45	1688.9	100	11379	100

When the n_h have been obtained, the corresponding $V(\hat{Y}_{Rs})$ is found by substituting in the formula

$$V(\hat{Y}_{Rs}) = \sum_h \frac{N_h(N_h - n_h)}{n_h} S_{dh}{}^2$$

where

$$S_{dh}{}^2 = S_{yh}{}^2 + R_h{}^2 S_{xh}{}^2 - 2R_h S_{yxh}$$

The quantities $S_{dh}{}^2$ are the same for all four allocations and are given on the extreme right of the top half of Table 6.3.

The variances and relative precisions are shown in Table 6.4.

There is not much to choose among the different allocations, as would be expected, since the n_h do not differ greatly in the four methods. Method 4, in which allocation is proportional to the total number of peach trees in the stratum, appears a trifle superior to the others.

TABLE 6.4

COMPARISON OF FOUR METHODS OF ALLOCATION

Method of Allocation: n_h Proportional to	Variance				Relative Precision
	Strata				
	1	2	3	Total	
1. N_h	49,824	105,833	376,215	531,872	100
2. $N_h S_{yh}$	35,144	131,847	343,446	510,437	104
3. $N_h \sqrt{\bar{X}_h}$	41,750	136,964	300,312	479,026	111
4. $N_h \bar{X}_h$	35,144	181,710	240,888	457,742	116

6.15   UNBIASED RATIO-TYPE ESTIMATES

In recent years there has been considerable interest in developing estimates of the ratio type that are unbiased or subject to a smaller bias than the ordinary ratio estimate. Such estimates might be useful in surveys with many strata and small samples in each stratum if the separate ratio estimate seems appropriate.

One estimate, due to Hartley and Ross (1954), can be derived by starting with the mean $\bar{r}$ of the ratios y_i/x_i and correcting it for bias.

$$\bar{r} = \frac{1}{n}\sum^n r_i = \frac{1}{n}\sum^n \frac{y_i}{x_i}$$

Now

$$\frac{1}{N}\sum_{i=1}^{N} r_i(x_i - \bar{X}) = \frac{1}{N}\sum_{i=1}^{N} \frac{y_i}{x_i}\cdot x_i - \left(\frac{1}{N}\sum_{i=1}^{N} r_i\right)\bar{X}$$

$$= \bar{Y} - \bar{X}E(r_i) = \bar{X}[R - E(r_i)]$$

But in simple random sampling $E(\bar{r}) = E(r_i)$. Hence

$$\text{bias in } \bar{r} = E(\bar{r}) - R = -\frac{1}{\bar{X}N}\sum_{i=1}^{N} r_i(x_i - \bar{X}) \qquad (6.28)$$

By theorem 2.3, an unbiased sample estimate of

$$\frac{1}{N-1}\sum_{i=1}^{N} r_i(x_i - \bar{X})$$

is

$$\frac{1}{n-1}\sum_{i=1}^{n} r_i(x_i - \bar{x}) = \frac{n}{n-1}(\bar{y} - \bar{r}\bar{x})$$

On substituting into (6.28), the estimate $\bar{r}$, corrected for bias, becomes

$$\bar{r}' = \bar{r} + \frac{n(N-1)}{(n-1)N\bar{X}}(\bar{y} - \bar{r}\bar{x}) \qquad (6.29)$$

The corresponding unbiased estimate of the population total $\hat{Y}$ is

$$\bar{r}'X = \bar{r}X + \frac{n(N-1)}{n-1}(\bar{y} - \bar{r}\bar{x}) \qquad (6.30)$$

Example.   Compute the estimated stratum total for the following simple random sample of size 8 from a stratum with $N = 16$, $X = 106$. From Table 6.5,

$$\bar{r}'X = (2.389)(106) + \frac{8(15)}{7}[11.000 - (2.389)(5.5)]$$

$$= 253.2 - 36.7 = 216.5$$

TABLE 6.5
COMPUTATION OF THE HARTLEY-ROSS ESTIMATE
Unit

	1	2	3	4	5	6	7	8	Mean
y_i	8	15	5	7	5	13	11	24	11.000
x_i	8	6	1	4	3	5	4	13	5.500
r_i	1.000	2.500	5.000	1.750	1.667	2.600	2.750	1.846	2.389

An exact formula for $V(\bar{r}'X)$ exists for any size of sample. If the fpc is negligible, the formula is

$$V(\bar{r}'X) = \frac{N^2}{n}(S_y^2 + \bar{r}_p^2 S_x^2 - 2\bar{r}_p S_{yx}) + \frac{N^2}{n(n-1)}(S_r^2 S_x^2 + S_{rx}^2) \quad (6.31)$$

where $\bar{r}_p$ and S_r^2 are the population mean and variance of the r_i and S_{rx} is the population covariance of r_i and x_i. This formula was given by Goodman and Hartley (1958), who also give an unbiased sample estimate of $V(\bar{r}'X)$. For the formula for the true variance when the fpc is not negligible, see Robson (1957).

General comparisons of the precision of $\bar{r}'X$ and the ordinary ratio estimate $\hat{Y}_R$ can be made only in samples large enough so that the approximate formula for $V(\hat{Y}_R)$ is valid. With n large, the second term in (6.31) can be omitted. The first term can be rewritten as

$$V(\bar{r}'X) \doteq \frac{N^2}{n} \sum_{i=1}^{N} \frac{[y_i - \bar{Y} - \bar{r}_p(x_i - \bar{X})]^2}{N - 1}$$

For $\hat{Y}_R$, the corresponding expression is

$$V(\hat{Y}_R) \doteq \frac{N^2}{n} \sum_{i=1}^{N} \frac{(y_i - Rx_i)^2}{N - 1}$$

Thus, as Goodman and Hartley point out, $\bar{r}'X$ is more precise in large samples if the line $\bar{Y} + \bar{r}_p(x_i - \bar{X})$ fits the values y_i more closely than the line Rx_i. Although extensive comparisons have not been made, it seems likely that in most applications in which ratio estimates are appropriate $V(\hat{Y}_R)$ will be smaller in large samples. Further comparisons of the estimates in small samples would be valuable, since these are the cases in which freedom from bias may be important.

As an alternative approach, Lahiri (1951) showed that the ordinary ratio estimate is unbiased if the sample is drawn with probability proportional to Σx_i. There are two ways of drawing the sample. One, due to Lahiri, is to draw a sample without replacement in the usual way. If T is the sum of the n largest values of x_i in the population, draw a random number between 1 and T, say ν. If $\Sigma x_i \geq \nu$ for the sample, retain it. Otherwise replace it and start again, drawing a new random number for each sample that is tried until one is found that can be retained. Clearly, the probability that a sample will be retained is proportional to Σx_i. A second method, Midzuno (1951), is to draw the first member of the sample with probability proportional to x_i and the remaining $(n - 1)$ members with equal probability. The following proof shows that $\hat{R}$ is unbiased.

If Σx_i is added over all simple random samples of size n, the total is $\binom{N - 1}{n - 1} X$, since every unit appears in $\binom{N - 1}{n - 1}$ samples. The probability that a specified sample will be drawn is therefore fore

$$P = \frac{\Sigma x_i}{\binom{N - 1}{n - 1} X}$$

For this method of sample selection, with $\hat{R}_L = \Sigma y_i / \Sigma x_i$,

$$E(\hat{R}_L) = \sum_{SrS} \left(P \frac{\Sigma y_i}{\Sigma x_i} \right)$$

where $\sum_{SrS}$ denotes a sum over all simple random samples. Substituting the value of P,

$$E(\hat{R}_L) = \sum_{SrS} \left[\frac{\Sigma x_i}{\binom{N - 1}{n - 1} X} \right] \cdot \frac{\Sigma y_i}{\Sigma x_i} = \frac{\binom{N - 1}{n - 1} Y}{\binom{N - 1}{n - 1} X} = R$$

No exact expression for $V(\hat{R}_L)$ has been found. It is easily shown that in large samples $\hat{R}_L$ has the same approximate variance as $\hat{R}$.

Example. This illustrates an artificial population in which the Lahiri estimate performed well. The population contains three strata with $N_h = 4$, $n_h = 2$ in each stratum. The population was deliberately constructed so that (a) R_h varies markedly from stratum to stratum, thus favoring a separate ratio estimate, and (b) the ratio estimate within each stratum is badly biased. Five methods of estimating the population total Y were compared.

Simple expansion:	$\Sigma N_h \bar{y}_h$
The combined ratio estimate:	$(\bar{y}_{st}/\bar{x}_{st}) X$
The separate ratio estimate:	$\sum_h (\bar{y}_h/\bar{x}_h) X_h$
The separate Hartley-Ross estimate:	$\sum_h (\bar{r}_h' X_h)$
The separate Lahiri estimate:	$\sum_h (\bar{y}_h/\bar{x}_h) X_h$

There are $6^3 = 216$ possible samples. Since estimates were made for every sample, biases and variances are exact. For the computations I am indebted to Joseph Sedransk.

TABLE 6.6

A SMALL ARTIFICIAL POPULATION

Stratum

	I		II		III	
	y	x	y	x	y	x
	2	2	2	1	3	1
	3	4	5	4	7	3
	4	6	9	8	9	4
	11	20	24	23	25	12
Totals	20	32	40	36	44	20
R_h	0.625		1.111		2.200	

TABLE 6.7

RESULTS FOR THE DIFFERENT ESTIMATES OF Y

Method	Variance	$(Bias)^2$	MSE
Simple expansion	820.3	0.0	820.3
Combined ratio	262.8	6.5	269.3
Separate ratio	35.9	24.1	60.0
Separate Hartley-Ross	153.6	0.0	153.6
Separate Lahiri	19.6	0.0	19.6

The results show several interesting features. For the combined ratio estimate, the contribution of the $(bias)^2$ to the mean square error is trivial, despite the extreme conditions. The separate ratio estimate is much more accurate than the combined estimate because of the wide variation in R_h, but it is badly biased. The Hartley-Ross separate estimate is superior to the combined ratio estimate but inferior, as judged by the mean square error, to the separate ratio estimate. The separate Lahiri estimate was easily the best of the group. The Lahiri method suits this population because the fourth unit in each stratum has a high probability of being drawn and samples containing this unit give good estimates of R_h.

No general conclusions can be drawn from this example. One practical limitation of the Lahiri method is that the sampler would probably not want to draw the sample with probability proportional to Σx_i unless he intended to use this type of ratio estimate for all the major items in the survey.

Quenouille (1956) has produced a method of adjustment, applicable to a broad class of estimates, which reduces the bias from order $1/n$ to order $1/n^2$. The utility of this method for ratio estimates was pointed out by Durbin (1959). The bias of estimates like $\hat{R}$, $\hat{Y}_R$ may be expanded in a Taylor series of the form

$$E(\hat{R}) = R + \frac{b_1}{n} + \frac{b_2}{n^2} + \cdots \qquad (6.32)$$

Let the sample be divided at random into g groups, each of size m, where $n = gm$. From (6.32)

$$E(g\hat{R}) = gR + \frac{b_1}{m} + \frac{b_2}{gm^2} + \cdots \qquad (6.33)$$

Now let $\hat{R}_j$ be the ordinary ratio $\Sigma y / \Sigma x$, computed from the sample after *omitting* the jth group. Since $\hat{R}_j$ is obtained from a simple random sample of size $m(g - 1)$, we have

$$E(\hat{R}_j) = R + \frac{b_1}{(g - 1)m} + \frac{b_2}{(g - 1)^2 m^2} + \cdots$$

Hence

$$E[(g - 1)\hat{R}_j] = (g - 1)R + \frac{b_1}{m} + \frac{b_2}{(g - 1)m^2} + \cdots$$

Subtraction from (6.33) gives, to order n^{-2},

$$E[g\hat{R} - (g - 1)\hat{R}_j] = R - \frac{b_2}{g(g - 1)m^2} = R - \frac{b_2}{n^2}\frac{g}{(g - 1)}$$

Thus the bias is now of order $1/n^2$. We can construct g estimates of this type, one for each group. Quenouille has shown that if their average is taken, that is,

$$\hat{R}_Q = g\hat{R} - (g - 1)\frac{\hat{R}_1 + \hat{R}_2 + \cdots + \hat{R}_g}{g}$$

its variance differs from that of $\hat{R}$ by terms of order $1/n^2$. Any increase in variance due to this adjustment for bias should therefore be negligible in moderately large samples.

The simplest estimate of this type is obtained by taking $g = 2$. The estimates $\hat{R}_1$ and $\hat{R}_2$ are those given by the two halves of the sample, and

$$\hat{R}_Q = 2\hat{R} - \frac{\hat{R}_1 + \hat{R}_2}{2}$$

At the other extreme we can take $g = n$. The advantages of one choice of g over another have not been investigated.

This method cannot be expected to help when small samples are taken within strata, as in the artificial example with $n_h = 2$ on p. 179. In samples of moderate size from populations showing wide variation in x, it may be worth applying as a precaution.

6.16 COMPARISON OF TWO RATIOS

In analytical surveys it is frequently necessary to estimate the difference $\hat{R} - \hat{R}'$ between two ratios and to compute the standard error of $\hat{R} - \hat{R}'$. The formulas given here are for the *estimated* variance of $\hat{R} - \hat{R}'$, since these are the ones most commonly required. The fpc terms are omitted for reasons presented in section 2.12.

Simple random sampling is assumed at first. Three cases can be distinguished.

The Two Ratios Are Independent

This occurs when the units are classified into two distinct classes and we wish to compare ratios estimated separately in the two classes. For instance, in a study of household expenditures a simple random sample of households might be subdivided into owned and rented houses in order to compare the proportions of income spent on upkeep of the house in the two classes. If the estimated ratios are denoted by $\hat{R} = \bar{y}/\bar{x}$, $\hat{R}' = \bar{y}'/\bar{x}'$, then

$$v(\hat{R} - \hat{R}') = v(\hat{R}) + v(\hat{R}')$$

The Two Ratios Have the Same Denominator

When the unit is a cluster of families, we might wish to compare the proportion of adult males who use electric shavers with the proportion who use razors. In any unit, y = number of adult males using electric shavers, y' = number of adult males using razors, and x = total number of adult males.

$$\hat{R} - \hat{R}' = \frac{\bar{y} - \bar{y}'}{\bar{x}}$$

If $d_i = y_i - y_i'$, the estimated variance of $\hat{R} - \hat{R}'$ may be computed as

$$v(\hat{R} - \hat{R}') \doteq \frac{1}{n(n-1)\bar{x}^2} \sum_{i=1}^{n} [d_i - (\hat{R} - \hat{R}')x_i]^2$$

The Two Ratios Have Different Denominators but May Be Correlated

An example is the comparison of the proportion of men who smoke with the proportion of women who smoke, in a survey in which the unit is a cluster of houses. Mathematically, this is the most general case.

$$v(\hat{R} - \hat{R}') = v(\hat{R}) + v(\hat{R}') - 2 \operatorname{cov}(\hat{R}\hat{R}')$$

The only unfamiliar term is $\operatorname{cov}(\hat{R}\hat{R}')$. Writing, in the usual way,

$$\hat{R} - R \doteq \frac{\bar{y} - R\bar{x}}{\bar{X}} \qquad \hat{R}' - R' \doteq \frac{\bar{y}' - R'\bar{x}'}{\bar{X}'}$$

we have

$$\operatorname{cov}(\hat{R}\hat{R}') \doteq \frac{1}{n\,\bar{X}\bar{X}'} \operatorname{cov}(y_i - Rx_i)(y_i' - R'x_i')$$

A sample estimate may be computed as follows:

$$\operatorname{cov}(\hat{R}\hat{R}') \doteq \frac{1}{n(n-1)\bar{x}\bar{x}'} \sum_{}^{n}(y_iy_i' - \hat{R}y_i'x_i - \hat{R}'y_ix_i' + \hat{R}\hat{R}'x_ix_i')$$

Example. The 1954 field trial of the Salk polio vaccine was conducted among children in the first three grades in all schools in a number of counties. The counties were not randomly selected, since those with a history of previous polio attacks were favored, but for this illustration it will be assumed that they are a random sample from some population.

Children whose parents did not give permission to participate in the trial were called the "not inoculated" group and, of course, received no shots. Half of the children who received permission were given three shots of an inert liquid and were called the "placebo" group. From the data in Table 6.8, compare the frequencies $\hat{R}$, $\hat{R}'$ of paralytic polio in the "not inoculated" and "placebo" groups. To reduce the amount of data, the comparison is restricted to 34 counties, each having more than 4000 children in the two groups combined.

In these data any variation in the polio attack rate from county to county would produce a positive correlation between $\hat{R}$ and $\hat{R}'$.

The following quantities are derived from the totals.

Placebo: $\qquad \hat{R} = \dfrac{88}{167.4} = 0.525687, \qquad \bar{x} = \dfrac{167.4}{34} = 4.9235$

Not inoculated: $\hat{R}' = \dfrac{99}{284.6} = 0.347857, \qquad \bar{x}' = \dfrac{284.6}{34} = 8.3706$

For $v(\hat{R})$, $v(\hat{R}')$ and $\operatorname{cov}(\hat{R}\hat{R}')$, all uncorrected sums of squares and products among the four variates are required.

$$v(\hat{R}) = \frac{1}{n(n-1)\bar{x}^2}\left(\sum y^2 - 2\hat{R}\sum yx + \hat{R}^2\sum x^2\right)$$

$$= \frac{1}{(34)(33)(4.9235)^2}[(564) - (1.05137)(822.2) + (0.27635)(1661.92)]$$

$$= 0.00584$$

TABLE 6.8

NUMBER OF CHILDREN (x, x') AND OF PARALYTIC CASES (y, y') PER COUNTY

$x*$	x'	$y\dagger$	y'	x	x'	y	y'
4.1	2.4	0	0	13.8	25.6	3	3
3.5	8.0	1	6	10.5	8.1	2	0
4.1	6.1	7	2	21.6	25.9	10	7
2.6	4.6	2	1	3.5	6.7	2	2
2.4	1.5	2	1	6.8	7.3	3	8
2.2	1.9	0	0	2.3	3.7	0	1
1.1	4.0	1	1	2.6	2.9	2	0
1.6	4.0	1	2	6.0	11.1	3	1
5.7	7.8	1	4	11.0	14.8	7	11
3.3	11.0	3	7	19.4	42.5	11	14
1.0	3.8	0	1	6.8	13.7	6	2
2.0	5.2	1	0	1.2	4.0	3	1
8.3	19.0	4	4	5.4	9.3	11	6
1.0	3.7	1	5	1.7	2.6	0	2
1.1	4.2	0	1	2.1	2.3	0	0
2.3	6.8	1	2	1.5	2.6	0	0
1.9	3.5	0	2	3.0	4.0	0	2
				Totals 167.4	284.6	88	99

* x, x' = numbers of "placebo" and "not inoculated" children (in 1000's)
† y, y' = numbers of paralytic polio cases in the placebo and not inoculated
groups

Similarly, we find $v(\hat{R}') = 0.00240$.

$$\text{cov}(\hat{R}\hat{R}') = \frac{1}{n(n-1)\bar{x}\bar{x}'}\left(\sum yy' - \hat{R}\sum y'x - \hat{R}'\sum yx' + \hat{R}\hat{R}'\sum xx'\right)$$

$$= \frac{(497) - (0.52569)(844.6) - (0.34786)(1397.4)}{(34)(33)(4.9235)(8.3706)} + (0.52569)(0.34786)(2690.8)$$

$$= 0.00127$$

Hence

$$\text{s.e.}(\hat{R} - \hat{R}') = \sqrt{0.00584 + 0.00240 - 0.00254} = 0.0754$$

Since $\hat{R} - \hat{R}' = 0.1778$, the difference approaches significance at the 5% level
(the distribution of $\hat{R} - \hat{R}'$ may be somewhat skew for this size of sample).
A possible explanation is that the not-inoculated children may have had more
natural protection against polio than the placebo children.

The same problem may arise in stratified samples in which the domains
of study cut across strata. If $\hat{R}_h$, $\hat{R}_h'$ appear to vary from stratum to stratum,
the comparison will probably be based on an examination of the values of

$\hat{R}_h - \hat{R}_h'$ in individual strata. By finding the standard errors of $\hat{R}_h - \hat{R}_h'$ it is possible to determine whether these differences vary from stratum to stratum and, if not, to compute an efficient over-all difference.

If the $\hat{R}_h$, $\hat{R}_h'$ exhibit no real variation from stratum to stratum, it may be sufficient to compare the combined estimates $\hat{R}_c$ and $\hat{R}_c'$. As before

$$v(\hat{R}_c - \hat{R}_c') = v(\hat{R}_c) + v(\hat{R}_c') - 2 \operatorname{cov}(\hat{R}_c \hat{R}_c')$$

where, putting $d_{hi} = (y_{hi} - \bar{y}_h) - \hat{R}_c(x_{hi} - \bar{x}_h)$,

$$v(\hat{R}_c) = \frac{1}{\bar{x}_{st}^2} \sum_h \frac{N_h^2}{n_h(n_h - 1)} \sum_i d_{hi}^2$$

$$\operatorname{cov}(\hat{R}_c \hat{R}_c') = \frac{1}{\bar{x}_{st}\bar{x}_{st}'} \sum_h \frac{N_h^2}{n_h(n_h - 1)} \sum_i d_{hi} d_{hi}'$$

A more thorough discussion of the comparison of ratios, including short-cut computing formulas when the sample permits them, has been given by Kish and Hess (1959).

6.17 MULTIVARIATE RATIO ESTIMATES

Olkin (1958) has extended the ratio estimate to the situation in which p auxiliary x-variables $(x_1, x_2, \cdots x_p)$ are available. For the population total, the proposed estimate, say $\hat{Y}_{MR}$ for *multivariate ratio*, is

$$\hat{Y}_{MR} = W_1 \frac{\bar{y}}{\bar{x}_1} X_1 + W_2 \frac{\bar{y}}{\bar{x}_2} X_2 + \cdots + w_p \frac{\bar{y}}{\bar{x}_p} X_p$$

$$= W_1 \hat{Y}_{R_1} + W_2 \hat{Y}_{R_2} + \cdots + W_p \hat{Y}_{R_p}$$

where the W_i are weights to be determined to maximize the precision of $\hat{Y}_{MR}$, subject to $\Sigma W_i = 1$. This type of estimate appears appropriate when the regression of y on x_i, x_2, $\cdots x_p$ is linear and passes through the origin. The population totals X_i must be known.

The method is described for two x-variates, since this should be the most frequent application. We have

$$\hat{Y}_{MR} - Y = W_1(\hat{Y}_{R_1} - Y) + W_2(\hat{Y}_{R_2} - Y)$$

Hence

$$V(\hat{Y}_{MR}) = W_1^2 V(\hat{Y}_{R_1}) + 2W_1 W_2 \operatorname{cov}(\hat{Y}_{R_1} \hat{Y}_{R_2}) + W_2^2 V(\hat{Y}_{R_2})$$

$$= W_1^2 V_{11} + 2W_1 W_2 V_{12} + W_2^2 V_{22}$$

where $V_{11} = V(\hat{Y}_{R_1})$, etc. The values of W_1, W_2, which minimize the variance, subject to $W_1 + W_2 = 1$, are found to be

$$W_1 = \frac{V_{22} - V_{12}}{V_{11} + V_{22} - 2V_{12}}, \qquad W_2 = \frac{V_{11} - V_{12}}{V_{11} + V_{22} - 2V_{12}}$$

and the minimum variance is

$$V_{min}(\hat{Y}_{MR}) = \frac{V_{11}V_{22} - V_{12}{}^2}{V_{11} + V_{22} - 2V_{12}}$$

With p variates, it is necessary to compute the inverse V^{ij} of the matrix V_{ij}. Then the optimum $W_i = \Sigma_i/\Sigma$, where Σ_i is the sum of the elements in the ith column of V^{ij} and Σ is the sum of all the p^2 elements of V^{ij}. The minimum variance is $1/\Sigma$.

In practice, the weights are determined from estimated variances and covariances v_{ij}. From (6.7) in section 6.3,

$$v_{11} = \frac{(1-f)\hat{Y}^2}{n}(c_{yy} + c_{11} - 2c_{y1})$$

$$v_{22} = \frac{(1-f)\hat{Y}^2}{n}(c_{yy} + c_{22} - 2c_{y2})$$

where $c_{yy} = s_y{}^2/\bar{y}^2$, etc. The covariance can be expressed as

$$v_{12} = \frac{(1-f)\hat{Y}^2}{n}(c_{yy} + c_{12} - c_{y1} - c_{y2})$$

A convenient method of computation is first to obtain the matrix

$$C = \begin{pmatrix} c_{yy} & c_{y1} & c_{y2} \\ c_{y1} & c_{11} & c_{12} \\ c_{y2} & c_{12} & c_{22} \end{pmatrix}$$

If $v_{ij}' = nv_{ij}/(1-f)\hat{Y}^2$, the matrix v_{ij}' is easily obtained by taking diagonal contrasts in C, that is,

$$v_{11}' = c_{yy} + c_{11} - c_{y1} - c_{y1}$$

$$v_{12}' = c_{yy} + c_{12} - c_{y1} - c_{y2} \qquad \text{etc.}$$

The factor $(1-f)\hat{Y}^2/n$ is not needed when computing the w_i, but it must be inserted when computing the minimum variance. Thus

$$v_{min}(\hat{Y}_{MR}) = \frac{(1-f)\hat{Y}^2}{n}\frac{(v_{11}'v_{22}' - v_{12}'^2)}{(v_{11}' + v_{22}' - 2v_{12}')}$$

In view of the amount of computation involved, this estimate will probably be restricted to smaller surveys of specialized scope. The method is capable of giving a marked increase in precision over $\hat{Y}_{R_1}$ or $\hat{Y}_{R_2}$ alone.

EXERCISES

* 6.1 A pilot survey of 21 households gave the following data for numbers of members (x), children (y_1), cars (y_2), and TV sets (y_3).

x	y_1	y_2	y_3	x	y_1	y_2	y_3	x	y_1	y_2	y_3
5	3	1	3	2	0	0	1	6	3	2	0
2	0	1	1	3	1	1	1	4	2	1	1
4	1	2	0	2	0	2	0	4	2	1	1
4	2	1	1	6	4	2	1	3	1	0	1
6	4	1	1	3	1	0	0	2	0	2	1
3	1	1	2	4	2	1	1	4	2	1	1
5	3	1	1	5	3	1	1	3	1	1	1

Assuming that the total population X is known, would you recommend that ratio estimates be used instead of simple expansions for estimating total numbers of children, cars, and TV sets?

* 6.2 In a field of barley the grain, y_i, and the grain plus straw, x_i, were weighed for each of a large number of sampling units located at random over the field. The total produce (grain plus straw) of the whole field was also weighed. The following data were obtained: $c_{yy} = 1.13$, $c_{yx} = 0.78$, $c_{xx} = 1.11$. Compute the gain in precision obtained by estimating the grain yield of the field from the ratio of grain to total produce instead of from the mean yield of grain per unit.

It requires 20 min to cut, thresh, and weigh the grain on each unit, 2 min to weigh the straw on each unit, and 2 hr to collect and weigh the total produce of the field. How many units must be taken per field in order that the ratio estimate may be more economical than the mean per unit?

6.3 For the data in Table 6.1, $\hat{Y}_R = 28,367$ and $c_{\bar{y}\bar{y}} = 0.0142068$, $c_{\bar{y}\bar{x}} = 0.0146541$, $c_{\bar{x}\bar{x}} = 0.0156830$. Compute the 95% quadratic confidence limits for Y and compare them with the limits found by the normal approximation.

* 6.4 The values of y, x in a population with $N = 6$ are as follows:

$$y \quad 3 \quad 5 \quad 7 \quad 6 \quad 8 \quad 13$$
$$x \quad 1 \quad 2 \quad 2 \quad 3 \quad 3 \quad 3$$

Check that the regression of y on x is a straight line through the origin. By computing $\hat{R}$ for all 15 simple random samples with $n = 2$ and all 20 simple random samples with $n = 3$, verify theorem 6.2 that $\hat{R}$ is unbiased in both cases.

* 6.5 The values of y and x are measured for each unit in a simple random sample from a population. If $\bar{X}$, the population mean of x, is known, which of the following procedures do you recommend for estimating $\bar{Y}/\bar{X}$? (a) Always use $\bar{y}/\bar{X}$. (b) Sometimes use $\bar{y}/\bar{X}$ and sometimes $\bar{y}/\bar{x}$. (c) Always use $\bar{y}/\bar{x}$. Give reasons for your answer.

* 6.6 The following data are for a small artificial population with $N = 8$ and two strata of equal size:

	Stratum 1		Stratum 2	
	x_{1i}	y_{1i}	x_{2i}	y_{2i}
a_1 2		0	b_1 10	7
a_2 5		3	b_2 18	15
a_3 9		7	b_3 21	10
a_4 15		10	b_4 25	16

For a stratified random sample in which $n_1 = n_2 = 2$, compare the MSE's of $\hat{Y}_{Rs}$ and $\hat{Y}_{Rc}$ by working out the results for all possible samples. To what extent is the difference in MSE's due to biases in the estimates?

6.7 In exercise 6.6 compute the variance given by using Lahiri's method of sample selection within each stratum and a separate ratio estimate.

6.8 Forty-five states of the United States (excluding the 5 largest) were arranged in nine strata with five states each, states in the same stratum having roughly the same ratio of 1950 to 1940 population. A stratified random sample with $n_h = 2$ gave the following results for 1960 population (y) and 1950 population (x), in millions.

	Stratum								
	1	2	3	4	5	6	7	8	9
y_{h1}	0.23	0.63	0.97	2.54	4.67	4.32	4.56	1.79	2.18
x_{h1}	0.13	0.50	0.91	2.01	3.93	3.96	4.06	1.91	1.90
y_{h2}	4.95	2.85	0.61	6.07	3.96	1.41	3.57	1.86	1.75
x_{h2}	2.78	2.38	0.53	4.84	3.44	1.33	3.29	2.01	1.32

Given that the 1950 population total X is 97.94, estimate the 1960 population by the combined ratio estimate. Find the standard error of your estimate by Keyfitz' short-cut method (section 6.13). The correct 1960 total was 114.99. Does your estimate agree with this figure within sampling errors?

6.9 In the example of a bivariate ratio estimate given by Olkin, a sample of 50 cities was drawn from a population of 200 large cities. The variates y, x_1, x_2 are the numbers of inhabitants per city in 1950, 1940, and 1930, respectively. For the population, $\bar{Y} = 1699$, $\bar{X}_1 = 1482$, $\bar{X}_2 = 1420$ (in 100's) and, for the sample, $\bar{y} = 1896$, $\bar{x}_1 = 1693$, $\bar{x}_2 = 1643$. The C matrix as defined in section 6.17 is

	y	x_1	x_2
y	1.213	1.241	1.256
x_1	1.241	1.302	1.335
x_2	1.256	1.335	1.381

Estimate $\bar{Y}$ by (a) the sample mean, (b) the ratio of 1950 to 1940 numbers of inhabitants, and (c) the bivariate ratio estimate. Compute the estimated standard error of each estimate.

6.10   Prove that with Midzuno's method of sample selection (section 6.15) the probability that any specific sample will be drawn is

$$\frac{(n - 1)!(N - n)!}{(N - 1)!} \frac{\sum\limits_{}^{n} (x_i)}{X}$$

REFERENCES

David, F. N. and Neyman, J. (1938). Extension of the Markoff theorem of least squares. *Stat. Res. Mem.*, **2**, 105.

Durbin, J. (1959). A note on the application of Quenouille's method of bias reduction to the estimation of ratios. *Biometrika*, **46**, 477–480.

Fieller, E. C. (1932). The distribution of the index in a normal bivariate population. *Biometrika*, **24**, 428–440.

Finkner, A. L. (1950). Methods of sampling for estimating commercial peach production in North Carolina. *North Carolina Agr. Exp. Sta. Tech. Bull.* 91.

Goodman, L. A., and Hartley, H. O. (1958). The precision of unbiased ratio-type estimators. *Jour. Amer. Stat. Assoc.*, **53**, 491–508.

Hájek, J (1958) Some contributions to the theory of probability sampling. *Int. Stat. Inst. Bull.*, **36**, 3, 127–134.

Hansen, M. H., Hurwitz, W. N., and Gurney, M. (1946). Problems and methods of the sample survey of business. *Jour. Amer. Stat. Assoc.*, **41**, 173–189.

Hansen, M. H., Hurwitz, W. N., and Madow, W. G. (1953). *Sample survey methods and theory*. John Wiley & Sons, New York.

Hartley, H. O., and Ross, A. (1954). Unbiased ratio estimates. *Nature*, **174**, 270–271.

Jessen, R. J., et al. (1947). On a population sample for Greece. *Jour. Amer. Stat. Assoc.*, **42**, 357–384.

Keyfitz, N. (1957). Estimates of sampling variance where two units are selected from each stratum. *Jour. Amer. Stat. Assoc.*, **52**, 503–510.

Kish, L., and Hess, I. (1959). On variances of ratios and their differences in multistage samples. *Jour. Amer. Stat. Assoc.*, **54**, 416–446.

Lahiri, D. B. (1951). A method for sample selection providing unbiased ratio estimates. *Int. Stat. Inst. Bull.*, **33**, 2, 133–140.

Midzuno, H. (1951). On the sampling system with probability proportionate to sum of sizes. *Ann. Inst. Stat. Math.*, **2**, 99–108.

Olkin, I. (1958). Multivariate ratio estimation for finite populations. *Biometrika*, **45**, 154–165.

Paulson, E. (1942). A note on the estimation of some mean values for a bivariate distribution. *Ann. Math. Stat.*, **13**, 440–444.

Quenouille, M. H. (1956). Notes on bias in estimation. *Biometrika*, **43**, 353–360.

Robson, D. S. (1957). Applications of multivariate polykays to the theory of unbiased ratio type estimation. *Jour. Amer. Stat. Assoc.*, **52**, 511–522.

Sukhatme, P. V. (1954). *Sampling theory of surveys with applications*. Iowa State College Press, Ames, Iowa.

CHAPTER 7

Regression Estimates

7.1 THE LINEAR REGRESSION ESTIMATE

Like the ratio estimate, the linear regression estimate is designed to increase precision by the use of an auxiliary variate x_i which is correlated with y_i. When the relation between y_i and x_i is examined, it may be found that although the relation is approximately linear the line does not go through the origin. This suggests an estimate based on the linear regression of y_i on x_i rather than on the ratio of the two variables.

We suppose that y_i and x_i are each obtained for every unit in the sample and that the population mean $\overline{X}$ of the x_i is known. The linear regression estimate of $\overline{Y}$, the population mean of the y_i, is

$$\bar{y}_{lr} = \bar{y} + b(\overline{X} - \bar{x}) \tag{7.1}$$

where the subscript lr denotes *linear regression* and b is an estimate of the change in y when x is increased by unity. The rationale of this estimate is that if $\bar{x}$ is below average we should expect $\bar{y}$ also to be below average by an amount $b(\overline{X} - \bar{x})$ because of the regression of y_i on x_i. For an estimate of the population total Y, we take $\hat{Y}_{lr} = N\bar{y}_{lr}$.

Watson (1937) used a regression of leaf area on leaf weight to estimate the average area of the leaves on a plant. The procedure was to weigh all the leaves on the plant. For a small sample of leaves, the area and the weight of each leaf were determined. The sample mean leaf area was then adjusted by means of the regression on leaf weight. The point of the application, is, of course, that the weight of a leaf can be found quickly but determination of its area is more time consuming.

This example illustrates a general situation in which regression estimates are helpful. Suppose that we can make a rapid estimate x_i of some characteristic for every unit and can also, by some more costly method, determine the correct value y_i of the characteristic for a simple random sample of the units. A rat expert might make a quick eye estimate of the number

189

of rats in each block in a city area and then determine, by trapping, the actual number of rats in each of a simple random sample of the blocks. In another application described by Yates (1960), an eye estimate of the volume of timber was made on each of a population of $\frac{1}{10}$-acre plots, and the actual timber volume was measured for a sample of the plots. The regression estimate

$$\bar{y} + b(\bar{X} - \bar{x})$$

adjusts the sample mean of the actual measurements by the regression of the actual measurements on the rapid estimates. The rapid estimates need not be free from bias. If $x_i - y_i = D$, so that the rapid estimate is perfect except for a constant bias D, then with $b = 1$ the regression estimate becomes

$$\bar{y} + (\bar{X} - \bar{x}) = \bar{X} + (\bar{y} - \bar{x})$$

$$= \text{(pop. mean of rapid estimate)} + \text{(adjustment for bias)}$$

Our knowledge of the properties of the regression estimate is of the same scope as our knowledge for the ratio estimate. The regression estimate is consistent, in the trivial sense that when the sample comprises the whole population, $\bar{x} = \bar{X}$, and the regression estimate reduces to $\bar{Y}$. As will be shown, the estimate is in general biased, but the ratio of the bias to the standard error becomes small when the sample is large. We possess a large-sample formula for the variance of the estimate, but more information is needed about the distribution of the estimate in small samples and about the value of n required for the practical use of large-sample results.

By a suitable choice of b, the regression estimate includes as particular cases both the mean per unit and the ratio estimate. Obviously if b is taken as zero, $\bar{y}_{lr}$ reduces to $\bar{y}$. If $b = \bar{y}/\bar{x}$,

$$\bar{y}_{lr} = \bar{y} + \frac{\bar{y}}{\bar{x}}(\bar{X} - \bar{x}) = \frac{\bar{y}}{\bar{x}}\bar{X} = \hat{\bar{Y}}_R \qquad (7.2)$$

7.2 REGRESSION ESTIMATES WITH PREASSIGNED b

Although, in most applications, b is estimated from the results of the sample, it is sometimes reasonable to choose the value of b in advance. In repeated surveys, previous calculations may have shown that the sample values of b remain fairly constant; or, if x is the value of y at a recent census, general knowledge of the population may suggest that b is not far from unity, so that $b = 1$ is chosen. Since the sampling theory of regression estimates when b is preassigned is both simple and informative, this case is considered first.

Theorem 7.1. In simple random sampling, in which b_0 is a preassigned constant, the linear regression estimate

$$\bar{y}_{lr} = \bar{y} + b_0(\bar{X} - \bar{x})$$

is unbiased, with variance

$$V(\bar{y}_{lr}) = \frac{1-f}{n} \frac{\sum_{i=1}^{N}[(y_i - \bar{Y}) - b_0(x_i - \bar{X})]^2}{N-1} \tag{7.3}$$

$$= \frac{1-f}{n}(S_y^2 - 2b_0 S_{yx} + b_0^2 S_x^2) \tag{7.4}$$

Note that no assumption is required about the relation between y and x in the finite population.

Proof. Since b_0 is constant in repeated sampling,

$$E(\bar{y}_{lr}) = E(\bar{y}) + b_0 E(\bar{x} - \bar{X}) = \bar{Y}$$

by theorem 2.1. Further, $\bar{y}_{lr}$ is the sample mean of the quantities $y_i - b_0(x_i - \bar{X})$, whose population mean is $\bar{Y}$. Hence by theorem 2.2

$$V(\bar{y}_{lr}) = \frac{1-f}{n} \cdot \frac{\sum_{i=1}^{N}[(y_i - \bar{Y}) - b_0(x_i - \bar{X})]^2}{N-1}$$

$$= \frac{1-f}{n}(S_y^2 - 2b_0 S_{yx} + b_0^2 S_x^2)$$

Corollary. An unbiased sample estimate of $V(\bar{y}_{lr})$ is

$$v(\bar{y}_{lr}) = \frac{1-f}{n} \frac{\sum_{i=1}^{n}[(y_i - \bar{y}) - b_0(x_i - \bar{x})]^2}{n-1}$$

$$= \frac{1-f}{n}(s_y^2 - 2b_0 s_{yx} + b_0^2 s_x^2)$$

This follows at once by applying theorem 2.4 to the variate $y_i - b_0(x_i - \bar{X})$.

A natural question at this point is: what is the best value of b_0? The answer is given in theorem 7.2.

Theorem 7.2. The value of b_0 which minimizes $V(\bar{y}_{lr})$ is

$$b_0 = B = \frac{S_{yx}}{S_x^2} = \frac{\sum_{i=1}^{N}(y_i - \bar{Y})(x_i - \bar{X})}{\sum_{i=1}^{N}(x_i - \bar{X})^2} \tag{7.5}$$

which may be called the linear regression coefficient of y on x in the finite population. The resulting minimum variance is

$$V_{min}(\bar{y}_{lr}) = \frac{1-f}{n} S_y^2 (1 - \rho^2)$$

where ρ is the population correlation coefficient between y and x.

Proof. In expression (7.4), for $V(\bar{y}_{lr})$, put

$$b_0 = B + d = \frac{S_{yx}}{S_x^2} + d$$

This gives

$$V(\bar{y}_{lr}) = \frac{1-f}{n}\left[S_y^2 - 2S_{yx}\left(\frac{S_{yx}}{S_x^2} + d\right) + S_x^2\left(\frac{S_{yx}^2}{S_x^4} + 2d\frac{S_{yx}}{S_x^2} + d^2\right)\right]$$

$$= \frac{1-f}{n}\left[\left(S_y^2 - \frac{S_{yx}^2}{S_x^2}\right) + d^2 S_x^2\right] \tag{7.6}$$

Clearly, this is minimized when $d = 0$. Since $\rho^2 = S_{yx}^2/S_y^2 S_x^2$,

$$V_{min}(\bar{y}_{lr}) = \frac{1-f}{n} S_y^2 (1 - \rho^2) \tag{7.7}$$

The same analysis may be used to show how far b_0 can depart from B without incurring a substantial loss of precision. From (7.6) and (7.7),

$$V(\bar{y}_{lr}) = \frac{1-f}{n} [S_y^2(1 - \rho^2) + (b_0 - B)^2 S_x^2]$$

$$= V_{min}(\bar{y}_{lr})\left[1 + \frac{(b_0 - B)^2 S_x^2}{S_y^2(1 - \rho^2)}\right]$$

Since $BS_x = \rho S_y$, this may be written

$$V(\bar{y}_{lr}) = V_{min}(\bar{y}_{lr})\left[1 + \left(\frac{b_0}{B} - 1\right)^2 \frac{\rho^2}{(1 - \rho^2)}\right]$$

Thus, if the proportional increase in variance is to be less than α, we must have

$$\left|\frac{b_0}{B} - 1\right| < \sqrt{\alpha(1 - \rho^2)/\rho^2} \tag{7.8}$$

For example, if $\rho = 0.7$, the increase in variance is less than 10%, ($\alpha = 0.1$), provided that

$$\left| \frac{b_0}{B} - 1 \right| < \sqrt{(0.1)(0.51)/(0.49)} = 0.32$$

Expression (7.8) makes it clear that in order to ensure a *small* proportional increase in variance b_0/B must be close to 1 if ρ is very high but can depart substantially from 1 if ρ is only moderate.

7.3 REGRESSION ESTIMATES WHEN b IS COMPUTED FROM THE SAMPLE

Theorem 7.2 suggests that if b must be computed from the sample an effective estimate is likely to be the familiar least squares estimate of B, that is,

$$b = \frac{\sum_{i=1}^{n}(y_i - \bar{y})(x_i - \bar{x})}{\sum_{i=1}^{n}(x_i - \bar{x})^2} \tag{7.9}$$

The theory of linear regression plays a prominent part in statistical methodology. The standard results of this theory are not entirely suitable for sample surveys because they require the assumptions that the population regression of y on x is linear, that the residual variance of y about the regression line is constant, and that the population is infinite. If the first two assumptions are violently wrong, a linear regression estimate will probably not be used. However, in surveys in which the regression of y on x is thought to be approximately linear, it is helpful to be able to use $\bar{y}_{lr}$ without having to assume exact linearity or constant residual variance.

Consequently, we present an approach that does not demand that the regression in the population be linear. The results hold only in large samples. They are analogous to the large-sample theory for the ratio estimate.

First we show that in samples of size n the quantity $(b - B)$ is of order $1/\sqrt{n}$. Define the variate e_i by the relation

$$e_i = y_i - \bar{Y} - B(x_i - \bar{X}) \tag{7.10}$$

It follows that

$$\sum_{i=1}^{N} e_i(x_i - \bar{X}) = \sum_{i=1}^{N}(y_i - \bar{Y})(x_i - \bar{X}) - B\sum_{i=1}^{N}(x_i - \bar{X})^2 = 0 \tag{7.11}$$

by definition of B. Now

$$b = \frac{\sum\limits_{i=1}^{n} y_i(x_i - \bar{x})}{\sum\limits_{i=1}^{n}(x_i - \bar{x})^2}$$

$$= \frac{\sum\limits_{i=1}^{n} [\bar{Y} + B(x_i - \bar{X}) + e_i](x_i - \bar{x})}{\sum\limits_{i=1}^{n}(x_i - \bar{x})^2} \qquad \text{using (7.10)}$$

$$= B + \frac{\sum\limits_{i=1}^{n} e_i(x_i - \bar{x})}{\sum\limits_{i=1}^{n}(x_i - \bar{x})^2} \qquad (7.12)$$

By theorem 2.3, $\sum\limits^{n} e_i(x_i - \bar{x})/(n - 1)$ is an unbiased estimate of $\sum\limits^{N} e_i(x_i - \bar{X})/(N - 1)$, which by (7.11) is zero. In repeated samples of size n the sample covariance $\sum\limits^{n} e_i(x_i - \bar{x})/(n - 1)$ is therefore distributed about a zero mean. The standard error of a sample covariance is known to be of order $1/\sqrt{n}$. Thus, in samples of size n, $\Sigma e_i(x_i - \bar{x})/(n - 1)$ will be of order $1/\sqrt{n}$. But the quantity $\Sigma (x_i - \bar{x})^2/(n - 1) = s_x^2$ is of order unity in samples of size n. Hence, from (7.12), $(b - B)$ is of order $1/\sqrt{n}$.

Theorem 7.3. If b is the least squares estimate of B and

$$\bar{y}_{lr} = \bar{y} + b(\bar{X} - \bar{x}) \qquad (7.13)$$

then in simple random samples of size n

$$V(\bar{y}_{lr}) = \frac{1 - f}{n} S_y^2(1 - \rho^2) \qquad (7.14)$$

provided that n is large enough so that terms of order $1/\sqrt{n}$ are negligible.

Proof. By averaging (7.10) over the units in the sample, we have

$$\bar{e} = \bar{y} - \bar{Y} - B(\bar{x} - \bar{X})$$

Substitution for $\bar{y}$ into expression (7.13) for $\bar{y}_{lr}$ gives

$$\bar{y}_{lr} = \bar{Y} + (b - B)(\bar{X} - \bar{x}) + \bar{e} \qquad (7.15)$$

From (7.10) it is clear that the population mean of the e_i is zero. Hence $\bar{e}$ is of order $1/\sqrt{n}$. But we have shown that $(b - B)$ is of order $1/\sqrt{n}$. Since $(\bar{X} - \bar{x})$ is also of order $1/\sqrt{n}$, their product $(b - B)(\bar{X} - \bar{x})$ is of order $1/n$. Consequently this product can be ignored relative to $\bar{e}$ if terms of order $1/\sqrt{n}$ are negligible. This gives

$$\bar{y}_{lr} - \bar{Y} \doteq \bar{e}$$

Since $E(\bar{e})$ is zero by (7.10) and theorem 2.1, $E(\bar{e}^2)$ is the variance of the mean of the quantities e_i in a simple random sample. Hence, by theorem 2.2,

$$V(\bar{y}_{lr}) = \frac{1-f}{n} S_e^2 = \frac{1-f}{n} \frac{\sum\limits_{i=1}^{N} e_i^2}{N-1} \tag{7.16}$$

Now

$$\sum_{i}^{N} e_i^2 = \sum_{i}^{N} [(y_i - \bar{Y}) - B(x_i - \bar{X})]^2$$

$$= \sum_{i}^{N} (y_i - \bar{Y})^2 - 2B \sum_{i}^{N} (y_i - \bar{Y})(x_i - \bar{X}) + B^2 \sum_{i}^{N} (x_i - \bar{X})^2$$

$$= \sum (y_i - \bar{Y})^2 - B^2 \sum (x_i - \bar{X})^2$$

by the definition of B, equation 7.5. But

$$\rho = \frac{\sum\limits_{i}^{N} (y_i - \bar{Y})(x_i - \bar{X})}{\sqrt{\sum\limits_{i}^{N} (y_i - \bar{Y})^2 \sum\limits_{i}^{N} (x_i - \bar{X})^2}} = B \sqrt{\frac{\sum (x_i - \bar{X})^2}{\sum (y_i - \bar{Y})^2}}$$

Thus

$$\sum_{i}^{N} e_i^2 = \sum (y_i - \bar{Y})^2 (1 - \rho^2)$$

so that, finally,

$$V(\bar{y}_{lr}) = \frac{1-f}{n} S_y^2 (1 - \rho^2) \tag{7.17}$$

As a sample estimate of $V(\bar{y}_{lr})$, valid in large samples, we may use

$$v(\bar{y}_{lr}) = \frac{1-f}{n(n-2)} \sum_{i=1}^{n} [(y_i - \bar{y}) - b(x_i - \bar{x})]^2 \tag{7.18}$$

$$= \frac{1-f}{n(n-2)} \left\{ \sum (y_i - \bar{y})^2 - \frac{[\sum (y_i - \bar{y})(x_i - \bar{x})]^2}{\sum (x_i - \bar{x})^2} \right\} \tag{7.19}$$

the latter being the usual short-cut computing formula. The derivation is as follows.

In theorem 7.3, equation (7.16), we had

$$V(\bar{y}_{lr}) \doteq \frac{(1-f)}{n} S_e^2$$

From theorem 2.4, an unbiased estimate of S_e^2 is

$$s_e^2 = \frac{1}{n-1} \sum_{i=1}^{n} (e_i - \bar{e})^2$$

Now, from equation (7.10),

$$e_i - \bar{e} = (y_i - \bar{y}) - B(x_i - \bar{x})$$
$$= [(y_i - \bar{y}) - b(x_i - \bar{x})] + (b - B)(x_i - \bar{x})$$

The second term on the right, of order $1/\sqrt{n}$, may be neglected in relation to the first term, which is of order unity. Hence in large samples we may use

$$\frac{1}{n-1} \sum_{i=1}^{n} [(y_i - \bar{y}) - b(x_i - \bar{x})]^2$$

as an estimate of S_e^2. The divisor $(n-2)$ instead of $(n-1)$ is suggested in (7.18) and (7.19) because it is used in standard regression theory and is known to give an unbiased estimate of S_e^2 if the population is infinite and the regression is linear.

7.4 ACCURACY OF THE LARGE-SAMPLE FORMULA FOR $V(\bar{y}_{lr})$

The preceding analysis leaves unanswered the question: how large must the sample be? A complete answer is not yet known, but some information is obtainable by considering an infinite population.

From (7.15) in theorem 7.3,

$$\bar{y}_{lr} - \bar{Y} = \bar{e} + (b - B)(\bar{X} - \bar{x})$$

Substituting for b from (7.12),

$$\bar{y}_{lr} - \bar{Y} = \bar{e} + \frac{\sum\limits_{}^{n} e_i(x_i - \bar{x})(\bar{X} - \bar{x})}{\sum (x_i - \bar{x})^2} \tag{7.20}$$

This expression for the error of the regression estimate will be used to find the leading terms in the variance and bias of $\bar{y}_{lr}$. For the variance, write

$$\bar{y}_{lr} - \bar{Y} = \sum_{i}^{n} e_i \left[\frac{1}{n} + \frac{(x_i - \bar{x})(\bar{X} - \bar{x})}{\sum (x_i - \bar{x})^2} \right]$$

Hence, in arrays in which the x_i are fixed,

$$V(\bar{y}_{lr} \mid x_i) = \frac{S_e^2}{n} \left[1 + \frac{n(\bar{x} - \bar{X})^2}{\sum (x_i - \bar{x})^2} \right]$$

where it is assumed that S_e^2 is the same for all x. The average value of this quantity over different selections of the x_i depends on the shape of the frequency distribution of x. If the x's are normally distributed, the average is

$$\frac{S_e^2}{n}\left(1 + \frac{1}{n-3}\right)$$

For a general distribution of x, the average may be shown to be (Cochran, 1942), to terms of order $1/n^3$,

$$V(\bar{y}_{lr}) \doteq \frac{S_e^2}{n}\left(1 + \frac{1}{n} + \frac{3 + 2\gamma_1^2}{n^2}\right) \tag{7.21}$$

where $\gamma_1^2 = k_3^2/S_x^3$ is the measure of relative skewness of the distribution of x.

Reverting to (7.20), the bias in $\bar{y}_{lr}$ arises from the second term on the right, since the average value of $\bar{e}$ is zero in simple random sampling. To obtain the leading term, we may replace $\Sigma(x_i - \bar{x})^2$ by its leading term, nS_x^2. Also write

$$\sum_{}^{n} e_i(x_i - \bar{x}) = \sum_{}^{n} e_i(x_i - \bar{X}) + n\bar{e}(\bar{X} - \bar{x})$$

Hence the leading term in the bias is the average of

$$\frac{\sum\limits_{}^{n} e_i(x_i - \bar{X})(\bar{X} - \bar{x})}{nS_x^2} + \frac{\bar{e}(\bar{x} - \bar{X})^2}{S_x^2} \tag{7.22}$$

Let u_i be the variate $e_i(x_i - \bar{X})$. From (7.11), its population mean $\bar{U} = 0$. The average of the first term in (7.22) may therefore be written

$$-\frac{E(\bar{u} - \bar{U})(\bar{x} - \bar{X})}{S_x^2} = -\frac{E(u - \bar{U})(x - \bar{X})}{nS_x^2} = -\frac{Ee(x - \bar{X})^2}{nS_x^2} \tag{7.23}$$

by theorem 2.3, (p. 24), letting $N \to \infty$. The average of the second term in (7.22) is easily shown to be of order $1/n^2$. Thus the leading term in the bias comes from the population covariance between e and $(x - \bar{X})^2$; it represents a contribution from the *quadratic* regression of y on x and vanishes if the relation between y and x is linear.

If ρ_2 denotes the correlation between e and $(x - \bar{X})^2$, the leading term in the bias may be expressed, alternatively, as

$$-\frac{\rho_2 S_e \sqrt{2 + \gamma_2}}{n} \tag{7.23}'$$

since the variance of $(x - \bar{X})^2$ is known to be $S_x^4(2 + \gamma_2)$, where $\gamma_2 = \kappa_4/S_x^4$ is Fisher's measure of relative kurtosis.

Finally, combining the bias in (7.23)' and the variance in (7.21), the mean square error of $\bar{y}_{lr}$, to terms of order $1/n^2$, is

$$\frac{S_y^2(1 - \rho^2)}{n}\left[1 + \frac{1 + \rho_2^2(2 + \gamma_2)}{n}\right] \tag{7.24}$$

This result suggests that if the kurtosis in the distribution of x is moderate, the large-sample formula for the variance of the regression estimate should be adequate in samples of size 50 or more.

A further consequence is that if n is large, so that terms in $1/n^2$ are negligible, an inefficient estimate b' of B can be used instead of the least squares estimate, since errors in b contribute only to terms in $1/n^2$. For instance, b might be computed from a subsample of the original data. Alternatively, if the units can be sorted conveniently into three equal-sized groups—low, middle, and high—according to the values of x, the estimate

$$b' = \frac{\bar{y}_{\text{high}} - \bar{y}_{\text{low}}}{\bar{x}_{\text{high}} - \bar{x}_{\text{low}}}$$

has an efficiency of about 8/9 (Bartlett, 1949).

7.5 FURTHER NOTES ON THE BIAS

In a finite population the leading term in the bias is obtained from (7.23) in section 7.4, except that in applying theorem 2.3 we do not let $N \to \infty$. The principal change is to bring in the fpc, giving,

$$\text{bias in } \bar{y}_{lr} \doteq -\frac{1 - f}{(n - 1)S_x^2}\left[\frac{\sum_{i}^{N} e_i(x_i - \bar{X})^2}{N - 1}\right]$$

The preceding analysis showed also that if the regression is linear in the infinite population, the leading term in the bias vanishes. Actually, it is a well-known result for infinite populations that if the regression is linear the bias vanishes completely, not merely its leading term. A corresponding result holds in finite populations if the regression of y on x is linear in the ordinary sense of this term. By a linear regression in a finite population, we mean that if

$$y_i = \bar{Y} + \beta(x_i - \bar{X}) + e_i \tag{7.25}$$

then $E(e_i \mid x_i) = 0$ for every fixed x_i. This implies that if a particular value of x appears on only one unit in the population, the value of e for that unit must be zero.

Theorem 7.4.　If the regression of y_i on x_i is linear, then

$$\bar{y}_{lr} = \bar{y} + b(\bar{X} - \bar{x})$$

where $b = \Sigma\,(y - \bar{y})(x_i - \bar{x})/\Sigma\,(x_i - \bar{x})^2$ is the least squares regression of y on x, is an unbiased estimate of $\bar{Y}$. The result requires that $\Sigma\,(x_i - \bar{x})^2 > 0$ in every sample. (If ν_{max} is the *largest* number of units in the population that all have the same value of x, the condition $\Sigma\,(x_i - \bar{x})^2 > 0$ is satisfied for any $n > \nu_{max}$.)

Proof. If (7.25) holds with $E(e_i \mid x_i) = 0$, it is easy to show that $\beta = B$, the population regression of y on x as defined in (7.5). From (7.25),

$$\sum_{}^{N} x_i(y_i - \bar{Y}) = \beta \sum_{}^{N} x_i(x_i - \bar{X}) + \sum_{}^{N} e_i x_i$$

Since $E(e_i \mid x_i) = 0$, $\displaystyle\sum^{N} e_i x_i = 0$, so that $\beta = B$. Hence, from (7.15) and (7.12),

$$\bar{y}_{lr} - \bar{Y} = \frac{(\bar{X} - \bar{x}) \displaystyle\sum^{n} e_i(x_i - \bar{x})}{\displaystyle\sum^{n} (x_i - \bar{x})^2} + \bar{e} \tag{7.26}$$

Now consider samples with the same set of values of x_i. Over such samples $(\bar{X} - \bar{x})$ and $\displaystyle\sum^{n}(x_i - \bar{x})^2$ remain constant. Further, if any value of x occurs m times in the sample and ν times in the population, each of the ν units will occur equally often in samples of this type. It follows that the average values of $\Sigma\,e_i(x_i - \bar{x})$ and $\bar{e}$ over this set of samples are both zero. Thus $E(\bar{y}_{lr} - \bar{Y}) = 0$ over this set of samples. Hence $\bar{y}_{lr}$ is unbiased over all simple random samples of size n.

7.6 COMPARISON WITH THE RATIO ESTIMATE AND THE MEAN PER UNIT

For these comparisons the sample size n must be large enough so that the approximate formulas for the variances of the ratio and regression estimates are valid. The three comparable variances for the estimated population mean $\bar{Y}$ are as follows:

$$V(\bar{y}_{lr}) = \frac{N - n}{Nn}\,S_y^{\,2}(1 - \rho^2) \qquad \text{(regression)}$$

$$V(\bar{y}_R) = \frac{N - n}{Nn}\,(S_y^{\,2} + R^2 S_x^{\,2} - 2R\rho S_y S_x) \qquad \text{(ratio)}$$

$$V(\bar{y}) = \frac{N - n}{Nn}\,S_y^{\,2} \qquad \text{(mean per unit)}$$

It is apparent that the variance of the regression estimate is smaller than that of the mean per unit unless $\rho = 0$, in which case the two variances are equal.

The variance of the regression estimate is less than that of the ratio estimate if

$$-\rho^2 S_y^{\,2} < R^2 S_x^{\,2} - 2R\rho S_y S_x$$

This is equivalent to the inequalities

$$(\rho S_y - RS_x)^2 > 0 \qquad \text{or} \qquad (B - R)^2 > 0$$

Thus the regression estimate is more precise than the ratio estimate unless $B = R$. This occurs when the relation between y_i and x_i is a straight line through the origin.

Example. The precision of the regression, ratio, and mean per unit estimates from a simple random sample can be compared by using data collected in the complete enumeration of peach orchards described on p. 174. In this example, y_i is the estimated peach production in an orchard and x_i the number of peach trees in the orchard. We will compare the estimates of the total production of the 256 orchards, made from a sample of 100 orchards. It is doubtful whether the sample is large enough to make the variance formulas fully valid, since the cv's of $\bar{y}$ and $\bar{x}$ are both somewhat higher than 10%, but the example will serve to illustrate the computations. The basic data are as follows:

$$S_y^{\,2} = 6409 \qquad S_{yx} = 4434 \qquad S_x^{\,2} = 3898$$
$$R = 1.270 \qquad \rho = 0.887 \qquad n = 100 \qquad N = 256$$

$$V(\hat{Y}_{lr}) = \frac{N(N - n)}{n} S_y^{\,2}(1 - \rho^2)$$

$$= \frac{(256)(156)}{100}(6409)(1 - 0.787) = 545{,}000$$

$$V(\hat{Y}_R) = \frac{N(N - n)}{n}(S_y^{\,2} + R^2 S_x^{\,2} - 2RS_{yx})$$

$$= \frac{(256)(156)}{100}[6409 + (1.613)(3898) - 2(1.270)(4434)]$$

$$= 573{,}000$$

$$V(\hat{Y}) = \frac{N(N - n)}{n} S_y^{\,2} = 2{,}559{,}000$$

There is little to choose between the regression and the ratio estimates, as might be expected from the nature of the variables. Both techniques are greatly superior to the mean per unit.

7.7 REGRESSION ESTIMATES IN STRATIFIED SAMPLING

As with the ratio estimate, two types of regression estimate can be made in stratified random sampling. In the first estimate $\bar{y}_{lrs}$ (s for separate), a separate regression estimate is computed for each stratum mean, that is,

$$\bar{y}_{lrh} = \bar{y}_h + b_h(\bar{X}_h - \bar{x}_h) \qquad (7.27)$$

Then

$$\bar{y}_{lrs} = \sum_h W_h \bar{y}_{lrh} \qquad (7.28)$$

This estimate is appropriate when it is thought that the true regression coefficients B_h vary from stratum to stratum.

The second regression estimate, $\bar{y}_{lrc}$ (c for combined), is appropriate when the B_h are presumed to be the same in all strata. To compute $\bar{y}_{lrc}$, we first find

$$\bar{y}_{st} = \sum_h W_h \bar{y}_h \qquad \bar{x}_{st} = \sum_h W_h \bar{x}_h$$

Then

$$\bar{y}_{lrc} = \bar{y}_{st} + b(\bar{X} - \bar{x}_{st}) \qquad (7.29)$$

The two estimates will be considered first in the case in which the b_h and b are chosen in advance, since their properties are unusually simple in this situation. From section 7.2, $\bar{y}_{lrh}$ is an unbiased estimate of $\bar{Y}_h$, so that $\bar{y}_{lrs}$ is an unbiased estimate of $\bar{Y}$. Further, since sampling is independent in different strata, it follows from theorem 7.1 that

$$V(\bar{y}_{lrs}) = \sum_h \frac{W_h^2(1 - f_h)}{n_h}(S_{yh}^2 - 2b_h S_{yxh} + b_h^2 S_{xh}^2) \qquad (7.30)$$

Theorem 7.2 shows that $V(\bar{y}_{lrs})$ is minimized when $b_h = B_h$, the true regression coefficient in stratum h. The minimum value of the variance may be written

$$V_{min}(\bar{y}_{lrs}) = \sum_h \frac{W_h^2(1 - f_h)}{n_h}\left(S_{yh}^2 - \frac{S_{yxh}^2}{S_{xh}^2}\right) \qquad (7.31)$$

Turning to the combined estimate with preassigned b, (7.29) shows that $\bar{y}_{lrc}$ is also an unbiased estimate of $\bar{Y}$. Since $\bar{y}_{lrc}$ is the usual estimate from a stratified sample for the variate $\bar{y}_{hi} + b(\bar{X} - x_{hi})$, we may apply theorem 5.3 to this variate, giving the result

$$V(\bar{y}_{lrc}) = \sum_h \frac{W_h^2(1 - f_h)}{n_h}(S_{yh}^2 - 2b S_{yxh} + b^2 S_{xh}^2) \qquad (7.32)$$

The value of b which minimizes this variance is

$$B_c = \sum_h \frac{W_h^2(1 - f_h)S_{yxh}}{n_h} \Big/ \sum_h \frac{W_h^2(1 - f_h)S_{xh}^2}{n_h} \qquad (7.33)$$

The quantity B_c is a weighted mean of the stratum regression coefficients $B_h = S_{yxh}/S_{xh}^2$. If we write

$$a_h = \frac{W_h^2(1 - f_h)}{n_h} S_{xh}^2$$

then $B_c = \sum a_h B_h / \sum a_h$.

From (7.31) and (7.32), with B_c in place of b, we find

$$V_{min}(\bar{y}_{lrc}) - V_{min}(\bar{y}_{lrs}) = \sum a_h B_h^2 - (\sum a_h) B_c^2$$
$$= \sum a_h (B_h - B_c)^2 \tag{7.34}$$

This result shows that with the optimum choices the separate estimate has a smaller variance than the combined estimate unless B_h is the same in all strata.

7.8 REGRESSION COEFFICIENTS ESTIMATED FROM THE SAMPLE

The preceding analysis is helpful in indicating the type of sample estimates b_h and b that may be efficient when used in regression estimates. With the separate estimate, the analysis suggests that we take

$$b_h = \frac{\sum\limits_i (y_{hi} - \bar{y}_h)(x_{hi} - \bar{x}_h)}{\sum\limits_i (x_{hi} - \bar{x}_h)^2}$$

the within-stratum least squares estimate of B_h.
Applying theorem 7.3 to each stratum, we have

$$V(\bar{y}_{lrs}) = \sum_h \frac{W_h^2 (1 - f_h)}{n_h} S_{yh}^2 (1 - \rho_h^2) \tag{7.35}$$

provided that the sample size n_h is large in all strata. To obtain a sample estimate of variance, substitute

$$s_{y \cdot xh}^2 = \frac{1}{n_h - 2} \left[\sum_i (y_{hi} - \bar{y}_h)^2 - b_h^2 \sum_i (x_{hi} - \bar{x}_h)^2 \right]$$

in place of $S_{yh}^2 (1 - \rho_h^2)$ in (7.35).

The estimate $\bar{y}_{lrs}$ suffers from the same difficulty as the corresponding ratio estimate, in that the ratio of the bias to the standard error may become appreciable. If follows from section 7.5 that the regression estimates $\bar{y}_{lrh}$ in the individual strata may have biases of order $1/n_h$ and the biases may be of the same sign in all strata, so that the over-all bias in $\bar{y}_{lrs}$ may also be of order $1/n_h$. Since the leading term in the bias comes from the quadratic regression of y_{hi} on x_{hi}, as shown in section 7.5, this danger is most acute when the relation between the variates approximate the quadratic rather than the linear type.

With the combined estimate, we saw that the variance is minimized when $b = B_c$, as defined in (7.33). This suggests that we take

$$b_c = \sum_h \frac{W_h^2 (1 - f_h)}{n_h(n_h - 1)} \sum_i (y_{hi} - \bar{y}_h)(x_{hi} - \bar{x}_h) \Big/ \sum_h \frac{W_h^2 (1 - f_h)}{n_h(n_h - 1)} \sum_i (x_{hi} - \bar{x}_h)^2$$

as a sample estimate of B_c. If the stratification is proportional and if we may replace the $(n_h - 1)$ in b_c by n_h, b_c reduces to the familiar pooled least squares estimate

$$b_c' = \sum_h \sum_i (y_{hi} - \bar{y}_h)(x_{hi} - \bar{x}_h) \Big/ \sum_h \sum_i (x_{hi} - \bar{x}_h)^2$$

In certain circumstances other estimates may be preferable to b_c or b_c'. For instance, if the true regression coefficients B_h are the same in all strata but the residual variances about the regression line differ substantially from one stratum to another, a different weighted mean of the b_h, weighting inversely as the estimated variance, may be more precise. However, the gain in precision as it affects $\bar{y}_{lrc}$ is likely to be small.

Since

$$\bar{y}_{lrc} - \bar{Y} = \bar{y}_{st} - \bar{Y} + b_c(\bar{X} - \bar{x}_{st})$$

$$= [\bar{y}_{st} - \bar{Y} + B_c(\bar{X} - \bar{x}_{st})] + (b_c - B_c)(\bar{X} - \bar{x}_{st})$$

it follows that if sampling errors of b_c are negligible

$$V(\bar{y}_{lrc}) = \sum_h \frac{W_h^2(1 - f_h)}{n_h} (S_{yh}^2 - 2B_c S_{yxh} + B_c^2 S_{xh}^2)$$

Further examination of the structure of b_c and b_c' shows that they are in general biased. If stratification is proportional and the residual variance about the regression line is approximately the same in all strata, the resulting bias in $\bar{y}_{lrc}$ is of order $1/n$, as is the contribution of $V(b_c)$ to the variance of $\bar{y}_{lrc}$. If, however, the contribution of one stratum to the variance is predominating, say the hth stratum, the contribution of $V(b_c)$ to $V(\bar{y}_{lrc})$ may be as large as $1/n_h$.

As an estimate of $V(\bar{y}_{lrc})$, we may take

$$v(\bar{y}_{lrc}) = \sum_h \frac{W_h^2(1 - f_h)}{n_h(n_h - 1)} \sum_i [(y_{hi} - \bar{y}_h) - b_c(x_{hc} - \bar{x}_h)]^2$$

The sum over i may, of course, be computed as

$$\sum_i (y_{hi} - \bar{y}_h)^2 - 2b_c \sum_i (y_{hi} - \bar{y}_h)(x_{hi} - \bar{x}_h) + b_c^2 \sum_i (x_{hi} - \bar{x}_h)^2$$

7.9 COMPARISON OF THE TWO TYPES OF REGRESSION ESTIMATE

Hard and fast rules cannot be given to decide whether the separate or the combined estimate is better in any specific situation: some exercise of judgment is required in making a choice. The defects of the separate estimate are that it is more liable to bias when samples are small within the individual strata and that its variance has a larger contribution from sampling errors in the regression coefficients. The defect of the combined estimate is that its variance is inflated if the population regression coefficients differ from stratum to stratum.

If we are confident that the regressions are linear and if B_h appears to be the same in all strata, so far as can be judged, the combined estimate is to be preferred. If the regressions appear linear (so that the danger of bias seems small) but B_h seems to vary from stratum to stratum, the separate estimate is advisable. If there is some curvilinearity in the regressions when a linear regression estimate is used, the combined estimate is probably safer unless the samples are large in all strata.

The development of estimates of the regression type that are unbiased has been discussed by Mickey (1959), but these estimates have not yet been extensively tried.

EXERCISES

7.1 An experienced farmer makes an eye estimate of the weight of peaches x_i on each tree in an orchard of $N = 200$ trees. He finds a total weight of $X = 11,600$ lb. The peaches are picked and weighed on a simple random sample of 10 trees, with the following results:

Tree Number

		1	2	3	4	5	6	7	8	9	10	Total
Actual wt.	y_i	61	42	50	58	67	45	39	57	71	53	543
Est. wt.	x_i	59	47	52	60	67	48	44	58	76	58	569

As an estimate of the total actual weight Y, we take

$$\hat{Y} = N[\bar{X} + (\bar{y} - \bar{x})]$$

Compute the estimate and find its standard error.

7.2 Does it appear that the linear regression estimate, with the sample least squares b, would give a more precise estimate in 7.1?

7.3 From the sample data in Table 6.1 (p. 156) compute the regression estimate of the 1930 total number of inhabitants in the 196 large cities. Find the approximate standard error of this estimate and compare its precision with that of the ratio estimate.

7.4 In exercise 7.3 find the estimated total number of inhabitants and its standard error if b is taken as 1.

7.5 In the following population with $N = 5$, verify (a) that the regression of y on x is linear and (b) that the linear regression estimate is unbiased in simple random samples with $n = 3$. The (y, x) pairs are (3, 0), (5, 0), (8, 2), (8, 3), (12, 3).

7.6 A rough measurement x, made on each unit, is related to the true measurement y on the unit by the equation

$$x = y + e + d$$

where d is a constant bias and e is an error of measurement, uncorrelated with y, which has mean zero and variance S_e^2 in the population, assumed infinite. In simple random samples of size n compare the variances of (a) the "difference" estimate $[\bar{y} + (\bar{X} - \bar{x})]$ of the mean $\bar{Y}$ and (b) the linear regression estimate, using the value of b which gives minimum variance. (The variances may depend on S_y^2).

7.7 By working out all possible cases, compare the precisions of the separate and combined regression estimates of the total Y of the following population, when simple random samples of size 2 are drawn from each stratum:

Stratum 1		Stratum 2	
x_{1i}	y_{1i}	x_{2i}	y_{2i}
4	0	5	7
6	3	6	12
7	5	8	13

Use the ordinary least squares estimates of the B's, b_h and b_c on p. 202.

REFERENCES

Bartlett, M. S. (1949). Fitting a straight line when both variables are subject to error. *Biometrics*, **5**, 207–212.

Cochran, W. G. (1942). Sampling theory when the sampling units are of unequal sizes. *Jour. Amer. Stat. Assoc.*, **37**, 199–212.

Mickey, M. R. (1959). Some finite population unbiased ratio and regression estimators. *Jour. Amer. Stat. Assoc.*, **54**, 594–612.

Watson, D. J. (1937). The estimation of leaf areas. *Jour. Agr. Sci.*, **27**, 474.

Yates, F. (1960). *Sampling methods for censuses and surveys*. Charles Griffin and Co., London, third edition.

CHAPTER 8

Systematic Sampling

8.1 DESCRIPTION

This method of sampling is at first sight quite different from simple random sampling. Suppose that the N units in the population are numbered 1 to N in some order. To select a sample of n units, we take a unit at random from the first k units and every kth unit thereafter. For instance, if k is 15 and if the first unit drawn is number 13, the subsequent units are numbers 28, 43, 58, and so on. The selection of the first unit determines the whole sample. This type is called an *every kth* systematic sample.

The apparent advantages of this method over simple random sampling are as follows:

1. It is easier to draw a sample and often easier to execute without mistakes. This is a particular advantage when the drawing is done in the field. Even when drawing is done in an office there may be a substantial saving in time. For instance, if the units are described on cards that are all of the same size and lie in a file drawer, a card can be drawn out every inch along the file as measured by a ruler. This operation is speedy, whereas simple random sampling would be slow. Of course, this method departs slightly from the strict "every kth" rule.

2. Intuitively, systematic sampling seems likely to be more precise than simple random sampling. In effect, it stratifies the population into n strata, which consist of the first k units, the second k units, and so on. We might therefore expect the systematic sample to be about as precise as the corresponding stratified random sample with *one* unit per stratum. The difference is that with the systematic sample the units occur at the same relative position in the stratum, whereas with the stratified random sample the position in the stratum is determined separately by randomization within each stratum (see Fig. 8.1). The systematic sample is spread more evenly over the population, and this fact has sometimes made systematic sampling considerably more precise than stratified random sampling.

206

× = systematic sample   ○ = stratified random sample

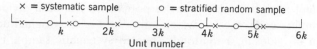

Unit number

Fig. 8.1 Systematic and stratified random sampling.

One variant of the systematic sample is to choose each unit at or near the center of the stratum; that is, instead of starting the sequence by a random number chosen between 1 and k, we take the starting number as $(k + 1)/2$ if k is odd and either $k/2$ or $(k + 2)/2$ if k is even. This procedure carries the idea of systematic sampling to its logical conclusion. If y_i can be considered a continuous function of a continuous variable i, there are grounds for expecting that this centrally located sample will be more precise than one randomly located. Little investigation of the efficacy of centrally located samples has been made for the types of population usually encountered in sample surveys, and attention will be confined to randomly located samples.

Since N is not in general an integral multiple of k, different systematic samples from the same finite population may vary by one unit in size. Thus, with $N = 23$, $k = 5$, the numbers of the units in the five systematic samples are shown in Table 8.1. The first three samples have $n = 5$ and the last

TABLE 8.1

THE POSSIBLE SYSTEMATIC SAMPLES FOR $N = 23$, $k = 5$

Systematic sample number

I	II	III	IV	V
1	2	3	4	5
6	7	8	9	10
11	12	13	14	15
16	17	18	19	20
21	22	23		

two have $n = 4$. This fact introduces a disturbance into the theory of systematic sampling. The disturbance is probably negligible if n exceeds 50 and will be ignored, for simplicity, in the presentation of theory. It is unlikely to be large even when n is small.

8.2 RELATION TO CLUSTER SAMPLING

There is another way of looking at systematic sampling. With $N = nk$, the k possible systematic samples are shown in the columns of Table 8.2.

It is evident from this table that the population has been divided into k large sampling units, each of which contains n of the original units. The operation of choosing a randomly located systematic sample is just the operation of choosing *one* of these large sampling units at random. Thus systematic sampling amounts to the selection of a *single* complex sampling

TABLE 8.2
COMPOSITION OF THE k SYSTEMATIC SAMPLES

Sample number

1	2	$\cdots$	i	$\cdots$	k
y_1	y_2		y_i		y_k
y_{k+1}	y_{k+2}		y_{k+i}		y_{2k}
$\cdots$	$\cdots$		$\cdots$		$\cdots$
$y_{(n-1)k+1}$	$y_{(n-1)k+2}$		$y_{(n-1)k+i}$		y_{nk}
Means $\bar{y}_1$	$\bar{y}_2$		$\bar{y}_i$		$\bar{y}_k$

unit which constitutes the whole sample. A systematic sample is a simple random sample of one cluster unit from a population of k cluster units.

8.3 VARIANCE OF THE ESTIMATED MEAN

Several formulas have been developed for the variance of $\bar{y}_{sy}$, the mean of a systematic sample. The three given below apply to any kind of cluster sampling in which the clusters contain n elements and the sample consists of one cluster.

If $N = nk$, it is easy to verify that $\bar{y}_{sy}$ is an unbiased estimate of $\bar{Y}$ for a randomly located systematic sample. If $N \neq nk$, this result does not hold, although the bias is unlikely to be important. The bias can be avoided by allotting a higher probability of selection to certain samples. Consider the example in Table 8.1. If a probability of selection $\frac{5}{23}$ is given to each of the first three samples and a probability $\frac{4}{23}$ to each of the last two, the sample mean is unbiased. A method of sample selection which has this property is to draw a random number between 1 and N, and take every kth unit thereafter, *going both forward and backward*. Thus, in Table 8.1, systematic sample I is drawn if the random number is 1, 6, 11, 16, or 21. Clearly, the probability is $\frac{5}{23}$ of selecting samples, I, II, or III, as against $\frac{4}{23}$ of selecting IV or V.

In the following analysis the symbol y_{ij} denotes the jth member of the ith systematic sample, so that $j = 1, 2, \cdots, n$, $i = 1, 2, \cdots, k$. The mean of the ith sample is denoted by $\bar{y}_{i.}$.

Theorem 8.1. The variance of the mean of a systematic sample is

$$V(\bar{y}_{sy}) = \frac{N-1}{N} S^2 - \frac{k(n-1)}{N} S^2_{wsy} \tag{8.1}$$

where

$$S^2_{wsy} = \frac{1}{k(n-1)} \sum_{i=1}^{k} \sum_{j=1}^{n} (y_{ij} - \bar{y}_{i.})^2$$

is the variance among units that lie within the same systematic sample. The denominator of this variance, $k(n-1)$, is constructed by the usual rules in the analysis of variance: each of the k samples contributes $(n-1)$ degrees of freedom to the sum of squares in the numerator.

Proof. By the usual identity of the analysis of variance

$$(N-1)S^2 = \sum_i \sum_j (y_{ij} - \bar{Y})^2$$
$$= n \sum_i (\bar{y}_{i.} - \bar{Y})^2 + \sum_i \sum_j (y_{ij} - \bar{y}_{i.})^2$$

But the variance of $\bar{y}_{sy}$ is by definition

$$V(\bar{y}_{sy}) = \frac{1}{k} \sum_{i=1}^{k} (\bar{y}_{i.} - \bar{Y})^2$$

Hence

$$(N-1)S^2 = nkV(\bar{y}_{sy}) + k(n-1)S^2_{wsy}$$

The result follows.

Corollary. The mean of a systematic sample is more precise than the mean of a simple random sample if and only if

$$S^2_{wsy} > S^2 \tag{8.2}$$

Proof. If $\bar{y}$ is the mean of a simple random sample of size n,

$$V(\bar{y}) = \frac{N-n}{N} \frac{S^2}{n}$$

From (8.1), $V(\bar{y}_{sy}) < V(\bar{y})$ if and only if

$$\frac{N-1}{N} S^2 - \frac{k(n-1)}{N} S^2_{wsy} < \frac{N-n}{N} \frac{S^2}{n}$$

that is, if

$$k(n-1)S^2_{wsy} > \left(N - 1 - \frac{N-n}{n}\right)S^2 = k(n-1)S^2$$

This important result, which applies to cluster sampling in general, states that systematic sampling is more precise than simple random sampling if the variance within the systematic samples is *larger* than the population variance as a whole. Systematic sampling is precise when units within the same sample are heterogeneous and is imprecise when they are homogeneous. The result is obvious intuitively. If there is little variation within a systematic sample relative to that in the population, the successive units in the sample are repeating more or less the same information.

Another form for the variance is given in theorem 8.2.

Theorem 8.2.

$$V(\bar{y}_{sy}) = \frac{S^2}{n}\left(\frac{N-1}{N}\right)[1 + (n-1)\rho_w] \qquad (8.3)$$

where ρ_w is the correlation coefficient between pairs of units that are in the same systematic sample. It is defined as

$$\rho_w = \frac{E(y_{ij} - \bar{Y})(y_{iu} - \bar{Y})}{E(y_{ij} - \bar{Y})^2}$$

where the numerator is averaged over all $kn(n-1)/2$ distinct pairs, and the denominator over all N values of y_{ij}. Since the denominator is $(N-1)S^2/N$, this gives

$$\rho_w = \frac{2}{(n-1)(N-1)S^2} \sum_{i=1}^{k} \sum_{j<u} (y_{ij} - \bar{Y})(y_{iu} - \bar{Y})$$

Proof.

$$n^2 k V(\bar{y}_{sy}) = n^2 \sum_{i=1}^{k} (\bar{y}_{i.} - \bar{Y})^2$$

$$= \sum_{i=1}^{k} [(y_{i1} - \bar{Y}) + (y_{i2} - \bar{Y}) + \cdots + (y_{in} - \bar{Y})]^2$$

The squared terms amount to the total sum of squares of deviations from $\bar{Y}$, that is, to $(N-1)S^2$. This gives

$$n^2 k V(\bar{y}_{sy}) = (N-1)S^2 + 2\sum_{i}\sum_{j<u}(y_{ij} - \bar{Y})(y_{iu} - \bar{Y}) ,$$

$$= (N-1)S^2 + (n-1)(N-1)S^2\rho_w$$

Hence

$$V(\bar{y}_{sy}) = \frac{S^2}{n}\left(\frac{N-1}{N}\right)[1 + (n-1)\rho_w]$$

This result shows that positive correlation between units in the same sample inflates the variance of the sample mean. Even a small positive correlation may have a large effect, because of the multiplier $(n-1)$.

The two preceding theorems express $V(\bar{y}_{sy})$ in terms of S^2, hence relate it to the variance for a simple random sample. There is an analogue of theorem 8.2 which expresses $V(\bar{y}_{sy})$ in terms of the variance for a stratified random sample in which the strata are composed of the first k units, the second k units, and so on. In our notation the subscript j in y_{ij} denotes the stratum. The stratum mean is written $\bar{y}_{.j}$.

Theorem 8.3.

$$V(\bar{y}_{sy}) = \frac{S_{wst}^2}{n}\left(\frac{N-n}{N}\right)\left[1 + (n-1)\rho_{wst}\right] \qquad (8.4)$$

where

$$S_{wst}^2 = \frac{1}{n(k-1)} \sum_{j=1}^{n}\sum_{i=1}^{k}(y_{ij} - \bar{y}_{.j})^2$$

This is the variance among units that lie in the same stratum. The divisor $n(k-1)$ is used because each of the n strata contributes $(k-1)$ degrees of freedom. Further

$$\rho_{wst} = \frac{E(y_{ij} - \bar{y}_{.j})(y_{iu} - \bar{y}_{.u})}{E(y_{ij} - \bar{y}_{.j})^2}$$

This quantity is the correlation between the deviations from the stratum means of pairs of items that are in the same systematic sample.

$$\rho_{wst} = \frac{2}{n(n-1)(k-1)} \sum_{i=1}^{k}\sum_{j<u} \frac{(y_{ij} - \bar{y}_{.j})(y_{iu} - \bar{y}_{.u})}{S_{wst}^2} \qquad (8.5)$$

The proof is similar to that of theorem 8.2.*

Corollary. A systematic sample has the same precision as the corresponding stratified random sample, with one unit per stratum, if $\rho_{wst} = 0$. This follows because for this type of stratified random sample $V(\bar{y}_{st})$ is (theorem 5.3, corollary 3)

$$V(\bar{y}_{st}) = \left(\frac{N-n}{N}\right)\frac{S_{wst}^2}{n}$$

Other formulas for $V(\bar{y}_{sy})$, appropriate to an autocorrelated population, have been given by W. G. and L. H. Madow (1944), who made the first theoretical study of the precision of systematic sampling.

Example. The data in Table 8.3 are for a small artificial population which exhibits a fairly steady rising trend. We have $N = 40$, $k = 10$, $n = 4$. Each column represents a systematic sample, and the rows are the strata. The example illustrates the situation in which the "within-stratum" correlation is positive. For instance, in the first sample each of the four numbers 0, 6, 18, and 26 lies below the mean of the stratum to which it belongs. This is consistently true, with a

* In the first edition slightly different definitions of ρ_w and ρ_{wst} were used.

few exceptions, in the first five systematic samples. In the last five samples, deviations from the strata means are mostly positive. Thus the cross-product terms in ρ_{wst} are predominantly positive. From theorem 8.3 we expect systematic sampling to be less precise than stratified random sampling with one unit per stratum.

TABLE 8.3

DATA FOR 10 SYSTEMATIC SAMPLES WITH $n = 4$, $N = kn = 40$

Strata	Systematic sample numbers										Strata means
	1	2	3	4	5	6	7	8	9	10	
I	0	1	1	2	5	4	7	7	8	6	4.1
II	6	8	9	10	13	12	15	16	16	17	12.2
III	18	19	20	20	24	23	25	28	29	27	23.3
IV	26	30	31	31	33	32	35	37	38	38	33.1
Totals	50	58	61	63	75	71	82	88	91	88	72.7

The variance $V(\bar{y}_{sy})$ is found directly from the systematic sample totals as

$$V(\bar{y}_{sy}) = V_{sy} = \frac{1}{k} \sum_{i=1}^{k} (\bar{y}_{i.} - \overline{Y})^2 = \frac{1}{n^2 k} \sum_{i=1}^{k} (n\bar{y}_{i.} - n\overline{Y})^2$$

$$= \frac{1}{160} \left[(50)^2 + (58)^2 + \cdots + (88)^2 - \frac{(727)^2}{10} \right] = 11.63$$

For random and stratified random sampling, we need an analysis of variance of the population into "between rows" and "within rows." This is presented in

TABLE 8.4

ANALYSIS OF VARIANCE

	df	ss	ms
Between rows (strata)	3	4828.3	
Within strata	36	485.5	$13.49 = S_{wst}^2$
Totals	39	5313.8	$136.25 = S^2$

Table 8.4. Hence the variances of the estimated means from simple random and stratified random samples are as follows:

$$V_{ran} = \left(\frac{N - n}{N} \right) \frac{S^2}{n} = \frac{9}{10} \cdot \frac{136.25}{4} = 30.66$$

$$V_{st} = \left(\frac{N - n}{N} \right) \frac{S_{wst}^2}{n} = \frac{9}{10} \cdot \frac{13.49}{4} = 3.04$$

Both stratified random sampling and systematic sampling are much more effective than simple random sampling, but, as anticipated, systematic sampling is less precise than stratified random sampling.

Table 8.5 shows the same data, with the order of the observations *reversed* in the second and fourth strata. This has the effect of making ρ_{wst} negative, because it makes the majority of the cross products between deviations from the strata means negative for pairs of observations that lie

TABLE 8.5

DATA IN TABLE 8.3, WITH THE ORDER REVERSED IN STRATA II AND IV

Strata	Systematic sample numbers										Strata means
	1	2	3	4	5	6	7	8	9	10	
I	0	1	1	2	5	4	7	7	8	6	4.1
II	17	16	16	15	12	13	10	9	8	6	12.2
III	18	19	20	20	24	23	25	28	29	27	23.3
IV	38	38	37	35	32	33	31	31	30	26	33.1
Totals	73	74	74	72	73	73	73	75	75	65	72.7

in the same systematic sample. In the first systematic sample, for instance, the deviations from the strata means are now -4.1, $+4.8$, -5.3, $+4.9$. Of the six products of pairs of deviations, four are negative. Roughly the same situation applies in every systematic sample.

This change does not affect V_{ran} and V_{st}. With systematic sampling, it brings about a dramatic increase in precision, as is seen when the systematic sample totals in Table 8.5 are compared with those in Table 8.3. We now have

$$V_{sy} = \frac{1}{160}\left[(73)^2 + (74)^2 + \cdots + (65)^2 - \frac{(727)^2}{10}\right] = 0.46$$

It is sometimes possible to exploit this result by numbering the units to create negative correlations within strata. Accurate knowledge of the trends within the population is required. However, as will be seen later, the situation in Table 8.5 is one in which it is difficult to obtain from the sample a good estimate of the standard error of $\bar{y}_{sy}$.

8.4 COMPARISON OF SYSTEMATIC WITH STRATIFIED RANDOM SAMPLING

The performance of systematic sampling in relation to that of stratified or simple random sampling is greatly dependent on the properties of the population. There are populations for which systematic sampling is extremely precise and others for which it is less precise than simple random sampling. For some populations and some values of n, $V(\bar{y}_{sy})$ may even *increase* when a larger sample is taken—a startling departure from good behavior. Thus it is difficult to give general advice about the situations in which systematic sampling is to be recommended. A knowledge of the structure of the population is necessary for its most effective use.

Two lines of research on this problem have been followed. One is to compare the different types of sampling on artificial populations in which y_i is some simple function of i. The other is to make the comparisons for natural populations. Some of the principal results are presented in the succeeding sections.

8.5 POPULATIONS IN "RANDOM" ORDER

Systematic sampling is sometimes used, for its convenience, in populations in which the numbering of the units is effectively random. This is so in sampling from a file arranged alphabetically by surnames, if the item that is being measured has no relation to the surname of the individual. There will then be no trend or stratification in y_i as we proceed along the file and no correlation between neighboring values.

In this situation we would expect systematic sampling to be essentially equivalent to simple random sampling and to have the same variance. For any single finite population, with given values of n and k, this is not exactly true, because V_{sy}, which is based on only k degrees of freedom, is rather erratic when k is small and may turn out to be either greater or smaller than V_{ran}. There are two results which show that on the average the two variances are equal.

Theorem 8.4. Consider all $N!$ finite populations which are formed by the $N!$ permutations of any set of numbers $y_1, y_2, \cdots, y_N$. Then, on the average over these finite populations,

$$E(V_{sy}) = V_{ran}$$

Note that V_{ran} is the same for all permutations.

This result, proved by W. G. and L. H. Madow (1944), shows that, if the order of the items in a specific finite population can be regarded as drawn at random from the $N!$ permutations, systematic sampling is on the average equivalent to simple random sampling.

The second approach is to regard the finite population as drawn at random from an infinite superpopulation which has certain properties. The result that is proved does not apply to any single finite population (i.e., to any specific set of values $y_1, y_2, \cdots, y_N$) but to the average of all finite populations that can be drawn from the infinite population. This approach may appear at first sight to have little relation to practical applications, but this impression is erroneous. Any sampling method is used in practice on a series of finite populations. One way of describing the class of finite populations for which a given sampling method is efficient is to describe the infinite superpopulation from which such finite populations might have been drawn at random.

The symbol $\mathscr{E}$ denotes averages over all finite populations which can be drawn from this superpopulation.

Theorem 8.5. If the variates y_i $(i = 1, 2, \cdots, N)$ are drawn at random from a superpopulation in which

$$\mathscr{E}y_i = \mu, \qquad \mathscr{E}(y_i - \mu)(y_j - \mu) = 0 \quad (i \neq j), \qquad \mathscr{E}(y_i - \mu)^2 = \sigma_i{}^2$$

then

$$\mathscr{E}V_{sy} = \mathscr{E}V_{ran}$$

The crucial conditions are that all y_i have the same mean μ, that is, there is no trend, and that no linear correlation exists between the values y_i and y_j at two different points. The variance $\sigma_i{}^2$ may change from point to point in the series.

Proof. For any specific finite population,

$$V_{ran} = \frac{N - n}{Nn} \frac{\sum\limits_{i=1}^{N} (y_i - \bar{Y})^2}{N - 1}$$

Now

$$\sum_{i=1}^{N} (y_i - \bar{Y})^2 = \sum_{i=1}^{N} [(y_i - \mu) - (\bar{Y} - \mu)]^2$$

$$= \sum_{i=1}^{N} (y_i - \mu)^2 - N(\bar{Y} - \mu)^2$$

Since y_i and y_j are uncorrelated $(i \neq j)$,

$$\mathscr{E}(\bar{Y} - \mu)^2 = \frac{1}{N^2} \sum_{i=1}^{N} \sigma_i{}^2$$

Hence

$$\mathscr{E}V_{ran} = \frac{N - n}{Nn(N - 1)} \left(\sum_{i=1}^{N} \sigma_i{}^2 - N \frac{\sum \sigma_i{}^2}{N^2} \right)$$

This gives

$$\mathscr{E}V_{ran} = \frac{N - n}{N^2 n} \sum_{i=1}^{N} \sigma_i{}^2$$

Turning to V_{sy}, let $\bar{y}_u$ denote the mean of the uth systematic sample. For any specific finite population,

$$V_{sy} = \frac{1}{k} \sum_{u=1}^{k} (\bar{y}_u - \bar{Y})^2$$

$$= \frac{1}{k} \left[\sum_{u=1}^{k} (\bar{y}_u - \mu)^2 - k(\bar{Y} - \mu)^2 \right]$$

By the theorem for the variance of the mean of an uncorrelated sample from an infinite population,

$$\mathscr{E}V_{sy} = \frac{1}{k} \left(\frac{\sum_{i=1}^{N} \sigma_i^2}{n^2} - \frac{k \sum_{i=1}^{N} \sigma_i^2}{N^2} \right)$$

$$= \frac{N-n}{N^2 n} \sum_{i=1}^{N} \sigma_i^2 = \mathscr{E}V_{ran}$$

8.6 POPULATIONS WITH LINEAR TREND

If the population consists solely of a linear trend, as illustrated in Fig. 8.2, it is fairly easy to guess the nature of the results. From Fig. 8.2, it looks as if V_{sy} and V_{st} (with one unit per stratum) will both be smaller than V_{ran}. Further, V_{sy} will be larger than V_{st}, for if the systematic sample is too low in one stratum it is too low in all strata, whereas stratified random sampling gives an opportunity for within-stratum errors to cancel.

To examine the effects mathematically, we may assume that $y_i = i$. We have

$$\sum_{i=1}^{N} i = \frac{N(N+1)}{2}, \qquad \sum_{i=1}^{N} i^2 = \frac{N(N+1)(2N+1)}{6}$$

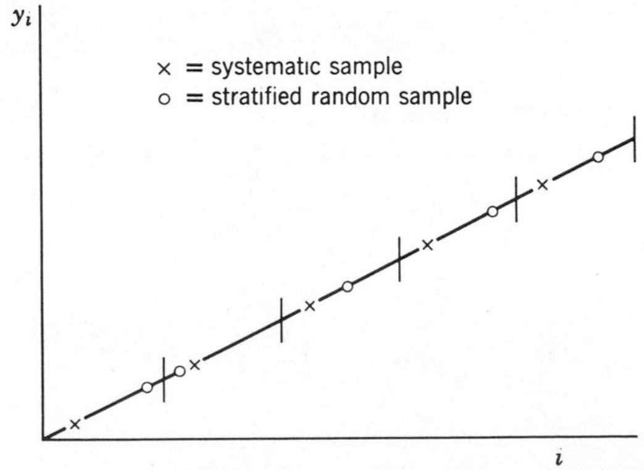

Fig. 8.2 Systematic sampling in a population with linear trend.

The population variance S^2 is given by

$$S^2 = \frac{1}{N-1}(\sum y_i{}^2 - N\bar{Y}^2)$$

$$= \frac{1}{N-1}\left[\frac{N(N+1)(2N+1)}{6} - \frac{N(N+1)^2}{4}\right] = \frac{N(N+1)}{12} \quad (8.6)$$

Hence the variance of the mean of a simple random sample is

$$V_{ran} = \frac{N-n}{N}\cdot\frac{S^2}{n} = \frac{n(k-1)}{N}\cdot\frac{N(N+1)}{12n} = \frac{(k-1)(N+1)}{12} \quad (8.7)$$

To find the variance within strata, $S_w{}^2$, we need only replace N by k in (8.6). This gives

$$V_{st} = \frac{N-n}{N}\cdot\frac{S_w{}^2}{n} = \frac{n(k-1)}{nk}\cdot\frac{k(k+1)}{12n} = \frac{(k^2-1)}{12n} \quad (8.8)$$

For systematic sampling, the mean of the second sample exceeds that of the first by 1; the mean of the third exceeds that of the second by 1, and so on. Thus the means $\bar{y}_u$ may be replaced by the numbers $1, 2, \cdots, k$. Hence, by a further application of (8.6),

$$\sum_{u=1}^{k}(\bar{y}_u - \bar{Y})^2 = \frac{k(k^2-1)}{12}$$

This gives

$$V_{sy} = \frac{1}{k}\sum(\bar{y}_u - \bar{Y})^2 = \frac{k^2-1}{12} \quad (8.9)$$

From the formulas (8.7), (8.8), and (8.9) we deduce, as anticipated,

$$V_{st} = \frac{k^2-1}{12n} \leq V_{sy} = \frac{k^2-1}{12} \leq V_{ran} = \frac{(k-1)(N+1)}{12}$$

Equality occurs only when $n = 1$. Thus, for removing the effect of a linear trend, suspected or unsuspected, the systematic sample is much more effective than the simple random sample but less effective than the stratified random sample.

The performance of systematic sampling in the presence of a linear trend can be improved in several ways. One is to use a centrally located sample. Another is to change the estimate from an unweighted to a weighted mean in which all internal members of the sample have weight unity (before division by n) but different weights are given to the first and last members. If the random number drawn between 1 and k is i, these weights are

$$1 \pm \frac{n(2i-k-1)}{2(n-1)k}$$

the $+$ sign being used for the first member, the $-$ sign for the last. For any i, the two weights obviously add to 2. The reader may verify that if the population consists of a linear trend and $N = nk$ the weighted sample mean gives the correct population mean. The performance of these *end corrections* has been examined by Yates (1948), to whom they are due.

8.7 POPULATIONS WITH PERIODIC VARIATION

If the population consists of a periodic trend, for example a simple sine curve, the effectiveness of the systematic sample depends on the value of k. This may be seen pictorially in Fig. 8.3. In this representation the height of the curve is the observation y_i. The sample points A represent the case least favorable to the systematic sample. This case holds whenever k is equal to the period of the sine curve or is an integral multiple of the period. Every observation within the systematic sample is exactly the same, so that the sample is no more precise than a single observation taken at random from the population.

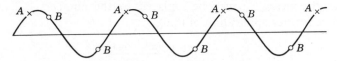

Fig. 8.3 Periodic variation.

The most favorable case (sample B) occurs when k is an odd multiple of the half-period. Every systematic sample has a mean exactly equal to the true population mean, since successive deviations above and below the middle line cancel. The sampling variance of the mean is therefore zero. Between these two cases the sample has various degrees of effectiveness, depending on the relation between k and the wavelength.

Populations that exhibit an exact sine curve are not likely to be encountered in practice. Populations with a more or less definite periodic trend are, however, not uncommon. Examples are the flow of road traffic past a point on a road over 24 hours of the day and store sales over seven days of the week. For estimating an average over a time period, a systematic sample daily at 4 p.m. or every Tuesday would obviously be unwise. Instead, the strategy is to stagger the sample over the periodic curve, for example, by seeing that every week-day is equally represented in the case of store sales.

Some populations have a kind of periodic effect that is less obvious. A series of weekly payrolls in a small sector of a factory may always list the workers in the same order and may contain between 19 and 23 names every week. A systematic sample of 1 in 20 names over a period of weeks might consist mainly of the records of one worker or of the records of two or three workers who are among the highest earners in the group. Similarly, a systematic sample of names from a city directory might contain too many heads of households, or too many children. If there is time to study the periodic structure, a systematic sample can usually be designed to capitalize on it. Failing this, a simple or stratified random sample is preferable when a periodic effect is suspected but not well known.

In some natural populations quasi-periodic variation may be present that would be difficult to anticipate. L. H. Madow (1946) found evidence pointing this way in a bed of hardwood seedling stock in a rather small population ($N = 420$). Finney (1950) discussed a similar phenomenon in timber volume per strip in the Dehra Dun forest, although in a re-examination of the data Milne (1959) suggested that the apparent periodicity might have been produced by the process of measurement. The effect of quasi-periodicity is that systematic sampling performs poorly at some values of n and particularly well for others. Whether this effect occurs frequently is not known. Matérn (1960) cites examples in which natural forces (e.g., tides) might produce a spatial periodic variation, but he is of the opinion that no clear case has been found in forest surveys.

8.8 AUTOCORRELATED POPULATIONS

With many natural populations, there is reason to expect that two observations y_i, y_j will be more nearly alike when i and j are close together in the series than when they are distant. This happens whenever natural forces induce a slow change as we proceed along the series. In a mathematical model for this effect we may suppose that y_i and y_j are positively correlated, the correlation between them being a function solely of their distance apart, $i - j$, and diminishing as this distance increases. Although this model is oversimplified, it may represent one of the salient features of many natural populations.

In order to investigate whether this model does apply to a population, we can calculate the set of correlations ρ_u for pairs of items that are u units apart and plot this correlation against u. This curve, or the function it represents, is called a *correlogram*. Even if the model is valid, the correlogram will not be a smooth function for any finite population because irregularities are introduced by the finite nature of the population. In a comparison of systematic with stratified random sampling for this model these irregularities make it difficult to derive results for any single finite population. The comparison can be made over the average of a whole series of finite populations, which are drawn at random from an infinite superpopulation to which the model applies. This technique has already been applied in theorem 8.5.

Thus we assume that the observations y_i $(i = 1, 2, \cdots, N)$ are drawn from a superpopulation in which

$$\mathscr{E}(y_i) = \mu, \quad \mathscr{E}(y_i - \mu)^2 = \sigma^2, \quad \mathscr{E}(y_i - \mu)(y_{i+u} - \mu) = \rho_u \sigma^2 \quad (8.10)$$

where

$$\rho_u \geq \rho_v \geq 0, \text{ whenever } u < v$$

The drawing of one set of y_i from this superpopulation creates a single finite population of size N.

The average variance for systematic sampling is denoted by

$$\mathscr{E}V_{sy} = \mathscr{E}E(\bar{y}_{sy} - \bar{Y})^2$$

For this class of populations it is easy to show that stratified random sampling is superior to simple random sampling, but no general result can be established about systematic sampling. Within the class there are superpopulations in which systematic sampling is superior to stratified random sampling, but there are also superpopulations in which systematic sampling is inferior to simple random sampling for certain values of k.

A general theorem can be obtained if it is further assumed that the correlogram is concave upwards.

Theorem 8.6. If, in addition to conditions (8.10), we have

$$\delta_i^2 = \rho_{i+1} + \rho_{i-1} - 2\rho_i \geq 0 \quad [i = 2, 3, \cdots, (kn - 2)]$$

then

$$\mathscr{E}V_{sy} \leq \mathscr{E}V_{st} \leq \mathscr{E}V_{ran}$$

for any size of sample. Further, unless $\delta_i^2 = 0$, $i = 2, 3, \cdots, (kn - 2)$,

$$\mathscr{E}V_{sy} < \mathscr{E}V_{st}$$

A proof has been given by Cochran (1946).

A sketch of the argument for $n = 2$ illustrates the role played by the "concave upwards" condition. In the systematic sample the members of the pair are always k units apart. Hence

$$\mathscr{E}V(\bar{y}_{sy}) = \tfrac{1}{4}(\sigma^2 + \sigma^2 + 2\rho_k \sigma^2) = \tfrac{1}{2}\sigma^2(1 + \rho_k)$$

With the stratified sample, there are k possible positions for the unit drawn from each stratum, making k^2 combinations of positions. The numbers of combinations 1, 2, $\cdots (2k - 1)$ units apart are as follows.

Distance	1	2	$\cdots$	$(k - 1)$	k	$(k + 1)$	$\cdots$	$(2k - 1)$	Total
Number	1	2	$\cdots$	$(k - 1)$	k	$(k - 1)$	$\cdots$	1	k^2

Hence the average value of $V(\bar{y}_{st})$, taken over the k^2 combinations, may be written

$$\mathscr{E}V(\bar{y}_{st}) = \frac{\sigma^2}{2k^2}\left[\sum_{i=1}^{k-1}i(2 + \rho_i + \rho_{2k-i}) + k(1 + \rho_k)\right]$$

Similarly, $\mathscr{E}V(\bar{y}_{sy})$ may be expressed as

$$\mathscr{E}V(\bar{y}_{sy}) = \frac{\sigma^2}{2k^2}\left[\sum_{i=1}^{k-1}i(2 + 2\rho_k) + k(1 + \rho_k)\right]$$

Hence

$$\mathscr{E}V(\bar{y}_{st}) - \mathscr{E}V(\bar{y}_{sy}) = \frac{\sigma^2}{2k^2}\left[\sum_{i}^{k-1}i(\rho_i + \rho_{2k-i} - 2\rho_k)\right]$$

But if

$$\rho_{i+1} + \rho_{i-1} \geq 2\rho_i \quad (i = 2, 3, \cdots)$$

it is easy to show that every term inside the brackets is positive. This completes the proof. In short, the *average* distance apart is k for both the systematic and the stratified sample, but on account of the concavity the stratified sample loses more in precision when the distance is less than k than it gains when the distance exceeds k.

Quenouille (1949) has shown that the inequalities in theorem 8.6 remain valid when two of the conditions are relaxed so that

$$\mathscr{E}(y_i) = \mu_i, \qquad \mathscr{E}(y_i - \mu_i)^2 = \sigma_i^2$$

In this event each of the three average variances is increased by the same amount.

As far as practical applications are concerned, correlograms that are concave upward have been proposed by several writers as models for specific natural populations. The function $\rho_u = \tanh(u^{-3/5})$ was suggested by Fisher and Mackenzie (1922) for the correlation between the weekly rainfall at two weather stations which are a distance u apart; the function $\rho_u = e^{-\lambda u}$ by Osborne (1942) and Matérn (1947) for forestry and land use surveys; and the function $\rho_u = (l - u)/l$ by Wold (1938) for certain types of economic time series.

8.9 NATURAL POPULATIONS

Investigations have been made on a variety of natural populations. The data are described in Table 8.6. The first three studies were made from maps. In the first study the finite population consists of 288 altitudes at successive distances of 0.1 mile in undulating country. In the next two the data are the fractions of the lengths of lines drawn on a cover-type map that lie in a certain type of cover (e.g., grass). These examples might be

TABLE 8.6

NATURAL POPULATIONS USED IN STUDIES OF SYSTEMATIC SAMPLING

Reference	N	Type of Data
Yates (1948), table 13	288	Altitudes read at intervals of 0.1 mile from ordnance survey map.
Osborne (1942)	*	Per cent of area in (a) cultivated land, (b) shrub, (c) grass, (d) woodland on parallel lines drawn on a cover-type map.
Osborne (1942)	*	Per cent of area in Douglas fir on parallel lines drawn on a cover-type map.
Yates (1948)	192	Soil temperature (12 in. under grass) for 192 consecutive days.
Yates (1948)	192	Soil temperature (4 in. under bare soil) for 192 days.
Yates (1948)	192	Air temperature for 192 days.
Yates (1948)	96	Yields of 96 rows of potatoes.
Finney (1948)	160	Volume of saleable timber per strip, 3 chains wide and of varying length (Mt. Stuart forest).
Finney (1948)	288	Volume of virgin timber per strip, 2.5 chains wide, 80 chains long (Black's Mountain forest).
Finney (1950)	292	Volume of timber per strip, 2 chains wide and of varying length (Dehra Dun forest).
Johnson (1943)	400†	Number of seedlings per 1-ft-bed-width in 4 beds of hardwood seedbed stock.
Johnson (1943)	400†	Number of seedlings per 1-ft-bed-width in 3 beds of coniferous seedbed stock.
Johnson (1943)	400†	Number of seedlings per 1-ft-bed-width in 6 beds of coniferous transplant stock.

* Theoretically, N is infinite, if lines that are infinitely thin can be envisaged.
† Approximately. The number varied from bed to bed.

considered the closest to continuous variation in the mathematical sense.

The next three studies are based on temperatures for 192 consecutive days: (a) 12 in. under the soil, (b) 4 in. under the soil, (c) in air. This trio represents a gradation in the direction of greater influence of erratic day-to-day changes in the weather compared with slow seasonal influences.

The remaining studies deal with plant or tree yields in sequences that lie along a line. In the study on potatoes, which is typical of the group, the finite population consists of the total yields of 96 rows in a field. Since no exhaustive search of the literature has been made, further data may be available.

In some of the studies V_{sy} is compared with the variance V_{st2} for a stratified random sample with strata of size $2k$ and two units per stratum.

This comparison is of interest because an unbiased estimate of V_{st2} can be obtained from the sample data. This cannot be done for V_{st1} (with strata of size k and 1 unit per stratum) or for V_{sy}. Other writers report comparisons of V_{sy} with both V_{st1} and V_{st2}. The majority of the sources do not present comparisons with V_{ran} in readily usable form, but it appears that in general V_{st2} gave gains in precision over V_{ran}.

In the papers by Yates and Finney comparisons are given for a range of values of n and k within each finite population. In these cases the data in Table 8.7 are the geometric means of the variance ratios for the individual

TABLE 8.7

RELATIVE PRECISION OF SYSTEMATIC AND STRATIFIED RANDOM SAMPLING

Data	Range of k	Relative Precision of Systematic to Stratified	
		V_{st1}/V_{sy}	V_{st2}/V_{sy}
Altitudes	2–20	2.99	5.68
Per cent area (4 cover types)		—	4.42
Per cent area (Douglas fir)		—	1.83
Soil temperature (12 in.)	2–24	2.42	4.23
Soil temperature (4 in.)	4–24	1.45	2.07
Air temperature	4–24	1.26	1.65
Potatoes	3–16	1.37	1.90
Timber volume (Mt. Stuart)	2–32	1.07	1.35
Timber volume (Black's Mt.)	2–24	1.19	1.44
Timber volume (Dehra Dun)	2–32	1.39	1.89
Hardwood seedlings	14	—	1.89
Coniferous seedlings	14–24	—	2.22
Coniferous transplant	12–22	—	0.93

values of k. The other writers make computations for only one value of k per population but may give data for different items or for several populations of the same natural type. Here, again, geometric means of the variance ratios were taken.

Although the data are limited in extent, the results are impressive. In the studies that permit comparison with V_{st1} systematic sampling shows a consistent gain in precision which, although modest, is worth having. The median of the ratios V_{st1}/V_{sy} is 1.4. The gains in comparison with V_{st2} are substantial, the median ratio being 1.9.

The internal trend of the results agrees with expectations, although not too much should be made of this in view of the small number of studies. The gains are largest for the types of data in which we would guess that variation would be nearest to continuous. The decline in V_{st1}/V_{sy} from soil to air temperatures would also be anticipated from this viewpoint. In the last three items (forest nursery data), the only one showing no gain is coniferous transplant stock, which is older and more uniform than seedling stock.

8.10 ESTIMATION OF THE VARIANCE FROM A SINGLE SAMPLE

From the results of a simple random sample with $n > 1$, we can calculate an unbiased estimate of the variance of the sample mean, the estimate being unbiased *whatever the form of the population*. Since a systematic sample can be regarded as a simple random sample with $n = 1$, this useful property does not hold for the systematic sample. As an illustration, consider the "sine curve" example. Let

$$y_i = m + a \sin \frac{\pi i}{2}$$

where $k = 4$ and $i = 1, 2, \cdots, 4n$. The successive observations in the population are

$$(m + a), m, (m - a), m, (m + a), m, (m - a), m, \cdots$$

If $i = 1$ is chosen as the first member, *all* members of the systematic sample have the value $(m + a)$. For the other three possible choices of i, all members have the values m, $(m - a)$, or m, respectively. Thus from a *single* sample we have no means of estimating the value of a. But the true sampling variance of the mean of the systematic sample is $a^2/2$. The illustration shows that it is impossible to construct an estimated variance that is unbiased if periodic variation is present.

These results do not mean that nothing can be done. Excluding the case of periodic variation, we might know enough about the structure of the population to be able to develop a mathematical model that adequately represents the type of variation present. We might then be able to manufacture a formula for the estimated variance that is approximately unbiased for this model, although it may be badly biased for other models. The decision to use one of these models must rest on the judgment of the sampler.

Some simple models with their corresponding estimated variances are presented below. No proofs are given.

The simplest models apply to populations in which y_i is composed of a trend plus a "random" component. Thus

$$y_i = \mu_i + e_i$$

where μ_i is some function of i. For the random component, we assume that there is a superpopulation in which

$$\mathscr{E}(e_i) = 0, \qquad \mathscr{E}(e_i^2) = \sigma_i^2, \qquad \mathscr{E}(e_i e_j) = 0 \qquad (i \neq j)$$

A proposed formula s_{sy}^2 for the estimated variance is called unbiased if

$$\mathscr{E}E(s_{sy}^2) = \mathscr{E}V_{sy}$$

that is, if it is unbiased over all finite populations that can be drawn from the superpopulation.

Population in "Random" Order

$$\mu_i = \text{constant} \qquad (i = 1, 2, \cdots, N)$$

$$s_{sy1}^2 = \frac{N - n}{Nn} \frac{\sum (y_i - \bar{y}_{sy})^2}{n - 1}$$

This case applies when we are confident that the order is essentially random with respect to the items being measured. The variance formula is the same as that for a simple random sample and is unbiased if the model is correct.

Stratification Effects Only

$$\mu_i = \text{constant} \qquad (rk + 1 \leq i \leq rk + k)$$

$$s_{sy2}^2 = \frac{N - n}{Nn} \frac{\sum (y_i - y_{i+k})^2}{2(n - 1)}$$

In this case the mean is constant within each stratum of k units. The estimate s_{sy2}^2, which is based on the mean square successive difference, is not unbiased. It contains an unwanted contribution from the difference between μ's in neighboring strata, and the first and last strata carry too little weight in estimating the random component of the variance. With a reasonably large sample, this estimate would in general be too high, assuming that the model is correct.

Linear Trend

$$\mu_i = \mu + \beta i$$

$$s_{sy3}^2 = \frac{N - n}{N} \frac{n'}{n^2} \frac{\sum (y_i - 2y_{i+k} + y_{i+2k})^2}{6(n - 2)} \qquad (1 \leq i \leq n - 2)$$

The estimate is based on successive quadratic terms in the sequence y_i. The sum of squares contains $(n - 2)$ terms. With a linear trend we have seen (section 8.6) that the trend can be eliminated by the use of end corrections. The term n'/n^2 is the sum of squares of the weights in $\bar{y}_{wsy}$. Unless n is small, n'/n^2 can be replaced by the usual factor $1/n$. Because the strata at the ends receive too little weight, the estimate is biased unless σ_i^2 is constant, but it should be satisfactory if n is large and the model is correct.

If continuous variation of a more complex type is present, the preceding formulas may give poor results. In Table 8.8 the second and third formulas

TABLE 8.8

VARIANCES OF SAMPLE MEAN NUMBERS OF SEEDLINGS (JOHNSON'S DATA)

	Bed	Actual V_{sy}	s_{sy2}^2	s_{sy3}^2
Silver maple	1	0.91	2.8	2.5
	2	0.74	3.6	2.9
American elm	1	4.8	28.4	12.6
	2	15.5	22.6	18.6
White spruce	1	5.5	17.2	11.2
	2	2.0	11.6	6.4
White pine	1	8.2	21.0	21.9

are applied to six forest nursery beds (Johnson, 1943). The quadratic formula is slightly better than that based on successive differences, but both give serious overestimates.

Various other formulas can be devised. Residuals from a fitted polynomial of higher degree may be effective if μ_i varies continuously and not too rapidly: tables have been provided by DeLury (1950) for this method.

Formulas developed from simple assumptions about the nature of the correlogram have been discussed by Osborne (1942), Cochran (1946), and Matérn (1947). Yates (1949) has investigated an estimate based on a quantity of the form

$$(y_u + y_{u+2k} + y_{u+4k} + \cdots) - (y_{u+k} + y_{u+3k} + \cdots)$$

The successive items in the sample are given alternatively $+$ and $-$ signs. If this expression is taken over the whole sample, only 1 df is available. In order to provide more degrees of freedom, the sample data can be broken into parts, which Yates suggests might contain nine observations each. If we denote the successive observations in the systematic sample by y_1', y_2', etc., and give weight $\frac{1}{2}$ to the first and last terms, we may write

$$d_1 = (\tfrac{1}{2}y_1' + y_3' + y_5' + y_7' + \tfrac{1}{2}y_9') - (y_2' + y_4' + y_6' + y_8')$$

The next difference, d_2, may start with $y_9{}'$, and so on. Then, for the estimated variance of $\bar{y}_{sy}$, we take

$$s_{sy}{}^2 = \frac{N - n}{Nn} \sum_{u=1}^{g} \frac{d_u{}^2}{7.5g}$$

The factor 7.5 is the sum of squares of the coefficients in any d_u, and g is the number of differences which the sample provides (g is approximately $n/9$). In the natural populations that Yates examined a formula of this type was superior to the formula s_{sy2}^2 based on successive differences, but it still overestimated the actual variance of $\bar{y}_{sy}$.

In conclusion, there is no dearth of formulas for the estimated variance, but all appear to have a limited range of applicability.

8.11 STRATIFIED SYSTEMATIC SAMPLING

We have seen that if the units are ordered appropriately systematic sampling provides a kind of stratification with equal sampling fractions. If we stratify by some other criterion, we may draw a separate systematic sample within each stratum with starting points independently determined. This is suitable if separate estimates are wanted for each stratum or if unequal sampling fractions are to be used. This method will, of course, be more precise than stratified random sampling if systematic sampling within strata is more precise than simple random sampling within strata.

If $\bar{y}_{syh}$ is the mean of the systematic sample in stratum h, the estimate of the population mean $\bar{Y}$ and its variance are

$$\bar{y}_{stsy} = \sum W_h \bar{y}_{syh}, \qquad V(\bar{y}_{stsy}) = \sum W_h{}^2 \, V(\bar{y}_{syh})$$

With only a few strata, the problem of finding a sample estimate of this quantity amounts to that already discussed of finding a satisfactory sample estimate of $V(\bar{y}_{syh})$ in each stratum.

When the strata are more numerous, an estimate based on the method of "collapsed strata" (section 5A.11) may be preferable. From the results in that section, it follows that the estimate

$$v(\bar{y}_{stsy}) = \sum{}' W_h{}^2 (\bar{y}_{syh} - \bar{y}_{syj})^2$$

where the sum extends over the pairs of strata, is on the average an overestimate, even if periodic variation is present within the strata.

An unbiased estimate of the error variance can be obtained if two systematic samples, with a different random start and an interval $2k$, are drawn within each stratum, one df being provided by each stratum. There will be some loss in precision if systematic sampling is effective. If there are many strata, one systematic sample can be used in most of them, drawing two in a random subsample of strata for the purposes of estimating the error.

8.12 SYSTEMATIC SAMPLING IN TWO DIMENSIONS

In sampling an area, the simplest extension of the one-dimensional systematic sample is the "square grid" pattern shown in Fig 8.4a. The sample is completely determined by the choice of a pair of random numbers to fix the coordinates of the upper left unit. The performance of the square grid has been studied both on theoretical and natural populations. Matérn (1960) has investigated the best type of sample when the correlation between any two points in the area is a monotone decreasing concave upward function of their distance apart d. For correlograms like $e^{-\lambda d}$ the square grid does well, being superior to simple or stratified random sampling with one unit per stratum, although Matérn gives reasons for expecting that the best pattern for this situation is a triangular network in which the points lie at the vertices of equilateral triangles.

In 14 agricultural uniformity trials, Haynes (1948) found that the square grid had about the same precision as simple random sampling in two dimensions. Milne (1959) examined the *central* square grid, in which the point lies at the center of the square, in 50 uniformity trials. It performed better than simple random sampling and perhaps slightly better than stratified random sampling, although this difference was not statistically significant. These results suggest that, at least for data of this type, autocorrelation effects are weak. For estimating the area covered by forest or by water on a map, Matérn found the square grid superior to the random methods in two examples.

Figure 8.4(*b*) shows an alternative systematic sample, called an *unaligned* sample. The coordinates of the upper left unit are selected first by a pair of random numbers. Two additional random numbers determine the

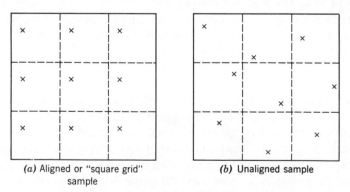

(*a*) Aligned or "square grid"   (*b*) Unaligned sample
      sample

Fig. 8.4   Two types of two-dimensional systematic sample.

horizontal coordinates of the remaining two units in the first *column* of strata. Another two are needed to fix the *vertical* coordinates of the remaining units in the first *row* of strata. The constant interval k (equal to the sides of the squares) then fixes the locations of all points. Investigations by Quenouille (1949) and Das (1950) for simple two-dimensional correlograms indicate that the unaligned pattern will often be superior both to the square grid and to stratified random sampling.

Further evidence of the superiority of an unaligned sample is obtained from experience in experimental design, in which the latin square has been found a precise method for arranging treatments in a rectangular field. The 5 x 5 latin square in Fig. 8.5a may be regarded as a division of the field into five systematic samples, one for each letter. There is some evidence that this particular square, which is called the "knight's move" latin square, is slightly more precise than a randomly chosen 5 × 5 square, probably because alignment is absent in the diagonals as well as in rows and columns.

The principle of the latin square has been used by Homeyer and Black (1946) in sampling rectangular fields of oats. Each field contained 21 plots. The three possible systematic samples are denoted by the letters A, B, and C, respectively, in Fig. 8.5b. This arrangement, with one of the letters chosen at random in each field, gave an increase in precision of around 25 % over stratified random sampling with rows as strata. The arrangement does not quite satisfy the latin square property because each letter appears three times in one column and twice in the other columns, but it approaches this property as nearly as possible.

```
A  B  C  D  E            A  B  C
D  E  A  B  C            B  C  A
B  C  D  E  A            C  A  B
E  A  B  C  D            A  B  C
C  D  E  A  B            B  C  A
                         C  A  B
                         A  B  C
```

(a) "Knight's move" latin square   (b) Systematic design for a 3 × 7 rectangular field

Fig. 8.5 Two systematic designs based on the latin square.

Yates (1960), who terms arrangements of this type *lattice sampling*, discusses their use in two- and three-dimensional sampling. In three dimensions each row, column, and vertical level can be represented in the sample by choosing p units out of the p^3 in the population. With p^2 units in the sample, each of the p^2 combinations of levels of rows and columns, of rows and vertical heights, and of columns and vertical heights can be represented. Patterson (1954) has investigated the arrangements that provide an unbiased estimate of error.

8.13 SUMMARY

Systematic samples are convenient to draw and to execute. In most of the studies reported in this chapter, both on artificial and on natural populations, they compared favorably in precision with stratified random samples. Their disadvantages are that they may give poor precision when unsuspected periodicity is present and that no trustworthy method for estimating $V(\bar{y}_{sy})$ from the sample data is known.

In the light of these results systematic sampling can safely be recommended in the following situations:

1. Where the ordering of the population is essentially random or contains at most a mild stratification. Here systematic sampling is used for convenience, with little expectation of a gain in precision. Sample estimates of error that are reasonably unbiased are available (section 8.10).

2. Where a stratification with numerous strata is employed and an independent systematic sample is drawn from each stratum. The effects of hidden periodicities tend to cancel out in this situation, and an estimate of error that is known to be an overestimate can be obtained (section 8.11). Alternatively, we can use half the number of strata and draw two systematic samples, with independent random starts, from each stratum. This method gives an unbiased estimate of error.

3. For subsampling the units (Chapter 10). In this case it turns out that an unbiased estimate of the sampling error can be obtained in most practical situations.

4. For sampling populations with variation of a continuous type, provided that an estimate of the sampling error is not regularly required. If a series of surveys of this type is being made, an occasional check on the sampling errors may be sufficient. Yates (1948) has shown how this may be done by taking supplementary observations.

EXERCISES.

8.1   The data in the Table are the numbers of seedlings for each foot of bed in a bed 200 ft. long.

Find the variance of the mean of a systematic sample consisting of every twentieth foot. Compare this with the variances for (a) a simple random sample, (b) a stratified random sample with two units per stratum, (c) a stratified random sample with one unit per stratum. All samples have $n = 10$. $[\sum (y_i - \bar{Y})^2 = 23{,}601.]$

• 8.2   A population of 360 households (numbered 1 to 360) in Baltimore is arranged alphabetically in a file by the surname of the head of the household. Households in which the head is nonwhite occur at the following numbers: 28, 31–33, 36–41, 44, 45, 47, 55, 56, 58, 68, 69, 82, 83, 85, 86, 89–94, 98, 99, 101, 107–110, 114, 154, 156, 178, 223, 224, 296, 298–300 302–304, 306–323, 325–331,

Numbers of Seedlings

	Feet										Systematic Sample Totals
	1–20 1	21–40 2	41–60 3	61–80 4	81–100 5	101–120 6	121–140 7	141–160 8	161–180 9	181–200 10	
	8	20	26	34	31	24	18	16	36	10	223
	6	19	26	21	23	19	13	12	8	35	182
	6	25	10	27	41	28	7	8	29	7	188
	23	11	41	25	18	18	9	10	33	9	197
	25	31	30	32	15	29	11	12	14	12	211
	16	26	55	43	21	24	20	20	13	7	245
	28	29	34	33	8	33	16	17	18	6	222
	21	19	56	45	22	37	9	12	20	14	255
	22	17	39	23	11	32	14	7	13	12	190
	18	28	41	27	3	26	15	17	24	15	214
	26	16	27	37	4	36	20	21	29	18	234
	28	9	20	14	5	20	21	26	18	4	165
	11	22	25	14	11	43	15	16	16	4	177
	16	26	39	24	9	27	14	18	20	9	202
	7	17	24	18	25	20	13	11	6	8	149
	22	39	25	17	16	21	9	19	15	8	191
	44	21	18	14	13	18	25	27	4	9	193
	26	14	44	38	22	19	17	29	8	10	227
	31	40	55	36	18	24	7	31	8	5	255
	26	30	39	29	9	30	30	29	10	3	235
Strata Totals	410	459	674	551	325	528	303	358	342	205	4155

333, 335–339, 341, 342. (The nonwhite households show some "clumping" because of an association between surname and color.)

Compare the precision of a 1-in-8 systematic sample with a simple random sample of the same size for estimating the proportion of households in which the head is nonwhite.

*8.3   A neighborhood contains three compact communities, consisting, respectively, of people of Anglo-Saxon, Polish, and Italian descent. There is an up-to-date directory. In it the persons in a house are listed in the following order: husband, wife, children (by age), others. Houses are listed in order along streets. The average number of persons per house is five.

The choice is between a systematic sample of every fifth person in the directory and a 20% simple random sample. For which of the following variables do you expect the systematic sample to be more precise? (a) Proportion of people of Polish descent, (b) proportion of males, (c) proportion of children. Give reasons.

*8.4   In a directory of 13 houses on a street the persons are listed as follows. M = male adult, F = female adult, m = male child, f = female child.

Household

1	2	3	4	5	6	7	8	9	10	11	12	13
M	M	M	M	M	M	M	M	M	M	M	M	M
F	F	F	F	F	F	F	F	F	F	F	F	F
f	f	m		m	f	f	m	m	m	f	f	
m	m	f		m	m	f	f		f	m		
f	f			f	m							

Compare the variances given by a systematic sample of one in five persons and a 20% simple random sample for estimating (a) the proportion of males, (b) the proportion of children, (c) the proportion of persons living in professional households (households 1, 2, 3, 12, and 13 are described as professional). Do the results support your answers to exercise 8.3? For the systematic sample, number down each column, then go to the top of the next column.

8.5   In exercise 8.1 we might estimate $V(\bar{y}_{sy})$ by (a) regarding each systematic sample as a simple random sample, (b) pretending that each 1-in-20 systematic sample is composed of two 1-in-40 systematic samples with a separate random start. For each method, compare the average of the estimated variances with the actual variance of $\bar{y}_{sy}$.

8.6   In a population consisting of a linear trend (section 8.6) show that a systematic sample is less precise than a stratified random sample with strata of size $2k$ and two units per stratum if $n > (4k + 2)/(k + 1)$.

8.7   A two-dimensional population with a linear trend may be represented by the relation
$$y_{ij} = i + j \qquad (i, j = 1, 2, \ldots, nk)$$
where y_{ij} is the item value in the ith row and jth column. The population contains $N^2 = n^2k^2$ units.

A systematic square grid sample is selected by drawing at random two independent starting coordinates i_0, j_0, each between 1 and k. The sample, of size n^2, contains all units whose coordinates are of the form
$$i_0 + \gamma k, j_0 + \delta k$$
where γ, δ are any two integers between 0 and $(n - 1)$, inclusive.

Show that the mean of this sample has the same precision as the mean of a simple random sample of size n^2.

8.8 If the comparison in exercise 8.7 were made for a three-dimensional population with linear trend, what result would you expect?

REFERENCES

Cochran, W. G. (1946). Relative accuracy of systematic and stratified random samples for a certain class of populations. *Ann. Math. Stat.*, **17**, 164–177.

Das, A. C. (1950). Two-dimensional systematic sampling and the associated stratified and random sampling. *Sankhya*, **10**, 95–108.

DeLury, D. B. (1950). *Values and integrals of the orthogonal polynomials up to $n = 26$.* University of Toronto Press.

Finney, D. J. (1948). Random and systematic sampling in timber surveys. *Forestry*, **22**, 1–36.

Finney, D. J. (1950). An example of periodic variation in forest sampling. *Forestry*, **23**, 96–111.

Fisher, R. A., and Mackenzie, W. A. (1922). The correlation of weekly rainfall. *Quart. Jour. Roy. Met. Soc.*, **48**, 234–245.

Haynes, J. D. (1948). An empirical investigation of sampling methods for an area. M.S. thesis, University of North Carolina.

Homeyer, P. G., and Black, C. A. (1946). Sampling replicated field experiments on oats for yield determinations. *Proc. Soil. Sci. Soc. America*, **11**, 341–344.

Johnson, F. A. (1943). A statistical study of sampling methods for tree nursery inventories. *Jour. Forestry*, **41**, 674–689.

Madow, L. H. (1946). Systematic sampling and its relation to other sampling designs. *Jour. Amer. Stat. Assoc.*, **41**, 207–214.

Madow, W. G., and Madow, L. H. (1944). On the theory of systematic sampling. *Ann. Math. Stat.*, **15**, 1–24.

Matérn, B. (1947). Methods of estimating the accuracy of line and sample plot surveys. *Medd. fr. Statens Skogsforsknings Institut*, **36**, 1–138.

Matérn, B (1960). Spatial variation. *Medd. fr. Statens Skogsforsknings Institut*, **49**, 5, 1–144.

Milne, A. (1959). The centric systematic area sample treated as a random sample. *Biometrics*, **15**, 270–297.

Osborne, J. G. (1942). Sampling errors of systematic and random surveys of cover-type areas. *Jour. Amer. Stat. Assoc.*, **37**, 256–264.

Patterson, H. D. (1954). The errors of lattice sampling. *Jour. Roy. Stat. Soc. B*, **16**, 140–149.

Quenouille, M. H. (1949). Problems in plane sampling. *Ann. Math. Stat.*, **20**, 355–375.

Wold, H. (1938). *A study of the analysis of stationary time series.* Uppsala.

Yates, F. (1948). Systematic sampling. *Phil. Trans. Roy. Soc. London*, **A241**, 345–377.

Yates, F. (1960), *Sampling methods for censuses and surveys.* Charles Griffin and Co., London. Third edition.

Not cited in text

Buckland, W. R. (1951). A review of the literature of systematic sampling. *Jour. Roy. Stat. Soc.*, **B13**, 208–215.

CHAPTER 9

Single-Stage Cluster Sampling

9.1 REASONS FOR CLUSTER SAMPLING

Several references have been made in preceding chapters to surveys in which the sampling unit consists of a group or *cluster* of smaller units that we have called *elements*. There are two main reasons for the widespread application of cluster sampling. Although the first intention may be to use the elements as sampling units, it is found in many surveys that no reliable list of the elements in the population is available and that it would be prohibitively expensive to construct such a list. In many countries there are no complete and up-to date lists of the people, the houses, or the farms in any large geographic region. From maps of the region, however, it can be divided into areal units such as blocks in the cities and segments of land with readily identifiable boundaries in the rural parts. In the United States these clusters are often chosen because they solve the problem of constructing a list of sampling units.

Even when a list of individual houses is available, economic considerations may point to the choice of a larger cluster unit. For a given size of sample, a small unit usually gives more precise results than a large unit. For example, a simple random sample of 600 houses covers a town more evenly than 20 city blocks containing an average of 30 houses apiece. But greater field costs are incurred in locating 600 houses and in travel between them than in locating 20 blocks and visiting all the houses in these blocks. When cost is balanced against precision, the larger unit may prove superior.

A rational choice between two types or sizes of unit may be made by the familiar principle of selecting the unit that gives the smaller variance for a given cost or the smaller cost for a prescribed variance. As in many practical decisions, there may be imponderable factors: one type of unit may have some special convenience or disadvantage that is difficult to include in a calculation of costs. In sampling a growing crop, some experiences suggest that a small unit may give biased estimates because of uncertainty

234

about the exact boundaries of the unit. Homeyer and Black (1946) found that units 2 × 2 ft gave yields of oats about 8 % higher than units 3 × 3 ft, possibly because samplers tend to place boundary plants inside the unit when there is doubt. Sukhatme (1947) cites similar results for wheat and rice.

9.2 A SIMPLE RULE

When the problem is to compare a few specific sizes or types of unit, the following result is helpful.

Theorem 9.1. This applies to simple random sampling in which the fpc is negligible. The quantity to be estimated is the population total. For the uth type of unit, let

$$M_u = \text{relative size of unit}$$
$$S_u{}^2 = \text{variance among the unit totals}$$
$$C_u = \text{relative cost of measuring one unit}$$

Then relative cost for specified precision or relative variance for specified cost $\propto C_u S_u{}^2 / M_u{}^2$.

Proof. Let V_u be the variance of the population total as given by the uth type of unit. Then

$$V(\hat{Y}) = V_u = \frac{N_u{}^2 S_u{}^2}{n_u}$$

The cost of taking these units is $C_u n_u$. Now the relative cost for a specified variance and the relative variance for a specified cost are both proportional to

$$C_u n_u V_u = C_u N_u{}^2 S_u{}^2 \propto \frac{C_u S_u{}^2}{M_u{}^2}$$

since $N_u M_u = \text{constant}$ for different units. This completes the proof.

Corollary 1. If we define the *relative net precision* of a unit as inversely proportional to the variance obtained for fixed cost, theorem 9.1 may be stated as

$$\text{relative net precision} \propto \frac{M_u{}^2}{C_u S_u{}^2} \tag{9.1}$$

Corollary 2. In the analysis of variance, the variances for units of different sizes are often computed on what is called a common basis— usually that applicable to the smallest unit. To put the variances on a common basis, the variance $S_u{}^2$ among totals of units of size M_u is divided by M_u. Let

$$S_u{}'^2 = \frac{S_u{}^2}{M_u} = \text{variance among unit totals (on a common basis)}$$

$$C_u{}' \propto \frac{C_u}{M_u} = \text{relative cost of taking a given bulk of sample}$$

Then theorem 9.1 and corollary 1 may be stated as follows:

$$\text{relative cost for equal precision} \propto \frac{C_u S_u{}^2}{M_u{}^2} \propto C_u{}' S_u{}'^2$$

$$\text{relative net precision} \propto \frac{1}{C_u{}' S_u{}'^2} \tag{9.2}$$

This result shows that if differences in the costs of taking the sample are ignored (i.e., assuming that $C_u{}'$ is constant) the relative net precision with the uth unit $\propto 1/S_u{}'^2$. In order to compare different units for the same total *bulk* of sample, the relevant quantities are the variances among units, expressed on a common basis.

Example. Johnson's data (1941) for a bed of white pine seedlings provide a simple example. The bed contained six rows, each 434 ft long. There are many ways in which the bed can be divided into sampling units. Data for four types of unit are shown in Table 9.1. Since the bed was completely counted, the data are correct population values.

TABLE 9.1

DATA FOR FOUR TYPES OF SAMPLING UNIT

	Type of Unit			
Preliminary Data	1-ft row	2-ft row	1-ft bed	2-ft bed
M_u = relative size of unit	1	2	6	12
N_u = number of units in pop.	2604	1302	434	217
$S_u{}^2$ = pop. variance per unit	2.537	6.746	23.094	68.558
Number of feet of row that can be counted in 15 min.	44	62	78	108

The units were
one foot of a single row
two feet of a single row
one foot of the width of the bed
two feet of the width of the bed

With the first two units it was assumed that sampling would be stratified by rows, so that the $S_u{}^2$ represent variances within rows. Simple random sampling was assumed for the last two units.

Since the principal cost is that of locating and counting the units, costs were estimated by a time study (last row of Table 9.1). With the larger units, a greater bulk of sample can be counted in 15 min, less time being spent in moving from one unit to another.

The quantity to be estimated is the total number of seedlings in the bed. In the notation of theorem 9.1, Table 9.1 gives the values of M_u and $S_u{}^2$. The relative values of C_u, expressed as the time required to count one unit, are as follows.

	1-ft row	2-ft row	1-ft bed	2-ft bed
C_u (in 15-min times)	$\frac{1}{44}$	$\frac{2}{62}$	$\frac{6}{78}$	$\frac{12}{108}$

By theorem 9.1, corollary 1, the relative net precisions are worked out in Table 9.2.

The last line of Table 9.2 gives the relative precisions when that of the smallest unit is taken as 100. The 1-ft bed appears to be the best unit.

TABLE 9.2

RELATIVE NET PRECISIONS OF THE FOUR UNITS

	1-ft row	2-ft row	1-ft bed	2-ft bed
$\dfrac{M_u{}^2}{C_u S_u{}^2}$	$\dfrac{44}{2.537} = 17.34$	$\dfrac{(4)(62)}{(2)(6.746)} = 18.38$	$\dfrac{(36)(78)}{(6)(23.094)} = 20.27$	$\dfrac{(144)(108)}{(12)(68.558)} = 18.90$
	100	106	117	109

The variances among units, expressed on a common basis, are also worth looking at. The values of $S_u{}'^2 = S_u{}^2/M_u$, applicable to a single foot of row, are, respectively, 2.537, 3.373, 3.849, 5.713. Note that these variances increase steadily with increasing size of unit. This result is commonly found (although exceptions may occur). Since the relative net precision $\propto 1/C_u{}'S_u{}'^2$, the cost of taking a given bulk of sample must decrease with the larger units if they are to prove economical.

Theorem 9.1 and its corollaries remain valid for stratified sampling with proportional allocation if all strata are of the same size and if $S_u{}^2$, $S_u{}'^2$ represent average variances within strata. This is so, under the conditions stated, because the variance of the estimated population total, ignoring the fpc, is $N^2 S_u{}^2/n$, and therefore assumes the same form as in simple random sampling. Theorem 9.1 does not hold for more complex types of sampling.

The preceding results are intended merely as an illustration of the general procedure. *Comparisons among units should always be made for the kind of sampling that is to be used in practice or, if this has not been decided, for the kinds that are under consideration.* Changes in the method of sampling or of estimation will alter the relative net precisions of the different units. Even with a fixed method of sampling and estimation, relative net precisions vary with size of sample if the cost is not a linear function of size or if the size is large enough so that the fpc must be taken into account.

There is usually more than one item to consider. One approach is to fix the total cost and work out the relative net precisions for each type of unit

TABLE 9.3

ESTIMATED STANDARD ERRORS (%) FOR FOUR SIZES OF UNIT, WITH SIMPLE RANDOM SAMPLING

Items	$S/4$	$S/2$	S	$2S$	Best Unit
Number of swine	5.0	4.9	5.3	6.2	$S/2$
Number of horses	3.4	3.3	3.6	4.2	$S/2$
Number of sheep	17.4	15.7	14.9	14.3	$2S$
Number of chickens	3.0	3.0	3.3	3.8	$S/4, S/2$
Number of eggs yesterday	5.7	5.2	4.9	4.7	$2S$
Number of cattle	4.7	4.6	4.8	5.5	$S/2$
Number of cows milked	3.7	3.6	3.8	4.4	$S/2$
Number of gallons of milk	4.4	4.2	4.4	4.9	$S/2$
Dairy products receipts	5.5	5.2	5.4	6.0	$S/2$
Number of farm acres	2.9	2.8	3.0	3.5	$S/2$
Number of corn acres	3.7	3.5	3.8	4.4	$S/2$
Number of oat acres	4.6	4.8	5.6	7.0	$S/4$
Corn yield	1.6	1.7	2.0	2.5	$S/4$
Oat yield	1.6	1.5	1.6	1.8	$S/2$
Commercial feed expenditures	12.6	13.6	16.7	21.8	$S/4$
Total expenditures, operator	7.8	8.1	9.6	12.0	$S/4$
Total receipts, operator	6.2	6.5	7.7	9.8	$S/4$
Net cash income, operator	6.8	6.9	7.8	9.5	$S/4$

and each item. Unless one type is uniformly superior, some compromise decision is made, giving principal weight to the most important items.

In view of the numerous factors that influence the results, a study of optimum size of unit in an extensive survey is a large task. A good example for farm sampling is described by Jessen (1942). An excerpt from his results is given in Table 9.3. This compares four sizes of unit—a quarter-section, a half-section, a section, and a block consisting of two contiguous sections. The section is an area 1 mile square, containing on the average slightly under four farms. In this comparison the total field cost ($1000), the length of questionnaire (60 min to complete), and the travel cost (5 cents per mile) are all specified, because relative net precisions change if any of these variables is altered. Costs are at a 1939 level.

The data in the table are the relative standard errors (in per cent) of the estimated means per farm for 18 items. No unit is best for all items. The half-section and the quarter-section are, however, superior to the larger units for all except two items, with little to choose between the half- and quarter-sections. The half-section would probably be preferred, because the problem of identifying the boundaries accurately is easier.

9.3 COMPARISONS OF PRECISION MADE FROM SURVEY DATA

In the nursery seedling example the variances for the different types of unit were obtained from a complete count of the population. Except with small populations, however, it is seldom feasible to conduct a survey solely for the purpose of comparison. Information about the optimum unit is more usually procured as an ingenious by-product of a survey whose main purpose is to make estimates.

Suppose that in a survey each unit can be divided into M smaller units. Instead of recording only the totals for each "large" unit in the sample, we record data separately for each of the M small units. A comparison can then be made of the precision of the large and small units. A simple random sample of size n will be assumed at first.

The analysis of variance in Table 9.4 can be computed from the sample.

TABLE 9.4

ANALYSIS OF VARIANCE OF THE SAMPLE DATA (ON A SMALL-UNIT BASIS)

	df	ms
Between large units	$(n - 1)$	s_b^2
Between small units within large	$n(M - 1)$	s_w^2
Between small units in sample	$nM - 1$	$s^2 = \dfrac{(n - 1)s_b^2 + n(M - 1)s_w^2}{nM - 1}$

The estimated variance of a large unit (on a small-unit basis) is s_b^2. It might be thought that an appropriate estimate of the variance of a small unit would be the mean square between all small units in the sample, that is,

$$s^2 = \frac{(n - 1)s_b^2 + n(M - 1)s_w^2}{nM - 1} \tag{9.3}$$

This estimate, although often satisfactory, is slightly biased because the sample is not a simple random sample of small units, since these are sampled in contiguous groups of M units.

An unbiased estimate is obtained from the sample by constructing an analysis of variance, as in Table 9.5, for the whole population, which contains N large units and NM small units.

TABLE 9.5

ANALYSIS OF VARIANCE FOR THE WHOLE POPULATION (ON A SMALL-UNIT BASIS)

	df	ms
Between large units	$N - 1$	S_b^2
Between small units within large units	$N(M - 1)$	S_w^2
Between small units in the population	$NM - 1$	$S^2 = \dfrac{(N - 1)S_b^2 + N(M - 1)S_w^2}{NM - 1}$

By its definition, the population variance among small units is given by the last line of the table, that is,

$$S^2 = \frac{(N - 1)S_b^2 + N(M - 1)S_w^2}{NM - 1}$$

With simple random sampling, s_b^2 in Table 9.4 is an unbiased estimate of S_b^2 (this follows from section 2.3). It may be shown easily that s_w^2 is an unbiased estimate of S_w^2. Hence an unbiased estimate of the variance S^2 among all small units in the population is

$$\hat{S}^2 = \frac{(N - 1)s_b^2 + N(M - 1)s_w^2}{NM - 1} \tag{9.4}$$

Clearly, this expression is almost the same as the simpler expression

$$\hat{S}^2 \doteq \frac{s_b^2 + (M - 1)s_w^2}{M} \tag{9.5}$$

If $n > 50$, (9.3) for s^2 also reduces to (9.5), so that s^2 is a satisfactory approximation to S^2 for $n > 50$.

The two estimates s_b^2 (for the large unit) and $\hat{S}^2$ (for the small unit) are on a common basis and may be substituted in theorem 9.1, corollary 2.

If the sample is large, the small units may be measured for a random subsample of the large units (say 100 out of 600). Alternatively, two small units, chosen at random from each large unit, might be measured. More than one size of small unit may be investigated simultaneously, provided that we take data that give an unbiased estimate of S_w^2 for each small unit. With stratified sampling, the variances for the large and small units can be estimated by these methods separately in each stratum and then substituted in the appropriate formula for the variance of the estimate from a stratified sample.

Example. The data come from a farm sample taken in North Carolina in 1942 in order to estimate farm employment (Finkner, Morgan, and Monroe, 1943). The method of drawing the sample was to locate points at random on the map and to choose as sampling units the three farms that were nearest to each point. This method is not recommended because a large farm has a greater

TABLE 9.6

SAMPLE ANALYSIS OF VARIANCE (NUMBER OF PAID WORKERS)
(SINGLE-FARM BASIS)

	df	ms
Between units within strata	825	6.218
Between farms within units	2768	2.918
Between farms within strata	3593	3.676

chance of inclusion in the sample than a small farm, and an isolated farm has a greater chance than another in a densely farmed area. Any effects of this bias will be ignored.

From the sample data for individual farms, the group of three farms can be compared with the individual farm as a sampling unit. The item chosen is the number of paid workers. The sample was stratified, the stratum being a group of townships similar in density of farm population and in ratio of cropland to farmland. Since the sampling fraction was 1.9%, the fpc can be ignored.

The variance of the estimated population total is

$$V(\hat{Y}_{st}) = \sum_h \frac{N_h^2 S_h^2}{n_h}$$

The correct procedure is to compute $N_h^2 S_h^2 / n_h$ separately within each stratum for the two types of unit, using an analysis of variance and expression (9.5). We shall use a simpler procedure as an approximation.

The strata contained in general between 300 and 450 farms, and either two or three 3-farm units were taken in each stratum to make the sampling approximately proportional. Assuming proportionality, that is, $n_h/N_h = n/N$, we may write

$$V(\hat{Y}_{st}) = \frac{N}{n} \sum N_h S_h^2 = \frac{N^2}{n} \bar{S}_h^2$$

if we assume further that the S_h^2 do not vary greatly among strata, so that they may be replaced by their average, $\bar{S}_h^2$.

Estimates of $\bar{S}_h^2$ are obtained from the analysis of variance in Table 9.6, which is on a single-farm basis.

For the group of three farms, the mean square $\bar{s}_{h3}^2 = 6.218$ serves as the estimate of $\bar{S}_h^2$ on a single-farm basis. For the individual farm, using (9.5), we have

$$\hat{S}^2 = \frac{6.218 + 2(2.918)}{3} = 4.018$$

By theorem 9.1, corollary 2, the two figures, 6.218 for the group of three farms and 4.018 for the individual farm, indicate the relative variances obtained for a fixed total size of sample. The group of farms gives about two thirds the precision of the single farm. Consideration of costs would presumably make the result more favorable to the three-farm unit.

9.4 VARIANCE IN TERMS OF INTRACLUSTER CORRELATION

Variance formulas are sometimes expressed in terms of the correlation coefficient ρ between elements in the same cluster. This approach has already been used for systematic sampling (section 8.3).

Let y_{ij} be the observed value for the jth element within the ith unit, and let y_i be the unit total. In cluster sampling we need to distinguish between two kinds of average: the mean per unit $\bar{Y} = \sum y_i/N$ and the mean per element $\bar{\bar{Y}} = \sum y_i/NM = \bar{Y}/M$. The variance among elements is

$$S^2 = \frac{\sum\limits_{i,j}(y_{ij} - \bar{\bar{Y}})^2}{NM - 1}$$

The intracluster correlation coefficient ρ was defined (section 8.3) as

$$\rho = \frac{E(y_{ij} - \bar{\bar{Y}})(y_{ik} - \bar{\bar{Y}})}{E(y_{ij} - \bar{\bar{Y}})^2} = \frac{2\sum\limits_{i}\sum\limits_{j<k}(y_{ij} - \bar{\bar{Y}})(y_{ik} - \bar{\bar{Y}})}{(M-1)(NM-1)S^2} \tag{9.6}$$

The number of terms (cross products) in the numerator E is $NM(M-1)/2$, and in the denominator E is $(NM-1)S^2/NM$.

Theorem 9.2. A simple random sample of n clusters, each containing M elements, is drawn from the N clusters in the population. Then the sample mean per element $\bar{y}$ is an unbiased estimate of $\bar{\bar{Y}}$ with variance

$$V(\bar{y}) = \frac{1-f}{n} \cdot \frac{NM-1}{M^2(N-1)} S^2[1 + (M-1)\rho]$$

$$\doteq \frac{1-f}{nM} S^2[1 + (M-1)\rho] \tag{9.7}$$

where ρ is the intracluster correlation coefficient.

Proof. Let y_i denote the total for the ith cluster and $\bar{y} = \sum\limits^{n} y_i/n$. By theorems 2.1 and 2.2, $\bar{y}$ is an unbiased estimate of $\bar{Y}$ with variance

$$V(\bar{y}) = \frac{(1-f)}{n} \frac{\sum (y_i - \bar{Y})^2}{N-1}$$

But $\bar{y} = M\bar{\bar{y}}$ and $\bar{Y} = M\bar{\bar{Y}}$. Hence $\bar{\bar{y}}$ is an unbiased estimate of $\bar{\bar{Y}}$ with variance

$$V(\bar{\bar{y}}) = \frac{1-f}{nM^2} \frac{\sum (y_i - \bar{Y})^2}{N-1} \tag{9.8}$$

But

$$(y_i - \bar{Y}) = (y_{i1} - \bar{\bar{Y}}) + (y_{i2} - \bar{\bar{Y}}) + \cdots + (y_{iM} - \bar{\bar{Y}})$$

Square and sum over all N clusters,

$$\sum_i^N (y_i - \bar{Y})^2 = \sum_i^N \sum_j^M (y_{ij} - \bar{\bar{Y}})^2 + 2\sum_i^N \sum_{j<k}^M (y_{ij} - \bar{\bar{Y}})(y_{ik} - \bar{\bar{Y}})$$

$$= (NM-1)S^2 + (M-1)(NM-1)\rho S^2$$

$$= (NM-1)S^2[1 + (M-1)\rho] \tag{9.8a}$$

using the definition of ρ in (9.6). Substitute in (9.8) for $V(\bar{\bar{y}})$. This gives

$$V(\bar{\bar{y}}) = \frac{1-f}{n} \cdot \frac{NM-1}{M^2(N-1)} S^2[1 + (M-1)\rho]$$

This completes the proof.

If a simple random sample of nM elements is taken, the formula for $V(\bar{\bar{y}})$ is the same as (9.7) except for the term in braces. The factor

$$1 + (M-1)\rho$$

shows by how much the variance is changed by the use of a cluster instead of an element as sampling unit. If $\rho > 0$, the cluster is less precise for a given bulk of sample. If $\rho < 0$, as sometimes happens, the cluster is more precise. This result is a simple extension of theorem 8.2.

An alternative expression can be given for ρ. Let S_b^2 denote the variance among cluster totals, on a single unit basis. Then

$$\sum (y_i - \bar{Y})^2 = (N-1)MS_b^2$$

Equation 9.8a can be rewritten as

$$(N-1)MS_b^2 = (NM-1)S^2[1 + (M-1)\rho]$$

so that

$$\rho = \frac{(N-1)MS_b^2 - (NM-1)S^2}{(NM-1)(M-1)S^2} \doteq \frac{S_b^2 - S^2}{(M-1)S^2}$$

A good discussion of the numerical values of ρ for different items and different sizes of cluster is given by Hansen, Hurwitz, and Madow (1953), who regard ρ as a "measure of homogeneity" of the cluster.

9.5 VARIANCE FUNCTIONS

In some types of surveys, for example, soil sampling, crop cutting, and surveys of farming that utilize an areal sampling unit, the size of the cluster unit may be capable of almost continuous variation. In the search for the best unit the problem is not that of choosing between two or three specific sizes that have been tried but of finding the optimum value of M regarded as a continuous variable. This problem requires a method of predicting the variance S_b^2 between units in the population as a function of M. By the analysis of variance, S_b^2 can be found if we know (a) the variance S^2 between all elements in the population and (b) the variance S_w^2 between elements that lie in the same unit. Our approach is to predict S_w^2 and S^2 and to find S_b^2 by the analysis of variance.

The sample data produce estimates of S^2 and S_w^2 for the size of unit actually used. Since S^2 is the variance among elements, it is not affected by the size of the unit. However, S_w^2 will be affected. It might be expected to increase as the size of the large unit increases. If the large units to be examined differ little in size from the unit actually used, a first approximation is to regard S_w^2 as constant, using the estimate given by the sample data. An investigation by McVay (1947) suggests that this approximation may often be satisfactory.

As a better approximation, attempts have been made (Jessen, 1942; Mahalanobis, 1944; Hendricks, 1944) to develop a general law to predict how S_w^2 changes with the size of unit. In several agricultural surveys, S_w^2 appeared to be related to M by the empirical formula

$$S_w^2 = AM^g \qquad (g > 0) \tag{9.9}$$

where A and g are constants that do not depend on M. In this formula S_w^2 increases steadily as M increases. Usually g is small. A curve of this type might be expected when there are forces that exert a similar influence on elements close together. Climate, soil type, topography, and access to markets tend to give neighboring farms similar features.

Theoretically, the formula is open to objection, since it makes S_w^2 increase without bound as M increases. If we assume, as seems reasonable, that there is no correlation between elements that are far apart, a formula in which S_w^2 approaches an upper bound with large M would be more appropriate. However, any formula will suffice if it gives a good fit over the range of M that is under investigation.

If this formula fits, $\log S_w^2$ should plot as a straight line against $\log M$. Values of S_w^2 for at least two values of M are needed in order to estimate the constants $\log A$ and g. At least three values of M are necessary for any appraisal of the linearity of the fit.

From the analysis of variance in Table 9.5 (p. 240) we find

$$S_b^2 = \frac{(NM - 1)S^2 - N(M - 1)S_w^2}{N - 1}$$

$$= \frac{(NM - 1)S^2 - N(M - 1)AM^g}{N - 1} \tag{9.10}$$

$$\doteq MS^2 - (M - 1)AM^g \tag{9.11}$$

Hendricks (1944) has pointed out that the complete population might be regarded as a single large sampling unit containing NM elements. If (9.9) holds, then $S^2 = A(NM)^g$. The advantage of this device is that the values of A and g can now be estimated from the data for a survey in which only one value of M was used. The two equations that lead to the estimates are

$$\log S_w^2 = \log A + g \log M$$
$$\log S^2 = \log A + g \log (NM)$$

The formula for S_b^2 becomes [from (9.10)]

$$S_b^2 = \frac{AM^g[(NM - 1)N^g - N(M - 1)]}{N - 1}$$

This method furnishes no check on the correctness of (9.9). It might happen that the formula held well enough for small values of M but failed for a value as large as NM. In this event the more general formulas (9.10) and (9.11) should be employed.

Formula 9.9 is presented as an example of the methodology rather than as a general law. The reader who faces a similar problem should construct and test whatever type of formula seems most appropriate to his material. In some cases $\log S_b^2$ might be a simple function of M.

9.6 A COST FUNCTION

In an extensive survey the nature of the field costs plays a large part in determining the optimum unit. As an illustration of the role of cost factors, we shall describe a cost function developed by Jessen (1942) for farm surveys in which the large units are clusters of neighboring farms.

Two components of field cost are distinguished. The component c_1Mn comprises costs that vary directly with the total number of elements (farms).

Thus c_1 contains the cost of the interview and the cost of travel from farm to farm within the cluster.

The second component, $c_2 \sqrt{n}$, measures the cost of travel between the clusters. Tests on a map showed that this cost, for a fixed population, varies approximately as the square root of the number of clusters. Total field cost is therefore

$$C = c_1 Mn + c_2 \sqrt{n} \qquad (9.12)$$

Assuming simple random sampling and ignoring the fpc, the variance of the mean per element $\bar{\bar{y}}$ is S_b^2/nM. From (9.11), this equals

$$V(\bar{\bar{y}}) = \frac{S^2 - (M-1)AM^{g-1}}{n} \qquad (9.13)$$

To determine the optimum size of unit, we find M, and incidentally n, to minimize V for fixed C. The general solution is complicated, although its application in a numerical problem presents no great difficulty.

By some manipulation we can obtain the equation that gives the optimum M. First solve the cost equation (9.12) as a quadratic in $\sqrt{n}$. This gives

$$\frac{2c_1 M \sqrt{n}}{c_2} = \left(1 + \frac{4Cc_1 M}{c_2{}^2}\right)^{\frac{1}{2}} - 1 \qquad (9.14)$$

The equation to be minimized is

$$C + \lambda V = c_1 Mn + c_2 \sqrt{n} + \lambda V$$

Differentiating, and noting that $\partial V/\partial n = -V/n$, we obtain the equations

n:
$$c_1 M + \tfrac{1}{2} c_2 n^{-\frac{1}{2}} = -\frac{\lambda \, \partial V}{\partial n} = \frac{\lambda V}{n} \qquad (9.15)$$

M:
$$c_1 n = -\frac{\lambda \, \partial V}{\partial M} \qquad (9.16)$$

Divide (9.16) by (9.15) to eliminate λ. This leads to

$$\frac{n}{V} \frac{\partial V}{\partial M} = -\frac{c_1 n}{c_1 M + \tfrac{1}{2} c_2 n^{-\frac{1}{2}}}$$

or

$$\frac{M}{V} \frac{\partial V}{\partial M} = -\frac{1}{1 + c_2/2c_1 M \sqrt{n}} \qquad (9.17)$$

If we substitute for $\sqrt{n}$ from (9.14), we obtain, after some simplification,

$$\frac{M}{V} \frac{\partial V}{\partial M} = \left(1 + \frac{4Cc_1 M}{c_2{}^2}\right)^{-\frac{1}{2}} - 1$$

By writing out the left side of this equation in full and changing signs on both sides, we find

$$\frac{AM^{g-1}[gM - (g - 1)]}{S^2 - (M - 1)AM^{g-1}} = 1 - \left(1 + \frac{4Cc_1M}{c_2{}^2}\right)^{-\frac{1}{2}}$$

This equation gives the optimum M. The left side does not involve any of the cost factors, being dependent only on the shape of the variance function. Both sides can be seen to be increasing functions of M, for $g > 0$, $M \geq 1$, within the region of interest. Suppose that the solution has been found for specified values of C, c_1, and c_2, and we wish to examine the effect of an increase in c_1 on this solution. The left side does not depend on c_1, but the right side increases as c_1 increases. Consequently the optimum value of M will decrease. A decrease in c_2 produces a similar effect.

Now c_1 increases if the length of interview increases, whereas c_2 decreases if travel becomes cheaper or if the farms in a given area become denser. These facts lead to the conclusion that the optimum size of unit becomes *smaller* when

> length of interview increases
> travel becomes cheaper
> the elements (farms) become more dense
> total amount of money used (C) increases

This conclusion is a consequence of the type of cost function and would require re-examination with a different function. It illustrates the fact that the optimum unit is not a fixed characteristic of the population, but depends also on the type of survey and on the levels of prices and wages.

Hansen, Hurwitz, and Madow (1953) give an excellent discussion of the construction of cost functions for surveys involving cluster sampling.

9.7 CLUSTER SAMPLING FOR PROPORTIONS

The same techniques apply to cluster sampling for proportions. Suppose that the M elements in any cluster can be classified into two classes and that $p_i = a_i/M$ is the proportion in class C in the ith cluster. A simple random sample of n clusters is taken, and the average p of the observed p_i in the sample is used as the estimate of the population proportion P.

It will be recalled (section 3.12) that we cannot use binomial theory to find $V(p)$ but must apply the formula for continuous variates to the p_i. This gives

$$V(p) = \frac{N - n}{Nn} \frac{\sum\limits_{i=1}^{N}(p_i - P)^2}{N - 1} \doteq \frac{N - n}{N^2n} \sum (p_i - P)^2$$

Alternatively, if we take a simple random sample of nM elements, the variance of p is obtained by binomial theory (theorem 3.2) as

$$V_{bin}(p) = \frac{(NM - nM)}{NM - 1}\frac{PQ}{nM} \doteq \frac{N - n}{N}\frac{PQ}{nM}$$

if N is large. Consequently the factor

$$\frac{V(p)}{V_{bin}(p)} \doteq \frac{M \sum (p_i - P)^2}{NPQ} \qquad (N \text{ large}) \qquad (9.18)$$

shows the relative change in the variance due to the use of clusters. Numerical values of this factor are helpful in making preliminary estimates of sample size with cluster sampling. The required sample size is first estimated by the binomial formula and then multiplied by the factor to indicate the size that will be necessary with cluster sampling. For an illustration, see Cornfield (1951).

If the cluster sizes M_i are variable, the estimate $p = \sum a_i / \sum M_i$ is a ratio estimate. Its variance is given approximately by the formula (section 3.12)

$$V(p) \doteq \frac{N - n}{Nn\bar{M}^2} \frac{\sum_{i=1}^{N} M_i^2 (p_i - P)^2}{N - 1}$$

where $\bar{M} = \sum M_i / N$ is the average size of cluster.

If this sample is compared with a simple random sample of $n\bar{M}$ elements, we find, as a generalization of (9.18),

$$\frac{V(p)}{V_{bin}(p)} \doteq \frac{\sum M_i^2 (p_i - P)^2}{N\bar{M}PQ} \qquad (9.19)$$

As with continuous variates, the relationship of size of cluster to between-cluster variance can be investigated, either by expressing the factor in (9.18) and (9.19) as a function of $\bar{M}$, or by seeking a relation between the within-cluster variance and $\bar{M}$. If we assign the value 1 to any unit that falls in class C and 0 to any other unit, the fundamental analysis of variance equation for fixed M is

$$NMP(1 - P) = M \sum (p_i - P)^2 + M \sum p_i(1 - p_i)$$

total ss = ss between clusters + ss within clusters

From this relation the mean square within clusters can be computed and plotted as a function of M. McVay (1947) describes how this analysis can be used to investigate optimum cluster size.

9.8 CLUSTER UNITS OF UNEQUAL SIZES

When the cluster units contain different numbers of elements, there are several methods of estimating population totals and means. These are discussed in the remainder of this chapter. Let M_i be the number of elements in the ith unit. As a practical point, note that in some surveys the values of all the M_i in the population are known exactly, or almost so, in advance—for instance, when the elements are the employees in a firm with up-to-date records and the cluster units are the firm's branches. In others the M_i are not known, except that the M_i for those units that fall in the sample become known during the field work. For any proposed estimate, the sampler must satisfy himself that he possesses the knowledge of the M_i that the estimate demands.

Consider first the estimation of the population *total* Y of the Y_{ij} from a simple random sample of n cluster units.

Unbiased Estimate

As before, let

$$y_i = \sum_{j=1}^{M_i} y_{ij} = M_i \bar{y}_i$$

denote the item *total* for the ith unit. By the corollary in theorem 2.1, an unbiased estimate of Y is

$$\hat{Y} = \frac{N}{n} \sum_{i=1}^{n} y_i \qquad (9.20)$$

By theorem 2.2, corollary 2, its variance is

$$V(\hat{Y}) = \frac{N^2(1-f)}{n} \frac{\sum_{i=1}^{N}(y_i - \bar{Y})^2}{N-1} \qquad (9.21)$$

where $\bar{Y} = Y/N$ is the population mean per unit.

The estimate $\hat{Y}$ is often found to be of poor precision. This occurs when the $\bar{y}_i$ (means per *element*) vary little from unit to unit and the M_i vary greatly. In this event the $y_i = M_i \bar{y}_i$ also vary greatly from unit to unit and the variance in (9.21) is large.

Ratio to Size Estimate

$$M_0 = \sum_{i=1}^{N} M_i = \text{total number of elements in the population}$$

If M_0 is known, an alternative is a ratio estimate in which M_i is taken as the auxiliary variate x_i.

$$\hat{Y}_R = M_0 \frac{\sum\limits_{i=1}^{n} y_i}{\sum\limits_{i=1}^{n} M_i} = M_0 \text{ (sample mean per element)}$$

In the notation of the ratio estimate the population ratio $R = Y/X = Y/M_0 = \overline{\overline{Y}}$, the population mean per element. By theorem 6.1, assuming that the number of clusters in the sample is large,

$$V(\hat{Y}_R) \doteq \frac{N^2(1-f)}{n} \frac{\sum\limits_{i=1}^{N}(y_i - M_i\overline{\overline{Y}})^2}{N-1} \tag{9.22}$$

$$\doteq \frac{N^2(1-f)}{n} \frac{\sum\limits_{i}^{N} M_i^2(\bar{y}_i - \overline{\overline{Y}})^2}{N-1} \tag{9.23}$$

As (9.23) shows, the variance of $\hat{Y}_R$ depends on the variability among the means per element and is often found to be much smaller than $V(\hat{Y})$. The corresponding estimates of the population *mean per element* are

$$\hat{\overline{\overline{Y}}} = \frac{\hat{Y}}{M_0} = \frac{N}{nM_0}\sum_{i}^{n} y_i, \qquad \hat{\overline{\overline{Y}}}_R = \frac{\hat{Y}_R}{M_0} = \frac{\sum\limits^{n} y_i}{\sum\limits^{n} M_i} = \text{sample mean per element}$$

Note that the unbiased estimate $\hat{\overline{\overline{Y}}}$ requires a knowledge of M_0, whereas the ratio estimate requires a knowledge of only the M_i that fall into the sample.

Mean of the Unit Means

A third possibility is to use the unweighted mean of the unit means, that is,

$$\bar{y}' = \frac{1}{n}(\bar{y}_1 + \bar{y}_2 + \cdots + \bar{y}_n) \tag{9.24}$$

When the M_i vary, this estimate is not only biased but inconsistent. The bias may, however, be unimportant if $\bar{y}_i$ is uncorrelated with M_i, and the estimate is occasionally useful. Its properties have been investigated by Sukhatme (1954).

9.9 SAMPLING WITH PROBABILITY PROPORTIONAL TO SIZE

If all the M_i are known, another technique, suggested by Hansen and Hurwitz (1943), is to select the units with probabilities proportional to their sizes M_i. This technique has found its principal use in surveys which employ subsampling (Chapter 11), but it is also applicable to the present problem. Sampling with probability proportional to size is illustrated in the following example of a small population of seven units:

Unit	Size M_i	$\sum M_i$	Assigned Range
1	3	3	1–3
2	1	4	4
3	11	15	5–15
4	6	21	16–21
5	4	25	22–25
6	2	27	26–27
7	3	30	28–30

The cumulative sum of the M_i is formed. To select a unit, we draw a random number between 1 and 30: suppose that this is 19. In the sum number 19 falls in unit 4, which covers numbers 16 to 21 inclusive. With this method of drawing, the probability that any unit is selected is proportional to the size of the unit.

If a second unit is to be selected, the process is repeated with a new random number between 1 and 30. However, contrary to our previous practice, we do not forbid the selection of unit 4 a second time. Selection with replacement is necessary, when n exceeds 1, in order to keep the probabilities of selection proportional to the sizes. This may be seen by the extreme case $n = 7$. If selection were made without replacement, all units would automatically be chosen, even though we had gone through the procedure of selection with probability proportional to size. For values of n between 1 and 7, selection without replacement leads to probabilities that are intermediate between equal probabilities and probabilities proportional to size.

The advantage of sampling with replacement is that the formulas for the true and estimated variances of the estimates are simple. In general, sampling with replacement is less precise than sampling without replacement. When n/N is small, however, the chance that the same unit appears twice in the sample is small, and sampling with replacement is almost equivalent to sampling without replacement. For situations in which the N's are small, as in stratified sampling, much research has been done in recent years to develop practicable methods of sampling with unequal probabilities and without replacement (see section 9.14).

9.10 THEORY FOR SELECTION WITH ARBITRARY PROBABILITIES

If the ith unit is selected with probability $z_i = M_i/M_0$ and with replacement, we shall show that an unbiased estimate of the population total Y is

$$\hat{Y}_{pps} = \frac{M_0}{n}(\bar{y}_1 + \bar{y}_2 + \cdots + \bar{y}_n)$$

$$= M_0 \text{ (mean of the unit means per element)} \qquad (9.25)$$

where $M_0 = \sum M_i =$ total number of elements in the population. Further,

$$V(\hat{Y}_{pps}) = \frac{M_0}{n} \sum_{i=1}^{N} M_i(\bar{y}_i - \bar{\bar{Y}})^2 \qquad (9.26)$$

so that the variance of $\hat{Y}_{pps}$, like that of $\hat{Y}_R$, depends on the variability of the unit means per element.

In some applications the sizes are known only approximately. In others the "size" is not the number of elements in the unit but simply a measure of its bigness that is thought to be highly correlated with the unit total y_i. For instance, the "size" of a hospital might be measured by the total number of beds or by the average number of occupied beds. Similarly, various measures of the "size" of a restaurant, a bank, or a farm can be devised. Consequently, we shall consider sampling with probability proportional to an *estimate* or measure of size M_i' (*ppes* sampling). If $z_i = M_i'/M_0'$ where $M_0' = \sum M_i'$, it will be shown that

$$\hat{Y}_{ppes} = \frac{1}{n} \sum_{i=1}^{n} \frac{y_i}{z_i} \qquad (9.27)$$

is an unbiased estimate of Y with variance

$$V(\hat{Y}_{ppes}) = \frac{1}{n} \sum_{i=1}^{N} z_i \left(\frac{y_i}{z_i} - Y\right)^2 \qquad (9.28)$$

Results (9.27) and (9.28) are generalizations of the results (9.25) and (9.26).

The proofs utilize a method introduced in section 2.8. Let t_i be the number of times that the ith unit appears in a specific sample of size n, where t_i may have any of the values $0, 1, 2, \cdots, n$. Consider the joint frequency distribution of the t_i for all N units in the population.

The method of drawing the sample is equivalent to the standard probability problem in which n balls are thrown into N boxes, the probability that a ball goes into the ith box being z_i at every throw. Consequently the joint distribution of the t_i is the multinomial expression

$$\frac{n!}{t_1! \, t_2! \cdots t_N!} \, z_1^{t_1} z_2^{t_2} \cdots z_N^{t_N}$$

For the multinomial, the following properties of the distribution of the t_i are well known:

$$E(t_i) = nz_i, \quad V(t_i) = nz_i(1 - z_i), \quad \mathrm{Cov}\,(t_i t_j) = -nz_i z_j \qquad (9.29)$$

Theorem 9.3. If a sample of n units is drawn with probabilities z_i and with replacement, then

$$\hat{Y}_{ppes} = \frac{1}{n} \sum_{i=1}^{n} \frac{y_i}{z_i} \qquad (9.27)$$

is an unbiased estimate of Y with variance

$$V(\hat{Y}_{ppes}) = \frac{1}{n} \sum_{i=1}^{N} z_i \left(\frac{y_i}{z_i} - Y \right)^2 \qquad (9.28)$$

Proof. We may write

$$\hat{Y}_{ppes} = \frac{1}{n} \left(t_1 \frac{y_1}{z_1} + t_2 \frac{y_2}{z_2} + \cdots + t_N \frac{y_N}{z_N} \right) = \frac{1}{n} \sum_{i=1}^{N} t_i \frac{y_i}{z_i}$$

where the sum extends over all units in the population. In repeated sampling the t's are the random variables, whereas the y_i and the z_i are a set of fixed numbers. Hence, since $E(t_i) = nz_i$ by (9.29),

$$E(\hat{Y}_{ppes}) = \frac{1}{n} \sum_{i=1}^{N} (nz_i) \frac{y_i}{z_i} = \sum_{i=1}^{n} y_i = Y$$

Further

$$V(\hat{Y}_{ppes}) = \frac{1}{n^2} \left[\sum_{i=1}^{N} \left(\frac{y_i}{z_i} \right)^2 V(t_i) + 2 \sum_{i<j}^{N} \frac{y_i}{z_i} \frac{y_j}{z_j} \mathrm{Cov}\,(t_i t_j) \right]$$

$$= \frac{1}{n} \left[\sum_{i=1}^{N} \left(\frac{y_i}{z_i} \right)^2 z_i(1 - z_i) - 2 \sum_{i<j}^{N} \frac{y_i}{z_i} \frac{y_j}{z_j} z_i z_j \right]$$

$$= \frac{1}{n} \left(\sum \frac{y_i^2}{z_i} - Y^2 \right) = \frac{1}{n} \sum z_i \left(\frac{y_i}{z_i} - Y \right)^2$$

since $\sum z_i = 1$.

Taking $z_i = M_i/M_0$ in theorem 9.3 gives the corresponding results for sampling with probability proportional to size.

Theorem 9.4. If a sample of n units is drawn with probabilities $z_i = M_i/M_0$ and with replacement, then

$$\hat{Y}_{pps} = \frac{M_0}{n}(\bar{y}_1 + \bar{y}_2 + \cdots + \bar{y}_n) \tag{9.25}$$

is an unbiased estimate of Y with variance

$$V(\hat{Y}_{pps}) = \frac{M_0}{n}\sum_{i=1}^{N}M_i(\bar{y}_i - \bar{\bar{Y}})^2 \tag{9.26}$$

Proof. Putting $z_i = M_i/M_0$ in theorem 9.3, we obtain

$$\hat{Y}_{ppes} = \frac{1}{n}\sum_{i=1}^{n}\frac{y_i}{z_i} = \frac{M_0}{n}\sum_{i=1}^{n}\frac{y_i}{M_i} = \frac{M_0}{n}\sum_{i=1}^{n}\bar{y}_i = \hat{Y}_{pps}$$

$$V(\hat{Y}_{pps}) = \frac{1}{n}\sum_{i=1}^{N}z_i\left(\frac{y_i}{z_i} - Y\right)^2$$

$$= \frac{1}{n}\sum_{i=1}^{N}\frac{M_i}{M_0}\left(\frac{M_0 y_i}{M_i} - Y\right)^2 = \frac{M_0}{n}\sum_{i=1}^{N}M_i(\bar{y}_i - \bar{\bar{Y}})^2$$

since $\bar{\bar{Y}} = Y/M_0$.

Corollary. An unbiased estimate of $\bar{\bar{Y}}$ is

$$\hat{\bar{Y}}_{pps} = \frac{1}{n}(\bar{y}_1 + \bar{y}_2 + \cdots + \bar{y}_n)$$

with variance

$$V(\hat{\bar{Y}}_{pps}) = \frac{1}{nM_0}\sum_{i=1}^{N}M_i(\bar{y}_i - \bar{\bar{Y}})^2 \tag{9.30}$$

The next two theorems show how to estimate the variance from the sample.

Theorem 9.5. Under the conditions of theorem 9.3, an unbiased estimate of $V(\hat{Y}_{ppes})$ is

$$v(\hat{Y}_{ppes}) = \sum_{i=1}^{n}\frac{[(y_i/z_i) - \hat{Y}_{ppes}]^2}{n(n-1)} \tag{9.31}$$

Proof. By the usual algebraic identity we may write

$$\sum_{i=1}^{n}\left(\frac{y_i}{z_i} - \hat{Y}_{ppes}\right)^2 = \sum_{i=1}^{n}\left(\frac{y_i}{z_i} - Y\right)^2 - n(\hat{Y}_{ppes} - Y)^2$$

Hence

$$E\sum_{i=1}^{n}\left(\frac{y_i}{z_i} - \hat{Y}_{ppes}\right)^2 = E\sum_{i=1}^{n}\left(\frac{y_i}{z_i} - Y\right)^2 - nV(\hat{Y}_{ppes})$$

since, by the definition of $V(\hat{Y}_{ppes})$, the mean value of the second term on the right is $-nV(\hat{Y}_{ppes})$. Introducing the variables t_i, we have

$$E \sum_{i=1}^{n} \left(\frac{y_i}{z_i} - \hat{Y}_{ppes}\right)^2 = E \sum_{i=1}^{N} t_i \left(\frac{y_i}{z_i} - Y\right)^2 - nV(\hat{Y}_{ppes})$$

$$= n \sum_{i=1}^{N} z_i \left(\frac{y_i}{z_i} - Y\right)^2 - nV(\hat{Y}_{ppes})$$

that is,

$$n(n-1)E[v(\hat{Y}_{ppes})] = n^2 V(\hat{Y}_{ppes}) - nV(\hat{Y}_{ppes}) = n(n-1)V(\hat{Y}_{ppes})$$

using (9.28) in theorem 9.3. This completes the proof.

Theorem 9.6. If units are drawn with probability $z_i = M_i/M_0$ and with replacement, then

$$v(\hat{Y}_{pps}) = \frac{M_0{}^2}{n(n-1)} \sum_{i=1}^{n} (\bar{y}_i - \bar{\bar{y}})^2 \tag{9.32}$$

is an unbiased estimate of $V(\hat{Y}_{pps})$, where $\bar{\bar{y}}$ is the unweighted mean of the $\bar{y}_i$.

This result is obtained by substituting $z_i = M_i/M_0$ in (9.31). Since $\hat{Y}_{pps} = M_0 \bar{\bar{y}}$, the estimated variance (apart from the multiplier) is the familiar sum of squares of deviations of the $\bar{y}_i$ from their mean.

9.11 THE OPTIMUM MEASURE OF SIZE

In cases in which the measure of size M_i' is some estimate of the bigness of the unit, a question of theoretical interest is: what measure of size minimizes the variance of $\hat{Y}_{ppes}$? Now,

$$V(\hat{Y}_{ppes}) = \frac{1}{n} \sum_{i=1}^{N} z_i \left(\frac{y_i}{z_i} - Y\right)^2 = \frac{1}{n} \left(\sum_{i=1}^{N} \frac{y_i{}^2}{z_i} - Y^2\right)$$

This expression becomes zero if $z_i \propto y_i$: that is, $z_i = y_i/Y$. If the y_i are all positive, this set of z_i is an acceptable set of probabilities. Consequently, the best measures of size are numbers proportional to the item totals y_i for the units.

This result is not of practical importance, for if the y_i were known in advance the sample would be unnecessary. The result suggests that if the y_i are relatively stable through time the most recently available previous values of the y_i may be the best measures of size for this item. In practice, of course, a *single* measure of size must be used for all items in selecting the sample. If there is a choice between different measures of size, the measure that is most nearly proportional to the unit totals of the principal items is likely to be best.

9.12 RELATIVE PRECISIONS OF THE TECHNIQUES

When sampling cluster units of unequal sizes, there is a choice of at least four techniques (assuming that the M_i are known if the technique requires them).

1. Selection: equal probabilities. Estimate $\hat{Y}$ or $\hat{\bar{Y}}$ (unbiased).
2. Selection: equal probabilities. Estimate $\hat{Y}_R$ or $\hat{\bar{Y}}_R$ (ratio).
3. Selection: probability $\propto$ size. Estimate $\hat{Y}_{pps}$ or $\hat{\bar{Y}}_{pps}$.
4. Stratify the units by size. Select with equal probabilities within strata. Estimate as usual for stratified sampling.

Initially, the first three techniques will be compared. There is no simple general rule for deciding which is most precise. The issue depends on the relation (if any) between $\bar{y}_i$ and M_i and on the variance of $\bar{y}_i$ as a function of M_i. The situation most favorable to the ratio and *pps* estimates is that in which the mean per element is unrelated to the size of the cluster ($\bar{y}_i$ uncorrelated with M_i). In order to include populations in which $\bar{y}_i$ may decrease or may increase as M_i increases, we adopt a model of the form

$$\bar{y}_i = \frac{\alpha}{M_i} + \beta + e_i \qquad (9.33)$$

where $E(e_i \mid M_i) = 0$.

Some assumption must also be made about the variance of e_i in clusters of given size. As discussed in section 9.4, the elements in a cluster often have a positive correlation ρ, usually small, which decreases as M_i increases. If we write $\rho = \rho_0 + \rho_1/M_i$, (9.7) in section (9.4) suggests that

$$V(e_i) = V(\bar{y}_i) = \frac{S^2}{M_i}\left[1 + (M_i - 1)\rho\right]$$

$$= S^2\left(\rho_0 + \frac{1 - \rho_0 + \rho_1}{M_i} - \frac{\rho_1}{M_i^2}\right)$$

As a simplification, we assume $V(e_i) = v/M_i^g$, where $g > 0$. Since ρ appears to change relatively slowly with M_i, it seems likely that g lies between 0 and 1. There are, however, variables for which the unit *total* is unrelated to M_i, and for these $g = 2$ may be appropriate.

The comparisons made from this model are based on work by Yates (1960), Des Raj (1954, 1958), Zarkovic (1960) and Cochran (1953), who used similar models.

The comparisons are restricted to surveys in which the fpc is negligible and n is large enough so that the approximate formula for the variance of the ratio estimate holds.

From (9.33), it follows that

$$y_i = \alpha + \beta M_i + e_i M_i$$
$$\bar{Y} = \alpha + \beta \bar{M} \qquad (\bar{M} = \sum M_i / N)$$
$$\bar{\bar{Y}} = \frac{\alpha}{\bar{M}} + \beta$$

For estimating the population mean per element, we have from (9.21), on dividing by $M_0^2 = N^2 \bar{M}^2$,

$$nV(\hat{\bar{Y}}) = \frac{E(y_i - \bar{Y})^2}{\bar{M}^2} = \frac{E[\beta(M_i - \bar{M}) + e_i M_i]^2}{\bar{M}^2}$$
$$= \beta^2 c^2 + \frac{vE(M_i^{2-g})}{\bar{M}^2}$$

where $c^2 = E(M_i - \bar{M})^2 / \bar{M}^2$ is the square of the coefficient of variation of the sizes M_i. For the ratio estimate, from (9.23),

$$nV(\hat{\bar{Y}}_R) = \frac{EM_i^2(\bar{y}_i - \bar{\bar{Y}})^2}{\bar{M}^2} = \frac{EM_i^2[\alpha(1/M_i - 1/\bar{M}) + e_i]^2}{\bar{M}^2}$$
$$= \frac{\alpha^2 c^2}{\bar{M}^2} + \frac{vE(M_i^{2-g})}{\bar{M}^2}$$

From (9.26), for the *pps* estimate,

$$nV(\hat{\bar{Y}}_{pps}) = \frac{EM_i(\bar{y}_i - \bar{\bar{Y}})^2}{\bar{M}} = \frac{EM_i[\alpha(1/M_i - 1/\bar{M}) + e_i]^2}{\bar{M}}$$
$$= \frac{\alpha^2}{\bar{M}} E\left(\frac{1}{M_i} - \frac{1}{\bar{M}}\right) + \frac{vE(M_i^{1-g})}{\bar{M}} \doteq \frac{\alpha^2 c^2}{\bar{M}^2} + \frac{vE(M_i^{1-g})}{\bar{M}}$$

Table 9.7 shows the results separately for $g = 0, 1, 2$, with the term involving v placed first.

Consider first $\alpha = 0$, the case in which $\bar{y}_i$ is unrelated to the size of cluster. In nV_R and nV_{pps}, the second term vanishes. It is clear that

(i) $$V_R < V_{un} \quad \text{for} \quad g = 0, 1, 2$$

If β (which in this case becomes $\bar{\bar{Y}}$) is large, the superiority of the ratio estimate may be great. Incidentally, the case $g = 1$, $\alpha = 0$, applies if elements are assigned to clusters at random; that is, if the cluster unit is as efficient as the element. This is also the case in which the ratio estimate is a best unbiased linear estimate. Further, if $\alpha = 0$,

(ii) $$V_{pps} < V_{un} \quad \text{for} \quad g = 0, 1$$

For $g = 2$, the comparable variances are

$$V_{un} = \frac{v}{\bar{M}^2} + c^2\beta^2, \qquad V_{pps} = \frac{v}{\bar{M}} E\left(\frac{1}{M_i}\right) \doteq \frac{v(1 + c^2)}{\bar{M}^2}$$

Hence pps sampling wins unless $v/\bar{M}^2 > \beta^2$.

When α is not zero, that is, when $\bar{y}_i$ either decreases or increases as M_i increases, the relative performances of the ratio and pps estimates to the simple expansion depend on the relative sizes of α and β. If $\beta = 0$, so

TABLE 9.7

COMPARABLE VALUES OF nV_{un}, nV_R, AND nV_{pps}

g	$V(\bar{y}_i)$	Equal Probability Unbiased Estimate	Equal Probability Ratio Estimate	pps
0	v	$v(1 + c^2) + c^2\beta^2$	$v(1 + c^2) + \dfrac{c^2\alpha^2}{\bar{M}^2}$	$v + \dfrac{\alpha^2}{\bar{M}}\left[E\left(\dfrac{1}{M_i}\right) - \dfrac{1}{\bar{M}}\right]$
1	$\dfrac{v}{M_i}$	$\dfrac{v}{\bar{M}} + c^2\beta^2$	$\dfrac{v}{\bar{M}} + \dfrac{c^2\alpha^2}{\bar{M}^2}$	$\dfrac{v}{\bar{M}} + \dfrac{\alpha^2}{\bar{M}}\left[E\left(\dfrac{1}{M_i}\right) - \dfrac{1}{\bar{M}}\right]$
2	$\dfrac{v}{M_i^2}$	$\dfrac{v}{\bar{M}^2} + c^2\beta^2$	$\dfrac{v}{\bar{M}^2} + \dfrac{c^2\alpha^2}{\bar{M}^2}$	$\dfrac{v}{\bar{M}} E\left(\dfrac{1}{M_i}\right) + \dfrac{\alpha^2}{\bar{M}}\left[E\left(\dfrac{1}{M_i}\right) - \dfrac{1}{\bar{M}}\right]$

that the unit *total* y_i is uncorrelated with M_i, the unbiased estimate always beats the ratio estimate and the pps estimate, except possibly when $g = 0$.

As regards the comparison between V_R and V_{pps}, the coefficients of α^2 are approximately the same in the two expressions. Hence we have, roughly,

$$V_R > V_{pps} \quad \text{if} \quad g = 0;$$
$$V_R = V_{pps} \quad \text{if} \quad g = 1;$$
$$V_R < V_{pps} \quad \text{if} \quad g = 2$$

Realistic comparisons with stratification by size of unit are difficult, since the issue depends on the amount of variation in the M_i that remains within the strata that are set up. If we assume that M_i is constant within strata (the case most favorable to stratified sampling), Table 9.8 shows the values of nV_{st}, comparable to those in Table 9.7, for proportional and Neyman optimum allocation.

The results are as follows. Note that with stratified samples the variance is unaffected by the value of α. If $\alpha = 0$, $V_{\text{prop}} = V_R$ for all three values of g. Further, V_{prop} beats *pps* sampling for $g = 2$, equals it for $g = 1$, and is inferior for $g = 0$. If α differs substantially from zero, stratified sampling is superior to ratio and *pps* sampling. If optimum allocation can be achieved, stratified sampling is never inferior and nearly always superior to the other methods (assuming M_i constant within strata).

TABLE 9.8

COMPARABLE VALUES OF nV_{st}

g	$V(\bar{y}_i)$	Proportional	Optimum
0	v	$v(1 + c^2)$	v
1	$\dfrac{v}{M_i}$	$\dfrac{v}{\bar{M}}$	$\dfrac{v(E\sqrt{M_i})^2}{\bar{M}^2} \doteq \dfrac{v}{\bar{M}}\left(1 - \dfrac{c^2}{8}\right)^2$
2	$\dfrac{v}{M_i^2}$	$\dfrac{v}{\bar{M}^2}$	$\dfrac{v}{\bar{M}^2}$

To summarize, if $\bar{y}_i$ shows no trend or only a slight trend as M_i increases, the ratio and *pps* methods are more precise than unbiased estimation with equal probabilities and may be much more precise. The unbiased estimate is superior if the unit total y_i is uncorrelated with M_i. There is less to choose between the ratio and the *pps* estimates. Since g is expected to lie mostly between 0 and 1, the *pps* estimate is probably more precise on the whole. On the other hand, the ratio estimate is easier to compute and less expensive if it costs more to obtain data from a large unit than from a small unit, since *pps* sampling tends to concentrate on the larger units. If strata can be constructed within which the M_i vary little, stratification performs well, particularly if optimum allocation is feasible. One advantage of the ratio and *pps* methods is that stratification can be used for some other purpose.

9.13 EXTENSION TO STRATIFIED SAMPLING

Selection within strata with probability proportional to an estimate of size is likely to be useful when a stratification has been made by some variable other than size. If the samples within each stratum are small and the total sample is not large, we have seen (section 6.10) that the available variance formulas for ratio estimates are somewhat suspect and that the separate ratio estimate may have a non-negligible bias.

With *ppes* sampling, the estimated population total is the sum of the estimates from the separate strata.

$$\hat{Y}_{ppes} = \sum_{h}^{L} \hat{Y}_h = \sum_{h}^{L} \frac{1}{n_h} \sum_{i}^{n_h} \frac{y_{hi}}{z_{hi}}$$

From theorems 9.3 and 9.5, we obtain

$$V(\hat{Y}_{ppes}) = \sum_{h} \frac{1}{n_h} \sum_{i}^{N_h} z_{hi} \left(\frac{y_{hi}}{z_{hi}} - Y_h \right)^2$$

$$v(\hat{Y}_{ppes}) = \sum_{h} \frac{1}{n_h(n_h - 1)} \sum_{i}^{n_h} \left(\frac{y_{hi}}{z_{hi}} - \hat{Y}_h \right)^2$$

9.14 SAMPLING WITH UNEQUAL PROBABILITIES WITHOUT REPLACEMENT

Much interesting work has been done on methods of selecting units with unequal probabilities but without replacement. In practice, this issue arises mainly in multistage stratified sampling (Chapter 11) in which large cluster units constitute the first stage of sampling. Stratification of the large units may be carried to the point at which the strata contain only a small number of units, so that the first-stage sampling fractions n_h/N_h are not negligible. However, most of the methods were developed first for single-stage sampling, in which the algebra is simpler.

Suppose that two units are to be drawn from a stratum. The first unit is drawn with probability proportional to size. Let the ith unit be selected at the first draw and let its relative size be z_i, where $\Sigma z_i = 1$. At the second draw one of the remaining units is selected with probability proportional to relative size, that is, with probability $z_j/(1 - z_i)$ for the jth unit. Hence the total probability that the ith unit will be selected at either the first or second draw is

$$\pi_i = z_i + \sum_{j \neq i}^{N} \frac{z_j z_i}{1 - z_j} \qquad (9.34)$$

$$= z_i + \sum_{j=1}^{N} \frac{z_i z_j}{1 - z_j} - \frac{z_i^2}{1 - z_i}$$

$$= z_i \left(1 + A - \frac{z_i}{1 - z_i} \right) \qquad (9.35)$$

where $A = \Sigma z_j/(1 - z_j)$ taken over all N units.

The expected number of units to be drawn is $\Sigma \pi_i$. Since two units are certain to be drawn by this process, we must have $\Sigma \pi_i = 2$, which is easily verified algebraically. Thus the relative probability that the ith unit will appear in the sample is $\pi_i/2 = z_i'$ (say). With this method of drawing, the z_i' are always closer to equality than the z_i. In the example given by Yates and Grundy (1953), with $N = 4$, $z_i = 0.1, 0.2, 0.3$, and 0.4, the z_i' are found to be $0.1173, 0.2206, 0.3042$, and 0.3579. The distortion of the probabilities is not great, considering that half the units are selected.

Suppose now that a sample of n units is selected, without replacement, by an extension of this method or by some other method. Let

π_i = probability that the ith unit is in the sample

π_{ij} = probability that the ith and jth units are both in the sample

The following relations hold:

$$\sum_i^N \pi_i = n, \qquad \sum_{j \neq i}^N \pi_{ij} = (n - 1)\pi_i, \qquad \sum_i^N \sum_{j > i}^N \pi_{ij} = \tfrac{1}{2}n(n - 1) \quad (9.36)$$

To establish the second relation, let $P(s)$ denote the probability of a sample consisting of n *specified* units. Then $\pi_{ij} = \Sigma P(s)$ over all samples containing the ith and jth units, and $\pi_i = \Sigma P(s)$ over all samples containing the ith unit. When we take $\Sigma \pi_{ij}$ for $j \neq i$, every $P(s)$ for a sample containing the ith unit is counted $(n - 1)$ times in the sum, since there are $(n - 1)$ other values of j in the sample. This proves the second relation. The third relation follows from the second.

We now show how to obtain an unbiased estimate of the stratum total Y and its variance and estimated variance. If $z_i' = \pi_i/n$, the estimate is

$$\hat{Y}_U = \frac{1}{n} \sum_i^n \frac{y_i}{z_i'} \quad (9.37)$$

where y_i is the measurement for the ith unit. Let t_i $(i = 1, 2, \cdots N)$ be a random variable which takes the value 1 if the ith unit is drawn and zero otherwise. Then t_i follows the binomial distribution for a sample of size 1, with probability π_i. Thus

$$E(t_i) = \pi_i = nz_i', \qquad V(t_i) = \pi_i(1 - \pi_i)$$

The value of $\mathrm{Cov}\,(t_i t_j)$ is also required. Since $t_i t_j$ is 1 only if both units appear in the sample,

$$\mathrm{Cov}\,(t_i t_j) = E(t_i t_j) - E(t_i)\,E(t_j) = \pi_{ij} - \pi_i \pi_j$$

Hence, regarding the y_i as fixed and the t_i as random variables,

$$E(\hat{Y}_U) = E\,\frac{1}{n}\left(\sum_{i=1}^N \frac{t_i y_i}{z_i'} \right) = \sum_{i=1}^N y_i = Y$$

$$V(\hat{Y}_U) = \frac{1}{n^2}\left[\sum_i^N \left(\frac{y_i}{z_i'}\right)^2 V(t_i) + 2\sum_i^N \sum_{j>i}^N \frac{y_i}{z_i'}\frac{y_j}{z_j'}\mathrm{Cov}\,(t_i t_j) \right]$$

$$= \frac{1}{n^2}\left[\sum_i^N \left(\frac{y_i}{z_i'}\right)^2 \pi_i(1 - \pi_i) + 2\sum_i^N \sum_{j>i}^N \frac{y_i}{z_i'}\frac{y_j}{z_j'}(\pi_{ij} - \pi_i \pi_j) \right] \quad (9.38)$$

These results were given by Horvitz and Thompson (1952). An alternative expression for the variance can be obtained by using the first two of the relations in (9.36). These give

$$\sum_{j \neq i} (\pi_{ij} - \pi_i \pi_j) = (n - 1)\pi_i - \pi_i(n - \pi_i) = -\pi_i(1 - \pi_i)$$

Hence, substituting for $\pi_i(1 - \pi_i)$ in (9.38),

$$V(\hat{Y}_U) = \frac{1}{n^2} \sum_i^N \sum_{j>i}^N \left\{ (\pi_i \pi_j - \pi_{ij}) \left[\left(\frac{y_i}{z_i{}'} \right)^2 + \left(\frac{y_j}{z_j{}'} \right)^2 - 2 \frac{y_i}{z_i{}'} \frac{y_j}{z_j{}'} \right] \right\}$$

This may be expressed as

$$V(\hat{Y}_U) = \frac{1}{n^2} \sum_i^N \sum_{j>i}^N (\pi_i \pi_j - \pi_{ij}) \left(\frac{y_i}{z_i{}'} - \frac{y_j}{z_j{}'} \right)^2 \qquad (9.39)$$

It follows that an unbiased sample estimate of this variance is

$$v(\hat{Y}_U) = \frac{1}{n^2} \sum_i^n \sum_{j>i}^n \frac{\pi_i \pi_j - \pi_{ij}}{\pi_{ij}} \left(\frac{y_i}{z_i{}'} - \frac{y_j}{z_j{}'} \right)^2 \qquad (9.40)$$

provided that π_{ij} does not vanish for any pair of units. This estimate is due to Yates and Grundy (1953).

These equations supply a sampling theory for selection without replacement. For practical application, there are difficulties. As n increases, it becomes harder with any method of selection to keep the $z_i{}'$ close to the original z_i. The quantities π_i and π_{ij} become complicated to calculate. The estimated variance (9.40) tends to be an unstable quantity because the terms $(\pi_i \pi_j - \pi_{ij})/\pi_{ij}$ vary widely, being sometimes negative. Some ingenious approaches that attempt to surmount these differences are described in the next section.

9.15 ALTERNATIVE APPROACHES

Narain (1951) constructed original probabilities of selection such that the final probabilities are proportional to the sizes. For example, consider $n = 2$. If we want $\pi_i = 2z_i$, (9.35) in section 9.14 shows that the original probabilities Z_i must satisfy the equations

$$2z_i = Z_i \left(1 + \sum^N \frac{Z_i}{1 - Z_i} - \frac{Z_i}{1 - Z_i} \right)$$

Methods for solving these equations are given by Narain and by Yates and Grundy. The computations are tedious for $n > 2$, and, as with all approaches, the method ultimately breaks down if n is large enough.

Murthy (1957), following work by Des Raj (1956a), uses as an estimate the weighted expression

$$\hat{Y}_M = \frac{\sum\limits^{n} P(s \mid i)y_i}{P(s)}$$

where $P(s \mid i) =$ conditional probability of getting the set of units that was drawn, given that the ith unit was drawn *first*;

$\quad P(s) =$ unconditional probability of getting the set of units that was drawn.

This method applies to any sampling plan in which the probability of drawing the remaining units in the sample does not depend on the *order* in which previous units were drawn, although it may, of course, depend on the sizes of the particular units. Under these conditions the estimate is unbiased, and general expressions for its variance and estimated variance have been given by Murthy. When $n = 2$, this plan has the advantage that the estimate of variance is always positive. The estimate then becomes

$$\hat{Y}_M = \frac{1}{2 - z_i - z_j}\left[(1 - z_j)\frac{y_i}{z_i} + (1 - z_i)\frac{y_j}{z_j}\right]$$

with estimated variance

$$v(\hat{Y}_M) = \frac{(1 - z_i)(1 - z_j)(1 - z_i - z_j)}{(2 - z_i - z_j)^2}\left(\frac{y_i}{z_i} - \frac{y_j}{z_j}\right)^2$$

Des Raj's technique (1956b) assumes that we know the values of an auxiliary variate x_i (which may be the sizes), such that the relation between y_i and x_i is linear. By methods of linear programming, he finds, for $n = 2$, the values of the π_{ij} such that $\pi_i \propto x_i$ and that $V(\hat{Y}_U)$, as given in (9.38), is minimized.

The two remaining methods are applications of techniques already discussed. The first, due to Hartley and Rao (1962), is to arrange the units in random order, cumulate the sizes, and draw an "every kth" systematic sample from the cumulated sizes. If a sample of n units is wanted, we take $k = M_0/n$, draw a random number r between 1 and k, and select the units that contain the numbers $r, r + k, r + 2k$, etc., in the cumulated sizes. If any unit is larger than M_0/n, it has a chance of being selected twice, but otherwise this plan selects with probabilities proportional to the original sizes. The average of the y_i/z_i is an unbiased estimate of Y.

Hartley and Rao give expressions for the variance and estimated variance for this plan in an expansion in inverse powers of N. Its efficiency appears to be similar to that of Narain's method, in which the probabilities also remain proportional to the original sizes. The systematic method avoids the computation of new original probabilities of selection.

Finally, we may subdivide the population into n groups and select *one* unit from each group with probabilities proportional to relative sizes within the group, as described in section 9.9. If the ith unit happens to fall in the first group, its probability of selection is z_i/Z_1, where $Z_1 = \Sigma z_i$, taken over the units in group 1. Consequently, in order to preserve the property of selection with probability proportional to size, the groups should be formed so that as nearly as possible $Z_1 = Z_2 = Z_3$, etc. An unbiased estimate of Y is

$$\hat{Y}_G = \sum_{j}^{n} Z_j \frac{y_j}{z_j}$$

where y_j, z_j are the value and the size for the unit drawn from group j. No unbiased estimate of variance is known, but an overestimate can be obtained by the method of collapsed strata (section 5A.11).

A variant of this plan is to assign units to groups at random, making the *number* of units per group as nearly equal as possible. If $N = Qn + k$, where Q is an integer and $k < n$, we make k of the groups contain $(Q + 1)$ units each. The remaining $(n - k)$ groups have Q units each. The estimate $\hat{Y}_G$ is unbiased. Since the Z_j are in general unequal under this plan, it does not keep the probabilities proportional to z_i. Its advantages, in addition to simplicity in operation, are that explicit expressions are available for the variances. Rao, Hartley, and Cochran (1962) have shown that

$$V(\hat{Y}_G) = \frac{1}{n}\left(1 - \frac{n-1}{N-1} + \frac{k(n-k)}{N(N-1)}\right) \sum_{i}^{N} z_i\left(\frac{y_i}{z_i} - Y\right)^2$$

$$= \left(1 - \frac{n-1}{N-1} + \frac{k(n-k)}{N(N-1)}\right) V(\hat{Y}_{pps})$$

where $\hat{Y}_{pps}$ is the estimate (section 9.10) for sampling with probabilities proportional to z_i and *with replacement*. The first term in parentheses plays the role of an fpc. The expression giving an unbiased estimate of variance is

$$v(\hat{Y}_G) = \frac{N^2 + k(n-k) - Nn}{N^2(n-1) - k(n-k)} \cdot \left[\sum_{j}^{n} z_j\left(\frac{y_j}{z_j} - \hat{Y}_G\right)^2\right]$$

9.16 SOME COMPARISONS FOR $n = 2$

The case $n = 2$ is likely to be the most frequent as well as the simplest. In the choice of a method relevant factors are (*a*) the ease with which the

SINGLE–STAGE CLUSTER SAMPLING

sample can be drawn, (b) the simplicity of the estimate, (c) the accuracy of the estimate and, (d) the availability of an estimate of the variance of the estimate.

No extensive comparisons of the performances of the methods have been made, although a number of them have been applied to three small populations with $N = 4$, $n = 2$, constructed by Yates and Grundy (1953). Six methods are compared here on three populations with $N = 5$, $n = 2$, constructed as follows. The sizes z_i of the units are the same in all three populations (A, B, C). In A the mean *per element*, which is proportional to y_i/z_i, is uncorrelated with z_i. In B the mean per element rises as the sizes increase, and in C the mean per element decreases as the sizes increase.

TABLE 9.9

THREE SMALL ARTIFICIAL POPULATIONS

Relative sizes (z_i)		0.1	0.1	0.2	0.3	0.3
Population A	y_i	0.3	0.5	0.8	0.9	1.5
	y_i/z_i	3	5	4	3	5
Population B	y_i	0.3	0.3	0.8	1.5	1.5
	y_i/z_i	3	3	4	5	5
Population C	y_i	0.5	0.5	0.8	0.9	0.9
	y_i/z_i	5	5	4	3	3

The plans compared are as follows. All give unbiased estimates.

1. The first unit is selected with probability proportional to z_i, the second with probability proportional to remaining sizes. Estimate: $\hat{Y}_U = \frac{1}{2}\Sigma y_i/z_i'$.

2. The original probabilities are chosen, as proposed by Narain, so that $\pi_i = 2z_i$. Estimate: $\hat{Y}_N = \frac{1}{2}\Sigma y_i/z_i$.

3. Units ordered at random and a systematic sample drawn. Estimate: $\hat{Y}_{SYS} = \frac{1}{2}\Sigma y_i/z_i$.

4. Population divided into two groups of equal total sizes. One group comprizes units of sizes 0.1, 0.1, 0.3; the other, units of sizes 0.2, 0.3. (It makes no difference which large unit is placed with the small units). Estimate: $\hat{Y}_{G1} = \Sigma Z_j(y_j/z_j)$.

5. Units arranged at random into one group of three units and one of two units. Estimate: $\hat{Y}_{G2} = \Sigma Z_j(y_j/z_j)$.

6. Units selected with *pps* and with replacement. Estimate: $\hat{Y}_{pps} = \frac{1}{2} \Sigma y_i/z_i$.

Table 9.10 presents the variances. On the average, there is little to choose between the first five methods, all being superior to sampling with replacement. The average variances may be misleading because population *A* may be more typical of the situations in which *pps* sampling is used than *B* and *C*, although cases in which y_i/z_i is correlated with z_i do occur.

TABLE 9.10

VARIANCES FOR THE ESTIMATED POPULATION TOTAL

Population	Estimate					
	$\hat{Y}_U$	$\hat{Y}_N$	$\hat{Y}_{SYS}$	$\hat{Y}_{G1}$	$\hat{Y}_{G2}$	$\hat{Y}_{pps}$
A	0.279	0.244	0.233	0.220	0.320	0.400
B	0.434	0.252	0.273	0.300	0.256	0.320
C	0.120	0.252	0.273	0.300	0.256	0.320
Average	0.278	0.249	0.260	0.273	0.277	0.347

In population *A* the two plans ($\hat{Y}_U$ and $\hat{Y}_{G2}$), which distort the probabilities of selection, appear less accurate than the three that preserve the probabilities.

Unbiased estimates of error are available by (9.40) for $\hat{Y}_U$ and $\hat{Y}_N$, with the drawbacks that the π_{ij} must be computed and the estimate may be rather erratic. The estimate $\hat{Y}_{G2}$ (subdivision into random groups) is the most favorably situated regarding the estimate of error.

EXERCISES

9.1 For the data in Table 9.1 compare the relative costs of using the four types of unit when the object is to estimate the total number of seedlings in the bed with a standard error of 200 seedlings. (Note that the fpc is involved.)

9.2 For the data in Table 3.5 (p. 66) estimate the relative precision of the household to the individual for estimating the sex ratio and the proportion of people who had seen a doctor in the past 12 months, assuming simple random sampling.

9.3 A population consisting of 2500 elements is divided into 10 strata, each containing 50 large units composed of five elements The analysis of variance of the population for an item is as follows, on an element basis:

	df	ms
Between strata	9	30.6
Between large units within strata	490	3.0
Between elements within large units	2000	1.6

Ignoring the fpc, is the relative precision of the large to the small unit greater with simple random sampling than with stratified random sampling (proportional allocation)?

9.4 A population containing $L\bar{N}M$ elements is divided into L strata, each having $\bar{N}$ large units, each of which contains M small units. The following quantities come from the analysis of variance of the population, on an element basis:

S_1^2 = mean square between strata

S_2^2 = mean square between large units within strata

S_3^2 = mean square between elements within strata

If $\bar{N}$ is large and the fpc is ignored, show that the relative precision of the large to the small unit (element) is improved by stratification if

$$\frac{(M-1)}{S_1^2} < \frac{M}{S_2^2} - \frac{1}{S_3^2}$$

9.5 In a rural survey in which the sampling unit is a cluster of M farms, the cost of taking a sample of n units is

$$C = 4tMn + 60\sqrt{n}$$

where t is the time in hours spent getting the answers from a single farmer. If \$2000 is spent on the survey, the values of n for $M = 1, 5, 10$; $t = \frac{1}{2}, 2$, work out as follows.

		M	
	1	5	10
$t = \frac{1}{2}$ hr	400	131	75
$t = 2$ hr	153	40	21

Verify two of these values to ensure that you understand the use of the formula.
The variance of the sample mean (ignoring the fpc) is

$$\frac{S^2}{Mn}[1 + (M-1)\rho]$$

If $\rho = 0.1$ for all M between 1 and 10, which size of unit is most precise for (a) $t = \frac{1}{2}$ hr, (b) $t = 2$ hr? How do you explain the difference in results?

9.6 If \$5000 were available for the survey, would you expect the optimum size of unit to decrease or increase (relative to that for \$2000)? Give reasons. You may, if you wish, find the optimum size in order to check your argument.

9.7 Horvitz and Thompson (1952) give the following data for eye estimates M_i of the numbers of households and for the actual numbers y_i in 20 city blocks in Ames, Iowa. To assist in the calculations, values of $\bar{y}_i$ and $\bar{y}_i^2/M_i$ are also given. A sample of $n = 1$ block is chosen. Compute the variances of the total number of households Y, as obtained by (a) the unbiased estimate in sampling with equal probabilities, (b) the ratio estimate in sampling with equal probabilities, (c) sampling with probability proportional to M_i. (For the ratio estimate, compute the true mean square error, not the approximate formula.)

M_i	y_i	$\bar{y}_i$	y_i^2/M_i	M_i	y_i	$\bar{y}_i$	y_i^2/M_i
9	9	1.0000	9.000	19	19	1.0000	19.000
9	13	1.4444	18.778	21	25	1.1905	29.762
12	12	1.0000	12.000	23	27	1.1739	31.696
12	12	1.0000	12.000	24	21	0.8750	18.375
12	14	1.1667	16.333	24	35	1.4583	51.042
14	17	1.2143	20.643	25	22	0.8800	19.360
14	15	1.0714	16.071	26	25	0.9615	24.038
17	20	1.1765	23.529	27	27	1.0000	27.000
18	19	1.0556	20.056	30	47	1.5667	73.633
18	18	1.0000	18.000	40	37	0.9250	34.225

Do the results agree with the discussion in section 9.12?

9.8   A questionnaire is to be sent to a sample of high schools to find out which schools provide certain facilities, for example, a course in Russian or a swimming pool. If M_i is the number of students in the ith school, the quantity to be estimated for any given facility is the proportion P of high-school students who are in schools having the facility, that is,

$$P = \frac{\displaystyle\sum_w M_i}{\displaystyle\sum_{i=1}^{N} M_i}$$

where $\sum_w$ is a sum over those schools *with* the facility.

A sample of n schools is drawn with probability proportional to M_i with replacement. For one facility, a schools out of n are found to possess it. (a) Show that $\hat{P} = a/n$ is an unbiased estimate of P and that its true variance is $P(1 - P)/n$. (*Hint.* In the corollary to theorem 9.4 let $y_i = M_i$ if the school has the facility and 0 otherwise.) (b) Show that an unbiased estimate of $V(\hat{P})$ is $v(\hat{P}) = \hat{P}(1 - \hat{P})/(n - 1)$.

9.9   The large units in a population arrange themselves into a finite number of size classes: all units in class h contain M_h small units. (a) Under what conditions does sampling with *pps* give, on the average, the same distribution of the size classes in the sample as stratification by size of unit, with optimum allocation for fixed sample size? (b) If the variance among large units in class h is kM_h, where k is a constant for all classes, what system of probabilities of selection of the units gives a sample in which the sizes have approximately the same distribution as a stratified random sample with optimum allocation for fixed sample size?

9.10   For a population with $N = 3$, $z_i = \frac{1}{2}, \frac{1}{3}, \frac{1}{6}$, $y_i = 7, 5, 2$, two units are drawn without replacement, the first with probability proportional to z_i, the second with probability proportional to the remaining sizes. (a) In the notation of section 9.14 verify that $\pi_1 = \frac{51}{60}, \pi_2 = \frac{44}{60}, \pi_3 = \frac{25}{60}$ and that $\pi_{12} = \frac{35}{60}, \pi_{13} = \frac{16}{60}, \pi_{23} = \frac{9}{60}$. (b) Compare the variances or MSE's of $\hat{Y}_U$, $\hat{Y}_{SYS}$, and $\hat{Y}_{G2}$ as defined in section 9.16. (For $\hat{Y}_U$ and $\hat{Y}_{G2}$, either construct all possible estimates or use the variance formulas. For $\hat{Y}_{SYS}$, construct all possible estimates.)

REFERENCES

Cornfield, J. (1951). The determination of sample size. *Amer. Jour. Pub. Health*, **41**, 654–661.

Des Raj (1954). On sampling with probabilities proportional to size. *Ganita*, **5**, 175–182.

Des Raj (1956a). Some estimators in sampling with varying probabilities without replacement. *Jour. Amer. Stat. Assoc.*, **51**, 269–284.

Des Raj (1956b). A note on the determination of optimum probabilities in sampling without replacement. *Sankhyā*, **17**, 197–200.

Des Raj (1958). On the relative accuracy of some sampling techniques. *Jour. Amer. Stat. Assoc.*, **53**, 98–101.

Finkner, A. L., Morgan, J. J., and Monroe, R. J. (1943). Methods of estimating farm employment from sample data in North Carolina. *N. C. Agr. Exp. Sta. Tech. Bull.* 75.

Hansen, M. H., and Hurwitz, W. N. (1943). On the theory of sampling from finite populations. *Ann. Math. Stat.*, **14**, 333–362.

Hansen, M. H., Hurwitz, W. N., and Madow, W. G. (1953). *Sample survey methods and theory*. Vol. I. John Wiley and Sons, New York.

Hartley, H. O., and Rao, J. N. K. (1962). Sampling with unequal probabilities and without replacement. *Ann. Math. Stat.*, **33**, 350–374.

Hendricks, W. A. (1944). The relative efficiencies of groups of farms as sampling units. *Jour. Amer. Stat. Assoc.*, **39**, 367–376.

Homeyer, P. G., and Black, C. A. (1946). Sampling replicated field experiments on oats for yield determinations. *Proc. Soil Sci. Soc. America*, **11**, 341–344.

Horvitz, D. G., and Thompson, D. J. (1952). A generalization of sampling without replacement from a finite universe. *Jour. Amer. Stat. Assoc.*, **47**, 663–685.

Jessen, R. J. (1942). Statistical investigation of a sample survey for obtaining farm facts. *Iowa Agr. Exp. Sta. Res. Bull.* 304.

Johnson, F. A. (1941). A statistical study of sampling methods for tree nursery inventories. M.S. thesis, Iowa State College.

McVay, F. E. (1947). Sampling methods applied to estimating numbers of commercial orchards in a commercial peach area. *Jour. Amer. Stat. Assoc.*, **42**, 533–540.

Mahalanobis, P. C. (1944). On large-scale sample surveys. *Phil. Trans. Roy. Soc. London*, **B231**, 329–451.

Murthy, M. N. (1957). Ordered and unordered estimators in sampling without replacement. *Sankhyā*, **18**, 379–390.

Narain, R. D. (1951). On sampling without replacement with varying probabilities. *Jour. Ind. Soc. Agric. Stat.*, **3**, 169–174.

Rao, J. N. K., Hartley, H. O., and Cochran, W. G. (1962). A simple procedure of unequal probability sampling without replacement. *Jour. Roy. Stat. Soc.*, **B, 24**, (in press).

Sukhatme, P. V. (1947). The problem of plot size in large-scale yield surveys. *Jour. Amer. Stat. Assoc.*, **42**, 297–310.

Sukhatme, P. V. (1954). *Sampling theory of surveys, with applications*, Iowa State College Press, Ames, Iowa.

Yates, F. (1960). Sampling methods for censuses and surveys. Charles Griffin & Sons, London, third edition.

Yates, F., and Grundy, P. M. (1953). Selection without replacement from within strata with probability proportional to size. *Jour. Roy. Stat. Soc.*, **B15**, 253–261.

Zarkovic, S. S. (1960). On the efficiency of sampling with various probabilities and the selection of units with replacement. *Metrika*, **3**, 53–60.

CHAPTER 10

Subsampling with Units
of Equal Size

10.1 TWO-STAGE SAMPLING

Suppose that each unit in the population can be divided into a number of smaller units, or elements. A sample of n units has been selected. If elements within a selected unit give similar results, it seems uneconomical to measure them all. A common practice is to select and measure a sample of the elements in any chosen unit. This technique is called *subsampling*, since the unit is not measured completely but is itself sampled. Another name, due to Mahalanobis, is *two-stage sampling*, because the sample is taken in two steps. The first is to select a sample of units, often called the *primary units*, and the second is to select a sample of elements from each chosen primary unit.

Subsampling has a great variety of applications, which go far beyond the immediate scope of sample surveys. Whenever any process involves chemical, physical, or biological tests that can be performed on a small amount of material, it is likely to be drawn as a subsample from a larger amount which is itself a sample.

In this chapter we consider the simplest case in which every unit contains the same number M of elements, of which m are chosen when any unit is subsampled. A schematic representation of a two-stage sample, in which $M = 9$ and $m = 2$, is shown in Fig. 10.1.

The principal advantage of two-stage sampling is that it is more flexible than one-stage sampling. It reduces to one-stage sampling when $m = M$, but, unless this is the best choice for m, we have the opportunity of taking some smaller value that appears more efficient. As usual, the issue reduces to a balance between statistical precision and cost. When elements in the same unit agree very closely, considerations of precision suggest a small value of m. On the other hand, it is sometimes almost as cheap to measure the whole of a unit as to subsample it; for example, when the unit is a

270

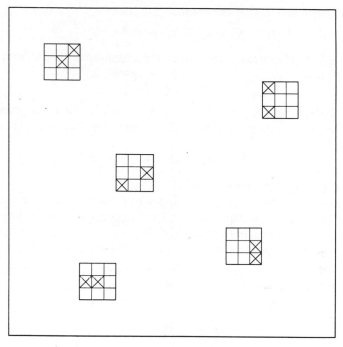

⊠ denotes an element in the sample

Fig. 10.1 Schematic representation of two-stage sampling ($N = 81, n = 5, M = 9,$ $m = 2$).

household and a single respondent can give accurate data about all members of the household.

10.2 TWO USEFUL RESULTS

In two-stage sampling expected values must be found not only over all possible samples of n primary units but also over all possible subsamples that can be drawn from the selected set of primary units. Fortunately, there is a close relation between variances in two-stage sampling and the corresponding variances already obtained for one-stage sampling. Two general results, due to Durbin (1953), will be proved.

If each primary unit contains M subunits, of which m are chosen, the simplest estimates of the population total and mean per subunit are, respectively,

$$\hat{Y} = \frac{NM}{n}(\bar{y}_1 + \bar{y}_2 + \cdots + \bar{y}_n), \qquad \bar{\hat{Y}} = \frac{1}{n}(\bar{y}_1 + \bar{y}_2 + \cdots + \bar{y}_n)$$

where $\bar{y}_i$ is the sample mean per subunit in the ith primary unit.

Both estimates are of the form

$$y' = y_1' + y_2' + \cdots + y_n'$$

where y_i' is an estimate made from the subsample drawn from the ith primary unit. Let

$$Y_i' = E(y_i' \mid i)$$

where the symbol $E(\mid i)$ denotes a mean taken over all subsamples drawn from the ith primary unit. If these means were known, we could construct the estimate

$$\hat{Y}' = Y_1' + Y_2' + \cdots + Y_n'$$

This is the one-stage analogue of y'.

The two theorems to be proved apply to primary units of unequal sizes as well as to those of equal sizes. They also apply when primary units are selected with unequal probability. The symbol π_i denotes the probability that the ith primary unit is drawn in the sample.

Theorem 10.1. If the primary units are drawn without replacement, and subsamples are chosen independently in different units, y' is an unbiased estimate of

$$Y' = \sum_i^N \pi_i Y_i'$$

with variance

$$V(y') = V(\hat{Y}') + \sum_i^N \pi_i \sigma_{2i}^2 \tag{10.1}$$

where

$$\sigma_{2i}^2 = E[(y_i' - Y_i')^2 \mid i]$$

is the variance of y_i' in repeated subsampling from the ith unit.

Proof. To find $E(y')$, average first over all samples that contain the same set of primary units. This average is denoted by $E(y' \mid pu)$. Clearly,

$$E(y' \mid pu) = Y_1' + Y_2' + \cdots + Y_n' = \hat{Y}'$$

When we average further over all selections of the n primary units, the term Y_i' will appear with relative frequency π_i. Hence

$$E(y') = \sum_i^N \pi_i Y_i' = Y'$$

For the variance, we have by definition

$$V(y') = E(y'^2) - [E(y')]^2$$

$$= E\left(\sum_i^n y_i'^2 + 2 \sum_i^n \sum_{j>i}^n y_i' y_j' \right) - [E(y')]^2 \tag{10.2}$$

Average first over samples containing the same set of n primary units. Now

$$E(y_i'^2 \mid i) = Y_i'^2 + \sigma_{2i}^2 \qquad (10.3)$$

Further, if subsampling is independent in different units,

$$E(y_i'y_j' \mid ij) = Y_i'Y_j' \qquad (10.4)$$

Hence, substituting in (10.2) and putting $\hat{Y}'$ for $E(y' \mid pu)$,

$$V(y' \mid pu) = \sum_i^n Y_i'^2 + 2\sum_i^n \sum_{j>i}^n Y_i'Y_j' + \sum_i^n \sigma_{2i}^2 - [E(\hat{Y}')]^2 \qquad (10.5)$$

The conditional variance may be rewritten as

$$V(y' \mid pu) = \hat{Y}'^2 - [E(\hat{Y}')]^2 + \sum_i^n \sigma_{2i}^2$$

Now average over all selections of the primary units. This gives

$$V(y') = V(\hat{Y}') + \sum_i^N \pi_i \sigma_{2i}^2$$

This proves the theorem.

This result may be phrased as follows. In two-stage sampling the variance of an estimate of the form y' consists of two parts. The first, $V(\hat{Y}')$, is the variance obtained by replacing the estimate y_i' from the subsample in the ith unit by its mean Y_i'. This is the between-primary unit component of the variance. The second, $\Sigma \pi_i \sigma_{2i}^2$, is the sum of the within-unit variances of the y_i', each weighted by its probability of selection in the sample.

Corollary 1. Theorem 10.1 is a generalization to two-stage sampling of the result given in (9.38) of section 9.14 for the variance of the estimate when units are chosen with arbitrary probabilities and without replacement. Revert to (10.5), and average over selections of the primary units. If π_{ij} is the probability that a sample contains both the ith and the jth units, this average may be written

$$V(y') = \sum_i^N \pi_i Y_i'^2 + 2\sum_i^N \sum_{j>i}^N \pi_{ij} Y_i'Y_j' + \sum_i^N \pi_i \sigma_{2i}^2 - \left(\sum_i^N \pi_i Y_i'\right)^2$$

$$= \sum_i^N \left[\pi_i(1 - \pi_i)Y_i'^2 + 2\sum_{j>i}^N (\pi_{ij} - \pi_i\pi_j)Y_i'Y_j'\right] + \sum_i^N \pi_i \sigma_{2i}^2 \qquad (10.6)$$

The between-units component reduces to (9.38) if we take $Y_i' = y_i/z_i'$.

Corollary 2. The reader may verify that theorem 10.1 also holds when primary units are drawn *with replacement*, provided that, if a primary unit is drawn more than once, the subsample is selected independently from the whole unit on each occasion. This condition guarantees that equation (10.4) in the proof remains valid.

Theorem 10.2 supplies a sample estimate of $V(y')$, given that we have an unbiased sample estimate $v(\hat{Y}')$ of $V(\hat{Y}')$. In its most general terms, the estimate $v(\hat{Y}')$ will be a quadratic of the form

$$v(\hat{Y}') = \sum_i^n a_{ijk}\ldots Y_i'^2 + 2\sum_i^n\sum_{j>i}^n b_{ijk}\ldots Y_i'Y_j'$$

where the subscripts in a denote the fact that in complex sampling the coefficient of $Y_i'^2$ may depend on the other units that are in the sample with the ith unit, and similarly for the subscripts in b.

Let $v_c(y')$ be a "copy" of $v(\hat{Y}')$, obtained by replacing Y_i' by y_i' wherever Y_i' appears; that is,

$$v_c(y') = \sum_i^n a_{ijk}\ldots y_i'^2 + 2\sum_i^n\sum_{j>i}^n b_{ijk}\ldots y_i'y_j'$$

Theorem 10.2. Under the conditions of theorem 10.1, an unbiased estimate of $V(y')$ is

$$v(y') = v_c(y') + \sum_i^n \pi_i \hat{\sigma}_{2i}^2 \tag{10.7}$$

where $\hat{\sigma}_{2i}^2$ is any unbiased sample estimate of σ_{2i}^2.

Proof. From the definition of $v_c(y')$ and relations (10.3) and (10.4), we have

$$E[v_c(y') \mid pu] = \sum_i^n a_{ijk}\ldots Y_i'^2 + 2\sum_i^n\sum_{j>i}^n b_{ijk}\ldots Y_i'Y_j' + \sum_i^n a_{ijk}\ldots\sigma_{2i}^2$$

$$= v(\hat{Y}') + \sum_i^n a_{ijk}\ldots\sigma_{2i}^2$$

When the average is taken over all selections of the primary units, the coefficient of σ_{2i}^2 is $E(a_{ijk}\ldots)$. From (10.6), this average must be $\pi_i(1 - \pi_i)$ if $v(\hat{Y}')$ is to be an unbiased estimate of $V(\hat{Y}')$. This gives

$$E[v_c(y')] = V(\hat{Y}') + \sum_i^N \pi_i(1 - \pi_i)\sigma_{2i}^2$$

But from theorem 10.1

$$V(y') = V(\hat{Y}') + \sum_i^N \pi_i\sigma_{2i}^2$$

Hence, to obtain an unbiased estimate of $V(y')$, we must add to $v_c(y')$ an unbiased estimate of $\sum^N \pi_i^2\sigma_{2i}^2$. Now

$$E\left(\sum_i^n \pi_i\hat{\sigma}_{2i}^2\right) = \sum_i^N \pi_i^2\sigma_{2i}^2$$

This completes the proof.

This theorem gives the following working rule. To find an unbiased sample estimate of $V(y')$, obtain from results in one-stage sampling an unbiased estimate $v(\hat{Y}')$ of $V(\hat{Y}')$. Compute a copy of this, $v_e(y')$, by replacing Y_i' by y_i' throughout. To this add the term $\sum\limits^{n} \pi_i \hat{\sigma}_{2i}{}^2$, where $\hat{\sigma}_{2i}{}^2$ is an unbiased sample estimate of the within-unit variance of y_i'.

Theorems 10.1 and 10.2 are more general than needed in this chapter, but they are given here because they are widely useful.

10.3 VARIANCE OF THE ESTIMATED MEAN IN TWO-STAGE SAMPLING

The following notation is used:

y_{ij} = value obtained for the jth element in the ith primary unit

$$\bar{y}_i = \sum_{j=1}^{m} \frac{y_{ij}}{m} = \text{sample mean per element in the } i\text{th primary unit}$$

$$\bar{\bar{y}} = \sum_{i=1}^{n} \frac{\bar{y}_i}{n} = \text{over-all sample mean per element}$$

$$S_1{}^2 = \frac{\sum\limits_{i=1}^{N}(\bar{Y}_i - \bar{\bar{Y}})^2}{N-1} = \text{variance among primary unit means}$$

$$S_2{}^2 = \frac{\sum\limits_{i=1}^{N}\sum\limits_{j=1}^{M}(y_{ij} - \bar{Y}_i)^2}{N(M-1)} = \begin{array}{l}\text{variance among elements within} \\ \text{primary units}\end{array}$$

Theorem 10.3. If the n units and the m subunits from each chosen unit are selected by simple random sampling, $\bar{\bar{y}}$ is an unbiased estimate of $\bar{\bar{Y}}$ with variance

$$V(\bar{\bar{y}}) = \left(\frac{N-n}{N}\right)\frac{S_1{}^2}{n} + \left(\frac{M-m}{M}\right)\frac{S_2{}^2}{mn} \qquad (10.8)$$

Proof. In the notation of theorem 10.1 take $y_i' = \bar{y}_i/n$. Then

$$\bar{\bar{y}} = y', \qquad Y_i' = \frac{1}{n}\bar{Y}_i, \qquad \hat{Y}' = \frac{1}{n}\sum^{n}\bar{Y}_i, \qquad \pi_i = \frac{n}{N}$$

From theorem 10.1,

$$E(\bar{\bar{y}}) = E(y') = \sum_{i}^{N} \pi_i Y_i' = \frac{1}{N}\sum_{i}^{N}\bar{Y}_i = \bar{\bar{Y}}$$

Now by theorem 2.2 (p. 22), for single-stage sampling, since $\hat{Y}'$ is the mean of the n values of $\bar{Y}_i$,

$$V(\hat{Y}') = \frac{N - n}{Nn} \frac{\sum_i^N (\bar{Y}_i - \bar{\bar{Y}})^2}{N - 1} = \frac{N - n}{N} \frac{S_1^2}{n} \qquad (10.9)$$

By the same theorem, since m units are selected out of M from the ith unit, the variance of $y_i' = \bar{y}_i/n$ as an estimate of $Y_i' = \bar{Y}_i/n$ is

$$\sigma_{2i}^2 = \frac{M - m}{Mn^2} \frac{S_{2i}^2}{m}$$

where S_{2i}^2 is the variance among subunits in the ith primary unit. Hence, by theorem 10.1,

$$V(\bar{\bar{y}}) = V(\hat{Y}') + \sum^N \pi_i \sigma_{2i}^2$$

$$= \frac{(N - n)}{N} \frac{S_1^2}{n} + \frac{1}{n^2} \sum_i^N \frac{n}{N} \left(\frac{M - m}{M} \right) \frac{S_{2i}^2}{m}$$

But $S_2^2 = \sum^N S_{2i}^2/N$. This gives

$$V(\bar{\bar{y}}) = \frac{(N - n)}{N} \frac{S_1^2}{n} + \left(\frac{M - m}{M} \right) \frac{S_2^2}{mn}$$

If $f_1 = n/N$ and $f_2 = m/M$ are sampling fractions in the first and second stages, a form of the result that is easier to remember is

$$V(\bar{\bar{y}}) = \frac{1 - f_1}{n} S_1^2 + \frac{1 - f_2}{mn} S_2^2 \qquad (10.10)$$

10.4 ESTIMATION OF THE VARIANCE

If the n primary unit means $\bar{Y}_i$ were known, an unbiased estimate of the variance of their mean $\hat{Y}'$ would be

$$v(\hat{Y}') = \frac{(1 - f_1)}{n} \frac{\sum^n (\bar{Y}_i - \hat{Y}')^2}{n - 1}$$

The copy of $v(\hat{Y}')$ from a two-stage sample is

$$v_c(y') = v_c(\bar{\bar{y}}) = \frac{(1 - f_1)}{n} \frac{\sum^n (\bar{y}_i - \bar{\bar{y}})^2}{n - 1} \qquad (10.11)$$

For theorem 10.2, we require also an unbiased estimate of σ_{2i}^2 in equation (10.1). Since subsamples are chosen by simple random sampling, this is given by

$$\hat{\sigma}_{2i}^2 = \frac{M-m}{M}\frac{s_{2i}^2}{mn^2} = \frac{(1-f_2)s_{2i}^2}{mn^2} \qquad (10.12)$$

where

$$s_{2i}^2 = \frac{\sum\limits_{j}^{m}(y_{ij}-\bar{y}_i)^2}{m-1}$$

Theorem 10.4. Under the conditions of theorem 10.3, an unbiased estimate of $V(\bar{\bar{y}})$ is

$$v(\bar{\bar{y}}) = \frac{1-f_1}{n}s_1^2 + \frac{f_1(1-f_2)}{mn}s_2^2 \qquad (10.13)$$

where

$$s_1^2 = \frac{\sum\limits_{i}^{n}(\bar{y}_i-\bar{\bar{y}})^2}{n-1} \qquad s_2^2 = \sum\limits_{i}^{n}\sum\limits_{j}^{m}\frac{(y_{ij}-\bar{y}_i)^2}{n(m-1)} \qquad (10.14)$$

Proof. By theorem 10.2, an unbiased estimate of $V(\bar{\bar{y}})$ is

$$v(\bar{\bar{y}}) = v_c(\bar{\bar{y}}) + \sum\limits_{i}^{n}\pi_i\hat{\sigma}_{2i}^2$$

Using (10.11), (10.12), and $\pi_i = n/N$, this gives

$$v(\bar{\bar{y}}) = \frac{1-f_1}{n}s_1^2 + \frac{1}{n^2}\sum\limits_{i}^{n}\frac{n}{N}\frac{1-f_2}{m}s_{2i}^2$$

But s_2^2, as defined in (10.14), equals $\sum\limits^{n}s_{2i}^2/n$. Hence

$$v(\bar{\bar{y}}) = \frac{1-f_1}{n}s_1^2 + \frac{f_1(1-f_2)}{mn}s_2^2$$

Corollary. A result that will be used later is

$$E(s_1^2) = S_1^2 - \frac{S_2^2}{M} + \frac{S_2^2}{m} \qquad (10.15)$$

Proof. Since $v(\bar{\bar{y}})$ is an unbiased estimate of $V(\bar{\bar{y}})$, (10.13) gives

$$\frac{1-f_1}{n}E(s_1^2) = \frac{1-f_1}{n}S_1^2 + \frac{1-f_2}{mn}S_2^2 - \frac{f_1(1-f_2)}{mn}S_2^2$$

$$= \frac{1-f_1}{n}\left(S_1^2 - \frac{S_2^2}{M} + \frac{S_2^2}{m}\right)$$

It follows that an unbiased estimate of S_1^2 is $[s_1^2 - s_2^2(1-f_2)/m]$.

Notes on Theorem 10.4. If $m = M$, that is, $f_2 = 1$, formula 10.13 becomes that appropriate to simple random sampling of the units. If $n = N$, the formula is that for proportional stratified random sampling, since primary units may then be regarded as strata, all of which are sampled. In this connection, two-stage sampling is a kind of incomplete stratification, with the units as strata.

In the common situation in which $f_1 = n/N$ is negligible, we obtain the useful result,

$$v(\bar{\bar{y}}) = \frac{s_1{}^2}{n} = \frac{\sum\limits_{i=1}^{n} (\bar{y}_i - \bar{\bar{y}})^2}{n(n-1)} \tag{10.16}$$

Thus the estimated variance can be computed from a knowledge of the unit means only. This result is particularly helpful when subsampling is systematic, because in this event we cannot compute an unbiased estimate of $S_2{}^2$. But (10.16) still applies, provided that n/N is small. If n/N is not small, it is easily seen that (10.16) gives an overestimate.

10.5 THE ESTIMATION OF PROPORTIONS

If the elements are classified into two classes and we estimate the proportion that falls in the first class, the preceding formulas can be applied by the usual device of defining y_{ij} as 1 if the corresponding element falls into this class and as zero otherwise. Let $p_i = a_i/m$ be the proportion falling in the first class in the subsample from the ith unit. The two estimated variances $s_1{}^2$ and $s_2{}^2$ required for theorem 10.4 work out as follows:

$$s_1{}^2 = \frac{\sum\limits_{i=1}^{n} (p_i - \bar{p})^2}{n-1}$$

$$s_2{}^2 = \frac{m}{n(m-1)} \sum\limits_{i=1}^{n} p_i q_i$$

where $\bar{p} = \Sigma p_i/n$. Consequently, by theorem 10.4,

$$v(\bar{p}) = \frac{1-f_1}{n(n-1)} \sum\limits_{i}^{n} (p_i - \bar{p})^2 + \frac{f_1(1-f_2)}{n^2(m-1)} \sum\limits_{i}^{n} p_i q_i$$

Example. In a study of plant disease the plants were grown in 160 small plots containing nine plants each. A random sample of 40 plots was chosen and three random plants in each sampled plot were examined for the presence of disease. It was found that 22 plots had no diseased plants (out of three), 11 had one, four had two, and three had three. Estimate the proportion of diseased plants and its s.e. The symbol ϕ denotes the frequencies 22, 11, 4, 3.

We have $N = 160$, $M = 9$, $n = 40$, $m = 3$. In finding s_1^2 and s_2^2, it is convenient to work at first with the numbers of diseased plants ($3p_i$) and the numbers of healthy plants ($3q_i$). The calculations are set out as follows:

$3p_i$	Frequency ϕ	$9p_iq_i$	$9\phi p_iq_i$	$3\phi p_i$	$9\phi p_i^2$
0	22	0	0	0	0
1	11	2	22	11	11
2	4	2	8	8	16
3	3	0	0	9	27
	40		30	28	54

$$\bar{p} = \frac{3\sum \phi p_i}{3\sum \phi} = \frac{28}{120} = 0.233$$

$$\sum \phi(p_i - \bar{p})^2 = \frac{1}{(9)}\left(54 - \frac{(28)^2}{40}\right) = 3.822$$

$$\sum \phi p_i q_i - \frac{30}{9} = 3.333$$

Hence, from the formula immediately before this example,

$$v(\bar{p}) = \frac{(3)(3.822)}{(4)(40)(39)} + \frac{(2)(3.333)}{(4)(3)(1600)(2)} = 0.00201$$

The proportion diseased is 0.233 with s.e. 0.045. The approximate formula $s_1/\sqrt{n}$, from (10.16), gives 0.049, a reasonably good estimate considering that $f_1 = \frac{1}{4}$.

10.6 OPTIMUM SAMPLING AND SUBSAMPLING FRACTIONS

These depend on the type of cost function. If travel costs between units are unimportant, one form that has proved useful is

$$C = c_1 n + c_2 nm$$

The first component of cost, $c_1 n$, is proportional to the number of primary units in the sample; the second, $c_2 nm$, to the total number of second-stage units or elements. From theorem 10.3, $V(\bar{y})$ may be written

$$V(\bar{y}) = \frac{1}{n}\left(S_1^2 - \frac{S_2^2}{M}\right) + \frac{1}{mn} S_2^2 - \frac{1}{N} S_1^2 \qquad (10.17)$$

The last term on the right does not depend on the choice of n and m. Minimizing V for fixed C, or C for fixed V, is equivalent to minimizing the product

$$\left(V + \frac{1}{N} S_1^2\right)C = c_1\left(S_1^2 - \frac{S_2^2}{M}\right) + c_2 S_2^2 + \frac{1}{m} c_1 S_2^2 + mc_2\left(S_1^2 - \frac{S_2^2}{M}\right)$$

Note that the first two terms are constant, whereas the last two depend on m but not on n. The minimizing value of m may be found by differentiation. But since, in practice, m must be an integer and is often small, a more accurate approach suggested by Eisenhart (Cameron, 1951) is used. Write

$$a = c_1 S_2^2, \qquad b = c_2 \left(S_1^2 - \frac{S_2^2}{M} \right)$$

We wish to find an integer m such that

$$\frac{a}{m} + bm \leq \frac{a}{m+1} + b(m+1), \qquad \text{that is, } m(m+1) \geq \frac{a}{b}$$

$$\frac{a}{m} + bm \leq \frac{a}{m-1} + b(m-1), \qquad \text{that is, } m(m-1) \leq \frac{a}{b}$$

These relations give the following rule. Compute

$$m_{opt} = \sqrt{a/b} = \frac{S_2}{\sqrt{S_1^2 - S_2^2/M}} \sqrt{c_1/c_2} \tag{10.18}$$

If m_{opt} lies between the integers m, $m + 1$, choose $(m + 1)$, that is, round upward, if $m_{opt}^2 > m(m + 1)$; otherwise round downward. Thus, if m_{opt} lies between $1.414 = \sqrt{2}$ and 2, we round upward to 2. If m_{opt} is greater than M, or if S_1^2 is less than S_2^2/M, we take $m = M$ and employ one-stage sampling.

The structure of (10.18) is as expected. If elements were assigned to units at random, that is, if the primary unit were as efficient as the element, the variance of a primary unit mean would be S_2^2/M, so that $(S_1^2 - S_2^2/M)$ would be zero. This gives $m_{opt} = $ infinity, that is, complete enumeration of the primary units. Conversely, the greater the variance S_1^2 among primary unit means relative to that within primary units, the smaller the value of m_{opt}. The greater the cost c_1 of access to the unit relative to the cost c_2 of obtaining data from any element in the unit, the higher the optimum m.

The value of n is found by solving either the cost equation or the variance equation, depending on which has been preassigned.

In most practical situations the optimum is relatively flat. An error of a few units in the choice of m produces only a small loss of precision, as the following example illustrates.

In the terminology of the analysis of variance, the quantity $(S_1^2 - S_2^2/M)$, which appears in the denominator of m_{opt}, is known as the component of variance between unit means. Write

$$S_u^2 = S_1^2 - \frac{S_2^2}{M} \tag{10.19}$$

Example. Let

$$c_1 = 10c_2, \qquad S_2 = 1.3S_u$$

then

$$m_{opt} = 1.3\sqrt{10} = 4.1$$

We will regard total cost as fixed and see how the variance of $\bar{y}$ changes with m. N is assumed large. From (10.17),

$$V(\bar{y}) = \frac{S_u^2}{n} + \frac{S_2^2}{nm}$$

$$= \left(S_u^2 + \frac{S_2^2}{m}\right)\frac{c_1 + mc_2}{C}$$

eliminating n by means of the cost equation. This gives

$$V(\bar{y}) = \frac{S_u^2 c_2}{C}\left(1 + \frac{S_2^2}{mS_u^2}\right)\left(\frac{c_1}{c_2} + m\right) = \frac{S_u^2 c_2}{C}\left(1 + \frac{1.69}{m}\right)(10 + m)$$

Omitting the constant factor, the relative variance can be calculated for different values of m. Table 10.1 shows these variances and the relative precisions (with the maximum precision for $m = 4$ taken as the standard).

TABLE 10.1

RELATIVE VARIANCES AND PRECISIONS FOR DIFFERENT VALUES OF m

$m =$	1	2	3	4	5	6	7	8	9	10
Rel. variance	29.59	22.14	20.32	19.92	20.07	20.51	21.10	21.80	22.56	23.38
Rel. precision	0.67	0.90	0.98	1.00	0.99	0.97	0.94	0.91	0.88	0.85

For any value of m between 2 and 9, the loss of precision relative to the optimum is less than 12%.

In practice, the choice of m requires estimates of c_1/c_2 and S_2/S_1 or equivalently S_2/S_u. Because of the flatness of the optimum, these ratios need not be obtained with high accuracy. If c_1/c_2 is known reasonably well and a value of m, say m_0, has been selected, a useful table (Brooks, 1955) shows the range of values of S_2^2/S_u^2 within which this m_0 gives a precision at least 90% of the optimum.

The table was obtained as follows. For given cost, assuming N large, the relative precision of m_0 to m_{opt} is found to be

$$\frac{V(\bar{y} \mid m_{opt})}{V(\bar{y} \mid m_0)} = \frac{(S_u\sqrt{c_1} + S_2\sqrt{c_2})^2}{S_u^2 c_1 + S_2^2 c_2 + m_0 c_2 S_u^2 + c_1 S_2^2/m_0} \tag{10.20}$$

The set of values of S_2/S_u for which this expression exceeds some assigned level L are those lying between the two roots

$$\frac{S_2}{S_u} = \frac{\gamma \pm \sqrt{L(1 - L)}(\sqrt{m_0} + \gamma^2/\sqrt{m_0})}{(L\gamma^2/m_0) - (1 - L)} \tag{10.21}$$

where $\gamma^2 = c_1/c_2$.

Table 10.2, adapted from Brooks (1955), shows the lower and upper limits of S_2^2/S_u^2 for $L = 0.9$. The wide interval between the lower and upper limits is striking in nearly all cases. Note that the range of m_0 changes in different parts of the table.

TABLE 10.2

LIMITS FOR S_2^2/S_u^2 WITHIN WHICH m_0 GIVES AT LEAST 90% OF THE MAXIMUM PRECISION

$c_1/c_2 =$ m_0	$\frac{1}{2}$		1		$c_1/c_2 =$ m_0	2		4	
	L	U	L	U		L	U	L	U
1	0.0	11	0.0	4	2	0.5	8	0.2	4
2	2.0	98	1.1	22	3	1.2	21	0.5	8
3	4.1	>*	2.4	72	4	2.2	44	1.0	16
4	6.6	>	4.0	>	5	3.3	82	1.6	27
5	9.5	>	5.9	>	6	4.7	>	2.4	42
6	13	>	8.1	>	7	6.3	>	3.3	61
7	16	>	11	>	8	8.0	>	4.3	87
8	20	>	13	>	9	10	>	5.4	>

$c_1/c_2 =$ m_0	8		16		$c_1/c_2 =$ m_0	32		64	
	L	U	L	U		L	U	L	U
6	1.0	17	0.3	8	5	0.1	3	0.0	2
7	1.5	24	0.5	11	10	0.4	12	0.1	7
8	2.0	32	0.7	15	15	1.2	26	0.3	14
9	2.6	42	1.0	19	20	2.7	46	0.7	24
10	3.3	53	1.3	23	25	4.5	74	1.5	37
15	7.6	>	3.5	55	30	6.9	>	2.5	52
20	13.3	>	6.6	>	35	9.7	>	3.7	71
25	20.4	>	10.5	>	40	13	>	5.2	93

* > denotes "> 100."

If we have a rough idea about the values of S_2^2/S_u^2 for the principal items in a survey, Table 10.2 may be used to select a value m_0. Note that if ρ is the correlation between elements in the same primary unit, as defined in section 9.4, the ratio S_2^2/S_u^2 is nearly equal to $(1 - \rho)/\rho$. A value of S_2^2/S_u^2 as low as 1 corresponds to $\rho = 0.5$. This would be an unusually high degree of intraunit correlation. Similarly, $\rho = 0.1$ gives $S_2^2/S_u^2 = 9$, whereas $\rho = 0.01$ gives $S_2^2/S_u^2 = 99$.

Example. Suppose that c_1/c_2 is about 1 and that S_2^2/S_u^2 is expected to lie between 5 and 100 for the principal items. The columns $c_1/c_2 = 1$ give $m_0 = 4$ as a satisfactory choice, since this covers ratios from 4 to more than 100 (actually to

196). With $c_1/c_2 = 16$ and the same desired range, the table suggests a value of m_0 somewhere between 15 and 20. Further calculation from (10.21) shows that $m_0 = 18$ is best. This covers the range from 5.2 to 84—not quite so wide as desired.

When the cost of travel between primary units is substantial, a more accurate cost function may be

$$C = c_1 n + c_t \sqrt{n} + c_2 nm \tag{10.22}$$

since travel costs tend to be proportional to $\sqrt{n}$. If a desired value of $V(\bar{y})$ has been specified, pairs of values of (n, m) that give this variance are easily computed from (10.17) for $V(\bar{y})$. The costs for different combinations are then computed from (10.22) and the combination giving the smallest cost is found. When cost is fixed in advance, Hansen, Hurwitz, and Madow (1953) give a method for determining the (n, m) combination that minimizes the variance and a table that facilitates a rapid choice. Note that their n is our m and vice versa.

10.7 ESTIMATION OF m_{opt} FROM A PILOT SURVEY

Sometimes estimates of S_2^2 and S_1^2 or S_u^2 are obtained from a pilot survey in which n' primary units are chosen, with m' elements taken from each unit. This section deals with the choice of n' and m'. If s_1^2 is the variance between unit means and s_2^2 is the variance between elements within units, as defined in section 10.4, (10.15) gives

$$E(s_1^2) = \left(S_1^2 - \frac{S_2^2}{M}\right) + \frac{S_2^2}{m'} = S_u^2 + \frac{S_2^2}{m'} \tag{10.23}$$

For the simple cost function $c_1 n + c_2 nm$, we had

$$m_{opt} = \frac{S_2}{\sqrt{S_1^2 - S_2^2/M}} \sqrt{c_1/c_2}$$

As an estimate of m_{opt} from the pilot survey, (10.23) suggests that we take

$$\hat{m}_{opt} = \frac{s_2}{\sqrt{s_1^2 - s_2^2/m'}} \sqrt{c_1/c_2} = \frac{\sqrt{m'}}{\sqrt{(m' s_1^2/s_2^2) - 1}} \sqrt{c_1/c_2} \tag{10.24}$$

The estimate $\hat{m}_{opt}$ is subject to a sampling error that depends on the sampling error of the ratio s_1^2/s_2^2. From the analysis of variance it is known that $m' s_1^2/s_2^2$ is distributed as

$$F\left(1 + m' \frac{S_u^2}{S_2^2}\right)$$

where F has $(n' - 1)$ and $n'(m' - 1)$ degrees of freedom, provided that the y_{ij} are normally distributed. This result leads to the sampling distribution of $\hat{m}_{opt}$ for given values of n' and m', that is,

$$\hat{m}_{opt} = \frac{\sqrt{m'c_1/c_2}}{\sqrt{F\left(1 + \frac{m'S_u^2}{S_2^2}\right) - 1}} \qquad (10.25)$$

Example. For the example in section 10.6, in which

$$c_1 = 10c_2, \qquad S_2 = 1.3S_u, \qquad m_{opt} = 1.3\sqrt{10} = 4.1$$

consider how well m_{opt} is estimated from a pilot sample with $n' = 10$ and $m' = 4$. From (10.25),

$$\hat{m}_{opt} = \frac{6.324}{\sqrt{F[1 + (4/1.69)] - 1}} = \frac{6.324}{\sqrt{3.367F - 1}}$$

where F has 9 and 30 df. To find the limits within which $\hat{m}_{opt}$ will lie 80% of the time, we have, from the 10% one-tailed significance levels of F,

$$F_{.10}\ (9, 30) = 1.8490, \qquad F_{.90}\ (9, 30) = 1/F_{.10}(30, 9) = 1/2.2547 = 0.4435$$

Substitution of these values of F gives

$$\text{lower limit,} \qquad \hat{m}_{opt} = 2.8; \qquad \text{upper limit,} \qquad \hat{m}_{opt} = 9.0$$

As shown previously in Table 10.1, any m in this range gives a degree of precision close to the optimum. Thus, with $n' = 10$, $m' = 4$, the chances are 8 in 10 that the loss of precision is small.

The 80 and 95% limits for $n' = 5, 10, 20$ and $m' = 4$ appear in Table 10.3.

TABLE 10.3

LOWER AND UPPER LIMITS FOR $\hat{m}_{opt}$

n'	80%	90%
5	2.5, ∞	1.8, ∞
10	2.8, 9.0	2.3, ∞
20	3.1, 6.4	2.7, 9.1

With $n' = 20$, we are almost certain to estimate m_{opt} with precision close to the optimum. This is not so with $n' = 5$.

If the ratio c_1/c_2 is the same in the pilot survey as in the main survey, the cost of the pilot survey will be proportional to $c_1n' + c_2n'm'$. Brooks (1955) gives a table of the values of (n', m') in the most economical pilot survey that provides an expected relative precision of 90% in the estimation of m_{opt}. Table 10.4 shows part of this table.

TABLE 10.4

PILOT SAMPLE DESIGNS HAVING AN EXPECTED RELATIVE PRECISION OF 90%

c_1/c_2	≤ 1		2		4		8		16		32		64	
S_2^2/S_u^2	n'	m'	n'	m'	n'	m'	n'	m'	n'	m'	n'	m'	n'	m'
1	7	3	6	4	6	5	5	6	5	7	4	10	4	12
2	8	5	7	7	6	9	6	9	5	13	5	14	4	20
4	9	9	8	11	8	12	7	14	7	15	5	25	5	27
8	10	14	10	15	9	17	9	18	8	22	6	32	5	44
16	10	25	10	27	10	27	10	28	8	37	7	46	6	60
32	10	46	10	47	10	48	10	49	9	58	8	69	6	102
64	10	92	10	93	10	96	10	100	10	104	8	137	7	169

The computations assume that N and M are large: the designs are conservative if fpc terms are taken into account. Note that no more than 10 primary units are required and that the designs are relatively insensitive to the ratio c_1/c_2.

10.8 THREE-STAGE SAMPLING

The process of subsampling can be carried to a third stage by sampling the subunits (elements) instead of enumerating them completely. For instance, in surveys to estimate crop production in India (Sukhatme, 1947), the village is a convenient sampling unit. Within a village, only some of the fields growing the crop in question are selected, so that the field is a subunit. When a field is selected, only certain parts of it are cut for the determination of yield per acre: thus the subunit itself is sampled. If physical or chemical analyses of the crop are involved, an additional subsampling may be used, since these determinations are often made on a part of the sample cut from a field.

The results are a straightforward extension of those for two-stage sampling and are given briefly. The population contains N first-stage units, each with M second-stage units, each of which has K third-stage units. The corresponding numbers for the sample are n, m, and k, respectively. Let y_{iju} be the value obtained for the uth third-stage unit in the jth second-stage unit drawn from the ith primary unit. The relevant population means per third-stage unit are as follows:

$$\overline{Y}_{ij} = \frac{\sum\limits_{u}^{K} y_{iju}}{K}, \qquad \overline{\overline{Y}}_i = \frac{\sum\limits_{j}^{M}\sum\limits_{u}^{K} y_{iju}}{MK}, \qquad \overline{\overline{\overline{Y}}} = \frac{\sum\limits_{i}^{N}\sum\limits_{j}^{M}\sum\limits_{u}^{K} y_{iju}}{NMK}$$

The following population variances are required:

$$S_1^2 = \frac{\sum\limits_{i}^{N} (\bar{\bar{Y}}_i - \bar{\bar{Y}})^2}{N - 1}$$

$$S_2^2 = \frac{\sum\limits_{i}^{N} \sum\limits_{j}^{M} (\bar{Y}_{ij} - \bar{\bar{Y}}_i)^2}{N(M - 1)}$$

$$S_3^2 = \frac{\sum\limits_{i}^{N} \sum\limits_{j}^{M} \sum\limits_{u}^{K} (y_{ijk} - \bar{Y}_{ij})^2}{NM(K - 1)}$$

Theorem 10.5. If simple random sampling is used at all three stages, the sample mean $\bar{\bar{y}}$ per third-stage unit is an unbiased estimate of $\bar{\bar{Y}}$ with variance

$$V(\bar{\bar{y}}) = \frac{1 - f_1}{n} S_1^2 + \frac{1 - f_2}{nm} S_2^2 + \frac{1 - f_3}{nmk} S_3^2 \qquad (10.26)$$

where $f_1 = n/N$, $f_2 = m/M$, $f_3 = k/K$ are the sampling fractions at the three stages.

Proof. Only the principal steps are indicated. Write

$$\bar{\bar{y}} - \bar{\bar{Y}} = (\bar{\bar{y}} - \bar{\bar{Y}}_{nm}) + (\bar{\bar{Y}}_{nm} - \bar{\bar{Y}}_n) + (\bar{\bar{Y}}_n - \bar{\bar{Y}})$$

where $\bar{\bar{Y}}_{nm}$ is the population mean of the nm second-stage units that were selected and $\bar{\bar{Y}}_n$ is the population mean of the n primary units that were selected. When we square and take the average, the cross-product terms vanish. The contributions of the squared terms turn out to be as follows:

$$E(\bar{\bar{y}} - \bar{\bar{Y}}_{nm})^2 = \frac{1 - f_3}{nmk} S_3^2$$

$$E(\bar{\bar{Y}}_{nm} - \bar{\bar{Y}}_n)^2 = \frac{1 - f_2}{nm} S_2^2$$

$$E(\bar{\bar{Y}}_n - \bar{\bar{Y}})^2 = \frac{1 - f_1}{n} S_1^2$$

When these three terms are added, the theorem is obtained.

Theorem 10.6. An unbiased estimate of $V(\bar{\bar{y}})$ from the sample is

$$v(\bar{\bar{y}}) = \frac{1 - f_1}{n} s_1^2 + \frac{f_1(1 - f_2)}{nm} s_2^2 + \frac{f_1 f_2(1 - f_3)}{nmk} s_3^2 \qquad (10.27)$$

where s_1^2, s_2^2, s_3^2 are the sample analogues of S_1^2, S_2^2, S_3^2, respectively.

Proof. This may be proved by the methods in section 10.4 or alternatively by showing that

$$E(s_1^2) = S_1^2 + \frac{1-f_2}{m} S_2^2 + \frac{1-f_3}{mk} S_3^2 \qquad (10.28)$$

$$E(s_2^2) = S_2^2 + \frac{1-f_3}{k} S_3^2$$

and $E(s_3^2) = S_3^2$. To obtain the first result, let $\bar{y}_{iK}$ denote the mean over the m second-stage units in the ith primary unit, given that all K elements were enumerated at the third stage. Let $\bar{\bar{y}}_K$ be the mean of the n values $\bar{y}_{iK}$. Then from (10.15) for two-stage sampling, it follows that

$$E\left[\frac{\sum\limits^{n}(\bar{y}_{iK} - \bar{\bar{y}}_K)^2}{n-1}\right] = S_1^2 + \frac{1-f_2}{m} S_2^2$$

Now, if $\bar{y}_i$ is the sample mean for the ith primary unit, write

$$(\bar{y}_i - \bar{\bar{y}}) = (\bar{y}_{iK} - \bar{\bar{y}}_K) + [(\bar{y}_i - \bar{y}_{iK}) - (\bar{\bar{y}} - \bar{\bar{y}}_K)]$$

By first averaging over samples in which the first-stage and second-stage units are fixed, it is easily shown that

$$\frac{1}{(n-1)} E \sum^{n} [(\bar{y}_i - \bar{y}_{iK}) - (\bar{\bar{y}} - \bar{\bar{y}}_K)]^2 = \frac{S_3^2}{mk}(1 - f_3)$$

and that the sum of the cross-product terms contributes nothing. This establishes the result for $E(s_1^2)$. That for $E(s_2^2)$ is found similarly. Hence

$$E[v(\bar{\bar{y}})] = \frac{1-f_1}{n}\left(S_1^2 + \frac{1-f_2}{m} S_2^2 + \frac{1-f_3}{mk} S_3^2\right)$$

$$+ \frac{f_1(1-f_2)}{nm}\left(S_2^2 + \frac{1-f_3}{k} S_3^2\right) + \frac{f_1 f_2(1-f_3)}{nmk} S_3^2$$

$$= \frac{1-f_1}{n} S_1^2 + \frac{1-f_2}{nm} S_2^2 + \frac{1-f_3}{nmk} S_3^2 = V(\bar{\bar{y}})$$

As with two-stage sampling, it is clear from (10.27) that if f_1 is negligible $v(\bar{\bar{y}})$ reduces to

$$v(\bar{\bar{y}}) = \frac{s_1^2}{n} = \frac{\sum\limits^{n}(\bar{y}_i - \bar{\bar{y}})^2}{n(n-1)} \qquad (10.29)$$

This estimate is conservative if f_1 is not negligible.

With a cost function of the form

$$C = c_1 n + c_2 nm + c_3 nmk$$

the optimum values of k and m are

$$k_{opt} = \frac{S_3}{\sqrt{S_2^2 - S_3^2/K}} \sqrt{c_2/c_3}, \qquad m_{opt} = \frac{\sqrt{S_2^2 - S_3^2/K}}{\sqrt{S_1^2 - S_2^2/M}} \sqrt{c_1/c_2} \qquad (10.30)$$

The extension of the results in this section to additional stages of sampling should be clear from the structure of the formulas.

10.9 STRATIFIED SAMPLING OF THE UNITS

Subsampling may be combined with any type of sampling of the primary units. The subsampling itself may employ stratification or systematic sampling. Variance formulas for these modifications can be built up from the formulas for the simpler methods.

Results are given for stratified sampling of the primary units in a two-stage sample. The primary unit sizes are assumed constant for a given stratum but may vary from stratum to stratum. This situation occurs when primary units are stratified by size so that sizes within a stratum become constant or nearly so.

The hth stratum contains N_h primary units, each with M_h second-stage units; the corresponding sample numbers are n_h and m_h. The estimated population mean per second-stage unit is

$$\bar{\bar{y}}_{st} = \frac{\sum_h N_h M_h \bar{y}_h}{\sum_h N_h M_h} = \sum_h W_h \bar{y}_h \qquad (10.31)$$

where $W_h = N_h M_h / \Sigma N_h M_h$ is the relative size of the stratum in terms of *second-stage units* and $\bar{y}_h$ is the sample mean in the stratum. By applying theorem 10.3 within each stratum, we have

$$V(\bar{\bar{y}}_{st}) = \sum_h W_h^2 \left(\frac{1 - f_{1h}}{n_h} S_{1h}^2 + \frac{1 - f_{2h}}{n_h m_n} S_{2h}^2 \right) \qquad (10.32)$$

where $f_{1h} = n_h/N_h, f_{2h} = m_h/M_h$.

From theorem 10.4, an unbiased sample estimate is

$$v(\bar{\bar{y}}_{st}) = \sum_h W_h^2 \left[\frac{1 - f_{1h}}{n_h} s_{1h}^2 + \frac{f_{1h}(1 - f_{2h})}{n_h m_h} s_{2h}^2 \right] \qquad (10.33)$$

Corresponding variances for the estimated population total are obtained by multiplying formulas (10.32) and (10.33) by $(\Sigma N_h M_h)^2$.

10.10 OPTIMUM ALLOCATION WITH STRATIFIED SAMPLING

This deals with the best choice of the n_h and the m_h. If travel costs between units are not a major factor, the cost may be represented adequately by the formula

$$C = \sum_h c_{1h} n_h + \sum_h c_{2h} n_h m_h \qquad (10.34)$$

From (10.32), the variance may be rewritten as

$$V(\bar{\bar{y}}_{st}) = \sum_h W_h^2 \left[\frac{1}{n_h} \left(S_{1h}^2 - \frac{S_{2h}^2}{M_h} \right) + \frac{1}{n_h m_h} S_{2h}^2 - \frac{1}{N_h} S_{1h}^2 \right]$$

The quantity

$$V(\bar{\bar{y}}_{st}) + \lambda \left(\sum_h c_{1h} n_h + \sum_h c_{2h} n_h m_h - C \right)$$

where λ is a Lagrange multiplier, is a function of the variables n_h and $(n_h m_h)$. Hence, to minimize V for fixed C, or vice versa, we have

$$n_h \sqrt{\lambda} = \frac{W_h}{c_{1h}} \sqrt{S_{1h}^2 - S_{2h}^2 / M_h} \qquad (10.35)$$

$$n_h m_h \sqrt{\lambda} = \frac{W_h S_{2h}}{\sqrt{c_{2h}}} \qquad (10.36)$$

These give

$$m_h = \frac{S_{2h}}{\sqrt{S_{1h}^2 - S_{2h}^2 / M_h}} \sqrt{c_{1h}/c_{2h}}$$

The formula for optimum m_h is exactly the same as in unstratified sampling [(10.18) in section 10.6].

From (10.35), since $W_h \propto N_h M_h$

$$n_h \propto \frac{N_h M_h S_{uh}}{\sqrt{c_{1h}}} \quad \text{where } S_{uh}^2 = S_{1h}^2 - \frac{S_{2h}^2}{M_h} \qquad (10.37)$$

It will be recalled that in one-stage stratified sampling (section 5.5), the optimum n_h is proportional to $N_h S_h / \sqrt{c_h}$, where S_h is the standard deviation among unit totals and c_h is the cost per unit. Referring to (10.37), the quantity S_{uh}^2 is the component of variance among primary unit means, as explained in section 10.6. Hence $M_h S_{uh}$ in (10.37) may be regarded as a kind of standard deviation among primary unit totals, except that we are now dealing with the component of variance rather than the total variance.

Since self-weighting estimates are convenient, we consider under what circumstances the optimum allocation leads to a self-weighting estimate. From (10.31), it follows that $\bar{\bar{y}}_{st}$ is self-weighting if $n_h m_h / N_h M_h = f_0 =$ constant, since in this event

$$\bar{\bar{y}}_{st} = \frac{\sum_h N_h M_h / n_h m_h \sum_i^{n_h} \sum_j^{m_h} y_{hij}}{\sum N_h M_h} = \frac{\sum_h \sum_i \sum_j y_{hij}}{f_0 \sum N_h M_h} = \frac{\sum_h \sum_i \sum_j y_{hij}}{\sum n_h m_h} = \bar{\bar{y}}$$

The condition is, as might be expected, that the over-all sampling fraction f_0 be the same in all strata.

From (10.36), the optimum allocation gives

$$f_{0h} = \frac{n_h m_h}{N_h M_h} \propto \frac{S_{2h}}{\sqrt{c_{2h}}}$$

Frequently c_{2h}, the cost per second-stage unit, will be approximately the same in large and small primary units; but S_{2h} may be greater in large units than in small. However, since the optimum is flat, a self-weighting sample will often be almost as precise as the optimum. Note that this result holds even if the optimum sampling of primary units is far from proportional.

EXERCISES

• 10.1   A set of 20,000 records are stored in 400 file drawers, each containing 50 records. In a two-stage sample, five records are drawn at random from each of 80 randomly selected drawers. For one item, the estimates of variance were $s_1^2 = 362$, $s_2^2 = 805$, as defined in section 10.4. (a) Compute the standard error of the mean per record from this sample. (b) Compare this with the standard error given by the approximate formula (10.16) in section 10.4.

10.2   From the results of a pilot two-stage sample, in which m' subunits were chosen from each of n' units, it is useful to be able to estimate the value of $V(\bar{y})$ that would be given by a subsequent sample having m subunits from each of n units. Show that an unbiased estimate of $V(\bar{y})$ is

$$\hat{V}(\bar{y}) = \left(\frac{N-n}{N}\right)\frac{s_1^2}{n} + \frac{s_2^2}{mn}\left(1 - \frac{m}{m'} + \frac{mn}{m'N} - \frac{mn}{MN}\right)$$

where s_1^2 and s_2^2 are computed from the preliminary sample. *Hint.* Use theorem 10.3 and the result

$$E(s_1^2) = S_1^2 - \frac{S_2^2}{M} + \frac{S_2^2}{m}$$

10.3   In sampling wheat fields in Kansas, with the field as a primary unit, King and McCarty (1941) report the following mean squares for yield in bushels per acre: $s_1^2 = 165$, $s_2^2 = 66$. Two subsamples were taken per field. For a sample of n fields, compare the variances of the sample mean as given by (a) the sample as actually taken, (b) four subsamples per field from n fields, (c) completely harvesting n fields.

N and M may be assumed large and constant. In (c) assume that complete harvesting is equivalent to single-stage sampling (i.e., to having $m = M$).

10.4   In the same survey, with two subsamples per field, the mean squares for the percentage of protein were $s_1^2 = 7.73$, $s_2^2 = 1.43$. How many fields are required to estimate the mean yield to within ±1 bushel and the mean protein percentage to within ±¼, apart from a 1-in-20 chance in each case? Perform the calculations (a) assuming that two subsamples per field are taken in the main survey, (b) assuming complete harvesting of a field in the main survey.

10.5   For the wheat-yield data in exercise 10.3, what is the value of c_1/c_2 in a linear cost function if the estimated optimum m is 2?

10.6 If m/M and n/N are both small and the cost function is linear, show that $m = 2$ gives a smaller value of $V(\bar{y})$ than $m = 1$ if

$$\frac{c_1}{c_2} > 2 \frac{S_1^2}{S_2^2}$$

10.7 A large department store handles about 20,000 accounts receivable per month. A 2% sample ($m = 400$) was verified each month over a two-year period ($n = 24$). The numbers of accounts found to be in error per month (out of 400) were (in order of magnitude) 0, 0, 1, 1, 2, 4, 4, 5, 5, 5, 5, 6, 6, 6, 7, 7, 8, 9, 9, 10, 10, 13, 14, 17, the time pattern being erratic. From the results in section 10.5, compute s_1^2 and s_2^2. Hence compute the standard error of $\bar{p}$, as an estimate of the percentage of accounts that are in error over a period of a year, that would be obtained from verifying (a) 1200 accounts from a single month, chosen at random, (b) 300 accounts from each of four random months, (c) 100 accounts each month. *Hint.* Either use the formula in exercise 10.2 with $m' = 400$ or obtain unbiased estimates of S_1^2 and S_2^2 and use theorem 10.3.

10.8 In planning a two-stage survey it was expected that c_1/c_2 would be about 4 and that S_2^2/S_u^2 would lie between 5 and 50. (a) What value of m would you choose from Table 10.2? (b) Suppose that after the survey was completed it was found that c_1/c_2 was close to 8 and S_2^2/S_u^2 was about 25. Compute the relative precision given by your m to that given by the optimum m. (c) Make the same computation for $c_1/c_2 = 4$, $S_2^2/S_u^2 = 100$.

10.9 If ρ is the correlation coefficient between second-stage units in the same primary unit, prove that

$$\frac{1 - \rho}{\rho} = \frac{S_2^2}{[(N - 1)/N] S_1^2 - S_2^2/M} = \frac{S_2^2}{S_u^2}$$

(This establishes a result used in section 10.6.)

10.10 Show that if $S_u^2 > 0$, in the notation of section 10.6, a simple random sample of n primary units, with 1 element chosen per unit, is more precise than a simple random sample of n elements ($n > 1$, $M > 1$). Show that the precision of the two methods is equal if n/N is negligible. Would you expect this intuitively?

REFERENCES

Brooks, S. (1955). The estimation of an optimum subsampling number. *Jour. Amer. Stat. Assoc.*, **50**, 398–415.

Cameron, J. M. (1951), Use of variance components in preparing schedules for the sampling of baled wool. *Biometrics*, **7**, 83–96.

Durbin, J. (1953). Some results in sampling theory when the units are selected with unequal probabilities. *Jour. Roy. Stat. Soc.* **B15**, 262–269.

Hansen, M. H., Hurwitz, W. N., and Madow, W. G. (1953). *Sample survey methods and theory.* Vol. I. John Wiley and Sons, New York.

King, A. J. and McCarty, D. E. (1941). Application of sampling to agricultural statistics with emphasis on stratified samples. *Jour. Marketing*, April, 462–474.

Sukhatme, P. V. (1947). The problem of plot size in large-yield surveys. *Jour. Amer. Stat. Assoc.*, **42**, 297–310.

CHAPTER 11

Subsampling with Units
of Unequal Sizes

11.1 INTRODUCTION

In sampling extensive populations, primary units that vary in size are encountered frequently. Moreover, considerations of cost often dictate the use of multistage sampling, so that the problems discussed in this chapter are of common occurrence. If the sizes do not vary greatly, one method is to stratify by size of primary unit, so that the units within a stratum become equal, or nearly so. The formulas in section 10.9 may then be an adequate approximation. Often, however, substantial differences in size remain within some strata, and sometimes it is advisable to base the stratification on other variables. In a review of the British Social Surveys, which are nationwide samples with districts as primary units, Gray and Corlett (1950) point out that size was at first included as one of the variables for stratification but that another factor was found more desirable when the characteristics of the population became better known.

Some concentrated effort is required in order to obtain a good working knowledge of multistage sampling when the units vary in size, because the technique is flexible. The units may be chosen either with equal probabilities or with probabilities proportional to size or to some estimate of size. Various rules can be devised to determine the sampling and subsampling fractions, and various methods of estimation are available. The advantages of the different methods depend on the nature of the population, on the field costs, and on the supplementary data that are at our disposal.

The first part of this chapter is devoted to a description of the principal methods that are in use. We shall begin with a population that consists of a single stratum. The extension to stratified sampling can be made, as in preceding chapters, by summing the appropriate variance formulas

292

over the strata. For simplicity, we assume at first that only a single primary unit is chosen, that is, that $n = 1$. This case is not so impractical as it might appear at first sight, because when there is a large number of strata we may achieve satisfactory precision in estimation even though $n_h = 1$. In a series of monthly surveys taken by the U.S. Census Bureau to estimate numbers of employed people, the primary unit is a county or a group of neighboring counties. This is a large unit, but it has administrative advantages that decrease costs. Since counties are far from uniform in their characteristics, stratification is extended to the point at which only one is selected from each stratum. Consequently, the theory to be discussed is applicable to a single stratum in this sampling plan.

As in preceding chapters, the quantities to be estimated may be the population total Y, the population mean (usually the mean per element $\bar{\bar{Y}}$), or a ratio of two variates.

Notation. The observation for the jth element within the ith unit is denoted by y_{ij}. The following symbols refer to the ith unit:

	Population	Sample
Number of elements	M_i	m_i
Mean per element	$\bar{Y}_i$	$\bar{y}_i$
Total	$Y_i = M_i \bar{Y}_i$	$y_i = m_i \bar{y}_i$

The following symbols refer to the whole population or sample:

	Population	Sample
Number of elements	$M_0 = \sum\limits_{}^{N} M_i$	$\sum\limits_{}^{n} m_i$
Total	$Y = \sum\limits_{}^{N} Y_i$	$\sum\limits_{}^{n} y_i$
Mean per element	$\bar{\bar{Y}} = Y/M_0$	$\bar{\bar{y}} = \sum y_i / \sum m_i$
Mean per primary unit	$\bar{Y} = Y/N$	$\bar{y} = \sum y_i / n$

11.2 SAMPLING METHODS WHEN $n = 1$

Suppose that the ith unit is selected and that it contains M_i elements, of which m_i are sampled at random. We consider three methods of estimating $\bar{\bar{Y}}$, the mean per element.

I. Units Chosen with Equal Probability

$$\text{Estimate} = \bar{y}_\text{I} = \bar{y}_i.$$

The estimate is the sample mean per element. It is biased, for in repeated sampling from the same unit the average of $\bar{y}_i$ is $\overline{Y}_i$, and, since every unit has an equal chance of being selected, the average of $\overline{Y}_i$ is

$$\frac{1}{N} \sum_{i=1}^{N} \overline{Y}_i = \overline{\overline{Y}}_a \quad \text{(say)}$$

But the population mean is

$$\overline{\overline{Y}} = \frac{\sum_{i=1}^{N} M_i \overline{Y}_i}{M_0} , \quad \text{where } M_c = \sum_{i=1}^{N} M_i$$

Hence the bias equals $(\overline{\overline{Y}}_a - \overline{\overline{Y}})$. Since the method is biased, we shall compute the mean square error (MSE) about $\overline{\overline{Y}}$. Write

$$\bar{y}_i - \overline{\overline{Y}} = (\bar{y}_i - \overline{Y}_i) + (\overline{Y}_i - \overline{\overline{Y}}_a) + (\overline{\overline{Y}}_a - \overline{\overline{Y}})$$

Square and take the expectation over all possible samples. All contributions from cross-product terms vanish. The expectations of the squared terms follow easily by the methods given in Chapter 10. We find

$$\text{MSE}(\bar{y}_\text{I}) = \frac{1}{N} \sum_{i=1}^{N} \underbrace{\frac{(M_i - m_i)}{M_i} \frac{S_{2i}{}^2}{m_i}}_{\text{within units}} + \underbrace{\frac{1}{N} \sum_{i=1}^{N} (\overline{Y}_i - \overline{\overline{Y}}_a)^2}_{\text{between units}} + \underbrace{(\overline{\overline{Y}}_a - \overline{\overline{Y}})^2}_{\text{bias}} \quad (11.1)$$

where

$$S_{2i}{}^2 = \frac{1}{M_i - 1} \sum_{j=1}^{M_i} (y_{ij} - \overline{Y}_i)^2$$

is the variance among elements in the ith unit.

The MSE of $\bar{y}_\text{I}$ contains three components: one arising from variation within units, one from variation between the true means of the units, and one from the bias.

The values of the m_i have not been specified. The most common choice is either to take all m_i equal or to take m_i proportional to M_i, that is, to subsample a fixed proportion of whatever unit is selected. The choice of the m_i affects only the *first* of the three components of the variance—the component that arises from variation within units.

II. Units Chosen with Equal Probability

$$\text{Estimate} = \bar{y}_\text{II} = \frac{N M_i \bar{y}_i}{M_0}$$

This estimate is *unbiased*. Since $\bar{y}_i$ is an unbiased estimate of $\overline{Y}_i$, the product $M_i \bar{y}_i$ is an unbiased estimate of the unit total Y_i. Hence $N M_i \bar{y}_i$ is an unbiased estimate of the population total Y. Dividing by M_0, the total number of elements in the population, we obtain an unbiased estimate of $\overline{\overline{Y}}$.

To find $V(\bar{y}_{\text{II}})$, which, of course, equals its MSE, we have

$$\bar{y}_{\text{II}} - \bar{\bar{Y}} = \frac{NM_i\bar{y}_i}{M_0} - \bar{\bar{Y}}$$

$$= \frac{NM_i}{M_0}(\bar{y}_i - \bar{Y}_i) + \left(\frac{NM_i}{M_0}\bar{Y}_i - \bar{\bar{Y}}\right)$$

Now $M_i\bar{Y}_i = Y_i$, the total for the unit, and $\bar{\bar{Y}} = N\bar{Y}/M_0$, where $\bar{Y}$ is the population mean per unit. This gives

$$\bar{y}_{\text{II}} - \bar{\bar{Y}} = \frac{NM_i}{M_0}(\bar{y}_i - \bar{Y}_i) + \frac{N}{M_0}(Y_i - \bar{Y})$$

Hence

$$V(\bar{y}_{\text{II}}) = \frac{N}{M_0^2}\sum_{i=1}^{N} M_i(M_i - m_i)\frac{S_{2i}^2}{m_i} + \frac{N}{M_0^2}\sum_{i=1}^{N}(Y_i - \bar{Y})^2 \qquad (11.2)$$

The between-units component of this variance (second term on the right) represents the variation among the unit *totals* Y_i. This component is affected both by variations in the M_i from unit to unit and by variations in the means $\bar{Y}_i$ per element. If the units vary considerably in size, this component is large even though the means per element $\bar{Y}_i$ are almost constant from unit to unit. Frequently this component is so large that $\bar{y}_{\text{II}}$ has a much higher MSE than the biased estimate $\bar{y}_{\text{I}}$. Thus neither method I nor method II is fully satisfactory.

III. Units Chosen with Probability Proportional to Size

$$\text{Estimate} = \bar{y}_{\text{III}} = \bar{y}_i = \text{sample mean}$$

This technique is due to Hansen and Hurwitz (1943). It gives a sample mean that is unbiased and is not subject to the inflation of the variance in method II.

In repeated sampling, the ith unit appears with relative frequency M_i/M_0. Hence

$$E(\bar{y}_{\text{III}}) = \sum_{i=1}^{N} \frac{M_i}{M_0}\bar{Y}_i = \bar{\bar{Y}}$$

Further,

$$\bar{y}_{\text{III}} - \bar{\bar{Y}} = (\bar{y}_{\text{III}} - \bar{Y}_i) + (\bar{Y}_i - \bar{\bar{Y}})$$

Average first over samples in which the ith unit is selected.

$$E_i(\bar{y}_{\text{III}} - \bar{\bar{Y}})^2 = \left(\frac{M_i - m_i}{M_i}\right)\frac{S_{2i}^2}{m_i} + (\bar{Y}_i - \bar{\bar{Y}})^2$$

Now average over all possible selections of the unit. Since the ith unit is selected with relative frequency M_i/M_0,

$$V(\bar{y}_{\text{III}}) = \frac{1}{M_0}\left[\sum_{i=1}^{N}(M_i - m_i)\frac{S_{2i}^2}{m_i} + \sum_{i=1}^{N}M_i(\bar{Y}_i - \bar{\bar{Y}})^2\right] \qquad (11.3)$$

Note that, as in method I, the between-units component arises from differences among the means per element $\bar{Y}_i$ in the successive units. If these means per element are nearly equal, this component is small.

Example. Let us apply these results to a small population, artificially constructed. The data are presented in Table 11.1. There are three units, with

TABLE 11.1
ARTIFICIAL POPULATION WITH UNITS OF UNEQUAL SIZES

Unit	y_{ij}	M_i	Y_i	$S_{2i}{}^2$	$\bar{Y}_i$	$\bar{Y}_i - \bar{\bar{Y}}$
1	0, 1	2	1	0.500	0.5	−2.25
2	1, 2, 2, 3	4	8	0.667	2.0	−0.75
3	3, 3, 4, 4, 5, 5	6	24	0.800	4.0	+1.25
	Totals	12	33			

2, 4, and 6 elements, respectively. The reader may verify the figures given for Y_i, $S_{2i}{}^2$, and $\bar{Y}_i$. The population mean $\bar{\bar{Y}}$ is $\frac{33}{12}$, or 2.75. The unweighted mean of the $\bar{Y}_i$ is 2.167 $= \bar{\bar{Y}}_a$, so that the bias in method I is −0.583. Its square, the contribution to the MSE, is 0.340.

One unit is to be selected and two elements sampled from it. We consider four methods, two of which are variants of method I.

Method Ia.
  Selection: unit with equal probability, $m_i = 2$.
  Estimate: $\bar{y}_i$ (biased).
Method Ib.
  Selection: unit with equal probability, $m_i = \frac{1}{2}M_i$.
  Estimate: $\bar{y}_i$ (biased).
Method II.
  Selection: unit with equal probability, $m_i = 2$.
  Estimate: $NM_i\bar{y}_i/M_0$ (unbiased).
Method III.
  Selection: unit with probability M_i/M_0, $m_i = 2$.
  Estimate: $\bar{y}_i$ (unbiased).

Method I_b (proportional subsampling) does not guarantee a sample size of 2 (it may be 1, 2, or 3), but the average sample size is 2.

By application of the sampling error formulas (11.1), (11.2), and (11.3), we obtain the results in Table 11.2.

TABLE 11.2
MSE's OF SAMPLE ESTIMATES OF $\bar{\bar{Y}}$

| Method | Contribution to MSE from | | | Total |
	Within Units	Between Units	Bias	MSE
Ia	0.145	2.056	0.340	2.541
Ib	0.183	2.056	0.340	2.579
II	0.256	5.792	0.000	6.048
III	0.189	1.813	0.000	2.002

Although the example is artificial, the results are typical of those found in comparisons made on many populations. Method III gives the smallest MSE because it has the smallest contribution from variation between units. Method II, although unbiased, is very inferior. Method Ia (equal size of subsample) is slightly better than method Ib (proportional subsampling).

Some comparisons of these methods have also been made on actual populations. For six items (total workers, total agricultural workers, total nonagricultural workers, estimated separately for males and females), Hansen and Hurwitz (1943) found that method III produced large reductions in the contribution from variation between units as compared with the unbiased method II, and reductions which averaged 30% as compared with method I. (They assumed the contribution from variation within units to be negligible.) In estimating typical farm items for the state of North Carolina, Jebe (1952) reported reductions in the total variance of the order of 15% as compared with methods of type I. In both studies the primary unit was a county.

11.3 SAMPLING WITH PROBABILITY PROPORTIONAL TO ESTIMATED SIZE

As mentioned in Chapter 9, the sizes M_i of the units are sometimes known only approximately from previous data, and in other surveys several possible measures of the size of a unit may be available. Let z_i be the probability or relative size assigned to the ith unit, where the z_i are any set of positive numbers that add to unity. We still assume $n = 1$.

Method IV. An unbiased estimate of $\overline{\overline{Y}}$ is

$$\bar{y}_{IV} = \frac{M_i \bar{y}_i}{z_i M_0} \tag{11.4}$$

This follows because, in repeated sampling, the ith unit appears with relative frequency z_i, so that

$$E(\bar{y}_{IV}) = \sum_{i=1}^{N} z_i \left(\frac{M_i \bar{y}_i}{z_i M_0} \right) = \sum_{i=1}^{N} \frac{M_i \bar{y}_i}{M_0} = \overline{\overline{Y}}$$

The variance of $\bar{y}_{IV}$ is obtained in the usual way. Write

$$\bar{y}_{IV} - \overline{\overline{Y}} = \frac{M_i \bar{y}_i}{z_i M_0} - \overline{\overline{Y}} \qquad \text{[by (11.4)]}$$

$$= \frac{1}{M_0} \left[\frac{M_i}{z_i} (\bar{y}_i - \overline{Y}_i) + \left(\frac{M_i}{z_i} \overline{Y}_i - M_0 \overline{\overline{Y}} \right) \right]$$

In the variance, each square receives a weight z_i. Hence

$$V(\bar{y}_{IV}) = \frac{1}{M_0^2}\left[\sum_{i=1}^{N}\frac{M_i(M_i - m_i)}{z_i}\frac{S_{2i}^2}{m_i} + \sum_{i=1}^{N}z_i\left(\frac{M_i\bar{Y}_i}{z_i} - M_0\bar{\bar{Y}}\right)^2\right] \quad (11.5)$$

If $z_i = M_i/M_0$, (11.5) reduces to (11.3) for $V(\bar{y}_{III})$. If $z_i = 1/N$ (initial probabilities equal), (11.5) reduces to (11.2) for the variance of the unbiased estimate when probabilities are equal.

Unless $z_i = M_i/M_0$, the between-units component in (11.5) is affected to some extent by variations in the sizes M_i as well as by variations in the means per element $\bar{Y}_i$.

TABLE 11.3

COMPUTATION OF $V(\bar{y}_{IV})$

Unit	M_i	M_i/M_0	z_i	m_i	$\dfrac{M_i(M_i - m_i)}{z_i m_i}$	S_{2i}^2	Y_i	$\dfrac{Y_i}{z_i}$	$\dfrac{Y_i}{z_i} - Y$
1	2	0.17	0.2	2	0	0.500	1	5	-28
2	4	0.33	0.4	2	10	0.667	8	20	-13
3	6	0.50	0.4	2	30	0.800	24	60	$+27$

Example. Table 11.3 shows the computations for finding $V(\bar{y}_{IV})$ in the artificial population in Table 11.1. The z_i have been taken as 0.2, 0.4, and 0.4, and the $m_i = 2$.

From (11.5), the variance comes out as follows:

$$\text{within-units contribution} = \sum\frac{M_i(M_i - m_i)S_{2i}^2}{z_i m_i}\bigg/ M_0^2 = 0.213$$

$$\text{between-units contribution} = \sum z_i\left(\frac{Y_i}{z_i} - Y\right)^2\bigg/ M_0^2 = 3.583$$

Comparison with Table 11.2 shows that method IV has a lower variance than the unbiased method II in which the primary unit is chosen with equal probabilities, but method IV is decidedly inferior to method I or method III. In this example method IV pays too high a price in order to obtain an unbiased estimate.

Consequently, it is natural to consider whether the sample mean (as in method I) would be better than the estimate adopted in method IV.

V. Units Chosen with Probability Proportional to Estimated Size

$$\text{Estimate} = \bar{y}_V = \bar{y}_i = \text{sample mean}$$

The estimate is biased, since, for example,

$$E(\bar{y}_i) = \sum z_i\bar{Y}_i = \bar{\bar{Y}}_z$$

If the z_i are good estimates, $\overline{\overline{Y}}_z$ is close to the correct mean $\overline{\overline{Y}} = \sum M_i \overline{Y}_i / M_0$ and the bias is small.

If we write

$$\bar{y}_V - \overline{\overline{Y}} = (\bar{y}_i - \overline{Y}_i) + (\overline{Y}_i - \overline{\overline{Y}}_z) + (\overline{\overline{Y}}_z - \overline{\overline{Y}})$$

the three components of the MSE work out as follows:

$$\text{MSE}(\bar{y}_V) = \sum_{i=1}^{N} \frac{z_i(M_i - m_i)}{M_i} \frac{S_{2i}^2}{m_i} + \sum_{i=1}^{N} z_i(\overline{Y}_i - \overline{\overline{Y}}_z)^2 + (\overline{\overline{Y}}_z - \overline{\overline{Y}})^2$$

Example. If the values of z_i and m_i are chosen as in Table 11.3, the reader may verify that the components of the variance of $\bar{y}_V$ are as shown in Table 11.4.

TABLE 11.4

CONTRIBUTIONS TO THE MSE IN METHOD V

Within Units	Between Units	Bias	Total MSE
0.173	1.800	0.062	2.035

This is superior to all methods except method III (pps) and is almost as good as method III.

The variances of these five estimates could have been found as particular cases of theorem 10.1, but with $n = 1$ they were easily found directly.

11.4 SUMMARY OF METHODS FOR $n = 1$

The five methods of estimating the mean per element $\overline{\overline{Y}}$ and their MSE's in the numerical example are summarized in Table 11.5.

TABLE 11.5

TWO-STAGE SAMPLING METHODS ($n = 1$)

Method	Probabilities in Selecting Units	Estimate of $\overline{\overline{Y}}$	Bias Status	MSE in Example
I	Equal	$\bar{y}_i$	Biased	Ia: 2.541 Ib: 2.579
II	Equal	$\dfrac{NM_i\bar{y}_i}{M}$	Unbiased	6.048
III	$\dfrac{M_i}{M_0} \propto$ size	$\bar{y}_i$	Unbiased	2.002
IV	$z_i \propto$ estimated size	$\dfrac{M_i\bar{y}_i}{z_iM_0}$	Unbiased	3.796
V	$z_i \propto$ estimated size	$\bar{y}_i$	Biased	2.035

11.5 SAMPLING METHODS WHEN $n > 1$

The principal sampling methods for $n > 1$ are natural extensions of those discussed in sections 9.8 to 9.12 for one-stage sampling from cluster units of unequal sizes. Consequently we can use both the variance formulas developed in these sections and the comparisons made between the methods.

In the following sections the formulas for the true and estimated MSE's for the most useful methods when $n > 1$ are presented. For each method the conditions under which the estimate becomes self-weighting are noted, in view of the practical convenience of self-weighting procedures.

11.6 UNITS SELECTED WITH EQUAL PROBABILITIES. RATIO-TO-SIZE ESTIMATE

For estimating the population *mean* $\overline{\overline{Y}}$, there are several possible extensions of method I. The one that seems most generally useful is

$$\hat{\overline{Y}}_R = \frac{\sum\limits_{}^{n} M_i \bar{y}_i}{\sum\limits_{}^{n} M_i}$$

This is a typical ratio estimate because both the numerator and the denominator vary from sample to sample. As is characteristic of ratio estimates, the estimate is biased, but the bias becomes negligible when n is large. To find the approximate MSE, write

$$\frac{\sum\limits_{}^{n} M_i \bar{y}_i}{\sum\limits_{}^{n} M_i} - \overline{\overline{Y}} = \frac{\sum\limits_{}^{n} M_i(\bar{y}_i - \overline{\overline{Y}})}{\sum\limits_{}^{n} M_i} \doteq \frac{\sum\limits_{}^{n} M_i(\bar{y}_i - \overline{\overline{Y}})}{n\overline{M}}$$

where $\overline{M} = M_0/N$ is the average size per primary unit.

To apply theorem 10.1, p. 272, write

$$y_i' = \frac{M_i(\bar{y}_i - \overline{\overline{Y}})}{n\overline{M}}, \qquad Y_i' = \frac{M_i(\overline{Y}_i - \overline{\overline{Y}})}{n\overline{M}}, \qquad \hat{Y}' = \sum\limits_{}^{n} Y_i', \qquad \pi_i = \frac{n}{N}$$

It follows that $\hat{Y}'$ is the unweighted mean of the variates $M_i(\overline{Y}_i - \overline{\overline{Y}})/\overline{M}$. Hence, by theorem 2.2,

$$V(\hat{Y}') = \frac{1 - f_1}{n\overline{M}^2} \frac{\sum\limits_{}^{N} M_i^2(\overline{Y}_i - \overline{\overline{Y}})^2}{N - 1}$$

Further, in the notation of theorem 10.1,

$$\sigma_{2i}^2 = E(y_i' - Y_i')^2 = \frac{1}{n^2 \bar{M}^2} E[M_i^2(\bar{y}_i - \bar{Y}_i)^2]$$

$$= \frac{1}{n^2 \bar{M}^2} \frac{M_i^2(1 - f_{2i})S_{2i}^2}{m_i}$$

Hence, by theorem 10.1,

$$MSE(\hat{\bar{Y}}_R) \doteq V(y') = V(\hat{Y}') + \sum^{N} \pi_i \sigma_{2i}^2$$

$$\doteq \frac{1 - f_1}{n \bar{M}^2} \sum^{N} \frac{M_i^2(\bar{Y}_i - \bar{\bar{Y}})^2}{N - 1} + \frac{1}{n N \bar{M}^2} \sum^{N} \frac{M_i^2(1 - f_{2i})S_{2i}^2}{m_i} \quad (11.6)$$

This estimate reduces to the sample mean, that is, becomes self-weighting if

$$f_{2i} = \frac{m_i}{M_i} = \text{constant} = \frac{\bar{m}}{\bar{M}} = f_2 \quad (\text{say})$$

In this event the within-units contribution may be expressed more simply, giving

$$MSE(\bar{\bar{y}}) \doteq \frac{1 - f_1}{n} \sum^{N} \frac{M_i^2(\bar{Y}_i - \bar{\bar{Y}})^2}{\bar{M}^2(N - 1)} + \frac{1 - f_2}{n \bar{m}} \sum^{N} \left(\frac{M_i}{M_0}\right) S_{2i}^2 \quad (11.7)$$

The resemblance to the corresponding formula when the primary units are of equal sizes may be noted. From (10.10), section 10.3, we had

$$V(\bar{\bar{y}}) = \frac{1 - f_1}{n} \sum^{N} \frac{(\bar{Y}_i - \bar{\bar{Y}})^2}{N - 1} + \frac{1 - f_2}{nm} \sum^{N} \left(\frac{1}{N}\right) S_{2i}^2 \quad (11.8)$$

The difference is that in (11.7) the contributions from the primary units to the MSE are weighted.

An approximate sample estimate of the MSE in (11.6) is given by theorem 10.2. For the between-units component $V(\hat{Y}')$ the usual sample estimate (subject to a bias of order $1/n$), is

$$v(\hat{Y}') = \frac{1 - f_1}{n \bar{M}^2} \sum^{n} \frac{M_i^2(\bar{Y}_i - \bar{\bar{Y}}_n)^2}{n - 1} \quad (11.9)$$

where $\bar{\bar{Y}}_n = \sum^{n} M_i \bar{Y}_i / \sum^{n} M_i$. The "copy" of this is

$$v_c(\hat{Y}') = \frac{1 - f_1}{n \bar{M}^2} \sum^{n} \frac{M_i^2(\bar{y}_i - \hat{\bar{Y}}_R)^2}{n - 1} \quad (11.10)$$

noting that $\hat{\bar{Y}}_R = \sum M_i \bar{y}_i / \sum M_i$ is the copy of $\bar{\bar{Y}}_n$.

For σ_{2i}^2, an estimate is

$$\hat{\sigma}_{2i}^2 = \frac{1}{n^2 \bar{M}^2} \frac{M_i^2(1-f_{2i})s_{2i}^2}{m_i}$$

where, as usual,

$$s_{2i}^2 = \frac{\sum(y_{ij}-\bar{y}_i)^2}{m_i-1}$$

Hence, by theorem 10.2, a sample estimate of the MSE is

$$v(\hat{\bar{Y}}_R) = v(y') = v_c(\hat{Y}') + \sum_{}^{n} \pi_i \hat{\sigma}_{2i}^2$$

$$= \frac{1-f_1}{n\bar{M}^2} \sum_{}^{n} \frac{M_i^2(\bar{y}_i - \hat{\bar{Y}}_R)^2}{n-1} + \frac{f_1}{n^2\bar{M}^2} \sum_{}^{n} \frac{M_i^2(1-f_{2i})s_{2i}^2}{m_i} \quad (11.11)$$

By a more detailed analysis, Sukhatme (1954) has given a more accurate estimate of the within-units component.

For a self-weighting sample, (11.11) simplifies to

$$v(\hat{\bar{Y}}_R) = \frac{1-f_1}{n\bar{M}^2} \sum_{}^{n} \frac{M_i^2(\bar{y}_i - \hat{\bar{Y}}_R)^2}{n-1} + \frac{f_1(1-f_2)}{n^2 \bar{m}\bar{M}} \sum_{}^{n} M_i s_{2i}^2 \quad (11.12)$$

In both (11.11) and (11.12) note that if f_1 is negligible the estimated variance reduces to its first term.

Example. From the volume *American Men of Science*, 20 pages were selected at random. On each page the ages of two scientists, from two biographies also selected at random, were recorded. The total number of biographies per page varies in general from about 14 to 21. Estimate the average age and its standard error from the data in Table 11.6.

From the extreme right column,

$$\hat{\bar{Y}}_R = \frac{\sum M_i \bar{y}_i}{\sum M_i} = \frac{17,121.5}{359} = 47.7 \text{ years}$$

Since n/N is negligible, we have from (11.11),

$$v(\hat{\bar{Y}}_R) \doteq \frac{\sum_{}^{n} M_i^2(\bar{y}_i - \hat{\bar{Y}}_R)^2}{n\bar{M}^2(n-1)}$$

The numerator is most easily computed as

$$\sum(M_i \bar{y}_i)^2 - 2\hat{\bar{Y}}_R \sum(M_i\bar{y}_i)M_i + \hat{\bar{Y}}^2 \sum M_i^2$$
$$= 15,375,020 - (95.3844)(309,747.5) + (2274.55)(6481) = 571,300$$

TABLE 11.6

AGES OF 40 SCIENTISTS IN *American Men of Science* ($n = 20$, $m = 2$)

Unit No.	M_i	Ages y_{i1}	Ages y_{i2}	Total y_i	$M_i \bar{y}_i$
1	15	47	30	77	577.5
2	19	38	51	89	845.5
3	19	43	45	88	836.0
4	16	55	41	96	768.0
5	16	59	45	104	832.0
6	19	39	38	77	731.5
7	18	43	43	86	774.0
8	18	49	51	100	900.0
9	18	45	35	80	720.0
10	18	46	59	105	945.0
11	20	71	64	135	1,350.0
12	18	35	46	81	729.0
13	19	61	54	115	1,092.5
14	19	45	87	132	1,254.0
15	18	31	38	69	621.0
16	16	64	39	103	824.0
17	16	63	47	110	880.0
18	19	36	33	69	655.5
19	19	61	39	100	950.0
20	19	54	34	88	836.0
Totals	359			1,904	17,121.5

Since $\bar{M} = 359/20$, as estimated from the sample, this gives

$$v(\hat{\bar{Y}}_R) = \frac{(20)(571,300)}{(19)(359)^2} = 4.67$$

$$s(\hat{\bar{Y}}_R) = 2.16 \text{ years}$$

When primary units are selected with equal probabilities, an alternative estimate of the population mean is

$$\frac{1}{n}(\bar{y}_1 + \bar{y}_2 + \cdots + \bar{y}_n)$$

This estimate is self-weighting if $m_i =$ constant, as in the preceding example. When M_i and $\bar{Y}_i$ are uncorrelated, this estimate may be satisfactory, but it is liable to a bias that does not vanish even with n large when M_i and $\bar{Y}_i$ are correlated.

11.7   UNITS SELECTED WITH EQUAL PROBABILITIES. UNBIASED ESTIMATE

The unbiased estimate (method II in section 11.2) is

$$\hat{\bar{Y}}_u = \frac{N}{nM_0} \sum_{}^{n} M_i \bar{y}_i = \frac{1}{n\bar{M}} \sum_{}^{n} M_i \bar{y}_i$$

To find the variance, separate the error as usual into the within-units and between-units components, by writing

$$\hat{\bar{Y}}_u - \bar{Y} = \frac{1}{n\bar{M}} \sum_{}^{n} M_i(\bar{y}_i - \bar{Y}_i) + \frac{1}{n\bar{M}} \sum_{}^{n} (Y_i - \bar{Y})$$

where we have used the facts that $Y_i = M_i \bar{Y}_i$ and that $\sum^{n} \bar{Y}/n\bar{M} = \bar{Y}/\bar{M} = \bar{\bar{Y}}$. By squaring and taking the average, we find (putting the between-units component first)

$$V(\hat{\bar{Y}}_u) = \frac{1 - f_1}{n\bar{M}^2} \frac{\sum^{N}(Y_i - \bar{Y})^2}{N - 1} + \frac{1}{nN\bar{M}^2} \sum^{N} \frac{M_i^2(1 - f_{2i})S_{2i}^2}{m_i} \quad (11.13)$$

Like the ratio-to-size estimate, the unbiased estimate becomes self-weighting if $f_{2i} = m_i/M_i = \text{constant} = f_2$. We then have

$$\hat{\bar{Y}}_u = \frac{1}{n\bar{M}} \sum_{}^{n} \frac{M_i y_i}{f_2 M_i} = \frac{1}{nf_2\bar{M}} \sum_{i=1}^{n} \sum_{j=1}^{m} y_{ij} \quad (11.14)$$

With a self-weighting estimate, the variance in (11.13) can be expressed as

$$V(\hat{\bar{Y}}_u) = \frac{1 - f_1}{n\bar{M}^2} \frac{\sum^{N}(Y_i - \bar{Y})^2}{N - 1} + \frac{1 - f_2}{n\bar{m}N} \sum^{N} \frac{M_i}{\bar{M}} S_{2i}^2 \quad (11.15)$$

For an unbiased estimate of (11.13) from the sample, the usual procedure leads to the formula

$$v(\hat{\bar{Y}}_u) \equiv \frac{1 - f_1}{n\bar{M}^2} \frac{\sum^{n}(M_i\bar{y}_i - \hat{\bar{Y}}_u)^2}{n - 1} + \frac{f_1}{n^2\bar{M}^2} \sum^{n} \frac{M_i^2(1 - f_{2i})s_{2i}^2}{m_i} \quad (11.16)$$

where $\hat{\bar{Y}}_u = \sum M_i \bar{y}_i/n$.

For the self-weighting estimate (11.14), this reduces to

$$v(\hat{\bar{Y}}_u) = \frac{1 - f_1}{n\bar{M}^2} \frac{\sum^{n}(M_i\bar{y}_i - \hat{\bar{Y}}_u)^2}{n - 1} + \frac{f_1(1 - f_2)}{n\bar{m}\bar{M}} \sum^{n} M_i s_{2i}^2 \quad (11.17)$$

Example. For the data in Table 11.6 the unbiased estimate requires a knowledge of N (the number of pages) and M_0 (the number of biographies in the book). N is 2823 and M_0 is given as about 50,000. Accepting this figure for illustration, we have

$$\hat{\bar{Y}}_u = \frac{2823}{(20)(50,000)} (17,121.5) = 48.3 \text{ years}$$

From (11.16), with $\bar{M} = 50,000/2823 = 17.712$,

$$v(\hat{\bar{Y}}_u) = \frac{1}{(20)(17.712)^2(19)} \left[(577.5)^2 + \cdots + (836.0)^2 - \frac{(17,121.5)^2}{20} \right] = 6.021$$

The s.e. of the estimate is 2.45 years.

11.8 UNITS SELECTED WITH PROBABILITY PROPORTIONAL TO A MEASURE OF SIZE. UNBIASED ESTIMATE

Primary units are selected with probabilities proportional to z_i. Selection *with replacement* is assumed for simplicity. Results for $z_i = M_i/M_0$ (probability proportional to size) follow as a special case.

The subsample of m_i subunits from the ith unit is assumed to be drawn without replacement. If the ith unit is drawn twice, we suppose that the whole subsample is replaced, and a new independent drawing of m_i subunits, again without replacement, is made.

An unbiased estimate of the population mean (extension of method IV) is

$$\hat{\bar{Y}}_{ppes} = \frac{1}{nM_0} \sum^n \frac{M_i \bar{y}_i}{z_i} \tag{11.18}$$

To find the variance, write

$$\hat{\bar{Y}}_{ppes} - \bar{Y} = \frac{1}{nM_0} \sum^n \frac{M_i(\bar{y}_i - \bar{Y}_i)}{z_i} + \frac{1}{nM_0} \sum^n \left(\frac{Y_i}{z_i} - Y \right) \tag{11.19}$$

The between-units component may be written

$$\frac{1}{nM_0} \sum^N t_i \left(\frac{Y_i}{z_i} - Y \right)$$

Its variance, V_1, is obtainable from theorem 9.3 as

$$V_1 = \frac{1}{nM_0^2} \sum^N z_i \left(\frac{Y_i}{z_i} - Y \right)^2 \tag{11.20}$$

The within-units contribution to the variance for a unit that is drawn once is, by theorem 2.2,

$$\frac{1}{n^2 M_0^2} \frac{M_i^2(1 - f_{2i})S_{2i}^2}{z_i^2 m_i}$$

If the unit is drawn t_i times, each drawing contributes the same amount, since successive drawings are independent. This gives

$$V_2(|pu) = \frac{1}{n^2 M_0^2} \sum_{}^{N} \frac{t_i M_i^2 (1 - f_{2i}) S_{2i}^2}{z_i^2 m_i}$$

Hence,

$$V_2 = E[V_2(|pu)] = \frac{1}{n M_0^2} \sum_{}^{N} \frac{M_i^2 (1 - f_{2i}) S_{2i}^2}{z_i m_i} \tag{11.21}$$

There are other ways in which the subsamples may be drawn. If the ith unit is selected t_i times, one variant is to draw a subsample of size $m_i t_i$ without replacement, provided, of course, that $M_i > m_i t_i$. This method is more precise but will be slightly costlier, since more subunits have to be measured. Sukhatme (1954) has shown that the within-units contribution to the variance for this method is

$$V_2 - \frac{n-1}{n M_0^2} \sum_{}^{N} M_i S_i^2 \tag{11.22}$$

where V_2 is as given in (11.21).

Another possibility is to draw a single sample of size m_i, no matter how many times the ith unit is selected. This sample receives a weight t_i in making the estimate. The within-units contribution to the variance is found to be

$$V_2 + \frac{n-1}{n M_0^2} \sum_{}^{N} \frac{M_i^2 (1 - f_{2i}) S_{2i}^2}{m_i}$$

The differences in precision among these three methods may be shown to be small if the over-all sampling fraction is small.

To continue with our first method of subsampling, we have from (11.20) and (11.21),

$$V(\hat{\bar{Y}}_{ppes}) = \frac{1}{n M_0^2} \sum_{}^{N} z_i \left(\frac{Y_i}{z_i} - Y \right)^2 + \frac{1}{n M_0^2} \sum_{}^{N} \frac{M_i^2 (1 - f_{2i}) S_{2i}^2}{z_i m_i} \tag{11.23}$$

To discover when the estimate becomes self-weighting, write

$$\hat{\bar{Y}}_{ppes} = \frac{1}{n M_0} \sum_{i}^{n} \frac{M_i}{z_i m_i} \sum_{j}^{m_i} y_{ij}$$

The necessary condition is therefore

$$\frac{M_i}{z_i m_i} = \text{constant} = \frac{n}{f_0} \quad \text{(say)} \tag{11.24}$$

so that the estimate becomes $\sum\sum y_{ij}/f_0 M_0$. The quantity f_0 may be defined as the *expected over-all sampling fraction*. For the expected number of subunits in the sample is

$$E\left(\sum^n m_i\right) = E\left(\sum^N t_i m_i\right) = n \sum^N z_i m_i = f_0 M_0$$

using (11.24).

From (11.24), $m_i/M_i = f_0/n z_i$. If f_0 is chosen in advance, the field worker can be told what subsampling fraction m_i/M_i to take before he goes to the primary unit. For example, suppose that an over-all sampling fraction of 2% is aimed at, so that $f_0 = 0.02$, and that $n = 60$ primary units have been selected. If $z_i = 0.0026$ for one unit, we must have $m_i/M_i = 0.02/(60)(0.0026)$ or 1 in 7.8.

An unbiased estimate of $V(\bar{\bar{Y}}_{ppes})$ is the simple expression

$$v(\bar{\bar{Y}}_{ppes}) = \frac{1}{n(n-1)M_0^2} \sum^n (y_i' - \bar{y}')^2 \tag{11.25}$$

where $y_i' = M_i \bar{y}_i/z_i$ and $\bar{y}'$ is the unweighted mean of the y_i'. For a self-weighting sample, $y_i' = n y_i/f_0$, where y_i is the sample total in the ith unit.

Proof. Theorem 9.5, section 9.10, showed that if the $Y_i = M_i \bar{Y}_i$ are known, an unbiased estimate of the between-units contribution (on dividing by M_0^2) is

$$\frac{1}{n(n-1)M_0^2} \sum^n \left[\frac{Y_i}{z_i} - \left(\frac{\bar{Y}}{z}\right)\right]^2 \quad \text{where } \left(\frac{\bar{Y}}{z}\right) = \frac{1}{n} \sum \frac{Y_i}{z_i}$$

Hence we write, in the usual way,

$$y_i' - \bar{y}' = \frac{Y_i}{z_i} - \left(\frac{\bar{Y}}{z}\right) + \left\{y_i' - \frac{Y_i}{z_i} - \left[\bar{y}' - \left(\frac{\bar{Y}}{z}\right)\right]\right\}$$

The within-units component of $\sum(y_i' - \bar{y}')^2$, for a fixed set of primary units, is

$$\frac{n-1}{n} \sum^N \frac{t_i M_i^2 (1 - f_{2i}) S_{2i}^2}{z_i^2 m_i}$$

Its over-all average is

$$E_2\left[\sum^n (y_i' - \bar{y}')^2\right] = (n-1) \sum^N \frac{M_i^2 (1 - f_{2i}) S_{2i}^2}{z_i m_i}$$

Hence, on dividing by $n(n-1)M_0^2$, we obtain the correct within-units contribution to $V(\bar{\bar{Y}}_{ppes})$ in (11.23). This establishes the result (11.25). With a self-weighting sample, (11.25) takes the simpler form

$$v(\bar{\bar{Y}}_{ppes}) = \frac{n}{(n-1)(f_0 M_0)^2} \sum_1^n (y_i - \bar{y})^2 \tag{11.25'}$$

where y_i is the sample total in the ith unit.

11.9 UNITS SELECTED WITH PROBABILITY PROPORTIONAL TO SIZE. UNBIASED ESTIMATE

If $z_i = M_i/M_0$, the unbiased estimate (11.18) reduces to

$$\hat{\bar{Y}}_{ppes} = \frac{1}{n}(\bar{y}_1 + \bar{y}_2 + \cdots + \bar{y}_n) \qquad (11.26)$$

Clearly, this estimate becomes the unweighted sample mean per subunit $\bar{\bar{y}}$ if $m_i = m$.

From (11.23), the variance is

$$V(\hat{\bar{Y}}_{pps}) = \frac{1}{n}\sum_{}^{N}\frac{M_i}{M_0}(\bar{Y}_i - \bar{\bar{Y}})^2 + \frac{1}{n}\sum_{}^{N}\frac{M_i}{M_0}\frac{1 - f_{2i}}{m_i}S_{2i}{}^2 \qquad (11.27)$$

and from (11.25), since $y_i{}'$ becomes $M_0\bar{y}_i$, an unbiased estimate of variance is

$$v(\hat{\bar{Y}}_{pps}) = \frac{1}{n(n-1)}\sum_{}^{n}(\bar{y}_i - \hat{\bar{Y}}_{pps})^2 \qquad (11.28)$$

If $m_i = m$, this may be written

$$v(\hat{\bar{Y}}_{pps}) = \frac{1}{n(n-1)m^2}\sum_{}^{n}(y_i - \bar{y})^2 \qquad (11.29)$$

where $y_i = m\bar{y}_i$ = sample total in the ith unit.

11.10 UNITS SELECTED WITH PROBABILITY PROPORTIONAL TO A MEASURE OF SIZE. ESTIMATE: RATIO TO SIZE.

In surveys in which selection of units with probability proportional to size appears highly efficient, but the sampler possesses only estimates z_i of the relative sizes, the unbiased estimate in section 11.8 may give too high a between-units contribution to the variance, as happened in the numerical example in section 11.3. An alternative estimate (extension of method V) is the biased estimate

$$\hat{\bar{Y}}_{Rppes} = \frac{\sum_{}^{n}M_i\bar{y}_i/z_i}{\sum_{}^{n}M_i/z_i} \qquad (11.30)$$

The numerator is an unbiased estimate of nY, and the denominator an unbiased estimate of nM_0. The estimate becomes the unweighted sample mean $\bar{\bar{y}}$ if $m_i/M_i = f_0/nz_i$, the same condition that held for the unbiased estimate.

Since this estimate is a particular case of the more general ratio estimate discussed in section 11.14, the variance formulas will be proved there. Assuming n large,

$$V(\hat{\bar{\bar{Y}}}_{Rpp es}) \doteq \frac{1}{nM_0^2} \sum_{}^{N} \frac{M_i^2}{z_i} (\bar{Y}_i - \bar{\bar{Y}})^2 + \frac{1}{nM_0^2} \sum_{}^{N} \frac{M_i^2(1 - f_{2i})S_{2i}^2}{z_i m_i} \qquad (11.31)$$

The estimate of variance (slightly biased) is

$$v(\hat{\bar{\bar{Y}}}_{Rpp es}) = \frac{1}{n(n-1)M_0^2} \sum_{}^{n} \left[\frac{M_i}{z_i} (\bar{y}_i - \hat{\bar{\bar{Y}}}_{Rpp es}) \right]^2 \qquad (11.32)$$

When the sampling is self-weighting, this can be written

$$v(\bar{\bar{y}}) = \frac{n}{(n-1)(f_0 M_0)^2} \sum_{}^{n} (y_i - m_i \bar{\bar{y}})^2 \qquad (11.33)$$

11.11 COMPARISON OF THE METHODS

In section 9.12 the precisions of the following three sampling plans were compared for one-stage sampling with units of unequal sizes:

Selection of units: equal probabilities. Unbiased estimate.
Selection of units: equal probabilities. Ratio-to-size estimate.
Selection of units: probability proportional to size. Unbiased estimate.

In two-stage sampling the conclusions drawn in section 9.12 remain valid for the between-units contribution to the variance, because this contribution is the same as the variance for the corresponding one-stage plan. To summarize from section 9.12, it was found that if $\bar{Y}_i$ is uncorrelated with M_i, or changes only slightly as M_i changes, the *pps* estimate and the ratio-to-size estimate are superior to the unbiased estimate. The superiority may be great if the M_i vary substantially. On the other hand, the unbiased estimate wins if unit totals Y_i are uncorrelated with M_i.

The relative performances of the ratio-to-size estimate and the *pps* estimate depend on the relation between the variance of $\bar{Y}_i$ and M_i. If $V(\bar{Y}_i)$ is proportional to M_i^{-g}, the *pps* estimate is more precise if $g < 1$ and less precise of $g > 1$. The condition $g < 1$ probably approximates the situation in the majority of applications.

For each sampling plan in section 11.5 to section 11.10, the self-weighting form of the estimate was given. Unless the within-unit variances S_{2i}^2 differ greatly from one another, the use of a self-weighting plan should not incur any material loss of precision. As we have seen, the choice of the m_i affects only the within-units contribution to the variance. As shown by (11.6) and (11.13), the within-units contributions are approximately the same for the ratio-to-size estimate and the unbiased estimate, that is,

$$V_2 = \frac{1}{nN\bar{M}^2} \sum^N \frac{M_i^2(1 - f_{2i})S_{2i}^2}{m_i} = \frac{1}{nN\bar{M}^2}\left(\sum^N \frac{M_i^2 S_{2i}^2}{m_i} - \sum^N M_i S_{2i}^2 \right)$$

If the m_i are chosen to minimize V_2 for a fixed total sample size Σm_i, we find $m_i \propto M_i S_{2i}$. The self-weighting estimate requires $m_i \propto M_i$. For the *pps* estimate, the reader may verify that the minimum V_2 is given by choosing $m_i \propto S_{2i}$, whereas the self-weighting plan has $m_i =$ constant.

In comparing the within-units variances for the different plans, we assume that the self-weighting forms are used. From (11.7) and (11.27) the V_2 terms are as follows:

$$\text{equal:} \quad V_2 = \frac{1}{n\bar{m}} \sum^N \left(1 - \frac{\bar{m}}{\bar{M}} \right) \frac{M_i}{M_0} S_{2i}^2$$

$$\text{pps:} \quad V_2 = \frac{1}{n\bar{m}} \sum^N \left(1 - \frac{\bar{m}}{M_i} \right) \frac{M_i}{M_0} S_{2i}^2$$

The two expressions differ only in one minor respect. With equal probabilities, the fpc term is the same in all units, whereas with *pps* sampling $\bar{m}/M_i$ is smaller in the larger units and therefore $(1 - \bar{m}/M_i)$ is larger in the larger units. Since S_{2i}^2 is often greater in large than in small units, *pps* sampling gives perhaps a higher within-units contribution. With the subsampling fractions that are common in practice, however, the difference should be trivial. In the example in Table 11.2, section 11.2, the V_2 contributions were 0.189 for *pps* sampling and 0.183 for the self-weighting form of the ratio estimate (method I*b*).

In a comparison of the three plans, the net effect of the within-units contribution is therefore to dilute the differences created by the between-units contributions so that relative precisions will not differ so greatly as with one-stage sampling. For instance, if the between-unit contributions for two plans are $V_2 = 2$ and $V_2 = 1$ and the within-unit contributions are $V_1 = 1$ in both plans, the relative precision of the poorer plan is increased from $\frac{1}{2}$ in one-stage sampling to $\frac{2}{3}$ in this two-stage sample.

In the preceding comparisons we have not included *ppes* sampling. If the estimates of size are fairly good, *ppes* sampling, with the ratio-to-size estimate (extension of method V), should perform about as well as *pps* sampling. With the unbiased estimate (extension of method IV), the precision should be intermediate between that for *pps* sampling and that for the unbiased estimate with units chosen with equal probabilities.

The choice of a sampling plan will be influenced by the amount of knowledge required about the M_i. In all the plans the M_i must, of course, be known for the n primary units that are in the sample, and *pps* sampling demands a knowledge of all the M_i in the population. For estimating the population *mean*, the unbiased estimates, with either equal probabilities or *ppes*, require a knowledge of M_0, the total number of subunits in the population, whereas the corresponding ratio-to-size estimates do not. For estimating the population *total*, the situation is reversed.

11.12   RATIOS TO ANOTHER VARIABLE

In two-stage sampling the quantity to be estimated is often a ratio Y/X. This happens for two different reasons. As mentioned previously, if x is the value of y at a recent census, the ratio y/x may be relatively stable. An estimate of the population total or mean of y that is based on this ratio may be more precise than the estimates considered in this chapter. This was found to be the case for sampling farm items in North Carolina [(L. H. Madow (1950); Jebe (1952)].

Ratio estimates of this type are encountered also in the estimation of proportions or means over parts of the population. In an urban survey with the city block as primary unit, an example of a proportion of this type is

number of employed males over 16 years

total number of males over 16 years

If $y_{ij} = 1$ for any employed male over 16 and $y_{ij} = 0$ otherwise, and $x_{ij} = 1$ for any male over 16 and $x_{ij} = 0$ otherwise, the population proportion is Y/X. Other examples for this type of survey are the average income of families that subscribe to a certain magazine or the average amount of pocket money per teen-age child.

11.13   VARIANCE OF THE RATIO WITH EQUAL PROBABILITIES OF SELECTION

Formulas for the MSE and estimated variance are easily found from results already established. Consider first the selection of units with equal probabilities. The ratio estimate is

$$\hat{R} = \frac{\sum\limits^{n} M_i \bar{y}_i}{\sum\limits^{n} M_i \bar{x}_i}$$

Now, with $R = Y/X$,

$$\hat{R} - R = \frac{\sum M_i(\bar{y}_i - R\bar{x}_i)}{\sum\limits^{n} M_i \bar{x}_i} \doteq \frac{1}{n\bar{X}} \sum\limits^{n} M_i(\bar{y}_i - R\bar{x}_i)$$

where we approximate as usual by replacing $\sum\limits^{n} M_i \bar{x}_i$ in the denominator by its expected value nX/N or $n\bar{X}$.

Let $d_{ij} = y_{ij} - Rx_{ij}$. By the definition of R, the population total D and the population mean per subunit $\bar{\bar{D}}$ both vanish. With the ratio-to-size estimate (section 11.6), the approximate error of the estimate was expressed as $\sum\limits^{n} M_i(\bar{y}_i - \bar{\bar{Y}})/n\bar{M}$. With the present ratio estimate, the approximate error may be written as $\sum\limits^{n} M_i(\bar{d}_i - \bar{\bar{D}})/n\bar{X}$. Hence variance formulas for $\hat{R}$ are obtainable from those in section 11.6 by replacing y_{ij} by d_{ij} and multiplying by $(\bar{M}/\bar{X})^2$.

For the true MSE, this gives, from (11.6),

$$\text{MSE}(\hat{R}) \doteq \frac{1-f_1}{n\bar{X}^2} \sum^{N} \frac{M_i^2(\bar{Y}_i - R\bar{X}_i)^2}{N-1} + \frac{1}{nN\bar{X}^2} \sum^{N} \frac{M_i^2(1-f_{2i})}{m_i} S_{d2i}^2 \quad (11.34)$$

where

$$S_{d2i}^2 = \frac{1}{M_i - 1} \sum_{j=1}^{Mi} [(y_{ij} - Rx_{ij}) - (\bar{Y}_i - R\bar{X}_i)]^2$$

If $f_{2i} = m_i/M_i = f_2 = $ constant, $\hat{R}$ reduces to the ratio of the sample totals $\Sigma\Sigma y_{ij}/\Sigma\Sigma x_{ij}$. The MSE then takes the form

$$\text{MSE}(\hat{R}) = \frac{1-f_1}{n\bar{X}^2} \sum^{N} \frac{M_i^2(\bar{Y}_i - R\bar{X}_i)^2}{N-1} + \frac{1-f_2}{n\bar{m}\bar{X}^2} \sum^{N} \frac{M_i}{M_0} S_{d2i}^2 \quad (11.35)$$

For the estimated variance, substitute d_{ij} for y_{ij} and $\bar{X}$ for $\bar{M}$ in (11.11) for $v(\bar{\bar{Y}}_R)$. The resulting expression contains R. Substitute $\hat{R}$ for R, noting that the term $\hat{\bar{\bar{Y}}}_R$ in (11.11) becomes zero. This gives

$$v(\hat{R}) \doteq \frac{1-f_1}{n\bar{X}^2} \sum^{n} \frac{M_i^2(\bar{y}_i - \hat{R}\bar{x}_i)^2}{n-1} + \frac{f_1}{n^2\bar{X}^2} \sum^{n} \frac{M_i^2(1-f_{2i})s_{d2i}^2}{m_i} \quad (11.36)$$

11.14 VARIANCE OF THE RATIO WITH *ppes* SELECTION

If primary units are selected with probabilities proportional to z_i, with replacement, the estimate is

$$\hat{R} = \frac{\sum\limits^{n} M_i \bar{y}_i/z_i}{\sum\limits^{n} M_i \bar{x}_i/z_i} \quad (11.37)$$

The numerator and denominator are unbiased estimates of nY and nX, respectively. To find the variance, write

$$\hat{R} - R = \frac{\sum\limits_{n}^{n} M_i(\bar{y}_i - R\bar{x}_i)/z_i}{\sum\limits^{n} M_i\bar{x}_i/z_i} \doteq \frac{1}{nX} \sum^{n} \frac{M_i(\bar{y}_i - R\bar{x}_i)}{z_i}$$

On comparing the approximate error of $\hat{R}$ with that of the unbiased estimate $\hat{\bar{Y}}_{ppes}$ (section 11.8), it follows that $V(\hat{R})$ can be derived from $V(\hat{\bar{Y}}_{ppes})$ by replacing y_{ij} by $d_{ij} = y_{ij} - Rx_{ij}$, and M_0 by X. From (11.23), this gives

$$V(\hat{R}) = \frac{1}{nX^2} \sum^{N} \frac{1}{z_i} (Y_i - RX_i)^2 + \frac{1}{nX^2} \sum^{N} \frac{M_i^2(1 - f_{2i})S_{d2i}^2}{z_i m_i} \qquad (11.38)$$

The estimate $\hat{R}$ reduces to the ratio of the sample totals if

$$\frac{M_i}{z_i m_i} = \text{constant} = \frac{n}{f_0}$$

this condition being the same as that for $\hat{\bar{Y}}_{ppes}$.

From (11.25), a sample estimate of $V(\hat{R})$ that is slightly biased is

$$v(\hat{R}) = \frac{1}{n(n-1)X^2} \sum^{n} (y_i' - \hat{R}x_i')^2 \qquad (11.39)$$

where $y_i' = M_i\bar{y}_i/z_i$ and $x_i' = M_i\bar{x}_i/z_i$.

11.15 CHOICE OF SAMPLING AND SUBSAMPLING FRACTIONS. EQUAL PROBABILITIES

This problem is discussed first for the ratio-to-size estimate when units are chosen with equal probabilities. The subsampling fraction m_i/M_i is assumed constant, so that the estimate is the sample mean per element. The simplest cost function contains three terms:

c_u = fixed cost per primary unit
c_2 = cost per subunit
c_l = cost of listing per subunit in a selected unit

The third term is included because the sampler must usually list the elements in any selected unit and verify their number in order to draw a subsample. Hence

$$\text{cost} = c_u n + c_2 \sum^{n} m_i + c_l \sum^{n} M_i \qquad (11.40)$$

This formula is not usable as it stands, since the cost depends on the particular set of units that is chosen. Instead, consider the average cost over n units, which equals

$$E(C) = c_u n + c_2 n \bar{m} + c_l n \bar{M} = (c_u + c_l \bar{M}) n + c_2 n \bar{m} = c_1 n + c_2 n \bar{m}$$

(11.41)

where c_1 now includes the average cost of listing a unit.

From (11.7) in section 11.6,

$$\text{MSE}(\bar{\bar{y}}) = \frac{1 - f_1}{n} \sum_{i}^{N} \frac{M_i^2 (\bar{Y}_i - \bar{\bar{Y}})^2}{\bar{M}^2 (N - 1)} + \frac{1 - f_2}{n \bar{m}} \sum_{i}^{N} \frac{M_i}{M_0} S_{2i}^2$$

Write

$$S_b^2 = \frac{\sum_{i}^{N} M_i^2 (\bar{Y}_i - \bar{\bar{Y}})^2}{\bar{M}^2 (N - 1)}$$

This is a weighted variance among unit means per element. It is analogous to the variance S_1^2 in section 10.6 and reduces to S_1^2 if all M_i are equal. We may also write

$$S_2^2 = \sum_{i}^{N} \frac{M_i}{M_0} S_{2i}^2$$

This is a weighted mean of the within-unit variances. It reduces to the S_2^2 of section 10.6 if all M_i are equal.

In this notation

$$\text{MSE}(\bar{\bar{y}}) = \frac{1}{n} \left(S_b^2 - \frac{S_2^2}{\bar{M}} \right) + \frac{1}{n \bar{m}} S_2^2 - \frac{1}{N} S_b^2$$

(11.42)

The cost and MSE equations (11.41) and (11.42) are of exactly the same form as those in section 10.6, except that $\bar{m}$ replaces m, S_b^2 replaces S_1^2 and c_1 includes the cost of listing. Hence, from (10.18),

$$\bar{m}_{opt} \doteq \frac{S_2}{\sqrt{S_b^2 - S_2^2 / \bar{M}}} \sqrt{\frac{c_1}{c_2}}$$

(11.43)

The methods given in section 10.6 for utilizing knowledge about the ratios S_2/S_b and c_1/c_2 to guide the selection of $\bar{m}_{opt}$ are applicable here. The unbiased estimate when units are drawn with equal probabilities can be handled similarly.

The next section presents a more general analysis of this problem.

11.16 SAMPLING AND SUBSAMPLING FRACTIONS FOR *ppes* SAMPLING

An important analysis by Hansen and Hurwitz (1949) shows how to determine simultaneously the optimum probabilities of selection of units and the optimum sampling and subsampling fractions. The analysis is presented for ratio estimates $\hat{R}$. Units are selected with probabilities proportional to z_i. The subsampling fractions are assumed chosen so that $\hat{R}$ reduces to $\Sigma\Sigma y_{ij}/\Sigma\Sigma x_{ij}$. From section 11.14 this requires $m_i = kM_i/z_i$, where we have used k in place of the previous f_0/n.

As in section 11.15, the cost function is

$$C = c_u n + c_2 \sum_{}^{n} m_i + c_l \sum_{}^{n} M_i$$

This cost function applies only if good preliminary estimates of the sizes of all units in the population are available, since listing costs are included only for those units that appear in the sample. If the whole population has to be listed in advance, *pps* sampling is seldom economical for a single survey unless listing is extremely cheap.

Since

$$E\left(\sum_{}^{n} m_i\right) = \sum_{}^{N} nz_i m_i = nk \sum_{}^{N} M_i = nkM_0$$

$$E\left(\sum_{}^{n} M_i\right) = \sum_{}^{N} nz_i M_i$$

the average cost of sampling n units is

$$C = c_u n + c_2 nkM_0 + c_l n \sum_{}^{N} z_i M_i$$

In attempting to minimize $V(\hat{R})$ for fixed average cost, the variables at our disposal are n, k and the probabilities z_i.

By (11.38) in section 11.14, the variance to be minimized is

$$V(\hat{R}) = \frac{1}{nX^2} \sum_{}^{N} \left[\frac{1}{z_i}(Y_i - RX_i)^2 + \frac{M_i(M_i - m_i)}{z_i m_i} S_{d2i}^2\right]$$

Since $d_{ij} = y_{ij} - Rx_{ij}$, we may write $(Y_i - RX_i) = M_i \bar{D}_i$. Noting further that $M_i/z_i m_i = 1/k$, we have

$$V(\hat{R}) = \frac{1}{nX^2} \sum_{}^{N} \left[\frac{M_i^2}{z_i}\bar{D}_i^2 + \frac{M_i}{k}S_{d2i}^2 - \frac{M_i}{z_i}S_{d2i}^2\right]$$

Combining the first and third terms inside the parentheses gives

$$V = X^2 V(\hat{R}) = \sum_{}^{N} \frac{1}{n}\left[\frac{M_i^2}{z_i}\left(\bar{D}_i^2 - \frac{S_{d2i}^2}{M_i}\right) + \frac{M_i}{k}S_{d2i}^2\right]$$

Finally, note that n appears only in the combinations nz_i and nk. Introduce the variables $z_i' = nz_i$ and $k' = nk$. Thus

$$V = \sum_{}^{N} \left[\frac{M_i^2}{z_i'}\left(\bar{D}_i^2 - \frac{S_{d2i}^2}{M_i}\right) + \frac{M_i}{k'}S_{d2i}^2\right] \qquad (11.44)$$

The problem is to minimize V with respect to variations in n, k' and the z_i', subject to the restrictions that average cost is fixed and that

$$\sum_{i}^{N} z_i = 1, \qquad \text{i.e., } \sum_{i}^{N} z_i' = n$$

Taking λ and μ as undetermined multipliers, we minimize

$$V + \lambda\left(c_u n + c_2 k' M_0 + c_l \sum_{i}^{N} z_i' M_i - C\right) + \mu\left(n - \sum_{i}^{N} z_i'\right) \quad (11.45)$$

Differentiation gives

$$n: \quad \lambda c_u + \mu = 0$$

$$z_i': \quad \frac{-M_i^2}{z_i'^2}\left(\bar{D}_i^2 - \frac{S_{d2i}^2}{M_i}\right) + \lambda c_l M_i - \mu = 0$$

that is,

$$\lambda z_i'^2 = \frac{M_i^2(\bar{D}_i^2 - S_{d2i}^2/M_i)}{c_u + c_l M_i}$$

Since $z_i = z_i'/n$ and $\Sigma z_i = 1$, it follows that

$$z_i = \frac{M_i D_{iu}/\sqrt{c_u + c_l M_i}}{\sum_{}^{N} M_i D_{iu}/\sqrt{c_u + c_l M_i}} \quad (11.46)$$

where

$$D_{iu}^2 = \bar{D}_i^2 - \frac{S_{d2i}^2}{M_i}$$

and it has been assumed that the D_{iu}^2 are positive. Equation (11.46) gives the optimum selection probabilities.

The quantity D_{iu}^2 must now be examined, since it may depend on the size of unit M_i. In section 9.4 the variance between cluster unit means was expressed in terms of the intraunit correlation coefficient. From equation 9.7, with $n = 1$ and N assumed large, the variance among the means of a group of primary units is given approximately by

$$V(\bar{Y}_i) \doteq \frac{S^2}{\bar{M}}[1 + (\bar{M} - 1)\rho_{\bar{M}}] \quad (11.47)$$

where S^2 is the variance among subunits in the population and $\bar{M}$ is the average size of the primary units. The intraunit correlation has been denoted by $\rho_{\bar{M}}$ as a reminder that the correlation may depend on the size of the unit.

Apply this result to an analysis of variance of the variate d_{ij} into the categories between units and within units. The symbol S_d^2 denotes the variance among all subunits in the population. Assuming N large and $M_i = \bar{M}$, we have

Total SS: $\qquad\qquad N\bar{M}S_d^2$

$$\text{SS between units: } \bar{M}\sum_{i}^{N} \bar{D}_i^2 = NS_d^2[1 + (\bar{M} - 1)\rho_{\bar{M}}] \qquad (11.48)$$

where we have used (11.47) and noted that $\bar{\bar{D}} = 0$ by the definition of R. Hence, by subtraction,

$$\text{SS within units: } N(\bar{M} - 1)S_d^2(1 - \rho_{\bar{M}}) = N(\bar{M} - 1)S_{d2}^2$$

where S_{d2}^2 is the variance within units. This gives

$$S_{d2}^2 = S_d^2(1 - \rho_{\bar{M}}) \qquad (11.49)$$

From (11.48) and (11.49) we obtain the average value of D_{iu}^2 for primary units of size $\bar{M}$, that is,

$$E(D_{iu}^2) = \frac{1}{N}\sum_{}^{N} \bar{D}_i^2 - \frac{S_{d2}^2}{\bar{M}} = \frac{S_d^2}{\bar{M}}[1 + (\bar{M} - 1)\rho_{\bar{M}} - (1 - \rho_{\bar{M}})] = \rho_{\bar{M}}S_d^2$$

If $\bar{M}$ does not vary greatly, the assumption that $\rho_{\bar{M}}$ is constant, hence that $E(D_{iu}^2)$ is constant, is often satisfactory. In general, however, $\rho_{\bar{M}}$ may be expected to *decrease* as $\bar{M}$ increases, since subunits that are far apart are less subject to common influences. As Hansen and Hurwitz (1949) suggest, the rate of decrease is usually small enough so that $\bar{M}\rho_{\bar{M}}$ increases, hence $\bar{M}E(D_{iu}^2)$ increases, as $\bar{M}$ increases. If $\rho_{\bar{M}}$ is zero or negative, many of the quantities D_{iu}^2 will be negative, and the solution given here breaks down. In this situation two-stage sampling is less efficient than one-stage.

We can now discuss the optimum choice of the z_i. From (11.46),

$$z_i \propto \frac{M_i D_{iu}}{\sqrt{c_u + c_l M_i}}$$

Since the values of the individual D_{iu} are not known, we replace D_{iu} by its average for units of size M_i, that is, by $\sqrt{E(D_{iu}^2 \mid M_i)} = \bar{D}_{u,\bar{M}_i}$ (say). The following deductions may be made.

1. Suppose that $c_l M_i$, the cost of listing per primary unit, is small relative to c_u, the fixed cost per primary unit. If $\bar{D}_{u,\bar{M}_i}$ is constant, then $z_i \propto M_i$, so that *pps* selection is best. If $\bar{D}_{u,\bar{M}_i}$ decreases with increasing M_i, optimum probabilities lie between $z_i \propto M_i$ and $z_i \propto \sqrt{M_i}$.

2. If the cost of listing predominates, optimum probabilities lie between $z_i \propto \sqrt{M_i}$ and $z_i = $ constant (equal probabilities).

3. If costs of listing and fixed costs are of the same order of magnitude, $z_i \propto \sqrt{M_i}$ is a good compromise.

The optimum k is found by differentiating (11.45) with respect to k'. The result is

$$k = \frac{\sqrt{\sum M_i S_{d2i}^2}}{\sqrt{M_0 c_2} \sum M_i D_{iu}/\sqrt{c_u + c_2 M_i}} \tag{11.50}$$

This result is similar to that obtained in section 11.15 for units chosen with equal probabilities. To see this, note that from (11.46) and (11.50) the optimum $m_i = kM_i/z_i$ is found to be

$$m_i = \frac{\sqrt{\sum(M_i/M_0)S_{d2i}^2}}{\bar{D}_{u,M_i}} \sqrt{(c_u + c_l M_i)/c_2} = \frac{S_{d2}'}{S_{du}'} \sqrt{(c_u + c_l M_i)/c_2}$$

In this form the result is the same as that for $\bar{m}_{opt}$ in (11.43), noting that c_1 in (11.43) is $c_u + c_l \bar{M}$.

Finally, the optimum n is found by solving the average cost equation.

11.17 STRATIFIED SAMPLING. UNBIASED ESTIMATES

For the unbiased methods the extension to stratified sampling is straight-forward. The subscript h denotes the stratum.

M_{0h} = total number of subunits in stratum h

$M_0 = \sum_h^L M_{0h}$ = total number of subunits in the population

The estimated population mean per subunit is

$$\bar{\bar{y}}_{st} = \sum_h^L W_h \bar{\bar{y}}_h, \qquad W_h = \frac{M_{0h}}{M_0}$$

where $\bar{\bar{y}}_h$ denotes the estimate of the stratum mean per subunit $\bar{\bar{Y}}_h$. Further,

$$V(\bar{\bar{y}}_{st}) = \sum_h^L W_h^2 V(\bar{\bar{y}}_h), \qquad v(\bar{\bar{y}}_{st}) = \sum_h^L W_h^2 v(\bar{\bar{y}}_h)$$

These variances are readily obtained from the formulas already given.

It is of interest to consider the conditions under which the estimates become self-weighting. For *ppes* sampling (section 11.8) the estimated population mean is, from equation (11.18),

$$\hat{\bar{\bar{Y}}}_{ppes} = \frac{1}{M_0} \sum_h^L \frac{1}{n_h} \sum_i^{n_h} \frac{M_{hi} y_{hi}}{m_{hi} z_{hi}}$$

where y_{hi} is the *total* over the m_{hi} subunits taken from the ith unit in stratum h. In section 11.8 we saw that the estimate is self-weighting within strata if $M_{hi}/m_{hi}z_{hi} = n_h/f_{0h}$. With this substitution, the estimate becomes

$$\hat{\bar{Y}}_{ppes} = \frac{1}{M_0} \sum_h^L \frac{1}{f_{0h}} \sum_i^{n_h} y_{hi}$$

Thus the estimate is completely self-weighting if f_{0h}, the expected over-all sampling fraction, is the same in all strata.

If units are of the same size within any stratum (i.e., $M_{hi} = M_h$), it was shown in section 10.10 that sample allocation leading to a completely self-weighting estimate is close to the optimum allocation, provided that $S_{2h}/\sqrt{c_{2h}}$ is reasonably constant. A similar result holds here. From (11.23), we have

$$V(\hat{\bar{Y}}_{ppes}) = \frac{1}{M_0^2}\left[\sum_h^L \frac{1}{n_h} \sum_i^{N_h} z_{hi}\left(\frac{Y_{hi}}{z_{hi}} - Y_h\right)^2 + \sum_h^L \frac{1}{f_{0h}} \sum_i^{N_h} M_{hi}S_{2hi}^2\left(1 - \frac{m_{hi}}{M_{hi}}\right) \right]$$

where $M_{hi}/z_{hi}m_{hi} = n_h/f_{0h}$, to make the estimate self-weighting within each stratum. The quantity f_{0h} enters this expression in the form

$$\frac{1}{M_0^2} \sum_h^L \frac{1}{f_{0h}} \sum_i^{N_h} M_{hi}S_{2hi}^2 \tag{11.51}$$

(The term in m_{hi}/f_{0h}, arising from the second-stage fpc, may be written $M_{hi}/z_{hi}n_h$ and thus is a term in $1/n_h$ rather than in $1/f_{0h}$.)

With a simple cost function, the expected cost may be written

$$C = \sum_h c_{1h}n_h + \sum_h c_{2h}f_{0h}M_{0h} \tag{11.52}$$

since $f_{0h}M_{0h}$ is the expected number of second-stage units to be drawn from stratum h. In this cost function listing costs have been included in c_{1h}.

Hence, from (11.51) and (11.52), the variance is minimized for fixed cost if

$$f_{0h} \propto \frac{\sqrt{\sum M_{hi}S_{2hi}^2}}{\sqrt{c_{2h}M_{0h}}} = \frac{1}{\sqrt{c_{2h}}} \sqrt{\sum (M_{hi}/M_{0h})S_{2hi}^2}$$

The term involving variances is a weighted mean of the S_{2hi}^2. This verifies the result.

The estimated variance is obtained from (11.25) in section 11.8. For a completely self-weighting estimate, (11.25') shows that v takes the form

$$v(\hat{\bar{Y}}_{ppes}) = \frac{1}{(f_0M_0)^2} \sum_h \frac{n_h}{n_h - 1} \sum_i (y_{hi} - \bar{y}_h)^2$$

11.18 STRATIFIED SAMPLING. RATIO ESTIMATES

With ratio estimates the familiar problem—whether to take a separate or a combined estimate—arises. The separate estimate is preferable if n_h is large in each stratum and the true ratio is likely to vary from stratum to stratum. Its variance formulas follow at once from those for a single stratum.

For the combined estimate, with *ppes* sampling, let

$$\hat{Y}_h = \frac{1}{n_h} \sum_{i=1}^{n_h} \frac{M_{hi}}{z_{hi}} \bar{y}_{hi}, \qquad \hat{X}_h = \frac{1}{n_h} \sum_{i=1}^{n_h} \frac{M_{hi}}{z_{hi}} \bar{x}_{hi}$$

The quantities $\hat{Y}_h$, $\hat{X}_h$ are unbiased estimates of the stratum totals Y_h, X_h. The combined ratio estimate is defined as

$$\hat{R}_c = \frac{\sum\limits_{h}^{L} \hat{Y}_h}{\sum\limits_{h}^{L} \hat{X}_h}$$

The approximate MSE of $\hat{R}_c$ is found as usual by writing

$$\hat{R} - R \doteq \frac{1}{X} \sum_h^L (\hat{Y}_h - R\hat{X}_h)$$

The quantity $\hat{Y}_h - R\hat{X}_h$ is an unbiased *ppes* estimate of the stratum total $Y_h - RX_h$ of the variate $d_{hij} = y_{hij} - Rx_{hij}$. Hence, from formula (11.23) in section 11.8, replacing y_{hij} by d_{hij}, we obtain

$$\text{MSE}(\hat{R}_c) \doteq \frac{1}{X^2} \sum_h^L \frac{1}{n_h} \sum_i^{N_h} \left[z_{hi} \left(\frac{D_{hi}}{z_{hi}} - D_h \right)^2 + \frac{M_{hi}^2 (1 - f_{2hi}) S_{d2hi}^2}{z_{hi} m_{hi}} \right]$$

where

$$D_{hi} = Y_{hi} - RX_{hi}$$

$$S_{d2hi}^2 = \frac{1}{M_{hi} - 1} \sum_j^{M_{hi}} [(y_{hij} - Rx_{hij}) - (\bar{Y}_{hi} - R\bar{X}_{hi})]^2$$

Similarly, the estimated variance of R_c is obtained from (11.25) as

$$v(\hat{R}_c) \doteq \frac{1}{X^2} \sum_h^L \frac{1}{n_h(n_h - 1)} \sum_i^{n_h} (d_{hi}' - \bar{d}_h')^2$$

where

$$d_{hi}' = \frac{M_{hi} \bar{d}_{hi}}{z_{hi}}, \qquad \bar{d}_h' = \frac{1}{n_h} \sum_i^{n_h} d_{hi}'$$

$$\bar{d}_{hi} = \bar{y}_{hi} - \hat{R}_c \bar{x}_{hi}$$

If X is not known, the sample estimate $\Sigma \hat{X}_h$ is substituted for it.

The estimate $\hat{R}_c$ reduces to the ratio of the sample totals of y_{hij} and x_{hij} if the over-all sampling fraction is the same in all strata.

11.19 SELECTION WITH UNEQUAL PROBABILITIES WITHOUT REPLACEMENT

In some surveys the strata contain relatively few primary units, say 5 to 15, of which 2 or 3 are selected in the sample. Thus the primary sampling fraction may lie between 10 and 50%. This situation has encouraged the search for a satisfactory method of selecting primary units without replacement, which might produce the reduction in variance associated with a finite population correction. Some of the principal methods were described for one-stage sampling in sections 9.14 and 9.15. In the numerical example in Table 9.10 (p. 266), with two primary units drawn out of five, it is noticeable that in population A, in which $\overline{Y}_i$ was uncorrelated with z_i, the three estimates $\hat{Y}_N$, $\hat{Y}_{SYS}$, and $\hat{Y}_{GI}$ gave reductions in variance of about 40% as compared with $\hat{Y}_{pps}$, in which selection was with replacement. (These were the estimates obtained by plans which did not distort the probabilities of selection.)

In two-stage sampling the gains in precision from selection without replacement will be smaller. The sampling variance formulas show that this gain affects only the between primary unit contribution to the variance. Although the within primary unit variances are not the same for sampling with and without replacement, they are of the same order of magnitude. Moreover, when the primary sampling fraction is large, the second-stage fraction is likely to be small, so that the second-stage variance is a major part of the total variance. These considerations suggest that for most purposes the need for methods of selection without replacement is not too pressing. Some of the simpler methods will be outlined, although at this time none has found widespread adoption.

For $n = 2$, Yates and Grundy (1953) suggest drawing the first unit with probability proportional to a measure of size z_i and the second with probability proportional to the remaining sizes. An estimate of the stratum total Y is

$$\frac{1}{2}\left(\frac{M_i \bar{y}_i}{z_i} + \frac{M_j \bar{y}_j}{z_j}\right) = \tfrac{1}{2}(y_i' + y_j')$$

The estimate is biased, since this method distorts the selection probabilities, but the bias appears to be unimportant. The quantity $(y_i' - y_j')^2/4$ should be an overestimate of the variance.

The three remaining methods have already been described. One is to arrange primary units in random order, drawing a systematic "every kth" sample from the cumulated z_i. Each primary unit in which a point of the systematic sample falls is included in the sample (Hartley and Rao, 1962). An unbiased estimate of Y is $\Sigma y_i'/n$. As with the Yates and Grundy method, the estimate is self-weighting if $m_i/M_i = f_0/nz_i$, where f_0 is the expected over-all sampling fraction.

In the third and fourth methods, the stratum is divided into n groups. One primary unit is drawn from each group with probability proportional to relative size within the group, that is, to z_i/Z_g, where $Z_g = \Sigma z_i$ taken over the group (say, the gth) in which the ith unit falls. An unbiased estimate of Y is

$$\hat{Y}_G = \sum_g^n \frac{Z_g M_i \bar{y}_i}{z_i} \tag{11.53}$$

In forming the groups, one way is to make Z_g constant, as far as possible, in order to keep the probabilities of selection proportional to the original z_i. It helps also if the group means $\bar{\bar{Y}}_g$ are approximately equal, since the estimate of variance uses the method of collapsed strata.

The fourth method is to assign units to groups at random, with the number of units in a group as nearly equal as possible (Rao, Hartley, and Cochran, 1962). The estimate $\hat{Y}_{G2}$ is as in (11.53). An estimate of variance that is unbiased for any n is

$$v(\hat{Y}_{G2}) = \frac{\left(\sum^n N_g^2 - N\right)}{(N^2 - \sum N_g^2)}\left[\sum^n Z_g y_i'^2 - \hat{Y}_{G2}^2\right] + \sum^n \frac{Z_g M_i^2}{z_i m_i}(1 - f_{2i})s_{2i}^2$$

where N_g is the number of units in the gth group, $y_i' = M_i \bar{y}_i/z_i$, and $N = \Sigma N_g$. As usual, $s_{2i}^2 = \Sigma(y_{ij} - \bar{y}_i)^2/(m_i - 1)$. If N is divisible by n, so that $N_g = N/n$, the term outside the square bracket becomes $(1 - f_1)/(n - 1)$.

11.20 SUMMARY COMMENTS

The efficient design of a multistage sample with primary units of unequal size requires a good deal of preliminary work. Selection of primary units with probabilities proportional to a measure of size z_i is at its most effective, relative to selection with equal probabilities, when the ratios Y_i/z_i are uncorrelated with the sizes z_i for the principal items in the survey and the sizes vary substantially. These conditions hold frequently in the sampling of records in which the sizes of the primary units (groups of records) are determined by administrative or economic considerations, the data in individual records being at about the same level in different units. The principal decisions to be made are the following:

1. Find out whether the sizes are known, known approximately, or unknown. In the last case consider whether some information about

sizes can be obtained relatively easily. For example, Jessen et al. (1947) conducted two-stage samples of blocks in some Greek towns in which no usable estimates of the numbers of households per block were available. They considered three approaches: (*a*) Drawing the blocks with equal probabilities. (*b*) Making a rapid tour of the town by jeep in order to tie together small blocks to build artificial blocks that appeared to have roughly the same numbers of households. Blocks which obviously had no households were eliminated in this process. The sample blocks were then chosen with equal probability. (*c*) Cruising the town slowly enough to permit estimates to be made of the number of households in each block. Blocks were then chosen with probability proportional to estimated sizes.

2. Consider whether to use size of unit as one of the variables for stratification: this is advisable unless it prevents the use of some other variable that might give a worthwhile increase in precision.

3. Decide how the units are to be selected within strata. If sizes are known at least approximately, selection with pps, or its square root, will often be the best procedure, although this depends on the nature of the field costs.

4. Select a method of estimation. For estimating the population mean or total, a ratio estimate using the value of the same item at a recent census is sometimes very successful, if available. Estimates based on the sample mean or weighted sample mean are often more precise than the unbiased estimates.

5. Decide on the sampling and subsampling fractions within strata. We have recommended that subsampling fractions be chosen so that the estimates are self-weighting within strata. Further control so that the sample is completely self-weighting is advisable unless it appears to be accompanied by a substantial loss of precision.

Accounts of the planning and conduct of surveys involving two-stage sampling with primary units of unequal sizes are contained in the following references.

Sampling From Records

Patton, R. (1952). The sampling of records. Public Health Reports, 67, No. 10. (Sampling from cards in file drawers.)

Trueblood, R. M., and Cyert, R. M. (1957). Sampling techniques in accounting. Prentice-Hall. (Sampling applied to the aging of accounts receivable.)

Urban Sampling

Bureau of the Census (1950). A chapter in population sampling. U.S. Government Printing Office.

Kish, L. (1952). A two-stage sample of a city. Amer. Sociological Review, **17**, 761–769.

More Extensive Populations

Gray, P. G. and Corlett, T. (1950). Sampling for the social survey. Jour. Roy. Stat. Soc., **A113**, 150–206.

Hemphill, F. M. (1952). A sample survey of home injuries. Public Health Reports, 67.

Peaker, G. F. (1953). A sampling design used by the Ministry of Education. Jour. Roy. Stat. Soc., **A116**, 140–165. (A survey of the reading abilities of children aged 15.)

See also the books by Hansen, Hurwitz, and Madow and by Yates.

EXERCISES

11.1 By working out the estimates for all possible samples which can be drawn from the artificial population in Table 11.1, by methods Ia, Ib, II, and III, verify the total MSE's given in Table 11.2.

11.2 For methods II (equal probabilities, unbiased estimate) and III (pps selection), recompute the variances of $\hat{\bar{Y}}$ for the example in Table 11.1 when $m_i = 1$. Show that the precision of method III in relation to method II is lower for $m_i = 1$ than for $m_i = 2$. What general result does this illustrate?

11.3 For the population in Table 11.1, if the estimated sizes z_i are 0.1, 0.3 and 0.6, with $m_i = 2$, show that the unbiased estimate (method IV) gives a smaller variance than pps sampling. What is the explanation of this result?

11.4 The elements in a population with three primary units are classified into two classes. The unit sizes M_i and the proportions P_i of elements which belong to the first class are as follows:

$$M_1 = 100, \ M_2 = 200, \ M_3 = 300, \qquad P_1 = 0.40, \ P_2 = 0.45, \ P_3 = 0.35$$

For a sample consisting of 50 elements from one primary unit, compare the MSE's of methods Ia, II, and III for estimating the proportion of elements in the first class in the population. (In the variance formulas in section 11.2, S_i^2 is approximately $P_i Q_i$.)

11.5 A sample of n primary units is selected with equal probabilities. From each chosen unit, a constant fraction f_2 of the subunits is taken. If a_i out of the m_i subunits in the ith unit fall in class C, show that the ratio-to-size estimate (section 11.6) of the population proportion in class C is $\bar{p} = \Sigma a_i / \Sigma m_i$. From formula (11.12), show that an estimate of MSE($\bar{p}$) is

$$v(\bar{p}) = \frac{1 - f_1}{n\bar{M}^2} \sum_{n}^{n} \frac{M_i^2(p_i - \bar{p})^2}{n - 1} + \frac{f_1(1 - f_2)}{n^2 \bar{m}\bar{M}} \sum^{n} \frac{M_i m_i}{m_1 - 1} p_i q_i$$

where $p_i = a_i / m_i$.

11.6 A firm with 36 factories decides to check the condition of some equipment of which $M_0 = 25{,}012$ pieces are in use. A random sample of 12 factories is taken, a 10% subsample being checked in each selected factory. The numbers of pieces checked (m_i) and the numbers found with signs of deterioration (a_i) are as follows.

Factory	m_i	a_i	$p_i = \dfrac{a_i}{m_i}$	Factory	m_i	a_i	$p_i = \dfrac{a_i}{m_i}$
1	65	8	0.123	7	85	18	0.212
2	82	21	0.256	8	73	11	0.151
3	52	4	0.077	9	50	7	0.140
4	91	12	0.132	10	76	9	0.118
5	62	1	0.016	11	64	20	0.312
6	69	3	0.043	12	50	2	0.040

Estimate the percentage and the total number of defective pieces in use and give estimates of their standard errors.

Note. Since $M_i/\bar{M} \doteq m_i/\bar{m}$, the between-units component of $v(\bar{p})$ may be computed as

$$\frac{1 - f_1}{n\bar{m}^2(n - 1)} \left(\sum a_i^2 - 2\bar{p} \sum a_i m_i + \bar{p}^2 \sum m_i^2 \right),$$

and since the m_i are fairly large, the within-units component as

$$\frac{f_1(1 - f_2)}{(n\bar{m})^2} \sum a_i q_i.$$

11.7 If primary units are selected with equal probabilities and f_2 is constant, show that in the notation of exercise 11.5 the unbiased estimate of a population proportion is $p = N \sum a_i / n M_0 f_2$ and that, if terms in $1/m_i$ are negligible, its variance may be computed as

$$v(p) = \frac{1 - f_1}{n(n - 1)\bar{m}^2} \sum^{n} (a_i - \bar{a})^2 + \frac{f_1(1 - f_2)}{(n\bar{m})^2} \sum^{n} a_i q_i.$$

Calculate p and its standard error for the data in exercise 11.6.

11.8 A sample of n primary units is chosen with probabilities proportional to estimated sizes z_i (with replacement) and with a constant expected over-all sampling fraction f_0. Show that the unbiased and the ratio-to-size estimates of the population total are, respectively, T/f_0 and $TM_0/\sum^{n} m_i$, where T is the sample total. (It follows that if M_0 is not known the unbiased estimate can be used, but not the ratio to size. For estimating the population mean per subunit, the situation is reversed.)

11.9 In a study of overcrowding in a large city one stratum contained 100 blocks of which 10 were chosen with probabilities proportional to estimated size (with replacement). An expected over-all sampling fraction $f_0 = 2\%$ was used. The sample totals in each block for number of rooms and number of persons are as follows.

Block	1	2	3	4	5	6	7	8	9	10
Rooms	60	52	58	56	62	51	72	48	71	58
Persons	115	80	82	93	105	109	130	93	109	95

(a) Estimate the total number of rooms and the total number of persons in the stratum and the average number of persons per room. (b) Compute standard errors for the total number of persons and for the average number of persons per room. (Use formulas 11.25′ and 11.39, noting that $m_i z_i / M_i = f_0 / n$.)

REFERENCES

Gray, P. G., and Corlett, T. (1950). Sampling for the social survey. *Jour. Roy. Stat. Soc.*, **A113**, 150–206.

Hansen, M. H., and Hurwitz, W. N. (1943). On the theory of sampling from finite populations. *Ann. Math. Stat.*, **14**, 333–362.

Hansen, M. H., and Hurwitz, W. N. (1949). On the determination of the optimum probabilities in sampling. *Ann. Math. Stat.*, **20**, 426–432.

Hartley, H. O., and Rao, J. N. K. (1962). Sampling with unequal probabilities without replacement. *Ann. Math. Stat.*, **33**, 350–374.

Jebe, E. H. (1952). Estimation for sub-sampling designs employing the county as a primary sampling unit. *Jour. Amer. Stat. Assoc.*, **47**, 49–70.

Jessen, R. J., et al. (1947). On a population sample for Greece. *Jour. Amer. Stat. Assoc.*, **42**, 357–384.

Madow, L. H. (1950). On the use of the county as a primary sampling unit for state estimates. *Jour. Amer. Stat. Assoc.*, **45**, 30–47.

Rao. J. N. K., Hartley, H. O., and Cochran, W. G. (1962). A simple procedure of unequal probability sampling without replacement. *Jour. Roy. Stat. Soc.*, **B24**.

Sukhatme, P. V. (1954). *Sampling theory of surveys, with applications.* Iowa State College Press, Ames, Iowa.

Yates, F., and Grundy, P. M. (1953). Selection without replacement from strata with probability proportional to size. *Jour. Roy. Stat. Soc.*, **B15**, 253–261.

CHAPTER 12

Double Sampling

12.1 DESCRIPTION OF THE TECHNIQUE

As we have seen, a number of sampling techniques depend on the possession of advance information about an auxiliary variate x_i. Ratio and regression estimates require a knowledge of the population mean $\bar{X}$. If it is desired to stratify the population according to the values of the x_i, their frequency distribution must be known.

When such information is lacking, it is sometimes relatively cheap to take a large preliminary sample in which x_i alone is measured. The purpose of this sample is to furnish a good estimate of $\bar{X}$ or of the frequency distribution of x_i. In a survey whose function is to make estimates for some other variate y_i, it may pay to devote part of the resources to this preliminary sample, although this means that the size of the sample in the main survey on y_i must be decreased. This technique is known as *double sampling* or *two-phase sampling*. As the discussion implies, the technique is profitable only if the gain in precision from ratio or regression estimates or stratification more than offsets the loss in precision due to the reduction in the size of the main sample.

Double sampling may be appropriate when the information about x_i is on file cards that have not been tabulated. For instance, in surveys of the German civilian population in 1945 the sample from any town was usually drawn from rationing registration lists. In addition to geographic stratification within the town, for which data were usually already available, stratification by sex and age was proposed. Since the sample had to be drawn in a hurry, and since the lists were in constant use, tabulation of the complete age and sex distribution was not feasible. A moderately large systematic sample could, however, be drawn quickly. Each person drawn was classified into the appropriate age-sex class. From these data the much smaller list of persons to be interviewed was selected.

12.2 DOUBLE SAMPLING FOR STRATIFICATION

The theory was first given by Neyman (1938).

The population is to be stratified into a number of classes according to the values of x_i. The first sample is a simple random sample of size n'. Let

$W_h = N_h/N$ = proportion of population falling into stratum h

$w_h = n_h'/n'$ = proportion of first sample falling into stratum h

Then w_h is an estimate of W_h.

The second sample is a stratified random sample of size n in which y_i is measured: n_h units are drawn from stratum h. The second sample is often a subsample from the first sample, but it may be drawn independently if this is more convenient.

The cost of the two samples is assumed to be

$$C = nc_n + n'c_{n'} \tag{12.1}$$

where c_n is usually large in relation to c_n'.

The problem is to choose n' and the n_h (and consequently n) to minimize the variance of the estimate for a given cost. We must then verify whether the minimum variance is smaller than can be attained by a single simple random sample in which y_i alone is measured.

The first step is to set up the estimate and determine its variance. The population mean is

$$\bar{Y} = \sum_{h=1}^{L} W_h \bar{Y}_h$$

As an estimate we use

$$\bar{y}_{st} = \sum_{h=1}^{L} w_h \bar{y}_h$$

Whenever a new sample is drawn, this implies a fresh drawing of both the first and the second samples. Thus the w_h and the sample means $\bar{y}_h$ are both random variables, subject to error. The problem is therefore one of stratification in which the strata totals are not known exactly. The strata boundaries are assumed fixed in repeated sampling.

In the theorems for the mean and variance of $\bar{y}_{st}$, a slight approximation is involved. It is assumed that every $w_h > 0$, that is, n', is assumed large enough so that the probability that any stratum contains no units in the large sample is negligible.

Theorem 12.1. The estimate $\bar{y}_{st}$ is unbiased.

Proof. Average first over samples in which the w_h are fixed. Since $\bar{y}_h$ is the mean of a simple random sample from the stratum, $E(\bar{y}_h) = \bar{Y}_h$, but, when the average is taken over different selections of the first sample, $E(w_h) = W_h$, since the first sample is also a simple random sample. Hence

$$E(\bar{y}_{st}) = E[E(\sum w_h \bar{y}_h \mid w_h)] = E(\sum w_h \bar{Y}_h) = \sum W_h \bar{Y}_h = \bar{Y}$$

Theorem 12.2. If the values of the n_h do not depend on the w_h,

$$V(\bar{y}_{st}) = \sum_{h=1}^{L} \left\{ \left[W_h^2 + \frac{g'W_h(1 - W_h)}{n'} \right] \frac{(1 - f_h)S_h^2}{n_h} + \frac{g'W_h(\bar{Y}_h - \bar{Y})^2}{n'} \right\} \quad (12.2)$$

where $g' = (N - n')/(N - 1)$ and $f_h = n_h/N_h$.

Proof. Average first over samples in which the w_h are fixed. Over these samples, the mean of $\bar{y}_{st}$ is $\sum w_h \bar{Y}_h$, so that there is a bias of amount $\sum(w_h - W_h)\bar{Y}_h$. The conditional variance of $\bar{y}_{st}$ is given by theorem 5.3. Hence the mean square error is

$$E[(\bar{y}_{st} - \bar{Y})^2 \mid w_h] = \sum_{h=1}^{L} \frac{w_h^2(1 - f_h)S_h^2}{n_h} + \left[\sum_{h=1}^{L} (w_h - W_h)\bar{Y}_h \right]^2 \quad (12.3)$$

Now average over selections of the w_h. (At this point we use the assumption that the n_h remain constant when the w_h vary.) By theorem 3.2,

$$V(w_h) = \frac{g'W_h(1 - W_h)}{n'}$$

so that

$$E(w_h^2) = [E(w_h)]^2 + V(w_h) = W_h^2 + \frac{g'W_h(1 - W_h)}{n'} \quad (12.4)$$

Also, it is easily shown that

$$E(w_h - W_h)(w_j - W_j) = -\frac{g'}{n'} W_h W_j \quad (h \neq j)$$

For the last term in (12.3), these results give

$$E\left[\sum_{h=1}^{L} (w_h - W_h)\bar{Y}_h \right]^2 = \frac{g'}{n'} \left[\sum_{h=1}^{L} W_h(1 - W_h)\bar{Y}_h^2 - 2\sum_{h=1}^{L} \sum_{j>h}^{L} W_h W_j \bar{Y}_h \bar{Y}_j \right]$$

$$= \frac{g'}{n'} \left(\sum_{h=1}^{L} W_h \bar{Y}_h^2 - \bar{Y}^2 \right) = \frac{g'}{n'} \sum W_h(\bar{Y}_h - \bar{Y})^2 \quad (12.5)$$

Finally, substituting from (12.4) and (12.5) into (12.3), we obtain

$$V(\bar{y}_{st}) = \sum_{h}^{L} \left\{ \left[W_h^2 + \frac{g'W_h(1 - W_h)}{n'} \right] \frac{(1 - f_h)S_h^2}{n_h} + \frac{g'W_h(\bar{Y}_h - \bar{Y})^2}{n'} \right\}$$

The term free from n' is the familiar expression for the variance when the strata sizes are known exactly. The effects of errors in the first sample are therefore to increase slightly the within-stratum contribution and to introduce a between-stratum component.

In most applications $f_h = n_h/N_h$ will be negligible. Frequently, n'/N is also small, so that g' can be replaced by 1. Under these conditions

$$V(\bar{y}_{st}) = \sum_{h}^{L} \left\{ \left[W_h^2 + \frac{W_h(1 - W_h)}{n'} \right] \frac{S_h^2}{n_h} + \frac{W_h(\bar{Y}_h - \bar{Y})^2}{n'} \right\} \quad (12.6)$$

Corollary 1. The result of theorem 12.2 changes slightly if n_h depends on w_h. For instance, if proportional stratification is desired, the sampler may take $n_h = nw_h$ in the small sample, since the w_h are the best available estimates of the W_h. More generally, we may have $n_h = n\lambda_h w_h/\Sigma\lambda_h w_h$. This substitution is made in (12.3) before finding the average over different selections of the w_h. After some algebraic manipulation the variance is found to be, assuming n_h/N_h negligible,

$$V(\bar{y}_{st}) = \sum_{h}^{L} \left\{ \frac{W_h S_h^2}{n} \left[\frac{Q}{\lambda_h} + \frac{g'}{n'} \left(1 - \frac{Q}{\lambda_h} \right) \right] + \frac{g'W_h(\bar{Y}_h - \bar{Y})^2}{n'} \right\}$$

where $Q = \Sigma\lambda_h W_h$. If $\lambda_h = 1$ (proportional stratification), then $Q = 1$ and we have

$$V(\bar{y}_{st}) = \sum_{h}^{L} \left[\frac{W_h S_h^2}{n} + \frac{g'W_h(\bar{Y}_h - \bar{Y})^2}{n'} \right]$$

Corollary 2. If a proportion is being estimated in the second sample,

$$S_h^2 = \frac{N_h}{N_h - 1} P_h Q_h \doteq P_h Q_h$$

$$(\bar{Y}_h - \bar{Y})^2 = (P_h - P)^2$$

Theorem 12.2 gives, with n_h/N_h negligible,

$$V(p_{st}) \doteq \sum_{h}^{L} \left\{ \left[W_h^2 + \frac{g'W_h(1 - W_h)}{n'} \right] \frac{P_h Q_h}{n_h} + \frac{g'W_h(P_h - P)^2}{n'} \right\} \quad (12.7)$$

where P_h is the proportion in stratum h.

Papers by Robson (1952) and Robson and King (1953) extend this theory to two-stage sampling, applying it to the estimation of magazine readership.

12.3 OPTIMUM ALLOCATION

The values of the n_h and n' that lead to the minimum variance are rather complicated. It follows from formula (12.2) and the cost function that, if n' and n are given, n_h should be proportional to

$$S_h\sqrt{W_h^2 + [g'W_h(1 - W_h)]/n'}$$

Since the second term inside the root is usually small compared with the first, Neyman (1938) suggests taking n_h proportional to $W_h S_h$. Thus

$$n_h = \frac{n W_h S_h}{\sum W_h S_h}$$

When these values are substituted into the variance (12.2), ignoring the term in $W_h(1 - W_h)$ and assuming n_h/N_h, n'/N negligible, we obtain

$$V_{opt} \doteq \frac{(\sum W_h S_h)^2}{n} + \frac{\sum W_h(\overline{Y}_h - \overline{Y})^2}{n'} \tag{12.8}$$

$$= \frac{V_n}{n} + \frac{V_{n'}}{n'} \quad \text{(say)} \tag{12.8'}$$

This approximate expression for the variance is now minimized by choice of n and n' for a given cost of

$$C = nc_n + n'c_{n'} \tag{12.1}$$

It is easily found that

$$\frac{n}{\sqrt{V_n c_{n'}}} = \frac{n'}{\sqrt{V_{n'} c_n}} \tag{12.9}$$

This equation and (12.1) determine n and n'.

An expression for the minimum variance is needed for later applications of double sampling. From (12.9),

$$\frac{n}{\sqrt{V_n c_{n'}}} = \frac{n'}{\sqrt{V_{n'} c_n}} = \frac{nc_n + n'c_{n'}}{\sqrt{c_n c_{n'}}(\sqrt{V_n c_n} + \sqrt{V_{n'} c_{n'}})}$$

$$= \frac{C}{\sqrt{c_n c_{n'}}(\sqrt{V_n c_n} + \sqrt{V_{n'} c_{n'}})} \tag{12.9'}$$

Substitute these solutions in (12.8') for V_{opt}. This gives

$$V_{opt} = \frac{(\sqrt{V_n c_n} + \sqrt{V_{n'} c_{n'}})^2}{C} \tag{12.10}$$

If the first sample is very cheap, the assumption that n'/N is negligible, that is, that $g' = 1$, may not hold. The solutions (12.9) for n and n' remain satisfactory, the only change needed being to subtract the term $V_{n'}/N$ from (12.10).

Example. This example is artificial, but it illustrates the calculations involved. We use the Jefferson county data previously considered (p. 171). The x_i variate, farm size, is employed to divide the population into two strata: farms up to 160 acres and farms of more than 160 acres. Assume that it costs 10 times as much to sample for corn acres (y_i) as for farm size (x_i), and let the cost be

$$C = 100 = n + 0.1n' \tag{12.11}$$

This means that if double sampling is not used ($n' = 0$) we can afford to take a sample of 100 farms to estimate corn acres.

The relevant data for the population are

Strata	W_h	$S_h{}^2$	S_h	$\bar{Y}_h$
1	0.786	312	17.7	19.404
2	0.214	922	30.4	51.626
Population		620		26.297

By (12.10) we could proceed at once to compute V_{opt}. However, the intermediate steps are given. We find

$$V_n = (\sum W_h S_h)^2 = 417$$
$$V_{n'} = \sum W_h(\bar{Y}_h - \bar{Y})^2 = 175$$

so that by (12.9)

$$\frac{n}{n'} = \sqrt{\frac{417}{175} \cdot \frac{1}{10}} = 0.488$$

From the cost equation (12.11) we obtain

$$n' = \frac{100}{0.588} = 170, \qquad n = 170 \times 0.488 = 83$$

At this point the reader may verify from the data in this example that the neglected term in $W_h(1 - W_h)$ in the variance formula (12.2) is in fact negligible. From (12.8) we then have

$$V_{opt} = \tfrac{417}{83} + \tfrac{175}{170} = 5.02 + 1.03 = 6.05$$

For a random sample of size 100, with no double sampling, we would have

$$V = \tfrac{620}{100} = 6.20$$

Evidently there would be only a trifling gain from double sampling.

Note. Reverting to corollary 1, of theorem 12.2, an alternative approach to the choice of the n_h is to write $n_h = n\lambda_h w_h/\sum\lambda_h w_h$ and to choose the λ_h to minimize $V(\bar{y}_{st})$ as given in corollary 1. It will be found that the optimum $\lambda_h \propto S_h$, assuming $1/n'$ negligible. For practical purposes this is the same solution as that already given.

12.4 ESTIMATED VARIANCE IN DOUBLE SAMPLING FOR STRATIFICATION

An unbiased estimate of $V(\bar{y}_{st})$ in (12.2) can be constructed without difficulty. We assume n_h/N_h and $1/N$ negligible.

Theorem 12.3. An unbiased estimate of $V(\bar{y}_{st})$ is

$$v(\bar{y}_{st}) = \frac{n'}{n'-1} \sum_h^L \left\{ \left[w_h^2 - \frac{g'w_h}{n'} \right] \frac{s_h^2}{n_h} + \frac{g'w_h(\bar{y}_h - \bar{y}_{st})^2}{n'} \right\} \quad (12.12)$$

where $g' = (N - n')/(N - 1)$.

Proof. By averaging first over samples with fixed w_h and then over the selections of the w_h, the expectations of the terms inside the braces work out as follows:

$$E \sum_h w_h^2 \frac{s_h^2}{n_h} = \sum_h \left[W_h^2 + \frac{g'W_h(1 - W_h)}{n'} \right] \frac{s_h^2}{n_h} \quad (12.13)$$

$$-E \sum_h \frac{g'w_h}{n'} \frac{s_h^2}{n_h} = -\sum_h \frac{g'W_h}{n'} \frac{S_h^2}{n_h} \quad (12.14)$$

$$E \sum_h \frac{g'w_h(\bar{y}_h - \bar{y}_{st})^2}{n'} = E\left(\sum_h \frac{g'w_h\bar{y}_h^2}{n'} - \frac{g'\bar{y}_{st}^2}{n'} \right)$$

$$= \sum_h \frac{g'W_h\bar{Y}_h^2}{n'} + \sum_h \frac{g'W_h}{n'} \frac{S_h^2}{n_h} - \frac{g'\bar{Y}^2}{n'} - \frac{g'V(\bar{y}_{st})}{n'} \quad (12.15)$$

Adding these three equations, we obtain, on comparing with (12.2),

$$\frac{(n'-1)Ev(\bar{y}_{st})}{n'} = V(\bar{y}_{st})\left(1 - \frac{g'}{n'}\right) = V(\bar{y}_{st})\frac{N(n'-1)}{(N-1)n'} = V(\bar{y}_{st})\frac{(n'-1)}{n'}$$

assuming $1/N$ negligible. This completes the proof.

If n' is large relative to the n_h, $v(\bar{y}_{st})$ reduces to

$$v(\bar{y}_{st}) \doteq \sum_h w_h^2 \frac{s_h^2}{n_h} \quad (12.16)$$

This expression is equivalent to assuming that errors in the strata weights w_h can be ignored.

Corollary. If p_h is the observed proportion of units in stratum h which fall into some defined class and $p_{st} = \sum w_h p_h / \sum w_h$ is the estimate of the population proportion, then an estimate of $V(p_{st})$ is

$$v(p_{st}) = \frac{n'}{n'-1} \sum_h \left[\left(w_h^2 - \frac{g'w_h}{n'} \right) \frac{p_h q_h}{n_h - 1} + \frac{g'w_h(p_h - p_{st})^2}{n'} \right]$$

In almost all cases this can be simplified to

$$v(p_{st}) \doteq \sum_h \left[\frac{w_h^2 p_h q_h}{n_h - 1} + \frac{w_h(p_h - p_{st})^2}{n'} \right]$$

Frequently the term in $1/n'$ can also be dropped.

Example. In a simple random sample of 374 households 292 were occupied by white families and 82 by nonwhite families. A subsample of about one in four households gave the following data as to ownership:

	Owned	Rented	Total
White:	31	43	74
Nonwhite:	4	14	18

Estimate the proportion of rented households in the area from which the sample was drawn and find the standard error of the estimate.

If the first stratum consists of the white-occupied households,

$$w_1 = \tfrac{292}{374} = 0.78, \qquad w_2 = \tfrac{82}{374} = 0.22$$

$$p_1 = \tfrac{43}{74} = 0.60, \qquad p_2 = \tfrac{14}{18} = 0.78$$

$$p_{st} = w_1 p_1 + w_2 p_2 = 0.64$$

$$n' = 374, \qquad n_1 = 74, \qquad n_2 = 18$$

It is readily found that only the leading term in $v(p_{st})$ is of importance. Hence

$$v(p_{st}) = \sum_h \frac{w_h^2 p_h q_h}{n_h - 1} = \frac{(0.78)^2 (0.60)(0.40)}{73} + \frac{(0.22)^2 (0.78)(0.22)}{17}$$

$$= 0.00248$$

$$s(p_{st}) = 0.049$$

The estimated proportion of rented households is 0.64 ± 0.049. The reader may verify that there is only a trifling gain in precision over a single-stage simple random sample of size 92. In view of the relatively small size of the nonwhite stratum, a greater difference between the proportions of rented households for whites and nonwhites would be necessary to make double sampling profitable.

12.5 REGRESSION ESTIMATES

In a number of the applications of double sampling the auxiliary variate x_i has been used to make a regression estimate of $\bar{Y}$. We shall assume that the population is infinite and that the relation between y_i and x_i is linear. Write as a model

$$y_{i\alpha} = \bar{Y} + B(x_i - \bar{X}) + e_{i\alpha} \tag{12.17}$$

where the second subscript α is introduced as a reminder that for fixed x_i the random variate $e_{i\alpha}$ follows a frequency distribution with mean 0 and variance $S_e^2 = S_y^2(1 - \rho^2)$.

In the first (large) sample, of size n', we measure only x_i; in the second, of size n, we measure both x_i and $y_{i\alpha}$. The estimate of $\bar{Y}$ is

$$\bar{y}_{lr} = \bar{y} + b(\bar{x}' - \bar{x})$$

where $\bar{x}'$, $\bar{x}$ are the means of x_i in the first and second samples, respectively, and b is the least squares regression coefficient of $y_{i\alpha}$ on x_i, computed from the second sample.

We now examine the error of estimate $(\bar{y}_{lr} - \bar{Y})$. From (12.17) we find

$$\bar{y} = \bar{Y} + B(\bar{x} - \bar{X}) + \bar{e} \qquad (12.18)$$

$$b = \frac{\sum_{i=1}^{n}(y_{i\alpha} - \bar{y})(x_i - \bar{x})}{\sum_{i=1}^{n}(x_i - \bar{x})^2}$$

$$= B + \frac{\sum_{i=1}^{n} e_{i\alpha}(x_i - \bar{x})}{\sum_{i=1}^{n}(x_i - \bar{x})^2} \qquad (12.19)$$

From (12.18) and (12.19), substitute for $\bar{y}$ and b in the error of estimate. This gives

$$\bar{y}_{lr} - \bar{Y} = (\bar{y} - \bar{Y}) + b(\bar{x}' - \bar{x})$$

$$= B(\bar{x} - \bar{X}) + \bar{e} + B(\bar{x}' - \bar{x}) + (\bar{x}' - \bar{x})\frac{\sum e_{i\alpha}(x_i - \bar{x})}{\sum(x_i - \bar{x})^2}$$

$$= \bar{e} + (\bar{x}' - \bar{x})\frac{\sum e_{i\alpha}(x_i - \bar{x})}{\sum(x_i - \bar{x})^2} + B(\bar{x}' - \bar{X}) \qquad (12.20)$$

In ordinary regression theory, in which $\bar{x}' = \bar{X}$, the standard practice is to discuss the *conditional* frequency distribution of the error of estimate $(\bar{y}_{lr} - \bar{Y})$ in repeated samples in which the x_i values are fixed. If this approach is adopted in the present problem, keeping the x_i values fixed in both the first and the second samples, we see that the estimate is biased in the conditional distribution, since

$$E_c(\bar{y}_{lr} - \bar{Y}) = B(\bar{x}' - \bar{X})$$

Hence the conditional mean square error (MSE) of $\bar{y}_{lr}$ is

$$\text{MSE}(\bar{y}_{lr}) = S_y^2(1 - \rho^2)\left[\frac{1}{n} + \frac{(\bar{x}' - \bar{x})^2}{\sum(x_i - \bar{x})^2}\right] + B^2(\bar{x}' - \bar{X})^2 \quad (12.21)$$

This expression is not suitable for comparison with other methods of sampling, since the MSE depends on the set of x_i which appears in the two samples. Instead, we need the average MSE over all possible drawings of the first and second samples.

A simple result is obtained under the assumption that (a) the first sample is drawn at random, (b) the second sample is a random subsample drawn from the first, and (c) the x_i are normally distributed. In this event the average MSE is found to be

$$V(\bar{y}_{lr}) = S_y^2(1 - \rho^2) \left[\frac{1}{n} + \left(\frac{1}{n} - \frac{1}{n'}\right)\frac{1}{(n-3)}\right] + \frac{B^2 S_x^2}{n'} \quad (12.22)$$

$$= \frac{S_y^2(1 - \rho^2)}{n} \left[1 + \frac{(n'-n)}{n'}\frac{1}{(n-3)}\right] + \frac{\rho^2 S_y^2}{n'} \quad (12.23)$$

since $B^2 S_x^2 = \rho^2 S_y^2$.

If the x_i are not normally distributed, the only term whose value is changed is that in $1/(n-3)$. In regard to assumption (b), the small sample might not be drawn *at random* from the large sample: it is preferable to select the small sample to obtain a wide spread in the values of x_i and reduce the sampling error of b. The effect is to reduce, perhaps considerably, the term in $1/(n-3)$.

In some applications the second sample is drawn independently of the first. In this event the argument given in this section remains unchanged down to (12.21). In (12.22) the term

$$\frac{1}{n} - \frac{1}{n'}$$

is replaced by

$$\frac{1}{n} + \frac{1}{n'}$$

This case of two independent samples was first considered by Chameli Bose (1943).

To summarize, there is some doubt about the exact value of the term in $1/(n-3)$ in the average variance. However, this term is of order $1/n^2$, negligible with large n. This gives the following theorem.

Theorem 12.4. If the first sample is size n', the second is size n, and $1/n$ is negligible, the variance of $\bar{y}_{lr}$, the regression estimate in double sampling, is given approximately by

$$V(\bar{y}_{lr}) \doteq \frac{S_y^2(1 - \rho^2)}{n} + \frac{\rho^2 S_y^2}{n'} \quad (12.24)$$

12.6 DOUBLE SAMPLING WITH REGRESSION VERSUS SINGLE SAMPLING

From the variance formula (12.24), double sampling with a regression estimate can be compared with a single simple random sample under the assumption that (a) the first sample is a simple random sample, (b) $1/n$ is negligible, and (c) the second sample is also a simple random sample. Results for this case should provide a rough guide to other cases.

Write

$$V(\bar{y}_{lr}) = \frac{V_n}{n} + \frac{V_{n'}}{n'}$$

where

$$V_n = S_y^2(1 - \rho^2), \qquad V_n' = \rho^2 S_y^2$$
$$\text{cost} = C = nc_n + n'c_{n'}$$

The problem of finding the optimum n and n' and the minimum variance is exactly the same as in double sampling for stratification (section 12.3). Equation 12.10 gives

$$V_{opt} = \frac{(\sqrt{V_n c_n} + \sqrt{V_{n'} c_{n'}})^2}{C}$$

$$= \frac{S_y^2[\sqrt{(1 - \rho^2)}c_n + \rho\sqrt{c_{n'}}]^2}{C} \tag{12.25}$$

where ρ is taken as positive.

If all resources are devoted to a single sample, with no adjustment for regression, this sample has size $n_s = C/c_n$ and the variance of its mean is

$$V(\bar{y}) = \frac{S_y^2}{n_s} = \frac{c_n S_y^2}{C} \tag{12.26}$$

Hence, double sampling gives a smaller variance if

$$c_n > [\sqrt{(1 - \rho^2)}c_n + \rho\sqrt{c_{n'}}]^2$$

This inequality may be expressed in two ways:

$$\frac{c_n}{c_{n'}} > \frac{(1 + \sqrt{1 - \rho^2})^2}{\rho^2} = \frac{\rho^2}{(1 - \sqrt{1 - \rho^2})^2} \tag{12.27}$$

or

$$\rho^2 > \frac{4c_n c_{n'}}{(c_n + c_{n'})^2} \tag{12.28}$$

Equation 12.27 shows that for a given value of ρ the ratio of the cost per unit in the second sample to the cost per unit in the first sample must exceed a critical value before double sampling brings an increase in precision. Given c_n and $c_{n'}$, (12.28) shows the critical value that must be exceeded by ρ^2 to make double sampling profitable.

Figure 12.1 plots the values of the ratio $c_n/c_{n'}$ (on a log scale) against ρ. Curve I is the relationship when double and single sampling are equally precise; curve II holds when $V_{opt} = 0.8V(\bar{y})$, that is, when double sampling gives a 25% increase in precision; and curve III refers to a 50% increase in precision. For example, when $\rho = 0.8$, double sampling equals single sampling in precision if $c_n/c_{n'}$ is 4, gives a 25% increase in precision if $c_n/c_{n'}$ is about $7\frac{1}{2}$, and a 50% increase if $c_n/c_{n'}$ is about 13.

For practical use, the curves overestimate the gains to be achieved from double sampling, because the best values of n and n' must either be estimated from previous data or be guessed. Some allowance for errors in these estimations should be made before deciding to adopt double sampling.

For any ρ, there is an upper limit to the gain in precision from double sampling. This occurs when information on $\bar{x}'$ is obtained free ($c_{n'} = 0$). The upper limit to the relative precision is $1/(1 - \rho^2)$.

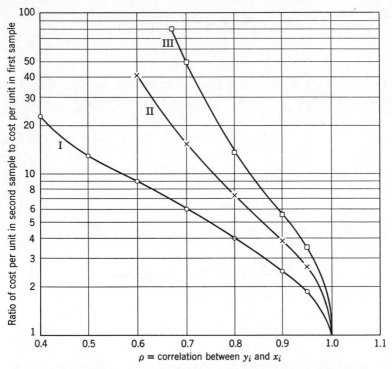

Fig. 12.1   Relation between $c_n/c_{n'}$ and ρ for three fixed values of the relative precision of double and single sampling.

      Curve I: double and single sampling equally precise.
      Curve II: double sampling gives 25 per cent increase in precision.
      Curve III: double sampling gives 50 per cent increase in precision.

12.7 ESTIMATED VARIANCE IN DOUBLE SAMPLING FOR REGRESSION

If terms in $1/n$ are negligible, $V(\bar{y}_{lr})$ is given by (12.24):

$$V(\bar{y}_{lr}) \doteq \frac{S_y^2(1 - \rho^2)}{n} + \frac{\rho^2 S_y^2}{n'}$$

With a linear regression model, the quantity

$$s_{y.x}^2 = \frac{1}{n - 2}\left[\sum_{i=1}^{n}(y_i - \bar{y})^2 - b^2 \sum_{i=1}^{n}(x_i - \bar{x})^2\right]$$

is an unbiased estimate of $S_y^2(1 - \rho^2)$, where the subscript α has now been dropped. Since

$$s_y^2 = \frac{\sum(y_i - \bar{y})^2}{n - 1}$$

is an unbiased estimate of S_y^2, it follows that

$$s_y^2 - s_{y.x}^2$$

is an unbiased estimate of $\rho^2 S_y^2$.

Thus a sample estimate of $V(\bar{y}_{lr})$ is

$$v(\bar{y}_{lr}) = \frac{s_{y.x}^2}{n} + \frac{s_y^2 - s_{y.x}^2}{n'} \tag{12.29}$$

If the second sample is very small and terms in $1/n$ are not negligible, a suggested estimate of variance is

$$v(\bar{y}_{lr}) = s_{y.x}^2\left[\frac{1}{n} + \frac{(\bar{x}' - \bar{x})^2}{\sum(x_i - \bar{x})^2}\right] + \frac{s_y^2 - s_{y.x}^2}{n'}$$

This is a hybrid of the conditional variance and the average variance.

12.8 RATIO ESTIMATES

If the first sample is used to obtain $\bar{x}'$ for a ratio estimate of $\bar{Y}$, the estimate is

$$\bar{y}_R = \frac{\bar{y}}{\bar{x}}\bar{x}' \tag{12.30}$$

To find the approximate variance, write

$$\bar{y}_R - \bar{Y} = \frac{\bar{y}}{\bar{x}} \bar{x}' - \bar{Y}$$

$$= \left(\frac{\bar{y}}{\bar{x}} \bar{X} - \bar{Y}\right) + \frac{\bar{y}}{\bar{x}} (\bar{x}' - \bar{X})$$

$$= \frac{\bar{X}}{\bar{x}} (\bar{y} - R\bar{x}) + \frac{\bar{y}}{\bar{x}} (\bar{x}' - \bar{X})$$

The first component is the error of the ordinary ratio estimate (section 2.9). In obtaining the approximate error variance in section 2.9, we replaced the factor $\bar{X}/\bar{x}$ by unity in this term. To the same order of approximation, we replace the factor $\bar{y}/\bar{x}$ in the second component by the population ratio $R = \bar{Y}/\bar{X}$. Thus

$$\bar{y}_R - \bar{Y} \doteq (\bar{y} - R\bar{x}) + R(\bar{x}' - \bar{X}) \tag{12.31}$$

If the first and second samples are drawn *independently*, we obtain

$$V(\bar{y}_R) = \frac{S_y^{\;2} - 2RS_{yx} + R^2 S_x^{\;2}}{n} + \frac{R^2 S_x^{\;2}}{n'} \tag{12.32}$$

where the fpc terms are assumed negligible.

If the second sample is a random subsample of the first, rearrange (12.31) in the form

$$\bar{y}_R - \bar{Y} = (\bar{y} - R\bar{X}) + R(\bar{x}' - \bar{x}) = (\bar{y} - \bar{Y}) + R(\bar{x}' - \bar{x})$$

It may be verified that, with the fpc ignored,

$$V(\bar{y} - \bar{Y}) = \frac{S_y^{\;2}}{n}$$

$$\text{cov}\,[(\bar{y} - \bar{Y})R(\bar{x}' - \bar{x})] = -RS_{yx}\left(\frac{1}{n} - \frac{1}{n'}\right)$$

$$V[R(\bar{x}' - \bar{x})] = R^2 S_x^{\;2}\left(\frac{1}{n} - \frac{1}{n'}\right)$$

Hence $V(\bar{y}_R)$ takes the form

$$V(\bar{y}_R) = \frac{S_y^{\;2} - 2RS_{yx} + R^2 S_x^{\;2}}{n} + \frac{2RS_{yx} - R^2 S_x^{\;2}}{n'} \tag{12.33}$$

Note that formulas (12.32) and (12.33) are both of the form

$$V(\bar{y}_R) = \frac{V_n}{n} + \frac{V_{n'}}{n'}$$

Hence the optimum choices of n and n', and the minimum variance for comparison with single sampling, are found by the same procedure as for stratification and regression estimates.

For sample estimates of variance, the quantities s_y^2, s_{yx}, s_x^2, and $\hat{R}$ may be substituted in (12.32) and (12.33). The resulting estimates $v(\bar{y}_R)$ are not unbiased but appear to be adequate to the order of approximation presented in the analysis.

12.9 REPEATED SAMPLING OF THE SAME POPULATION

As confidence in sampling has increased, the practice of relying on samples for the collection of important series of data that are published at regular intervals has become common. In part, this is due to a realization that with a dynamic population a census at infrequent intervals is of limited use. Highly precise information about the characteristics of a population in July 1950 and July 1960 may not help much in planning that demands a knowledge of the population in 1964. A series of small samples at annual or even shorter intervals may be more serviceable.

When the same population (apart from the changes that the passage of time introduces) is sampled repeatedly, the sampler is in an ideal position to make realistic estimates both of costs and of variances and to apply the techniques that lead to optimum efficiency of sampling. One important question is how frequently and in what manner the sample should be changed as time progresses. Many considerations affect the decision. People may be unwilling to give the same type of information time after time. The respondents may be influenced by information which they receive at the interviews, and this may make them progressively less representative as time proceeds. Sometimes, however, cooperation is better in a second interview than in the first, and when the information is technical or confidential the second visit may produce more accurate data than the first.

The remainder of this chapter considers the question of replacement of the sample and the related question of making estimates from the series of repeated samples. The topic is appropriate to the present chapter because double sampling techniques can be utilized.

Given the data from a series of samples, there are three kinds of quantity for which we may wish estimates:

1. The change in $\overline{Y}$ from one occasion to the next
2. The average value of $\overline{Y}$ over all occasions
3. The average value of $\overline{Y}$ for the most recent occasion

In most surveys, interest centers on the current average (3), particularly if the characteristics of the population are likely to change rapidly with time. With a population in which time changes are slow, on the other hand, an annual average (2) taken over 12 monthly samples or four quarterly samples may be adequate for the major uses. This would be the situation in a study of the prevalence of chronic diseases of long duration. With a disease whose prevalence shows marked seasonal variation, the current data are of major interest, but annual averages are also useful for comparisons between different regions and different years. Estimates of change (1) are wanted mainly in attempts to study the effects of forces that are known to have acted on the population. For instance, if a bill is passed which is supposed to stimulate the building of houses, it is interesting to know whether the building rate of new houses has increased in the succeeding year (with a realization that an increase may not be entirely due to the bill).

Suppose that we are free to alter or retain the composition of the sample and that the total size of sample is to be the same on all occasions. If we wish to maximize precision, the following statements can be made about replacement policy:

1. For estimating change, it is best to retain the same sample throughout all occasions.

2. For estimating the average over all occasions, it is best to draw a new sample on each occasion.

3. For current estimates, equal precision is obtained either by keeping the same sample or by changing it on every occasion. Replacement of part of the sample on each occasion may be better than these alternatives.

Statements 1 and 2 hold because there is nearly always a *positive* correlation between the measurements on the same unit on two successive occasions. The estimated change on a unit has variance $S_1^2 + S_2^2 - 2\rho S_1 S_2$, where the subscripts refer to the occasions. If the change is estimated from two *different* units, the variance is $S_1^2 + S_2^2$. In estimating the over-all mean for the two occasions, the variance is $(S_1^2 + S_2^2 + 2\rho S_1 S_2)/4$ if the same unit is retained and $(S_1^2 + S_2^2)/4$ if a new unit is chosen.

Statement 3, which is less obvious, is investigated in succeeding sections.

12.10 SAMPLING ON TWO OCCASIONS

Suppose that the samples are of the same size n on both occasions and that the current estimates are of primary interest. Replacement policy has been examined by Jessen (1942). For simplicity, we assume that simple random sampling is used and that the population variance S^2 of y_i is the same on both occasions.

The mean of the first sample has variance S^2/n, there being no previous information to utilize. In selecting the second sample, m of the units in the first sample are retained (m for matched). The remaining u units (u for unmatched) are discarded and replaced by a new selection.

Notation.

$\bar{y}_{hu}$ = mean of unmatched portion on occasion h
$\bar{y}_{hm}$ = mean of matched portion on occasion h
$\bar{y}_{h}$ = mean of whole sample on occasion h

The unmatched and matched portions of the second sample provide independent estimates $\bar{y}_{2u}'$, $\bar{y}_{2m}'$ of $\bar{Y}_2$, as shown in Table 12.1. In the

TABLE 12.1
ESTIMATES FROM THE UNMATCHED AND MATCHED PORTIONS

	Estimate	Variance	
Unmatched:	$\bar{y}_{2u}' = \bar{y}_{2u}$	$\dfrac{S^2}{u}$	$= \dfrac{1}{W_{2u}}$
Matched:	$\bar{y}_{2m}' = \bar{y}_{2m} + b(\bar{y}_1 - \bar{y}_{1m})$	$\dfrac{S^2(1 - \rho^2)}{m} + \rho^2\dfrac{S^2}{n}$	$= \dfrac{1}{W_{2m}}$

matched portion we use a double-sampling regression estimate, where the "large" sample is the first sample and the auxiliary variate x_i is the value of y_i on the first occasion. The variance of $\bar{y}_{2m}'$ comes from (12.24), p. 336: note that our m and n correspond to n and n', respectively, in (12.24).

The best combined estimate of $\bar{Y}_2$ is found by weighting the two independent estimates inversely as their variances. If W_{2u}, W_{2m} are the inverse variances, this estimate is

$$\bar{y}_2' = \phi_2\bar{y}_{2u}' + (1 - \phi_2)\bar{y}_{2m}' \qquad (12.34)$$

where

$$\phi_2 = \frac{W_{2u}}{W_{2u} + W_{2m}}$$

By least squares theory, the variance of $\bar{y}_2'$ is

$$V(\bar{y}_2') = \frac{1}{W_{2u} + W_{2m}}$$

From Table 12.1, this works out after simplification as

$$V(\bar{y}_2') = \frac{S^2(n - u\rho^2)}{n^2 - u^2\rho^2} \qquad (12.35)$$

Note that if $u = 0$ (complete matching) or if $u = n$ (no matching) this variance has the same value, S^2/n.

The optimum value of u is found by minimizing (12.35) with respect to variation in u. This gives

$$\frac{u}{n} = \frac{1}{1 + \sqrt{1 - \rho^2}}, \qquad \frac{m}{n} = \frac{\sqrt{1 - \rho^2}}{1 + \sqrt{1 - \rho^2}} \qquad (12.36)$$

When the optimum u is substituted in (12.35), the minimum variance works out as

$$V_{opt}(\bar{y}_2') = \frac{S^2}{2n}[1 + \sqrt{1 - \rho^2}] \qquad (12.37)$$

Table 12.2 shows for a series of values of ρ the optimum per cent that should be matched and the relative gain in precision compared with no

TABLE 12.2

OPTIMUM % MATCHED

ρ	Optimum % matched	% gain in precision	% gain with $\frac{m}{n} = \frac{1}{3}$	% gain with $\frac{m}{n} = \frac{1}{4}$
0.5	46	7	7	6
0.6	44	11	11	9
0.7	42	17	17	15
0.8	38	25	25	23
0.9	30	39	39	39
0.95	24	52	50	52
1.0	0	100	67	75

matching. The best percentage to match never exceeds 50% and decreases steadily as ρ increases. When $\rho = 1$, the formula suggests $m = 0$, which lies outside the range of our assumptions, since m has been assumed reasonably large. The correct procedure in this case is to take $m = 2$. The two matched units are sufficient to determine the regression line exactly.

The greatest attainable gain in precision is 100% when $\rho = 1$. Unless ρ is high, the gains are modest.

Although the optimum percentage to match varies with ρ, only a single percentage can be used in practice for all items in a survey. The right-hand columns of Table 12.2 show the per cent gains in precision when one third and one fourth of the units are matched. Both are good compromises, except for items in which ρ exceeds 0.95.

12.11 SAMPLING ON MORE THAN TWO OCCASIONS

The general problem of replacement has been studied by Yates (1960) and Patterson (1950), with respect to both current estimates and estimates of change. When there are more than two occasions, the opportunities for a flexible use of the data are increased. On occasion h we may have parts of the sample that are matched with occasion $h - 1$, parts that are matched with both occasions $h - 1$ and $h - 2$, and so on. In attempting to improve the current estimate, we might try a multiple regression involving all matchings to previous occasions. It is also possible to *revise*

TABLE 12.3

ESTIMATES OF $\bar{Y}_h$ ON THE hth OCCASION

Estimate	Variance
Unmatched: $\bar{y}_{hu}' = \bar{y}_{hu}$	$\dfrac{S^2}{u} = \dfrac{1}{W_{hu}}$
Matched: $\bar{y}_{hm}' = \bar{y}_{hm} + b(\bar{y}_{h-1}' - \bar{y}_{h-1,m})$	$\dfrac{S^2(1 - \rho^2)}{m} + \rho^2 V(\bar{y}_{h-1}') = \dfrac{1}{W_{3m}}$

the current estimate for occasion $h - 1$ after the data for occasion h are known. In the revised estimate the regression of occasion $h - 1$ on both occasion $h - 2$ and occasion h could be utilized, assuming that suitably matched portions of the sample were available.

The present section contains an introduction to the subject. Attention will be restricted to current estimates in which only the regression on the sample immediately preceding is used. This results in some loss of precision, but since the correlation ρ usually decreases as the time interval between the occasions is increased the loss of precision will seldom be great. The variance S^2 and the correlation coefficient ρ between the item values on the same unit on two successive occasions are assumed constant throughout.

On the hth occasion let m_h and u_h be the numbers of units that are matched and unmatched, respectively, with the $(h - 1)$th occasion. The two estimates of $\bar{Y}_h$ that can be made are given in Table 12.3. The only change in procedure from the second occasion (Table 12.1) is that in the regression adjustment of the estimate from the matched portion we use the improved estimate $\bar{y}_{h-1}'$ instead of the sample mean $\bar{y}_{h-1}$.

The variance of the matched estimate $\bar{y}_{hm}'$ in Table 12.3 is derived from (12.24) at the end of section 12.5. Note that (*a*) our m corresponds to the

n in (12.24) and (b) the term $\rho^2 S_y^2/n'$, which comes from the term $B^2 E(\bar{x}' - \bar{X})^2$ in (12.21), is replaced by $\rho^2 V(\bar{y}'_{h-1})$, since $B = \rho$ and $\bar{y}'_{h-1}$ corresponds to $\bar{x}'$ in the earlier analysis.

We now examine the precision obtained if the optimum m_h and u_h and the optimum weights are used on every occasion. It will be found that the optimum m_h/n_h increases steadily on successive occasions, rapidly approaching a limiting value of $\frac{1}{2}$.

Weighting inversely as the variance, the best estimate of $\bar{y}_h$ is

$$\bar{y}_h' = \phi_h \bar{y}_{hu}' + (1 - \phi_h)\bar{y}_{hm}' \tag{12.38}$$

where $\phi_h = W_{hu}/(W_{hu} + W_{hm})$. This gives

$$V(\bar{y}_h') = \frac{1}{W_{hu} + W_{hm}} = \frac{g_h S^2}{n}$$

where g_h denotes the ratio of the variance on occasion h to that on the first occasion. Substituting for W_{hu}, W_{hm} from Table 12.3, we have

$$\frac{S^2}{V(\bar{y}_h')} = \frac{n}{g_h} = S^2(W_{hu} + W_{hm}) = u_h + \frac{1}{\dfrac{(1 - \rho^2)}{m_h} + \dfrac{\rho^2 g_{h-1}}{n}} \tag{12.39}$$

We now choose m_h and u_h to maximize this quantity and therefore to minimize $V(\bar{y}_h')$. Writing $u_h = n - m_h$ and differentiating the right side of (12.39) with respect to m_h we obtain

$$\frac{1 - \rho^2}{m_h^2} = \left(\frac{1 - \rho^2}{m_h} + \frac{\rho^2 g_{h-1}}{n}\right)^2$$

This gives, on solving for the optimum $\hat{m}_h$, say,

$$\frac{\hat{m}_h}{n} = \frac{\sqrt{1 - \rho^2}}{g_{h-1}(1 + \sqrt{1 - \rho^2})} \tag{12.40}$$

When this value is substituted in (12.39), the relation becomes, after some algebraic manipulation,

$$\frac{1}{g_h} = 1 + \frac{1 - \sqrt{1 - \rho^2}}{g_{h-1}(1 + \sqrt{1 - \rho^2})} \tag{12.41}$$

This relation may be written

$$r_h = 1 + b r_{h-1}$$

where $r_h = 1/g_h$ and $r_1 = 1/g_1 = 1$. Repeated use of this recurrence relation gives

$$\frac{1}{g_h} = r_h = 1 + b + b^2 + \cdots + b^{h-1} = \frac{1 - b^h}{1 - b}$$

where, from (12.41), $b = (1 - \sqrt{1 - \rho^2})/(1 + \sqrt{1 - \rho^2})$. Since $0 < b < 1$, the limiting variance factor g_∞ is

$$g_\infty = 1 - b = \frac{2\sqrt{1 - \rho^2}}{1 + \sqrt{1 - \rho^2}} \qquad (12.42)$$

Hence the variance of $\bar{y}_h{}'$ tends to

$$V(\bar{y}_\infty') = \frac{S^2}{n}\left(\frac{2\sqrt{1 - \rho^2}}{1 + \sqrt{1 - \rho^2}}\right) \qquad (12.43)$$

Finally, the limiting value of $\hat{m}_h$ is obtained from (12.40) as

$$\frac{\hat{m}_\infty}{n} = \frac{\sqrt{1 - \rho^2}}{g_\infty(1 + \sqrt{1 - \rho^2})} = \frac{1}{2}$$

irrespective of the value of ρ.

Table 12.4 shows the optimum percentage to match—$100\hat{m}_h/n$, as found from (12.40)—and the resulting variances for $\rho = 0.7$, 0.8, 0.9 and 0.95 and for a series of values of h.

TABLE 12.4

OPTIMUM % MATCHED AND VARIANCES

	% matched $100\hat{m}_h/n$				$g_h = nV(\bar{y}_h')/S^2$			
	$\rho =$				$\rho =$			
h	0.7	0.8	0.9	0.95	0.7	0.8	0.9	0.95
2	42	38	30	24	0.857	0.800	0.718	0.656
3	49	47	42	36	0.837	0.762	0.646	0.556
4	50	49	47	43	0.834	0.753	0.622	0.515
5	50	50	49	46	0.833	0.751	0.613	0.495
∞	50	50	50	50	0.833	0.750	0.607	0.476

By the fourth occasion, the optimum per cent matched is close to 50 for all the values of ρ shown, although a smaller amount of matching is indicated for the second and third occasions. The reductions in variance, that is, $(1 - g_h)$, are modest if ρ is less than 0.8.

12.12 SIMPLIFICATIONS AND FURTHER DEVELOPMENTS

In practical application the preceding analysis may need modification. We assumed that all replacement policies cost the same and are equally feasible. With human populations, field costs are likely to be lower if the same units are retained for a number of occasions. If estimates of the change in the population total or mean are of interest, this factor also points toward matching more than half the units from one occasion to the next.

It is convenient also to keep the weights and the proportion matched constant, rather than to change them on every occasion. Consequently, we shall investigate the variances of $\bar{y}_h'$ and of the estimated change $(\bar{y}_h' - \bar{y}_{h-1}')$ when m, u, and ϕ are held constant. We continue to write $V(\bar{y}_{h'}) = g_h S^2/n$, although the actual value of g_h will be different from that in the preceding section.

The estimate is now

$$\bar{y}_h' = \phi \bar{y}_{hu}' + (1 - \phi)\bar{y}_{hm}'$$

Substituting the expressions for the two variances (from Table 12.3), we have

$$V(\bar{y}_h') = \frac{g_h S^2}{n} = \phi^2 V(\bar{y}_{hu}') + (1 - \phi)^2 V(\bar{y}_{hm}')$$

$$= S^2\left[\frac{\phi^2}{u} + \frac{(1 - \phi)^2(1 - \rho^2)}{m}\right] + \frac{S^2\rho^2(1 - \phi)^2 g_{h-1}}{n}$$

Hence

$$g_h = \left[\frac{\phi^2}{\mu} + \frac{(1 - \phi)^2(1 - \rho^2)}{\lambda}\right] + \rho^2(1 - \phi)^2 g_{h-1} \qquad (12.44)$$

where $\mu = u/n$, $\lambda = m/n$. Write this relation as

$$g_h = a + bg_{h-1}$$

By repeated application, we have, since $g_1 = 1$,

$$g_h = \frac{a(1 - b^{h-1})}{1 - b} + b^{h-1}$$

Since $b = \rho^2(1 - \phi)^2$ is less than 1, the limiting value is

$$g_\infty = \frac{a}{1 - b} = \frac{\lambda\phi^2 + \mu(1 - \phi)^2(1 - \rho^2)}{\lambda\mu[1 - \rho^2(1 - \phi)^2]} \qquad (12.45)$$

The value of the weight ϕ which minimizes the limiting variance may be found by differentiating (12.45). This leads to a quadratic equation whose appropriate root is

$$\phi_{opt} = \frac{\sqrt{1 - \rho^2}[\sqrt{1 - \rho^2 + 4\lambda\mu\rho^2} - \sqrt{1 - \rho^2}]}{2\lambda\rho^2}$$

In practice, the value of ρ will not be known exactly and will differ from item to item. A simple compromise value can usually be chosen. Clearly,

ϕ_{opt} will be less than $\mu = u/n$, since the matched part of the sample gives higher precision per unit than the unmatched part. For example, with $\mu = 0.25$, that is, $\frac{1}{4}$ of the sample unmatched, ϕ_{opt} turns out to be 0.216, 0.198, and 0.164 for $\rho = 0.7, 0.8, 0.9$. The choice of $\phi = 0.2$ would be adequate for this range of ρ.

For the estimate of change, we have

$$V(\bar{y}_h{}' - \bar{y}_{h-1}') = V(\bar{y}_h{}') + V(\bar{y}_{h-1}') - 2\,\mathrm{Cov}\,(\bar{y}_h{}'\bar{y}_{h-1}') \quad (12.46)$$

To find the covariance term, note that if y_{hi}, $y_{h-1,i}$ are the values for the ith unit in the matched set on occasions h and $(h-1)$, our model is

$$y_{hi} = \bar{Y}_h + \rho(y_{h-1,i} - \bar{Y}_{h-1}) + e_{hi}$$

where the e_{hi} are independent of the y's. From this model it is found by substitution that

$$\bar{y}_{hm}{}' = \bar{y}_{hm} + \rho(\bar{y}_{h-1}' - \bar{y}_{h-1,m}) = \bar{Y}_h + \rho(\bar{y}_{h-1}' - \bar{Y}_{h-1}) + \bar{e}_{hm}$$

Hence the covariance of $\bar{y}_{hm}{}'$ and $\bar{y}_{h-1}'$ is $\rho V(\bar{y}_{h-1}')$. But

$$\mathrm{Cov}\,(\bar{y}_h{}'\bar{y}_{h-1}') = \mathrm{Cov}\,\{[\phi\bar{y}_{hu} + (1 - \phi)\bar{y}_{hm}{}']\bar{y}_{h-1}'\} = \rho(1 - \phi)V(\bar{y}_{h-1}')$$

since $\bar{y}_{hu}$ is independent of $\bar{y}_{h-1}'$. From (12.46), this gives

$$V(\bar{y}_h{}' - \bar{y}_{h-1}') = \frac{S^2}{n}\{g_h + g_{h-1}[1 - 2\rho(1 - \phi)]\} \quad (12.47)$$

From (12.44) and (12.47), the variances of $\bar{y}_h{}'$ and $(\bar{y}_h{}' - \bar{y}_{h-1}')$ may be computed for any values of m, ϕ, and ρ. Table 12.5 shows these variances for $\lambda = m/n = \frac{1}{2}$ and $\frac{3}{4}$. The weight ϕ was taken as 0.35 for $\lambda = \frac{1}{2}$ and 0.2 for $\lambda = \frac{3}{4}$.

The results indicate that an increase in the proportion retained from $\frac{1}{2}$ to $\frac{3}{4}$ produces only small increases in the variance of the current estimate and gives substantially larger reductions in the variance of the estimate of change. For example, with $\rho = 0.8$, the increase in $V(\bar{y}_h{}')$ is about 5%, whereas the decrease in $V(\bar{y}_h{}' - \bar{y}_{h-1}')$ is more than 20%. This suggests that retention of $\frac{2}{3}$, $\frac{3}{4}$, or $\frac{4}{5}$ from one occasion to the next may be a good practical policy if current estimates and estimates of change are both wanted.

Comparison of $V(\bar{y}_h{}')$ for $\lambda = \frac{1}{2}$ in Table 12.5 with the optimum variances in Table 12.4 shows that little precision is lost by using a constant weight and a fixed $\lambda = \frac{1}{2}$.

If ρ exceeds 0.8, the regression coefficient $b = \rho$ may be replaced by 1 with only a small additional loss of precision. This gives an estimate $\bar{y}_h{}''$ of the form

$$\bar{y}_h{}'' = \phi\bar{y}_{hu}{}' + (1 - \phi)(\bar{y}_{h-1}'' + \bar{y}_{hm} - \bar{y}_{h-1,m}) \quad (12.48)$$

TABLE 12.5

Effect of the Proportion Matched on $V(\bar{y}_h')$ and $V(\bar{y}_h' - \bar{y}_{h-1}')$

	$nV(\bar{y}_h')/S^2$								$nV(\bar{y}_h' - \bar{y}_{h-1}')/S^2$							
	$\rho =$								$\rho =$							
	0.7		0.8		0.9		0.95		0.7		0.8		0.9		0.95	
h	$\frac{1}{2}$*	$\frac{3}{4}$*	$\frac{1}{2}$	$\frac{3}{4}$	$\frac{1}{2}$	$\frac{3}{4}$	$\frac{1}{2}$	$\frac{3}{4}$	$\frac{1}{2}$	$\frac{3}{4}$	$\frac{1}{2}$	$\frac{3}{4}$	$\frac{1}{2}$	$\frac{3}{4}$	$\frac{1}{2}$	$\frac{3}{4}$
2	0.88	0.91	0.82	0.88	0.75	0.84	0.71	0.82	0.97	0.79	0.78	0.60	0.58	0.40	0.47	0.30
3	0.86	0.88	0.77	0.83	0.66	0.76	0.60	0.72	0.94	0.77	0.74	0.58	0.53	0.39	0.43	0.29
4	0.85	0.87	0.76	0.81	0.63	0.72	0.56	0.66	0.93	0.77	0.73	0.57	0.52	0.38	0.41	0.28
5	0.85	0.87	0.75	0.80	0.62	0.69	0.54	0.62	0.93	0.76	0.72	0.57	0.51	0.38	0.41	0.28
∞	0.85	0.87	0.75	0.79	0.62	0.67	0.53	0.58	0.93	0.76	0.72	0.57	0.51	0.37	0.40	0.28

* Value of λ = proportion matched or retained.

In the important Current Population Survey taken monthly by the U.S. Bureau of the Census, one quarter of the second-stage units are replaced each month, so that an individual household remains in the sample during four consecutive months. The household is omitted for the eight succeeding months but is then brought back for another four months, thus increasing slightly the precision of year-to-year comparisons.

The composite estimate used in this survey is of a form related to (12.48) but slightly different.

$$\bar{y}_h'' = (1 - K)\bar{y}_h + K(\bar{y}_{h-1}'' + \bar{y}_{hm} - \bar{y}_{h-1,m})$$ (12.49)

where K is a constant weighting factor. The difference is that $\bar{y}_h$, the current estimate for the whole sample, takes the place of the $\bar{y}_{hu}$ in (12.48). The quantities $\bar{y}_{hm}$, $\bar{y}_{h-1,m}$, $\bar{y}_h$ in (12.49) are ratio estimates of a fairly complex type. The variance of $\bar{y}_h''$ (due to Bershad) is given in Hansen, Hurwitz, and Madow (1953). Since the primary units remain unchanged, only the within-units component of $V(\bar{y}_h'')$ is affected by this replacement policy.

In another rotation policy a new sample is drawn on each occasion, with no matching. With monthly sampling, this plan is appropriate when annual estimates, and to a lesser extent semiannual or quarterly estimates, are of primary importance, for example, in an illness survey with emphasis on chronic diseases. If the questionnaire obtains for any unit the results for the preceding month as well as for the current month, we can consider composite estimates of the form

$$\bar{y}_h' = \bar{y}_h + \phi_h(\bar{y}_{h-1}' - \bar{y}_{h-1,h})$$ (12.50)

where $\bar{y}_h$ = estimate made from current data in the current sample,

$\bar{y}_{h-1,h}$ = estimate made from previous month's data in the current sample,

$\bar{y}_{h-1}'$ = composite estimate for the previous month.

The theory is discussed by Hansen, Hurwitz, and Madow (1953) and Woodruff (1959), who apply it to a survey of retail sales, and by Eckler (1955). In the Retail Trade Survey the composite estimate involves a ratio estimate, being of the form

$$\bar{y}_h'' = (1 - W)\bar{y}_h + W\left(\frac{\bar{y}_h}{\bar{y}_{h-1,h}}\right)\bar{y}_{h-1}''$$

where W is a weighting factor. Since month-to-month correlations are very high, averaging around 0.98, the gains in precision are substantial. One month later a revised composite estimate for month h is computed, using the results for month h from the new sample taken in month $(h + 1)$.

With this method, it is essential that the data obtained for the preceding month from the current sample are accurate. This may not be so when the data depend on the unrecorded memory of the respondent, though the method may work successfully if the data are of a type that the respondent records carefully as a routine matter.

EXERCISES

12.1 $3000 is allocated for a survey to estimate a proportion. The main survey will cost $10 per sampling unit. Information is available in files, at a cost of $0.25 per sampling unit, that enables the units to be classified into two strata of about equal sizes. If the true proportion is 0.2 in stratum 1 and 0.8 in stratum 2, estimate the optimum n, n', and the resulting value of $V(p_{st})$. Does double sampling produce a gain in precision over single sampling? (The ratios n'/N, n_h/N_h may be ignored.)

12.2 For the W_h, P_h in exercise 12.1, find the cost ratios c_n/c_n' for which double sampling is more economical than single sampling.

12.3 A population contains L strata of equal size. If V_{ran} denotes the variance of the mean of a simple random sample and V_{st}, V_{ds} are the corresponding variances for stratified random sampling with proportional allocation and for double sampling with stratification, show that, approximately,

$$nV_{ran} = \bar{S}_h^2 + \frac{\sum_h (\bar{Y}_h - \bar{Y})^2}{L}$$

$$nV_{st} = \bar{S}_h^2$$

$$nV_{ds} = \bar{S}_h^2 + \frac{n}{n'} \frac{\sum_h (\bar{Y}_h - \bar{Y})^2}{L}$$

where $\bar{S}_h^2$ is the average variance within strata. (N and n' may both be assumed large relative to L, and the n_h in double sampling may be assumed equal to n/L.)

Hence, if $(RP)_{st}$ denotes the relative precision of the stratified sample to the simple random sample, with a corresponding definition for $(RP)_{ds}$, show that

$$(RP)_{ds} = \frac{(RP)_{st}}{1 + (n/n')[(RP)_{st} - 1]}$$

For $(RP)_{st} = 2$, plot $(RP)_{ds}$ against n/n'. How small must this ratio be in order that $(RP)_{ds} = 1.9$?

12.4 If $\rho = 0.8$ in double sampling for regression, how large must n' be relative to n, if the loss in precision due to sampling errors in the mean of the large sample is to be less than 10%?

12.5 In an application of double sampling for regression, the small sample was of size 87 and the large sample of size 300. The following computations apply to the small sample:

$$\sum (y_i - \bar{y})^2 = 17{,}283, \quad \sum (y_i - \bar{y})(x_i - \bar{x}) = 5114, \quad \sum (x_i - \bar{x})^2 = 3248$$

Compute the standard error of the regression estimate of $\bar{Y}$.

12.6 For $\rho = 0.95$, verify the data given in Table 12.4 for the optimum percentage which should be matched and for the gain in precision relative to no matching. Compute the corresponding per cent gains in precision if one third of the units are retained from the first to the second occasion and one half of the units are retained on each subsequent occasion.

12.7 In simple random sampling on two occasions, suppose that the estimate on the second occasion is, in the notation of section 12.10,

$$\bar{y}_2'' = (1 - \phi)(\bar{y}_1 + \bar{y}_{2m} - \bar{y}_{1m}) + \phi\bar{y}_{2u}$$

(a) Ignoring the fpc, show that

$$V(\bar{y}_2'') = \frac{S^2}{n}\left\{(1 - \phi)^2 \frac{[1 + \mu(1 - 2\rho)]}{\lambda} + \frac{\phi^2}{\mu}\right\}$$

where $\lambda = m/n$, $\mu = u/n$. (b) For given ρ, λ, μ, find the value of ϕ that minimizes $V(\bar{y}_2'')$. Show that if ρ exceeds $\frac{1}{2}$ the best weight ϕ lies between μ and $\mu/(1 + \mu)$.

12.8 For $\mu = \frac{1}{4}$, $\mu = \frac{1}{2}$, $\rho = 0.8$, and $\rho = 0.9$, compare $V(\bar{y}_2'')$ in the preceding exercise with the variance of the optimum composite regression estimate $\bar{y}_2'$, as given by equation 12.35. (In $\bar{y}_2''$ take $\phi = 0.2$ when $\mu = \frac{1}{4}$ and $\phi = 0.4$ when $\mu = \frac{1}{2}$.) Verify that for these values of ρ the estimate $\bar{y}_2''$ is almost as precise as $\bar{y}_2'$ for both $\mu = \frac{1}{4}$ and $\mu = \frac{1}{2}$.

12.9 An independent sample of size n is drawn each month. From the sample taken in any month, data are obtained for the current and the preceding month. A composite estimate $\bar{y}_h'$ is made as in (12.50), section 12.12.

The model is

$$\bar{y}_h' = \bar{y}_h + \phi_h(\bar{y}_{h-1}' - \bar{y}_{h-1,h})$$

$$y_{hi} = \bar{Y}_h + \rho(y_{h-1,i} - \bar{Y}_{h-1}) + e_{hi}$$

where e_{hi} is independent of the y's and has variance $(1 - \rho^2)$. Show that
(a)

$$\bar{y}_h' - \bar{Y}_h = \bar{e}_h + \phi_h(\bar{y}_{h-1}' - \bar{Y}_{h-1}) + (\rho - \phi_h)(\bar{y}_{h-1,h} - \bar{Y}_{h-1})$$

(b) If $V(\bar{y}_h') = g_h S^2/n$, where S^2 is constant on all occasions,

$$g_h = (1 - \rho^2) + \phi_h^2 g_{h-1} + (\rho - \phi_h)^2$$

(c) The optimum $\phi_h = \rho/(1 + g_{h-1})$ and the resulting optimum g_h is

$$g_h = 1 - \frac{\rho^2}{1 + g_{h-1}}$$

(d) The limiting g_h is $g_\infty = \sqrt{1 - \rho^2}$. These results were given by Eckler (1955).

REFERENCES

Bose, Chameli (1943). Note on the sampling error in the method of double sampling. *Sankhya*, **6**, 330.

Eckler, A. R. (1955). Rotation sampling. *Ann. Math. Stat.*, **26**, 664–685.

Hansen, M. H., Hurwitz, W. N., and Madow, W. G. (1953). *Sample survey methods and theory.* John Wiley and Sons, New York.

Jessen, R. J. (1942). Statistical investigation of a sample survey for obtaining farm facts. *Iowa Agr. Exp. Sta. Res. Bull.* 304.

Neyman, J. (1938). Contribution to the theory of sampling human populations. *Jour. Amer. Stat. Assoc.*, **33**, 101–116.

Patterson, H. D. (1950). Sampling on successive occasions with partial replacement of units. *Jour. Roy. Stat. Soc.*, **B12**, 241–255.

Robson, D. S. (1952). Multiple sampling of attributes. *Jour. Amer. Stat. Assoc.*, **47**, 203–215.

Robson, D. S., and King, A. J. (1953). Double sampling and the Curtis impact survey. *Cornell Univ. Agr. Exp. Sta. Mem.* 231.

Woodruff, R. S. (1959). The use of rotating samples in the Census Bureau's Monthly Surveys. *Proc. Social Statistics Section. Amer. Stat. Assoc.*, 130–138.

Yates, F. (1960). *Sampling methods for censuses and surveys.* Charles Griffin and Co., London, third edition.

CHAPTER 13

Sources of Error in Surveys

13.1 INTRODUCTION

The theory presented in preceding chapters assumes throughout that some kind of probability sampling is used and that the observation y_i on the ith unit is the correct value for that unit. The error of estimate arises solely from the random sampling variation that is present when n of the units are measured instead of the complete population of N units.

These assumptions hold reasonably well in the simpler types of surveys in which the measuring devices are accurate and the quality of work is high. In complex surveys, particularly when difficult problems of measurement are involved, the assumptions may be far from true. Three additional sources of error that may be present are as follows:

1. Failure to measure some of the units in the chosen sample. This may occur by oversight, or, with human populations, because of failure to locate some individuals or their refusal to answer the questions when located.

2. Errors of measurement on a unit. The measuring device may be biased or imprecise. With human populations the respondents may not possess accurate information or they may give biased answers.

3. Errors introduced in editing, coding, and tabulating the results.

These sources of error necessitate a modification of the standard theory of sampling. The principal aims of such a modification are to provide guidance about the allocation of resources between the reduction of random sampling errors and the reduction of the other errors and to develop methods for computing standard errors and confidence limits that remain valid when the other errors are present.

13.2 EFFECTS OF NONRESPONSE

We shall use the term *nonresponse* to refer to the failure to measure some of the units in the selected sample. In the study of nonresponse it is convenient to think of the population as divided into two "strata," the first consisting of all units for which measurements would be obtained if the units happened to fall in the sample, the second of the units for which no measurements would be obtained. The compositions of the two strata depend intimately on the methods used to find the units and obtain the data. A survey in which at least three calls are made, if necessary, on every house and in which a supervisor with exceptional powers of persuasion calls on all persons who refuse to give data will have a much

TABLE 13.1

RESPONSES TO THREE REQUESTS IN A MAILED INQUIRY

	Number of Growers	% of Population	Average Number of Fruit Trees per Grower
Response to first mailing	300	10	456
Response to second mailing	543	17	382
Response to third mailing	434	14	340
Nonrespondents after 3 mailings	1839	59	290
Total population	3116	100	329

smaller "nonresponse" stratum than one in which only a single attempt is made for every house.

This division into two distinct strata is, of course, an oversimplification. Chance plays a part in determining whether a unit is found and measured in a given number of attempts. In a more complete specification of the problem we would attach to each unit a probability representing the chance that it would be measured by a given field method if it fell in the sample.

The sample provides no information about the nonresponse stratum 2. This would not matter if it could be assumed that the characteristics of stratum 2 are the same as those of stratum 1. Where checks have been made, however, it has often been found that units in the "nonresponse" stratum differ from units that are measurable. An illustration appears in Table 13.1. The data come from an experimental sampling of fruit orchards in North Carolina in 1946. Three successive mailings of the same questionnaire were sent to growers. For one of the questions— number of fruit trees—complete data were available for the population (Finkner, 1950).

The steady decline in the number of fruit trees per grower in the successive responses is evident, these numbers being 456 for respondents to the first mailing, 382 in the second mailing, 340 in the third, and 290 for the refusals to all three letters. The total response was poor, more than half the population failing to give data even after three attempts.

We now consider the effects of nonresponse on the sample estimate. Let N_1, N_2 be the numbers of units in the two strata and let $W_1 = N_1/N$, $W_2 = N_2/N$, so that W_2 is the proportion of nonresponse in the population. Assume that a simple random sample is drawn from the population. When the field work is completed, we have data for a simple random sample from stratum 1 but no data from stratum 2. Hence the amount of bias in the sample mean is

$$E(\bar{y}_1) - \bar{Y} = \bar{Y}_1 - \bar{Y} = \bar{Y}_1 - (W_1\bar{Y}_1 + W_2\bar{Y}_2)$$
$$= W_2(\bar{Y}_1 - \bar{Y}_2) \qquad (13.1)$$

The amount of bias is the product of the proportion of nonresponse and the difference between the means in the two strata. Since the sample provides no information about $\bar{Y}_2$, the size of the bias is unknown unless bounds can be placed on $\bar{Y}_2$ from some source other than the sample data. With a continuous variate, the only bounds that can be assigned with certainty are often so wide as to be useless.

Consequently, with continuous data, any sizable proportion of nonresponse usually makes it impossible to assign useful confidence limits to $\bar{Y}$ from the sample results. We are left in the position of relying on some guess about the size of the bias, without data to substantiate the guess.

In sampling for proportions the situation is a little easier, since the unknown proportion P_2 in stratum 2 must lie between 0 and 1. If W_2 is known, these bounds for P_2 enable us to construct confidence limits for the population proportion P. Suppose that a simple random sample of n units is drawn and that measurements are obtained for n_1 of the units in the sample. Assuming n_1 large enough, 95% confidence limits for P_1 are given by

$$p_1 \pm 2\sqrt{p_1 q_1/n_1}$$

where p_1 is the sample proportion and the fpc is ignored.

When we try to derive a confidence statement about P, we are on safe ground if we assume $P_2 = 0$ when finding $\hat{P}_L$ and $P_2 = 1$ when finding $\hat{P}_U$. Thus we might take, for 95% limits,

$$\hat{P}_L = W_1(p_1 - 2\sqrt{p_1 q_1/n_1}) + W_2(0) \qquad (13.2)$$
$$\hat{P}_U = W_1(p_1 + 2\sqrt{p_1 q_1/n_1}) + W_2(1) \qquad (13.3)$$

It is easy to verify that these limits are conservative, that is, that

$$Pr(\hat{P}_L \le P \le \hat{P}_U) > 0.95$$

The limits can be narrowed a little by a more careful argument (Cochran, Mosteller, and Tukey, 1954), since P_2 cannot be 0 and 1 simultaneously, as assumed above.

The limits are distressingly wide unless W_2 is very small. Table 13.2 shows the average limits for a sample size $n = 1000$ and a series of values of W_2 and p_1. Since the limits in (13.2) and (13.3) depend on the value of n_1 (number of respondents in the sample), we have taken $n_1 = nW_1$, its average value, in computing Table 13.2.

TABLE 13.2

95% Confidence Limits for P (%) when $n = 1000$

% Nonresponse, $100W_2$	Sample Percentage, $100p_1$			
	5	10	20	50
0	(3.6, 6.4)	(8.1, 11.9)	(17.5, 22.5)	(46.7, 53.2)
5	(3.4, 11.1)	(7.6, 16.3)	(16.5, 26.5)	(44.4, 55.6)
10	(3.2, 15.8)	(7.2, 20.8)	(15.6, 30.4)	(42.0, 58.0)
15	(3.0, 20.5)	(6.8, 25.2)	(14.7, 34.3)	(39.6, 60.4)
20	(2.8, 25.2)	(6.3, 29.7)	(13.7, 38.3)	(37.2, 62.8)

The rapid increase in the width of the confidence interval with increasing W_2 is evident. It is of interest to examine what values of n would be needed to give the same widths of confidence interval if W_2 were zero. This is easily done when p_1 is 50%. For $W_2 = 5\%$, Table 13.2 shows that the half-width of the confidence interval is 5.6. The equivalent sample size n_e, assuming no nonresponse, is found from the equation

$$5.6 = 2\sqrt{(50)(50)/n_e}$$
$$n_e = 320$$

For $W_2 = 10$, 15, and 20%, the values of n_e are 155, 90, and 60, respectively. It is evidently worthwhile to devote a substantial proportion of the resources to the reduction of nonresponse.

An interesting method of finding sample size when nonresponse is present has been given by Birnbaum and Sirken (1950a, 1950b). The proportion W_2 of nonresponse is assumed known from previous experience in the particular type of survey. No advance knowledge of P_1, P_2, or P is assumed. Thus, if there were no nonresponse and if we wished the absolute error in the sample proportion to be less than d, we would take (by section 4.4)

$$n = \frac{t_\alpha^2 PQ}{d^2}$$

where t_α is the normal deviate corresponding to the risk α that the error exceeds d. With no advance information about P, we would take $P = 0.5$ as the least favorable case, giving

$$n = \frac{t_\alpha^2}{4d^2} \qquad (13.4)$$

By taking the least favorable combination of the bias $W_2(P_1 - P_2)$ and

TABLE 13.3

SMALLEST VALUE OF n FOR GIVEN LIMIT OF ERROR d, WITH RISK $\alpha = 0.05$

% Nonresponse, $100W_2$	$d(\%)$			
	20	15	10	5
0	24	43	96	384
2	27	50	122	653
4	31	60	166	2000
6	36	75	255	....
8	43	99	521	....
10	53	142	...	....
15	112	...	...	....

the value of P_1, Birnbaum and Sirken show that a value of n which still guarantees an error less than d, with risk α, is

$$n \doteq \frac{t_\alpha^2}{4d(d - W_2)W_1} - 1 \qquad (13.5)$$

Note that no value of n suffices if $W_2 > d$. If $W_2 = 0$, this equation reduces to (13.4) apart from the term -1, which comes from an approximation in the analysis. Some values of n given by Birnbaum and Sirken's method are shown in Table 13.3.

This table tells the same sad story as Table 13.2. If we are content with a crude estimate $(d = 20)$, amounts of nonresponse up to 10% can be handled by doubling the sample size. However, any sizable percentage of nonresponse makes it impossible or very costly to attain a highly guaranteed precision by increasing the sample size among the respondents.

13.3 TYPES OF NONRESPONSE

Some methods for handling the nonresponse problem are described in succeeding sections. A rough classification of the types of nonresponse is as follows.

1. *Noncoverage*—failure to locate or to visit some units in the sample. This is a problem with areal sampling units, in which the interviewer must find and list all dwellings (according to some definition) in a city block. It arises also from the use of incomplete lists. Sometimes weather or poor transportation facilities make it impossible to reach certain units during the period of the survey.

2. *Not-at-homes*. This group contains persons who reside at home but are temporarily away from the house. Families in which both parents work and families without children are harder to reach than families with very young children or with old people confined to the house.

3. *Unable to answer*. The respondent may not have the information wanted in certain questions or may be unwilling to give it. Skillful wording and pretesting of the questionnaire are a safeguard.

4. *The "hard core."* Persons who adamantly refuse to be interviewed, who are incapacitated, or who are far from home during the whole time available for field-work constitute this sector. It represents a source of bias that persists no matter how much effort is put into completeness of returns.

The detection and measurement of noncoverage are difficult. With areal sampling, one method is to revisit the primary units, making a careful listing that serves as a check. Comparisons of counts of numbers of people or dwellings with those in another survey sometimes give a warning that some have been missed. When the principal frame is a directory of street addresses, it may be supplemented by an area sample, the purpose of which is to sample parts of the town (new building) not adequately covered by the directory and, in parts in which the directory seems accurate, to search for addresses missing from the directory. Surveys using these methods, with a discussion of the problem of noncoverage, are described by Kish and Hess (1958) and Woolsey (1956).

In regard to the not-at-homes, the problem is easier in surveys in which *any* adult in the home is capable of answering the questions than in those in which a single adult, chosen at random, is to be interviewed. A single adult is usually preferred if the survey is one of individuals in which one person cannot report accurately for another or if intrahousehold cor-relations are expected to be high, so that the measurement of more than one person per family is uneconomical. In this connection, a useful method of selecting a single person from a household was developed by Kish (1949). The original plan was intended for households that may contain as many as six eligible persons, but the procedure can be adapted for smaller or larger households.

The interviewer lists on the schedule the eligible persons in the household and then numbers them: males first in order of decreasing age, then females in order of decreasing age. Each schedule has printed on it *one* of the sets of instructions in Table 13.4.

Each eligible person in a household of a given size has an equal chance of being selected, except that adults 3 and 5 in households of size 5 are slightly overrepresented. Since male respondents are concentrated in

TABLE 13.4

INSTRUCTIONS FOR SELECTING A SINGLE RESPONDENT

Relative Frequency of Use	Table Number	If Number of Adults in Household is					
		1	2	3	4	5	6
		Select Adult Numbered					
1/6	A	1	1	1	1	1	1
1/12	B1	1	1	1	1	2	2
1/12	B2	1	1	1	2	2	2
1/6	C	1	1	2	2	3	3
1/6	D	1	2	2	3	4	4
1/12	E1	1	2	3	3	3	5
1/12	E2	1	2	3	4	5	5
1/6	F	1	2	3	4	5	6

Tables A, B, and C, the interviewer can devote evening calls to households so designated.

13.4 CALL-BACKS

A standard technique is to specify the number of call-backs, or a minimum number, that must be made on any unit before abandoning it as "unable to contact." Stephan and McCarthy (1958) give data from a number of surveys on the percentage of the total sample obtained at each call. Average results are shown in Table 13.5.

TABLE 13.5

NUMBER OF CALLS REQUIRED FOR COMPLETED INTERVIEWS

	% of Sample contacted on				
Respondent	First Call	Second Call	Third or Later Call	Per Cent Nonresponse	Total
Any adult*	70	17	8	5	100
Random adult	37	32	23	8	100

* Two surveys in which the respondent was a housewife and a farm operator, respectively, have been included in the "any adult" group.

In surveys in which any adult in the house could answer the questions, the first call obtained about 70% of the sample and the first two calls, 87%. The increased cost of sampling when a randomly chosen adult is to be interviewed is evident, the first call producing only 37% of the required interviews. The marked success of the second call reflects the work of the interviewer in finding out in advance when the desired respondent would be at home and available.

Little has been published on the relative costs of later calls to the first call. Later calls would be expected to be more expensive per completed interview, since the houses are more sparsely located in the area assigned to the interviewer and since the occupants are presumably people who spend more than an average amount of time away from home. From British experience, Durbin (1954) suggests that later calls may be less expensive than would be anticipated. The following figures show estimated relative costs per completed interview (i.e., money spent on ith calls divided by number of new interviews obtained) for each call up to the fifth in a special study reported by Durbin and Stuart (1954).

TABLE 13.6

RELATIVE COSTS PER NEW COMPLETED INTERVIEW AT THE iTH CALL

Call	1	2	3	4	5
Relative cost	100	112	127	151	250

The estimation of these costs requires care. If the desired respondent is not at home at the first call, the interviewer may spend time inquiring when this person will be at home and making a tentative appointment. In the costing such time should be assigned to the second call rather than to an unsuccessful first call.

A more useful measure is the average cost per completed interview *over all interviews obtained up to the ith call.* These figures give the relative costs of obtaining n completed interviews when we insist on i calls before the interviewer gives up. In order to compute these figures, we must know how many interviews are obtained at each call. In Table 13.7 these calculations are made under two sets of assumptions. The first simulates surveys in which any adult can answer the questions, the second those demanding a random adult. The data on numbers of interviews obtained were taken from Table 13.5.

The details of the calculation are shown only for the first assumption, the method being exactly the same for the second. The symbol n_0 denotes the *original* sample size.

Insistence on up to three calls costs only 4% more *per completed interview* than single calls if any adult is a satisfactory respondent, and only 10% more if a random adult must be interviewed. How typical these results are is not known, but the method provides realistic estimates of the cost of insisting on call-backs if the necessary cost and sample size

TABLE 13.7

RELATIVE COSTS PER COMPLETED INTERVIEW UP TO THE ith CALL

Respondent = Any Adult

| Call | Relative Cost | At ith Call | | Up to ith Call | | | "Random" Adult | |
		No. of Ints.*	Cost of Ints.	Total No. of Ints.	Total Cost	Cost per Int.	No. of Ints.	Cost per Int.
1	100	$0.70n_0$	$70n_0$	$0.70n_0$	$70n_0$	100	$0.37n_0$	100
2	112	$0.17n_0$	$19.04n_0$	$0.87n_0$	$89.04n_0$	102	$0.32n_0$	106
3	127	$0.07n_0$	$8.89n_0$	$0.94n_0$	$97.93n_0$	104	$0.16n_0$	110
4	151	$0.04n_0$	$6.04n_0$	$0.98n_0$	$103.97n_0$	106	$0.09n_0$	114
5	250	$0.02n_0$	$5.00n_0$	$1.00n_0$	$108.97n_0$	109	$0.06n_0$	122

* Interviews

data have been collected. There is also the time-factor: call-backs delay the final results.

13.5 A MATHEMATICAL MODEL OF THE EFFECTS OF CALL-BACKS

Deming (1953) developed a useful and flexible mathematical model for examining in more detail the consequences of different call-back policies. The population is divided into r classes, according to the probability that the respondent will be found at home. Let

w_{ij} = probability that a respondent in the jth class will be reached on or before the ith call

p_j = proportion of the population falling in the jth class

μ_j = item mean for the jth class

σ_j^2 = item variance for the jth class

For simplicity we assume $w_{ij} > 0$ for all classes, though the method is easily adapted to include persons impossible to reach. If $\bar{y}_{ij}$ is the mean for those in class j who were reached on or before the ith call, it is also assumed that $E(\bar{y}_{ij}) = \mu_j$.

The true population mean for the item is

$$\bar{\mu} = \sum_j p_j \mu_j \tag{13.6}$$

Consider the composition of the sample after i calls. The persons in the sample can be classified into $(r + 1)$ classes as follows: in the first class and interviewed; in the second class and interviewed; and so on. The $(r + 1)$th class consists of all those not yet interviewed after i calls. If the fpc is ignored, the numbers falling in these $(r + 1)$ classes are distributed according to the multinomial

$$[w_{i1}p_1 + w_{i2}p_2 + \cdots + w_{ir}p_r + (1 - \sum w_{ij}p_j)]^{n_0}$$

where n_o is the initial size of the sample.

It follows that the number n_i who have been interviewed in the course of i calls is binomially distributed with number of trials $= n_o$ and probability of success $\sum w_{ij}p_j$. Hence

$$E(n_i) = \text{expected number of interviews in } i \text{ calls} = n_o \sum_j^r w_{ij}p_j \tag{13.7}$$

For fixed n_i, the numbers of interviews n_{ij} obtained $(j = 1, 2, r)$ follow a multinomial with probabilities $w_{ij}p_j/\sum w_{ij}p_j$. It follows that

$$E(n_{ij} \mid n_i) = \frac{n_i w_{ij}p_j}{\sum w_{ij}p_j}$$

Hence, if $\bar{y}_i$ is the sample mean obtained after i calls,

$$E(\bar{y}_i \mid n_i) = E\left(\frac{\sum n_{ij}\bar{y}_{ij}}{n_i}\right) = \frac{\sum n_i w_{ij}p_j\mu_j}{n_i \sum w_{ij}p_j} = \frac{\sum w_{ij}p_j\mu_j}{\sum w_{ij}p_j} \tag{13.8}$$

Since this result does not depend on n_i, the unconditional mean of $\bar{y}_i$ is also $\bar{\mu}_i$. The bias in the estimate $\bar{y}$ is therefore $(\bar{\mu}_i - \bar{\mu})$.

The conditional variance of $\bar{y}_i$ for given n_i is found similarly to be

$$V(\bar{y}_i \mid n_i) = \frac{\sum_j^r w_{ij}p_j[\sigma_j^2 + (\mu_j - \bar{\mu}_i)^2]}{n_i \sum_j^r w_{ij}p_j} \tag{13.9}$$

The unconditional variance, ignoring terms of order $1/n_i^2$, is given approximately by replacing n_i in (13.9) by its expected value from (13.7).

Finally, the mean square error of the estimate obtained after i calls is

$$\text{MSE}(\bar{y}_i \mid i) = V(\bar{y}_i \mid i) + (\bar{\mu}_i - \bar{\mu})^2 \tag{13.10}$$

The cost of making i calls must also be considered. The expected number of *new* interviews obtained in the kth call is $\Sigma(w_{kj} - w_{k-1,j})p_j$. Hence, if c_k is the cost per completed interview at the kth call, the expected total cost of making i calls is $n_oC(i)$, where

$$C(i) = c_1 \sum w_{1j}p_j + c_2 \sum (w_{2j} - w_{1j})p_j + \cdots + c_i \sum (w_{ij} - w_{i-1,j})p_j$$

Example. A population with three classes is shown in Table 13.8. The p_j and w_{ij} are intended to represent surveys in which a random adult is interviewed. At the first call the probabilities w_{1j} of obtaining an interview are taken as 0.6,

TABLE 13.8

CHARACTERISTICS OF THE THREE CLASSES

	Class		
	1	2	3
p_j	0.45	0.50	0.05
w_{ij}	$0.6 + (0.4)[1 - (0.1)^{i-1}]$	$0.3 + (0.7)[1 - (0.5)^{i-1}]$	$0.1 + (0.9)[1 - (0.8)^{i-1}]$
I μ_j	55	50	45
II μ_j	60	50	40

TABLE 13.9

NUMBER OF INTERVIEWS, COSTS PER INTERVIEW AND BIASES

Number of Calls Required	Number of Interviews Obtained	Average Cost per Interview	I Bias	II Bias
1	$0.425n_o$	100	+1.118	+2.235
2	$0.771n_o$	105	+0.711	+1.421
3	$0.882n_o$	108	+0.421	+0.842
4	$0.933n_o$	110	+0.266	+0.532
5	$0.960n_o$	114	+0.180	+0.360

0.3, and 0.1 in the three classes. At the second and subsequent calls, the conditional probabilities of interviewing a person missed previously are 0.9, 0.5, and 0.2. These figures were made higher than the corresponding probabilities at the first call in order to represent the effect of intelligent inquiry by the interviewer.

The item being estimated is a binomial percentage close to 50%. Two sets of μ_j are considered (I, II). For simplicity, the within-class variances $\sigma_j^2 = \mu_j (100 - \mu_j)$ were all taken as 2500. The relative costs per completed interview at successive calls were those given in Table 13.6.

Table 13.9 shows (a) expected total number of interviews obtained for a total of i calls, (b) the average cost of these calls per interview and (c) the bias ($\bar{\mu}_i - \bar{\mu}$) in the estimate $\bar{y}$ under assumptions I and II about the μ_j.

In II, for example, the true population mean $\bar{\mu}$ is 54%. The mean $\bar{\mu}_1$ obtained from first calls is 56.235%, giving the bias of +2.235% shown in the table. A policy that requires three calls reduces this bias to +0.842%.

The values of MSE($\bar{y}$) obtained from a given expenditure of money were compared for the different call-back policies. In the first comparisons the amount of money is sufficient to take $n_0 = 500$ if only one call is made. From Table 13.9 the expected number of interviews obtained in the first call is $E(n_1) = (500)(0.425) = 212.5$. If two calls are made, this expected number must be reduced to $E(n_2) = 212.5/1.05 = 202.4$. to maintain the same cost, and similarly for 3, 4, and 5 call-backs. These values of $E(n_i)$ were substituted in equation (13.9) to give $V(\bar{y})$ and hence MSE($\bar{y}$).

TABLE 13.10

VALUES OF MSE($\bar{y}$) FOR DIFFERENT CALL-BACK POLICIES
COSTING THE SAME AMOUNT

Number of Calls Required	$n_0 = 500$ (for first calls only)			$n_0 = 1000$		$n_0 = 2000$	
	No Bias	I*	II*	I	II	I	II
1	**11.8**	13.0	16.9	7.1	10.9	4.2	8.0
2	12.4	12.9	14.6	6.7	8.3	3.6	5.2
3	12.7	**12.9**	13.6	**6.5**	7.1	3.4	3.9
4	13.0	13.1	**13.4**	6.6	**6.9**	**3.3**	3.6
5	13.5	13.5	13.8	6.8	6.9	3.4	**3.5**

* These represent populations with smaller (I) and greater (II) amounts of bias, as defined in Table 13.8.

Table 13.10 presents the resulting MSE's for three amounts of expenditure, corresponding to $n_0 = 500, 1000, 2000$ for a single call. When $n_0 = 500$, the values of MSE($\bar{y}$) are also given for the "no bias" situation in which every $\mu_j = 50$. This column shows the effect of call-backs when they are unnecessary, since no bias results from confining the survey to a single call.

The policies giving the lowest MSE's are shown in boldface type. Consider first the smallest sample size, $n_0 = 500$. If call-backs are unnecessary, a policy demanding as many as four call-backs results in only a modest increase in the MSE. In I, involving the smaller amount of bias, the different policies produce about the same accuracy, although three is the optimum. In II, three to five call-backs are satisfactory, a single call giving a MSE about 25% above the minimum.

For the larger sample sizes the optimum number of call-backs increases to four or five, and the use of a single call results in more substantial losses of accuracy.

This is, of course, only an illustration. The importance of the method is that as information accumulates about costs and relative biases an economical policy can be worked out for any specific type of survey.

13.6 OPTIMUM SAMPLING FRACTION AMONG THE NONRESPONDENTS

After the first attempt to reach the persons in the sample has been made, another approach, due to Hansen and Hurwitz (1946), is to take a random subsample of the persons who have not been reached and make a major effort to interview everyone in the subsample. This technique was first developed for surveys in which the initial attempt was made by mail, a subsample of persons who did not return the completed questionnaire being approached by the more expensive method of a personal interview.

The first step is to take a simple random sample of n units, using the ordinary field methods. Let n_1 be the number of units in the sample that provide the data sought and n_2 the number in the nonresponse group. By more intensive efforts, the data are later obtained from a random sample of r_2 out of the n_2. Let

$$n_2 = kr_2 \quad (k > 1) \tag{13.11}$$

Then the average sampling fraction in the first stratum is k times that in the second. This follows because if k is fixed in advance

$$E\left(\frac{n_1}{N_1}\right) = E\left(\frac{n_2}{N_2}\right) = kE\left(\frac{r_2}{N_2}\right)$$

The values of n (initial size of sample) and k are chosen to give a specified precision for the lowest cost.

The cost of taking the sample is

$$C = c_0 n + c_1 n_1 + c_2 r_2$$

where the c's are costs per unit: c_0 is the cost of making the first attempt, c_1 is the cost of processing the results from the first attempt, and c_2 is the cost of getting and processing the data in the second stratum. Since the values of n_1 and n_2 are not known until the first attempt is made, the *expected* cost is used in planning the sample. The expected values of n_1 and r_2 are, respectively, $W_1 n$ and $W_2 n/k$, where W_1, W_2 are the true proportions in the two strata. Thus expected cost is

$$c_0 n + c_1 W_1 n + \frac{c_2 W_2 n}{k} \tag{13.12}$$

Let $\bar{y}_1$, $\bar{y}_{2r}$ be the sample means in the two strata. The subscript r is introduced as a reminder that the sample in the second stratum is of size r_2. As an estimate of the population mean, we take

$$\bar{y}' = \frac{1}{n}(n_1 \bar{y}_1 + n_2 \bar{y}_{2r}) \tag{13.13}$$

Note that the second stratum receives a weight n_2, although the sample is only of size r_2. This is done in order to obtain an unbiased estimate.

This procedure is an application of double sampling with stratification. The first or "large" sample of size n gives an estimate n_1/n_2 of the relative size of the strata. The second or "small" sample is of size n_1 in the first stratum and r_2 in the second stratum.

To find $V(\bar{y}')$, write

$$\bar{y}' = \frac{1}{n}(n_1\bar{y}_1 + n_2\bar{y}_{2n}) + \frac{n_2}{n}(\bar{y}_{2r} - \bar{y}_{2n}) \qquad (13.14)$$

where $\bar{y}_{2n}$ is the mean of the whole sample of size n_2 from stratum 2.

The first term on the right is the mean of a random sample of size n from the whole population. Its variance is therefore

$$\frac{(N-n)}{N}\frac{S^2}{n}$$

where S^2 is the variance of the whole population. Further, when we find the variance of $\bar{y}'$, there is no contribution from cross products between the first and second terms. For

$$E[\bar{y}_{2n}(\bar{y}_{2r} - \bar{y}_{2n})] = 0$$

over all random samples of size r_2 that can be drawn from a fixed sample of size n_2.

Consider the second term on the right of (13.14). If $\bar{Y}_2$ is the population mean of the nonresponse stratum, we have

$$(\bar{y}_{2r} - \bar{Y}_2) = (\bar{y}_{2r} - \bar{y}_{2n}) + (\bar{y}_{2n} - \bar{Y}_2)$$

so that

$$E(\bar{y}_{2r} - \bar{Y}_2)^2 = E(\bar{y}_{2r} - \bar{y}_{2n})^2 + E(\bar{y}_{2n} - \bar{Y}_2)^2$$

there being no contribution from cross-product terms for the same reason as before. Now $\bar{y}_{2r}$ is the mean of a simple random sample of size r_2 from the second stratum, and $\bar{y}_{2n}$ is the mean of a simple random sample of size n_2 from the same stratum. Hence, *for fixed n_2 and r_2,*

$$\frac{(N_2 - r_2)}{N_2}\frac{S_2^2}{r_2} = E(\bar{y}_{2r} - \bar{y}_{2n})^2 + \frac{(N_2 - n_2)}{N_2}\frac{S_2^2}{n_2}$$

where S_2^2 is the variance within the nonresponse stratum. This gives

$$E(\bar{y}_{2r} - \bar{y}_{2n})^2 = S_2^2\left(\frac{1}{r_2} - \frac{1}{n_2}\right) = S_2^2\frac{n_2 - r_2}{n_2 r_2} = S_2^2\frac{k-1}{n_2}$$

since $n_2 = kr_2$.

Hence, adding the variances of the two terms in (13.14), we find, for fixed n_2,

$$V(\bar{y}') = \frac{(N - n)}{N} \frac{S^2}{n} + \left(\frac{n_2}{n}\right)^2 \frac{(k - 1)}{n_2} S_2^{\,2}$$

$$= \frac{(N - n)}{N} \frac{S^2}{n} + \frac{(k - 1)}{n^2} n_2 S_2^{\,2} \tag{13.15}$$

Since $E(n_2) = n W_2$, this gives for the expected variance

$$\bar{V}(\bar{y}') = \frac{(N - n)}{N} \frac{S^2}{n} + \frac{(k - 1)W_2}{n} S_2^{\,2} \tag{13.16}$$

The first term is the variance that would be obtained if all n_2 in the nonresponse group were sampled. The second term is the increase in variance from sampling only r_2 of the n_2.

The quantities n and k are then chosen to minimize average cost (13.12) for a preassigned value of the expected variance (13.16).

The solutions are

$$k_{opt} = \sqrt{\frac{c_2(S^2 - W_2 S_2^{\,2})}{S_2^{\,2}(c_0 + c_1 W_1)}} \tag{13.17}$$

$$n_{opt} = \frac{N[S^2 + (k - 1)W_2 S_2^{\,2}]}{NV + S^2} \tag{13.18}$$

where V is the value specified for the variance of the estimated population mean.

The solutions require a knowledge of W_2; this can often be estimated from previous experience. In addition to S^2, whose value must be estimated in advance in any "sample size" problem, the solutions also involve $S_2^{\,2}$, the variance in the nonresponse stratum. The value of $S_2^{\,2}$ is naturally harder to predict; it will probably not be the same as S^2. For instance, in surveys made by mail of most kinds of economic enterprise, the respondents tend to be larger operators, with larger between-unit variances than the nonrespondents.

If W_2 is not well known, a satisfactory approximation is to work out the value of n_{opt} for a range of assumed values of W_2 between 0 and a safe upper limit. The maximum n_{opt} in this series is adopted as the initial sample size n. When the replies to the mail survey have been received, the value of n_2 is known. The variance formula (13.15) is then solved to find the value of k that gives the desired variance V. The cost for this method is usually only slightly higher than the optimum cost which would have applied if W_2 were known.

Example. This example is condensed from the paper by Hansen and Hurwitz (1946). The first sample is taken by mail and the response rate W_1 is expected to be 50%. The precision desired is that which would be given by a simple random sample of size 1000 if there were no nonresponse. The cost of mailing a questionnaire is 10 cents, and the cost of processing the completed questionnaire is 40 cents. To carry out a personal interview costs $4.10.

How many questionnaires should be sent out and what percentage of the nonrespondents should be interviewed?

In terms of the cost function (13.12) the unit costs in dollars are as follows:

c_0 = cost of first attempt   = 0.1
c_1 = cost of processing data for a respondent = 0.4
c_2 = cost of obtaining and processing data
     for a nonrespondent   = 4.5

The optimum n and k can be found from (13.17) and (13.18). If the variances S^2 and S_2^2 are assumed equal and N is assumed to be large, then

$$k_{opt} = \sqrt{\frac{c_2(1 - W_2)}{c_0 + c_1 W_1}} = \sqrt{\frac{(4.5)(0.5)}{0.1 + (0.4)(0.5)}} = \sqrt{7.5} = 2.739$$

$$n_{opt} = \frac{S^2[1 + (k - 1)W_2]}{V} = 1000\{1 + (1.739)(0.5)\}$$

$$= 1870$$

Note that we have put $S^2/V = 1000$, or $V = S^2/1000$, since this is the variance that the sample mean would have if a sample of 1000 were taken and complete response were obtained.

Consequently, 1870 questionnaires should be mailed. Of the 935 that are not returned, we interview a random subsample of 935/2.739, or 341. The cost is $2095.

As Durbin (1954) has pointed out, subsampling is unlikely to show a marked profit unless c_2 is large in relation to $(c_0 + c_1 W_1)$. The two quantities are comparable, since $(c_0 + c_1 W_1)$ is the expected cost per unit of making the first attempt and processing the results and c_2 has the same meaning for the second attempt. From the equations it can be shown that the ratio of the cost of obtaining a prescribed V with $k = 1$ (no subsampling) to the minimum cost for optimum k is

$$\frac{S^2(c_0 + c_1 W_1 + c_2 W_2)}{[\sqrt{(S^2 - W_2 S_2^2)(c_0 + c_1 W_1)} + \sqrt{c_2 W_2 S_2}]^2} = \frac{c_0 + c_1 W_1 + c_2 W_2}{[\sqrt{W_1(c_0 + c_1 W_1)} + \sqrt{c_2 W_2}]^2}$$

if S^2 and S_2^2 are approximately equal. If r is the ratio of c_2 to $(c_0 + c_1 W_1)$, the cost ratio becomes

$$\frac{1 + rW_2}{(\sqrt{W_1} + \sqrt{r W_2})^2}$$

For instance, if $r = 4$, the cost ratio is 1.029 for $W_1 = 0.5$, 1.074 for

$W_1 = 0.8$, and 1.061 for $W_1 = 0.9$. If, however, S^2 is substantially greater than $S_2{}^2$, there is more to be gained from subsampling.

With stratified sampling, the optimum values of the n_h and the k_h in the individual strata are rather complex. A good approximation is to estimate first, by the methods in sections 5.5 and 5.6, the sample sizes n_{oh} that would be required in the strata if there were no nonresponse. Now from (13.18), if $W_2 = 0$, we have

$$n_o = \frac{NS^2}{NV + S^2}$$

Hence (13.18) can be rewritten as

$$n_{opt} = n_o \left[1 + \frac{(k - 1)W_2 S_2{}^2}{S^2} \right]$$

This equation, applied separately to each stratum, gives an approximation to the optimum n_h. The values of k_h are found by applying (13.17) in each stratum.

These techniques can be used with ratio or regression estimates. With the ratio estimate, the quantities S^2 and $S_2{}^2$ are replaced by $S_d{}^2$ and $S_{2d}{}^2$, where $d_i = y_i - Rx_i$. With a regression estimate, S^2 becomes $S^2(1 - \rho^2)$ and $S_2{}^2$ becomes $S_2{}^2(1 - \rho^2)$.

13.7 ADJUSTMENTS FOR BIAS WITHOUT CALL-BACKS

An ingenious method of diminishing the biases present in the results of the first call was suggested by Hartley (1946) and developed by Politz and Simmons (1949, 1950) and Simmons (1954). Suppose that all calls are made during the evening on the six week-nights. The respondent is asked whether he was at home, at the time of the interview, on each of the five preceding week-nights. If the respondent states that he was at home t nights out of five, the ratio $(t + 1)/6$ is taken as an estimate of the frequency π with which he is at home during interviewing hours.

The results from the first call are sorted into six groups according to the value of t, (0, 1, 2, 3, 4, 5). In the tth group let n_t be the number of interviews obtained and $\bar{y}_t$, the item mean. The Politz-Simmons estimate of the population mean μ is

$$\bar{y}_{PS} = \frac{\sum\limits_{t=0}^{5} 6n_t \bar{y}_t/(t + 1)}{\sum\limits_{t=0}^{5} 6n_t/(t + 1)}$$

This approach recognizes that the first call results are unduly weighted with persons who are at home most of the time. Since a person who is at home, on the average, a proportion π of the time has a relative chance

π of appearing in the sample, his response should receive a weight $1/\pi$. The quantity $6/(t + 1)$ is used as an estimate of $1/\pi$. Thus $\bar{y}_{PS}$ is less biased than the sample mean $\bar{y}$ from the first call, but its variance is greater, because an unweighted mean is replaced by a weighted mean with estimated weights.

In presenting the mean and variance of $\bar{y}_{PS}$, we use the notation of section 13.5. The population is divided into classes, people in the jth class being at home a fraction π_j of the time. Note that the tth group (i.e., persons at home t nights out of the preceding five) will contain persons from various classes. Let n_{jt}, $\bar{y}_{jt}$ be the number and the item mean for those in class j and group t. Then $\bar{y}_{PS}$ may be written as follows:

$$\bar{y}_{PS} = \frac{\sum\sum 6n_{jt}\bar{y}_{jt}/(t + 1)}{\sum\sum 6n_{jt}/(t + 1)} = \frac{N}{D} \quad \text{(say)}$$

This is a ratio type of estimate. In large samples its mean is approximately $E(N)/E(D)$.

If n_o is the initial size of sample (responses plus not-at-homes) and n_j is the number from class j who are interviewed, the following assumptions are made:

(i) $\dfrac{n_j}{n_o}$ is a binomial estimate of $p_j\pi_j$

(ii) $E(n_{jt} \mid n_j) = n_j \dfrac{5!}{t!\,(5 - t)!} \pi_j^{\,t}(1 - \pi_j)^{5-t}$

(iii) $E(\bar{y}_{jt}) = \mu_j$, for any j and t

Assumption (ii) is open to question. Without giving a detailed discussion, it assumes that people report correctly whether they were at home. For given j, using assumption (ii),

$$E\sum_{t=1}^{5} n_{jt}\left(\frac{6}{t + 1}\right) = n_j \sum_{t=1}^{5} \left(\frac{6}{t + 1}\right)\frac{5!}{t!\,(5 - t)!} \pi_j^{\,t}(1 - \pi_j)^{5-t}$$

$$= \frac{n_j}{\pi_j}[1 - (1 - \pi_j)^6]$$

Hence

$$E(D) = \sum_{j=1}^{r} \frac{E(n_j)}{\pi_j}[1 - (1 - \pi_j)^6] = n_o \sum_{j=1}^{r} p_j[1 - (1 - \pi_j)^6]$$

using assumption (i). Further, since $E(\bar{y}_{jt}) = \mu_j$ for any j and t, this gives the result

$$E(\bar{y}_{PS}) = \bar{\mu}_{PS} \doteq \frac{\sum\limits_{j=1}^{r} p_j\mu_j[1 - (1 - \pi_j)^6]}{\sum\limits_{j=1}^{r} p_j[1 - (1 - \pi_j)^6]}$$

Since the true mean $\bar{\mu} = \Sigma\, p_j\mu_j$, some bias remains in $\bar{y}_{PS}$. In a certain sense, this estimate has the same bias as $\bar{y}_6$, the sample mean given by the call-back method with a requirement that as many as six calls be made if necessary. In section 13.5, equation 13.8, it was shown that the call-back method, with a total of i calls, gives an unbiased estimate of $\bar{\mu}_i = \Sigma\, w_{ij}p_j\mu_j / \Sigma\, w_{ij}p_j$, where w_{ij} is the probability that a person in class j who falls in the sample will be interviewed. Now $w_{1j} = \pi_j$. If at subsequent calls the probability of finding at home a person not previously reached remains at π_j, then

$$w_{ij} = [1 - (1 - \pi_j)^i]$$

so that $\bar{\mu}_{PS} = \bar{\mu}_6$. However, with the call-back method the probability of an interview at a later call may be greater than π_j as a result of information obtained by the interviewer at the first or earlier calls. In this event the call-back method has less bias after six calls.

The variance of $\bar{y}_{PS}$ is rather complicated. With the usual approximation for a ratio estimate, it may be expressed, following Deming (1953), as

$$V(\bar{y}_{PS}) \doteq \frac{1}{n_oU} \left\{ \Sigma\, \pi_j p_j B_j [\sigma_j{}^2 + (\mu_j - \bar{\mu}_{PS})^2] \right.$$
$$\left. + (n_o - 1) \Sigma\, (\pi_j p_j)^2 (B_j - A_j{}^2)(\mu_j - \bar{\mu}_{PS})^2 \right\}$$

where

$$U = 1 - \Sigma\, p_j(1 - \pi_j)^6$$

$$A_j = \frac{1}{\pi_j} [1 - (1 - \pi_j)^6]$$

$$B_j = \sum_{t=0}^{5} \left[\frac{6}{(1 + t)} \right]^2 \frac{5!}{t!\,(5 - t)!}\, \pi_j{}^t(1 - \pi_j)^{5-t}$$

Although this expression is difficult to appraise without applying it to specific populations, two comments can be made. If the μ_j do not differ greatly, that is, if the bias from first calls is moderate, the dominating term is the first:

$$\frac{1}{n_oU} \Sigma\, \pi_j p_j B_j \sigma_j{}^2$$

This expression tends to be 25 to 35% higher than the variance of the unweighted mean of the first calls. Also, $V(\bar{y}_{PS})$ contains a term that does not decrease as n_o increases and becomes important in very large samples.

To summarize, comparisons made on simulated populations by Deming (1953), Durbin (1954), and this author suggest that this method shows to best advantage, in relation to call-backs, when the biases from early calls are substantial and the sample is large. The reductions in MSE for the same outlay are small, however, unless call-backs cost substantially more than postulated here. The Politz-Simmons technique has the advantage of saving time. Errors and incompleteness in the values of t, not considered in the analysis, are a disadvantage. The method may also be applied, as suggested by Simmons (1954), in conjunction with several call-backs.

Several other methods for mitigating the "not-at-home" bias have been proposed. Bartholomew's (1961) applies to a survey with two calls. He supposes that, for those not at home on the first call, the interviewer, by careful inquiry, can make the probability of finding them on the second call approximately equal. If this is so, the n_2 persons interviewed at the second call are a random subsample of the $(n_o - n_1)$ persons missed at the first call. Hence $[n_1 \bar{y}_1 + (n_o - n_1)\bar{y}_2]/n_o$ is an unbiased estimate of the mean of the initial target sample. The method worked well on some British surveys to which Bartholomew applied it. In repeated surveys Kish and Hess (1959) suggest that nonresponses from recent surveys may serve as a replacement for nonresponses in a current survey. Wherever the bias from early calls shows a systematic pattern, as in Table 13.1, Hendricks (1949) has outlined extrapolation methods to estimate the average results that would be given by nonrespondents.

13.8 A MATHEMATICAL MODEL FOR ERRORS OF MEASUREMENT

Conceptually, we can imagine that a large number of independent repetitions of the measurement on the ith unit are possible. Let $y_{i\alpha}$ be the value obtained in the αth repetition. Then

$$y_{i\alpha} = \mu_i + e_{i\alpha}$$

where μ_i = correct value,

$e_{i\alpha}$ = error of measurement.

The idea of a "correct value" requires a little discussion. With some items the concept is simple and concrete. For instance, in a inventory taken by sampling the correct value may be the number of fan belts lying on a shelf at 12 noon on a specified day. In some cases the correct value can be defined operationally. A person's correct diastolic blood pressure at a specified time might be defined as the value obtained when it is measured by a certain standard instrument under carefully prescribed conditions. We may realize, however, that our standard instrument is itself subject to errors of measurement, and we may expect that in course of time a more precise instrument will be developed. With other items, for instance some aspect of an employee's attitude toward his employer or of a person's feelings of ability to cope with his day-to-day problems, nobody may claim to have a satisfactory method of measuring the "correct value." Nevertheless, the concept is useful even in such cases.

Under repeated measurements of the same unit, the errors $e_{i\alpha}$ will follow a frequency distribution. For the ith unit, let $e_{i\alpha}$ have mean β_i and variance σ_i^2. The term β_i represents a bias in the measurements. The magnitudes of β_i and σ_i^2 will, of course, depend on the nature of the item being measured and on the measuring instrument. They may depend also on numerous other factors. With human populations the prevailing economic and political climate and the amount and type of advance publicity received by the survey may influence the responses to the questionnaire.

The next step is to consider how the errors of measurement change when we move from one unit to another. Various complications can arise.

For the bias component β_i, there may be a constant bias, say, $E(\beta_i) = \beta$, that affects all units in the population. There will also be a component $(\beta_i - \beta)$ that follows a frequency distribution over the population. This component may be correlated with the correct value μ_i; for instance, the measuring device may consistently underestimate high values of μ_i and overestimate low values.

There may be a correlation between the values of $e_{i\alpha}$ on different units in the same sample. The simplest example is the "interviewer bias." Dramatic differences are sometimes found in the mean values of $y_{i\alpha}$ obtained by different interviewers who are sampling comparable parts of the same population [see Lienau (1941), Mahalanobis (1946), and Barr (1957)].

A similar effect has appeared when samples of a growing crop are cut by different teams and when chemical or biological analyses are done in different laboratories. The human factor is not the only cause for correlations among units that are measured at about the same time. Many measuring processes are affected by the weather; some use raw materials whose quality varies from batch to batch. In estimating the current sale price of homes built some years ago, Hansen, Hurwitz, and Bershad (1961) point out that if some houses in the sample have been sold recently their prices establish a level that guides the interviewer and the householder in assigning values to houses that have not been sold for many years. In fact, the average price recorded for the sample may depend on the order in which the recently sold houses appear in the sample.

In order to handle these intrasample correlations in their most general terms, a more complex model than that presented here is required. In particular, the notation for $e_{i\alpha}$ and β_i would have to indicate that their values may depend on the other units present in the sample. However, the types of correlation that are believed to be most common in practice can be represented by the present model or by simple extensions of it.

The components of the error of measurement are summarized in Table 13.11.

We have noted further that values of β_i and $d_{i\alpha}$ on different units in the same sample may be correlated with one another.

TABLE 13.11

COMPONENTS OF THE ERROR OF MEASUREMENT ON THE ith UNIT

Symbol	Nature of Component
β	Constant bias over all units
$\beta_i - \beta$	Variable component of bias, which follows some frequency distribution with mean zero as i varies and may be correlated with the correct value μ_i
$d_{i\alpha} = e_{i\alpha} - \beta_i$	Fluctuating component of error, which follows some frequency distribution with mean zero and variance σ_i^2 as α varies for fixed i

Models that are in general similar to the above have been developed by Hansen et al. (1951), Sukhatme and Seth (1952) and Hansen, Hurwitz, and Bershad (1961).

13.9   EFFECTS OF CONSTANT BIAS

Suppose that the measurements y_i on all units are subject to a constant bias β whose magnitude is unknown. Then the mean $\bar{y}$ of a simple random sample is also subject to bias β. In the estimated error variance, which we attach to the sample mean, the bias cancels out, since this estimate is derived from a sum of squares of terms $(y_i - \bar{y})^2$. Consequently, the usual computation of confidence limits for $\bar{Y}$ from the sample data takes no account of the bias. The same results hold in stratified random sampling.

The situation is essentially the same with regression and ratio estimates. Consider the regression estimate

$$\bar{y}_{lr} = \bar{y} + b(\bar{X} - \bar{x})$$

where both the y_i and the x_i may be subject to constant biases β_y and β_x, respectively. Since the least squares estimate b remains unchanged and since the bias β_x cancels out of the term $(\bar{X} - \bar{x})$, it follows that $\bar{y}_{lr}$ is subject to a bias β_y. It is easy to verify that the sample estimate of $V(\bar{y}_{1r})$ contains no contribution due to the biases.

With the ratio estimate

$$\bar{y}_R = \frac{\bar{y}}{\bar{x}} \, \bar{X}$$

the bias is also β_y, to a first approximation, since in large samples $E(\bar{X}/\bar{x})$ is approximately 1 even if the x_i are subject to a constant bias. In large samples the sample estimate of variance

$$v(\bar{y}_R) = \frac{(N - n)}{Nn} \frac{\sum (y_i - \hat{R}x_i)^2}{n - 1}$$

will be almost free from bias as an estimate of

$$E(\bar{y}_R - \bar{Y})^2$$

that is, as an estimate of the variance about the *biased* mean $\bar{Y}$.

To summarize, a constant bias passes undetected by the sample data. As we have seen (section 1.7), the 95% confidence probabilities are almost unaffected if the ratio of β_y to the standard error of the estimated mean is less than 0.1, but as the ratio increases beyond this value the computation of confidence limits becomes misleading. Estimates of *change* from one time period to another, or from one stratum to another, remain unbiased, provided that the bias is constant throughout.

13.10 EFFECTS OF ERRORS THAT ARE UNCORRELATED WITHIN THE SAMPLE

If constant bias is ignored and errors of measurement are uncorrelated within the sample, the ordinary formulas for estimating the standard errors of sample estimates remain valid, provided that fpc terms are negligible. This result is proved for simple random sampling.

The model can be written

$$y_{i\alpha} = \mu_i + \beta_i + d_{i\alpha} = \mu_i' + d_{i\alpha} \tag{13.19}$$

where $\mu_i' = \mu_i + \beta_i$ is the average value given by the measuring process on the ith unit. Since constant bias is ignored,

$$E(\beta_i) = 0, \qquad E(\mu_i') = \mu = \text{correct population mean}$$

We suppose, as holds in most surveys, that only one measurement is made on each unit. The sample means of $y_{i\alpha}$, μ_i', and $d_{i\alpha}$ are denoted by $\bar{y}_\alpha$, $\bar{\mu}'$, and $\bar{d}_\alpha$. From (13.19)

$$\bar{y}_\alpha - \mu = (\bar{\mu}' - \mu) + \bar{d}_\alpha$$

Since $E(d_{i\alpha} \mid i) = 0$, by the definition of $d_{i\alpha}$, it follows that $\bar{y}_\alpha$ is an unbiased estimate of μ under simple random sampling. Further,

$$(\bar{y}_\alpha - \mu)^2 = (\bar{\mu}' - \mu)^2 + \bar{d}_\alpha{}^2 + 2\bar{d}_\alpha(\bar{\mu}' - \mu) \qquad (13.20)$$

Hence

$$V(\bar{y}_\alpha) = E(\bar{\mu}' - \mu)^2 + E(\bar{d}_\alpha{}^2) \qquad (13.21)$$

the cross-product term vanishing because the $d_{i\alpha}$ have means zero for any i.

Average first over repeated measurements on the same set of n units. Since the $d_{i\alpha}$ on different units are independent,

$$E(\bar{d}_\alpha)^2 = \frac{1}{n^2} \sum_i^n \sigma_i{}^2$$

When we average subsequently over all simple random samples, we have

$$V(\bar{y}_\alpha) = \frac{1-f}{n} \frac{\sum_i^N (\mu_i' - \mu)^2}{N-1} + \frac{1}{nN} \sum_i^N \sigma_i{}^2$$

$$= \frac{1-f}{n} S_{\mu'}{}^2 + \frac{1}{n} \sigma_d{}^2 \qquad (13.22)$$

where $\sigma_d{}^2$ denotes the average of the variances of the errors of measurement.

Note that $S_{\mu'}{}^2$ is the population variance of $(\mu_i + \beta_i)$. It will usually be larger than $S_\mu{}^2$, the population variance of the correct values μ_i, though it can be smaller if μ_i and β_i are negatively correlated. If $n = N$, that is, the sample is a complete census, $V(\bar{y}_\alpha)$ does not vanish, because the errors of measurement give a contribution $\sigma_d{}^2/N$.

Equation 13.22 produces an interesting result, due to Hansen, Hurwitz, and Bershad (1961), when a population proportion P is being estimated. For any unit, let the correct value μ_i be 1 if the unit is in class C and zero otherwise, with

$$E(\mu_i) = P, \qquad S_\mu{}^2 = \frac{\sum_i^N (\mu_i - \mu)^2}{N-1} = \frac{N}{N-1} PQ \qquad (13.23)$$

If errors of measurement occur, this means that some units are incorrectly classified. For any such unit, the recorded value $y_{i\alpha}$ in repeated measurements is sometimes 1 and sometimes 0. Let P_i denote the proportion of measurements on the ith unit for which $y_{i\alpha} = 1$. Then $y_{i\alpha}$ is a binomial variate with mean $\mu_i' = P_i$, and the variance of $d_{i\alpha}$ is P_iQ_i. Hence, if $p_\alpha = \bar{y}_\alpha$ is the sample estimate, (13.22) becomes

$$V(p_\alpha) = \frac{1 - f}{n} \frac{\sum\limits_{i}^{N}(P_i - P)^2}{N - 1} + \frac{1}{nN} \sum\limits_{i}^{N} P_iQ_i \qquad (13.22)$$

$$< \frac{1}{n(N - 1)}\left[\sum\limits_{i}^{N}(P_i - P)^2 + \sum\limits_{i}^{N} P_iQ_i\right]$$

$$= \frac{1}{n(N - 1)}\left(\sum\limits_{i}^{N} P_i^2 - NP^2 + \sum\limits_{i}^{N} P_i - \sum\limits_{i}^{N} P_i^2\right)$$

$$= \frac{N}{n(N - 1)} PQ = \frac{S_\mu^2}{n} \qquad (13.24)$$

using (13.23).

The quantity S_μ^2/n is the variance that would be obtained for $V(p_\alpha)$ if no errors in classification occurred and if n/N were negligible. When errors of classification are present, the result in (13.24) that $V(p_\alpha) \leq S_\mu^2/n$ is reassuring. The result may appear paradoxical, however, since we might expect these errors to have more effect on $V(p_\alpha)$. The explanation is that in the estimation of a proportion μ_i and β_i are always negatively correlated. When $\mu_i = 1$, $\beta_i \leq 0$, since $P_i = (\mu_i + \beta_i) \leq 1$, and when $\mu_i = 0$, $\beta_i \geq 0$, since $P_i \geq 0$.

To revert to the case of a continuous variable, the ordinary formula for the sample estimate of $V(\bar{y}_\alpha)$ is

$$v(\bar{y}_\alpha) = \frac{1 - f}{n} s^2 = \frac{1 - f}{n} \frac{\sum\limits_{i}^{n}(y_{i\alpha} - \bar{y}_\alpha)^2}{n - 1}$$

From (13.19)

$$y_{i\alpha} - \bar{y}_\alpha = (\mu_i' - \bar{\mu}') + (d_{i\alpha} - \bar{d}_\alpha)$$

By squaring and averaging first over repeated measurements and then over different selections of the sample, we obtain

$$E(s^2) = E\left[\frac{\sum\limits^{n}(y_{i\alpha} - \bar{y}_\alpha)^2}{n - 1}\right] = S_\mu^2 + \sigma_d^2$$

Hence

$$Ev(\bar{y}_\alpha) = \frac{1 - f}{n} S_\mu^2 + \frac{1 - f}{n} \sigma_d^2 \qquad (13.25)$$

By comparison with (13.22), we see that $v(\bar{y}_\alpha)$ has a negative bias of amount σ_d^2/N. On the other hand, if the fpc term $(1 - f)$ is omitted from $v(\bar{y}_\alpha)$, we obtain an overestimate of amount S_μ^2/N.

In the same way it can be shown that the formulas given in preceding chapters for the sample estimates of error variances remain valid for stratified sampling and for multistage sampling and that the approximate formulas for ratio and regression estimates remain valid in large samples, provided that errors of measurement in $y_{i\alpha}$ and $x_{i\alpha}$ are uncorrelated within the sample and that the fpc's can be ignored. (The error in $y_{i\alpha}$ may be correlated with that in the corresponding $x_{i\alpha}$.)

These results raise the question: in what kinds of surveys are errors of measurement uncorrelated within the sample? Since intrasample correlations can enter in the process of measurement, in copying the measurements, in editing and coding, particularly if subjective decisions are involved, and in transferring the data to tabulating equipment, the assumption that there is no correlation cannot be made glibly. The risk of correlation should, however, be minimized in surveys taken from records, in self-filled questionnaires (as in mail surveys) in which individuals in the same sample do not consult one another, and in surveys of inanimate populations in which the measurement is objective.

13.11   EFFECTS OF INTRASAMPLE CORRELATION BETWEEN ERRORS

Under the model

$$y_{i\alpha} = \mu_i + \beta_i + d_{i\alpha} = \mu_i' + d_{i\alpha}$$

some of the most common types of intrasample correlation can be represented by supposing that values of $d_{i\alpha}$ for units in the same sample are correlated. In finding $V(\bar{y}_\alpha)$, the analysis given in section 13.8 proceeds without change down to equation (13.21).

Now

$$V(\bar{y}_\alpha) = E(\bar{\mu}' - \mu)^2 + E(\bar{d}_\alpha^2) \tag{13.21}$$

$$\bar{d}_\alpha^2 = \frac{1}{n^2}\left(\sum_i^n d_{i\alpha}^2 + 2\sum_{j>i}^n d_{i\alpha}d_{j\alpha}\right)$$

Hence

$$E(\bar{d}_\alpha^2) = \frac{1}{n}\sigma_d^2 + \frac{2n(n-1)}{2n^2}E(d_{i\alpha}d_{j\alpha}) \tag{13.26}$$

where the products are taken over all pairs of units in the same sample. By analogy with cluster sampling, the average intrasample correlation coefficient ρ_w may be defined by the equation

$$E(d_{i\alpha}d_{j\alpha}) = \rho_w\sigma_d^2$$

This gives, from (13.22) and (13.26),

$$V(\bar{y}_\alpha) = \frac{1-f}{n}S_\mu^2 + \frac{\sigma_d^2}{n}[1 + (n-1)\rho_w] \tag{13.27}$$

The average value of $v(\bar{y}_\alpha)$ is found in the same way to be

$$Ev(\bar{y}_\alpha) = \frac{1-f}{n} S_{\mu'}^2 + \frac{1-f}{n} \sigma_d^2(1 - \rho_w) \qquad (13.28)$$

Since ρ_w is likely to be positive for most types of measurement error, the standard formula $v(\bar{y}_\alpha)$ is usually an underestimate. Whether the underestimation is serious depends on the relative sizes of $S_{\mu'}^2$, σ_d^2 and $n\rho_w$.

This model represents only the simplest type of intrasample correlation. With stratified sampling, for instance, a coder may process results from several strata and through a misunderstanding of instructions may introduce correlated errors that extend over the strata. The mathematical model can be adapted to apply to situations of this type.

13.12 SUMMARY OF THE EFFECTS OF ERRORS OF MEASUREMENT

In terms of the model, the mean $\bar{y}$ of a simple random sample would be unbiased, with variance S_{μ}^2/n (ignoring the fpc), if all measurements were fully accurate. As a result of the types of errors of measurement discussed here, the mean may be subject to a bias of amount β, and its mean square error is

$$\text{MSE}(\bar{y}_\alpha) = \frac{1}{n} \{S_{\mu'}^2 + \sigma_d^2[1 + (n-1)\rho_w]\} + \beta^2 \qquad (13.29)$$

where $\mu_i' = \mu_i + \beta_i$.

Formula 13.29 contains two terms, $S_{\mu'}^2/n$ and $\sigma_d^2(1 - \rho_w)/n$, that decrease as $1/n$. The remaining two terms, $\rho_w\sigma_d^2$ and β^2, appear at first sight to be independent of n. This is probably an oversimplification. Any material change in the size of sample may require a change in the field methods of measurement, and this may affect ρ_w and β^2. However, these two terms should change relatively slowly, if at all, with n. Thus in large samples the MSE is likely to be dominated by these two terms, the ordinary sampling variance becoming unimportant and misleading as a guide to the real accuracy of the results.

13.13 THE STUDY OF ERRORS OF MEASUREMENT

In recent years much of the research on sampling practice has been devoted to the study of errors of measurement. The objectives are to discover the components that make a large contribution to the MSE and to find ways of decreasing these contributions. Some of the principal methods are described in this and the following sections. It is already clear that progress will be slow and expensive. One reason is that, as already mentioned, the measurement errors depend intimately both on the items and on the measuring process. Results about measurement errors found in one survey can seldom be assumed to apply to other surveys.

Ideally, the best method of studying errors of measurement is to obtain the correct values μ_i. In practice, this approach is limited to items for which a feasible method of finding μ_i exists and by problems of expense and execution. Examples are given by Belloc (1954), who compared data on hospitalization as reported in household interviews with the hospital records for the individual, and by Gray (1955), who compared employees' statements of sick leave with the personnel office records. Checks of this type—sometimes called "record-checks"—are possible with items such as age, occupation, number of years of schooling, and price paid for car. One difficulty is that sometimes the records contain no exact match of the person interviewed.

Failing a method of determining the correct value, an alternative is to remeasure by an independent method that is considered more accurate. Kish and Lansing (1954) engaged professional appraisers to estimate the selling prices of homes that had already been reported by the home owners. In surveys of illness respondents' replies have been compared either with doctors' records on the respondents or with the results of a complete medical examination [Sagen, Dunham, and Simmons (1959), Trussell and Elinson (1959)]. The results of such comparisons are not easy to interpret in terms of the model, since the superior instrument is itself subject to measurement errors, but the comparisons will at least indicate the items for which the routine instrument agrees well with the superior instrument and those for which it does not.

Another possibility in household surveys is to reinterview a subsample of the respondents. In one variant of the method the reinterviewing team is a more accurate measuring instrument, the best interviewers being chosen and the questionnaire being more detailed and probing. In this approach the emphasis is on discovering the items for which the first response was inaccurate and the reasons for the inaccuracy. In another variant the second team is intended to be of the same quality as the first. If the two teams could be regarded as giving two independent measurements, $y_{i\alpha} = \mu_i' + d_{i\alpha}$ and $y_{i\alpha'} = \mu_i' + d_{i\alpha'}$, the squared difference $(y_{i\alpha} - y_{i\alpha'})^2/2$ would be an estimate of the response variance σ_i^2 for this item. Both approaches face the difficulty that the second response may not be independent of the first. The respondent may simply repeat from memory the answer given on the first occasion, so that the discrepancies underestimate σ_i^2. If the time interval between the two visits is lengthened in order to minimize this effect, the respondent on the second occasion may not remember clearly his situation at the earlier time, so that the discrepancies overestimate σ_i^2.

Occasionally, over-all comparisons between the results of two different surveys are feasible. For a number of items, the results of the U.S. Census can be compared with those given by the Current Population Survey taken at the same time. Since the Survey is considered more accurate, particularly for items difficult to measure, rough estimates of the measurement bias β in the Census data can be made [Hansen, Hurwitz, and Bershad (1961)]. A number of comparisons between the results of quota samples and probability samples are discussed by Stephan and McCarthy (1958).

13.14 INTERPENETRATING SUBSAMPLES

This technique, particularly useful for the study of correlated errors, was proposed by Mahalanobis (1946). To present it in the simplest terms, a random sample of n units is divided *at random* into k subsamples, each subsample containing $m = n/k$ units. The field work and processing of the sample are planned so that there is no correlation between the errors of measurement of any two units in different subsamples. For instance, suppose that the correlation with which we have to deal arises solely from biases of the interviewers. If each of k interviewers is assigned to a different subsample and if there is no correlation between errors of measurement for different interviewers, we have an example of the technique.

With the same mathematical model, it is convenient to label the units by double subscripts. Let

$$y_{ij\alpha} = \mu'_{ij} + d_{ij\alpha}$$

where i denotes the subsample (interviewer) and j the member within the subsample. The fpc is ignored.

Since the ith subsample is a random subsample, it is itself a simple random sample of size m. Hence, by (13.27), the variance of its mean is

$$V(\bar{y}_{i\alpha}) = \frac{1}{m} \{S_{\mu'}^2 + \sigma_d^2[1 + (m - 1)\rho_w]\}$$

where ρ_w is the correlation between the $d_{ij\alpha}$ obtained by the same interviewer. Since errors are independent in the different subsamples,

$$V(\bar{y}_\alpha) = \frac{1}{k} V(\bar{y}_{i\alpha}) = \frac{1}{n} \{S_{\mu'}^2 + \sigma_d^2[1 + (m - 1)\rho_w]\} \qquad (13.30)$$

From the sample results, we can compute an analysis of variance into the components "between interviewers (subsamples)" and "within interviewers." It is easy to verify that the expected values of the mean squares work out as in Table 13.12.

TABLE 13.12

EXPECTATIONS OF THE MEAN SQUARES (ON A SINGLE-UNIT BASIS)

	df	ms	E(ms)
Between interviewers (subsamples)	$k - 1$	$s_b^2 = \dfrac{m \sum (\bar{y}_{i\alpha} - \bar{y}_\alpha)^2}{k - 1}$	$s_{\mu'}^2 + \sigma_d^2[1 + (m - 1)\rho_w]$
Within interviewers	$k(m - 1)$	$s_w^2 = \dfrac{\sum \sum (y_{ij\alpha} - \bar{y}_{i\alpha})^2}{k(m - 1)}$	$s_{\mu'}^2 + \sigma_d^2(1 - \rho_w)$

This analysis contains two important results. By comparison with (13.30) we see that s_b^2/n is an unbiased estimate of $V(\bar{y}_\alpha)$. Thus the method provides an estimate of error that takes account of interviewer biases. The analysis also supplies information about ρ_w. The F-ratio s_b^2/s_w^2 gives a test of significance of the null hypothesis $\rho_w = 0$. The quantity $(s_b^2 - s_w^2)/m$ is an unbiased estimate of $\rho_w \sigma_d^2$. This result enables us to answer the question: how much do the interviewer biases contribute to $V(\bar{y}_\alpha)$? The situation in which there are no interviewer biases can be represented by putting $\rho_w = 0$ and assuming that σ_d^2 remains unchanged. Under this supposition $V(\bar{y}_\alpha)$ becomes

$$V'(\bar{y}_\alpha) = \frac{1}{n}(S_{\mu'}^2 + \sigma_d^2)$$

An unbiased estimate is

$$v'(\bar{y}_\alpha) = \frac{1}{n}\left[s_w^2 + \frac{(s_b^2 - s_w^2)}{m}\right] = \frac{1}{n}\frac{[(m - 1)s_w^2 + s_b^2]}{m}$$

This is to be compared with s_b^2/n, an estimate of the actual $V(\bar{y}_\alpha)$.

An alternative model that produces the same results represents the bias of the ith interviewer by a term g_i, which has mean zero and variance σ_I^2 as i varies. Thus

$$y_{ij\alpha} = \mu_{ij}' + g_i + d_{ij\alpha} \tag{13.31}$$

where the $d_{ij\alpha}$ are now uncorrelated with each other and with the g_i. For this model,

$$V(\bar{y}_\alpha) = \frac{1}{n}(S_{\mu'}^2 + m\sigma_I^2 + \sigma_d^2) \tag{13.32}$$

and $s_b{}^2$ in the analysis of variance is found to be an unbiased estimate of $nV(\bar{y}_\alpha)$ as before. The situation in which interviewer biases are removed is represented by deleting g_i and replacing $\sigma_d{}^2$ by $(\sigma_I{}^2 + \sigma_d{}^2)$ to leave the error variance of the interviewer's estimate of a single unit unchanged.

As the name *interpenetrating* subsamples implies, it is essential that the subsamples be chosen at random. A common practice is to assign each interviewer to the units lying in a small geographic area near his home, in order to decrease travel costs. Any real differences between the averages $\bar{y}_i$ for different areas then appear in the analysis of variance as if they were interviewer biases. Thus $s_b{}^2/n$ becomes an overestimate of $V(\bar{y}_\alpha)$.

The technique extends to stratified and multistage sampling. If the sole interest is in an unbiased estimate of $V(\bar{y}_\alpha)$, all that is necessary is that the sample consist of a number of subsamples of the same structure in which we are sure that errors of measurement are independent in different subsamples. Strictly, this requires that different interviewing teams, supervisors, and data processors be used in different subsamples. If $\bar{y}_{i\alpha}$ is the mean of the ith subsample, the quantity $\Sigma(\bar{y}_{i\alpha} - \bar{y}_\alpha)^2/k(k-1)$ is an unbiased estimate of $V(\bar{y}_\alpha)$, with $(k-1)$ df. This result holds because the subsample can be regarded as a single complex sampling unit, the sample being in effect a simple random sample of these complex units, with uncorrelated errors of measurement between different complex units. Consequently, the results in section 13.10 apply.

Numerous applications of this method, sometimes called *replicated sampling*, are described by Deming (1960), who has used the method extensively. For other discussions of its advantages, see Jones (1955) and Koop (1960). Travel costs of interviewers are usually increased by interpenetration, but this can be mitigated if the sample is stratified into compact areas. For instance, each stratum might consist of two random subsamples, assigned to a different interviewer. Each interviewer is required to travel over the whole stratum instead of over only half the stratum. Every stratum provides 1 df for the estimate of $V(\bar{y}_\alpha)$.

13.15 EXTENSION TO MORE COMPLEX PLANS

In general, the interpretation of the analysis of variance depends on the nature of the plan and must usually be worked out separately. As an illustration, consider a two-stage stratified sample with L strata. In each stratum $n'k$ primary units are selected, each of the k interviewers being assigned to a random subsample of n' primary units. The primary units are assumed to be of equal size. Since the population is compact, each interviewer works in every stratum. The Bengal Labour Enquiry 1941–1942 described by Mahalanobis (1946) and the health survey in the

Arsenal district of Pittsburgh described by Horvitz (1952) were roughly of this type.

In terms of the alternative model in (13.31), the mean for the jth primary unit of the ith interviewer in stratum h may be written

$$\bar{y}_{hij\alpha} = \bar{\mu}_h + g_i + w_{hi} + (\bar{\mu}'_{hij} - \bar{\mu}_h) + \bar{d}_{hij\alpha}$$

where $\bar{\mu}_h$ is the correct mean for the stratum. As before, $\bar{\mu}'_{hij} = \bar{\mu}_{hij} + \bar{\beta}_{hij}$. It is assumed that $(\bar{\mu}'_{hij} - \bar{\mu}_h)$ averages to zero over the stratum and has variance $\sigma_{\bar{\mu}'}^2$. The $\bar{d}_{hij\alpha}$ are uncorrelated, with mean zero for any h, i, j, and variance $\sigma_{\bar{d}}^2$.

The equation contains a new term w_{hi}, denoting an interviewer $\times$ stratum interaction. There is not much evidence that this term is needed to make the model realistic, although, if there are marked differences between strata in economic level, an interviewer might show a differential bias in different strata. The w_{hi} are assumed distributed with mean zero and variance σ_{IS}^2.

The expectations of the mean squares of the useful terms in the analysis of variance work out as follows. The unit of analysis is the mean per subunit for a single primary unit.

	df	ms	E(ms)
Between interviewers	$k - 1$	s_b^2	$\sigma_{\bar{\mu}'}^2 + \sigma_{\bar{d}}^2 + n'\sigma_{IS}^2 + n'L\sigma_I^2$
Interviewers $\times$ strata	$(k - 1)(L - 1)$	s_{IS}^2	$\sigma_{\bar{\mu}'}^2 + \sigma_{\bar{d}}^2 + n'\sigma_{IS}^2$
Between pu within interviewers	$kL(n' - 1)$		$\sigma_{\bar{\mu}'}^2 + \sigma_{\bar{d}}^2$

This analysis enables us to estimate both the components σ_{IS}^2 and σ_I^2. If n/N is negligible, the "between interviewers" mean square gives an unbiased estimate of $kn'LV(\bar{y}_\alpha)$.

Example. In Horvitz' data $L = 6$, $k = 18$, $n' = 1$. The mean squares (in our units) were $s_b^2 = 0.0759$. $s_{IS}^2 = 0.0147$, for number of persons ill per household during the preceding month. Estimate the contribution of interviewer biases to $V(\bar{y}_\alpha)$.

In terms of the model, the analysis of variance gives

$$s_b^2 = 0.0759 \sim \sigma_{\bar{\mu}}^2 + \sigma_{\bar{d}}^2 + \sigma_{IS}^2 + 6\sigma_I^2$$
$$s_{IS}^2 = 0.0147 \sim \sigma_{\bar{\mu}}^2 + \sigma_{\bar{d}}^2 + \sigma_{IS}^2$$

The third term (between pu within interviewers) cannot be computed, since $n' = 1$.

The estimate of σ_I^2 is $(0.0759 - 0.0147)/6 = 0.0102$. With $n' = 1$, it is not possible to estimate σ_{IS}^2. To similate the situation in which there are no interviewer biases, we shall assume that the interviewer's contribution to the error of measurement of a single subunit (household) has a variance $\sigma_{IS}^2 + \sigma_I^2$ but that these contributions are independent from household to household. Since the assignment of an interviewer in a single stratum contained about 26 households, the *total* variance of a mean per primary unit would be

$$\sigma_{\bar{\mu}'}^2 + \sigma_{\bar{d}}^2 + \tfrac{1}{26}(\sigma_{IS}^2 + \sigma_I^2)$$

Unless $\sigma_{IS}^2 = 0$, we cannot estimate this quantity. The quantity

$$0.0147 + \tfrac{1}{26}(0.0102) = 0.0151 \sim \sigma_{\bar{\mu}'}^2 + \sigma_{\bar{d}}^2 + \sigma_{IS}^2 + \tfrac{1}{26}\sigma_I^2$$

is an overestimate which should not be seriously wrong if σ_{IS}^2 is small. This is to be compared with 0.0759, the actual variance on a primary unit mean basis. The contribution of interviewer biases to the total variance is about 80%. The estimate given by Horvitz (1952), who used a different value for s_{IS}^2, is 72%.

13.16 CONTROLLED EXPERIMENTS IMBEDDED IN SURVEYS

An extension of the idea of interpenetrating subsamples is to build into a survey an experimental comparison of some aspect of the measuring process or field operations. Perhaps the oldest example is the split schedule. Two forms q, q' of the questionnaire are prepared, differing in the wording of certain questions or in the order of the questions. In one plan each questionnaire is given to a random half of the units in the sample or in a part of it. For any item, the mean difference $\bar{y}_q - \bar{y}_{q'}$ and its standard error can be computed and a test of the relative bias performed. If appropriate, the variance ratio $s_q^2/s_{q'}^2$ can be tested to see whether one form gives more erratic responses than the other. An alternative plan is to arrange the units in pairs so that both members of a pair are expected to show similar responses. Each questionnaire is given to one member of each pair. If pairing is effective, this plan provides a more precise estimate of $\bar{y}_q - \bar{y}_{q'}$, although a less precise estimate of the variance ratio.

The idea is to make part of the survey a controlled experiment using the precautions, including randomization, that are typical of good experimentation. In more complex surveys considerable care must be exercised in planning to ensure that unbiased estimates of the effects that are of interest are obtainable. Two illustrations are given.

In the 1950 U.S. Census an experiment designed to estimate the effect of interviewer biases was conducted in 24 counties in two states. More than 700 interviewers participated. The counties were divided into 125 areas of average population 6500. An area contained on the average enough work for six interviewers, although the sizes of the areas varied. An area with enough work for k interviewers was divided into $2k$ subareas, two of which were allotted at random to each interviewer. Within each area the interviewer variance can be estimated by an analysis of variance of the kind in Table 13.12. Descriptions and results are given by Hanson and Marks (1958) and Hansen, Hurwitz, and Bershad (1961).

In the example described by Durbin and Stuart (1954) the experiment was the principal purpose of the survey rather than incidental to it. The aims were to estimate (a) the effects of two types of clustering of interviews on response rates, costs of interviewing, and precision, and (b) the effects of interviewer biases in urban surveys in parts of six towns. Three survey agencies supplied two interviewers each for every town, making 3 × 2 × 6 or 36 interviewers in the main part of the experiment. The sampling frame was the Electoral Register, one registration area being sampled in each town.

For the unclustered sample (type 1), a systematic sample of 30 names was drawn from the Register for each interviewer. In type 2 a systematic

TABLE 13.13

DESIGN OF A SURVEY ON CLUSTERING AND INTERVIEWER BIASES

Agency	Town					
	I	II	III	IV	V	VI
A	1	2	1	3	3	2
B	2	3	2	1	1	3
C	3	1	3	2	2	1

sample of 15 names was drawn from each of two polling districts within the area. In type 3 the sample from each polling district was taken from a single street or group of small streets. Thus type 3 has the most clustering, type 2 being intermediate. The over-all design, in a latin square pattern, is given in Table 13.13.

In town II, for instance, the two interviewers from agency A worked on separate type-2 samples, and so on. This cell provides 1 df for "between interviewers" and 2 df for "between clusters within interviewers." The analysis of the effects of clustering, which has several points of interest, is not given here.

These techniques have two advantages. Since money specifically earmarked for field research on measurement or sampling techniques is seldom available, the only way of conducting the research may be to implant it in an ongoing survey. Moreover, its results are more likely to apply to practical conditions if they are obtained in this way. Nevertheless, it is hard to simulate exactly the ordinary conditions of a survey when part of it consists of a controlled experiment. Even if efforts are made to conceal this fact, supervisors and interviewers are likely to be aware that there is something special about part of their work, and a controlled experiment always disrupts the usual procedures in some way or other. Much can be done to ensure useful information if this problem is anticipated and studied in advance.

13.17   SUMMARY

In regard to their effects on the formulas given in preceding chapters, nonsampling errors may be classified as follows:

1. With noncoverage and nonresponse, the most important consequence is that estimates may become biased, because the part of the population that is not reached may differ from the part that is sampled. There is now ample evidence that these biases vary considerably from item to item and from survey to survey, being sometimes negligible and sometimes large. A second consequence is, of course, that the variances of estimates are increased because the sample actually obtained is smaller than the target sample. This factor can be allowed for, at least approximately, in selecting the size of the target sample.

2. Errors of measurement that are independent from unit to unit within the sample and average to zero over the whole population are properly taken into account in the usual formulas for computing the standard errors of the estimates, provided that fpc terms are negligible. Such errors decrease the precision of the estimates, and it is worthwhile to find out whether this decrease is serious.

3. If errors of measurement on different units in the sample are correlated, the usual formulas for the standard errors are biased. The standard errors are likely to be too small, since the correlations are mostly positive in practice. This type of disturbance is easily overlooked and may often have passed unnoticed.

4. A constant bias that effects all units alike is hardest of all to detect. No manipulations of the sample data will reveal this bias.

As this chapter has indicated, the study of these problems is slow and difficult. Nevertheless, a good beginning has been made. Much ingenuity has been shown in devising techniques for the assessment and control of nonsampling errors. Although this is a field in which broad generalizations are hard to attain, information should gradually accumulate about the nature and magnitudes of errors of measurement in different types of survey. More needs to be learned also about what can be accomplished with good training and supervision of the interviewers, with pretesting, with mechanisms to control the quality of the field work, and with a postsurvey appraisal of the successes and weaknesses in the operation.

EXERCISES

13.1 Suppose that, by field methods of different intensities, it is possible to make the "response" stratum consist of 60, 80, 90, or 95% of the whole population. For a percentage that is to be estimated, the true "response" stratum means are: 60% stratum, 40.7; 80% stratum, 43.5; 90% stratum, 44.8; 95% stratum, 45.4; last 5%, 59.0. (a) For a method that samples only the 60% stratum, show that the root mean square error of the estimated percentage for the whole population is

$$\sqrt{(2414/n)} + 28.94$$

where n is the number of completed questionnaires obtained. (b) Show that a root mean square error of 5% cannot be achieved by a method with 60% response but can be obtained with slightly over 100 completed questionnaires for the methods that have a response of 80% or better. (c) If a root mean square error of 2% is prescribed, what methods can achieve it and what sample sizes are needed?

13.2 In 13.1 (c) suppose that it costs $5 per completed questionnaire for the field method that has a 90% response. To obtain a completed questionnaire from the *next* 5% of the population costs $20. For a root mean square error of 2%, is it cheaper to use the method with 90% response rate or that with 95% response rate?

13.3 A population consists of two strata of equal sizes. The probability of finding the respondent at home and willing to be interviewed at any call is 0.9 for persons in stratum 1 and 0.4 for persons in stratum 2. (a) In the notation of section 13.5 show that

$$w_{i1} = 1 - (0.1)^i, \qquad w_{i2} = 1 - (0.6)^i$$

(b) If the original sample size is n_o, compute the total expected number of interviews obtained for 1, 2, 3, 4, and 5 calls. (c) If the relative costs per completed interview at the ith call are 100, 120, 150, 200, and 300 for $i = 1, 2, 3, 4, 5$, respectively, compute the average cost per interview for all interviews obtained up to the ith call. (d) The money available for the survey is enough to pay for 300 completed first calls. If the policy is to insist on i calls, what are the expected total numbers of completed interviews that can be obtained for the same amount of money when $i = 1, 2, 3, 4, 5$?

13.4 In exercise 13.3 persons in stratum 1 have a mean of 40% for some binomial percentage that is being estimated and persons in stratum 2 have a mean of 60%. (a) Compute the bias in the sample mean for $i = 1, 2, 3, 4, 5$ calls. (b) Compute the variances of the sample means for the cost situation in part (d) of exercise 13.3. (To save computing, the variance may be taken as $2600/n_i$, where n_i is the expected total number of interviews obtained.) (c) Which policy gives the lowest MSE?

13.5 In section 13.6 (subsampling of the nonrespondents) show that the product VC, where V is the prescribed variance $V(\bar{y}')$ and C is the expected cost, is

$$S'^2C' + c_2W_2^2S_2^2 + kW_2S_2^2C' + \frac{1}{k}c_2W_2S'^2$$

where
$$S'^2 = S^2 - W_2 S_2^2, \qquad C' = c_0 + c_1 W_1$$
and that the minimum value of VC is
$$(S' \sqrt{C'} + \sqrt{c_2 W_2 S_2})^2$$

13.6 In a survey on poultry and pigs kept in gardens and certain small holdings (Gray, 1957) a postal inquiry with several reminders was followed by interviews of a subsample of nonrespondents. By advance judgment, $k = 2$ was chosen (i.e., a 50% subsample). The following data were available after the survey for one important item, in the notation of exercise 13.5.

$$\frac{c_1}{c_0} \doteq 0.15, \qquad \frac{c_2}{c_0} \doteq 9.5, \qquad W_1 \doteq 0.8, \qquad S^2 \doteq S_2^2$$

By finding VC for $k = 2$ and for the optimum k, determine whether $k = 2$ was a good choice.

13.7 In a survey by the Politz-Simmons method 390 respondents in an initial sample of 660 were found at home on the first call. The numbers who stated that they were at home on 0, 1, $\cdots$, 5 of the five previous nights and the number answering yes to a question in the survey were as follows.

	0/5	1/5	2/5	3/5	4/5	5/5
Number	14	35	55	74	94	118
Yes answers	4	13	20	30	42	56

Compute the Politz-Simmons estimate of the proportion of Yes answers in the population and compare it with the simple binomial estimate.

13.8 A population with $N = 6$ contains three units for which the correct answer to a question is yes and three for which it is no. Owing to errors of measurement, the probability of obtaining a "yes" response on a yes unit is 0.9. and the probability of obtaining a "no" response on a no unit is also 0.9. (a) By working out the distribution of all possible responses for samples of size 2, show that the probabilities are 0.218, 0.564, and 0.218 that the sample gives 0, 1, 2 "yes" responses. (b) Show that the variance of the estimated proportion of "yes" responses is 0.1090. Verify results (13.22)' and (13.24) in section 13.10. (c) What would be the variance of the estimated proportion of "yes" responses if there were no errors of measurement?

13.9 In part of the 1942 Bengal Labour Enquiry (Mahalanobis, 1946) a random sample of about 175 families was taken in each of three strata. The sample in each stratum was divided into five random subsamples, each assigned to a different interviewer. The five interviewers worked in all three strata. For expenditure on food, the relevant part of the analysis of variance (on a *single-family* basis) is as follows:

	df	ms	E(ms)
Between interviewers	4	22.3	$\sigma_\mu^2 + \sigma_d^2 + 35\sigma_{IS}^2 + 105\sigma_I^2$
Interviews × strata	8	9.6	$\sigma_\mu^2 + \sigma_d^2 + 35\sigma_{IS}^2$
Within subsamples	510	9.9	$\sigma_\mu^2 + \sigma_d^2$

In the notation of section 13.15 the model for a single family is

$$y_{hij\alpha} = \bar{\mu}_h + g_i + w_{hi} + (\mu'_{hij} - \bar{\mu}_h) + d_{hij\alpha}$$

Variances: σ_I^2 σ_{IS}^2 $\sigma_{\mu'}^2$ σ_d^2

Verify the expressions given for $E(ms)$ and estimate the proportion of the total variance of the mean that may be ascribed to enumerator biases.

REFERENCES

Barr, A. (1957). Differences between experienced interviewers. *App. Stat.* 6, 180–188.

Bartholomew, D. J. (1961). A method of allowing for "Not-at-home" bias in sample surveys. *App. Stat.*, 10, 52–59.

Belloc, N. B. (1954). Validation of morbidity survey data by comparison with hospital records. *Jour. Amer. Stat. Assoc.*, 49, 832–846.

Birnbaum, Z. W., and Sirken, M. G. (1950a). Bias due to nonavailability in sampling surveys. *Jour. Amer. Stat. Assoc.*, 45, 98–111.

Birnbaum, Z. W., and Sirken, M. G. (1950b). On the total error due to non-interview and to random sampling. *Int. Jour. Opinion and Attitude Res.*, 4, 179–191.

Cochran, W. G., Mosteller, F., and Tukey J. W. (1954). *Statistical problems of the Kinsey Report.* American Statistical Association, Washington, D.C., p. 280.

Deming, W. E. (1953). On a probability mechanism to attain an economic balance between the resultant error of non-response and the bias of non-response. *Jour. Amer. Stat. Assoc.*, 48, 743–772.

Deming, W. E. (1960). *Sample design in business research.* John Wiley and Sons, New York.

Durbin, J. (1954). Non-response and call-backs in surveys. *Bull. Int. Stat. Inst.*, 34, 2, 72–86.

Durbin, J., and Stuart, A. (1954). Callbacks and clustering in sample surveys: an experimental study. *Jour. Roy. Stat. Soc.*, A,117, 387–428.

Finkner, A. L. (1950). Methods of sampling for estimating commercial peach production in North Carolina. *North Carolina Agr. Exp. Stat. Tech. Bull.* 91.

Gray, P. G. (1955). The memory factor in social surveys. *Journ. Amer. Stat. Assoc.*, 50, 344–363.

Gray, P. G. (1957). A sample survey with both a postal and an interview stage. *App. Stat.*, 6, 139–153.

Hansen, M. H., et al. (1951). Response errors in surveys. *Jour. Amer. Stat. Assoc.*, 46, 147–190.

Hansen, M. H., and Hurwitz, W. N. (1946). The problem of nonresponse in sample surveys. *Jour. Amer. Stat. Assoc.*, 41, 517–529.

Hansen, M. H., Hurwitz, W. N., and Bershad, M. (1961). Measurement errors in censuses and surveys. *Bull. Int. Stat. Inst.* 38, 2, 359–374.

Hanson, R. H., and Marks, E. S. (1958). Influence of the interviewer on the accuracy of survey results. *Jour. Amer. Stat. Assoc.*, 53, 635–655.

Hartley, H. O. (1946). Discussion of paper by F. Yates. *Jour. Roy. Stat., Soc.* 109, 37.

Hendricks, W. A. (1949). Adjustment for bias by non-response in mailed surveys. *Agr. Econ. Res.*, 1, 52–56.

Horvitz, D. G. (1952). Sampling and field procedures of the Pittsburgh morbidity survey. *Pub. Health Reports*, 67, 1003–1012.

Jones, H. W. (1955). Investigating the properties of a sample mean by employing random subsample means. *Jour. Amer. Stat. Assoc.*, 51, 54–83.

Kish, L. (1949). A procedure for objective respondent selection within the household. *Jour. Amer. Stat. Assoc.*, **44**, 380–387.

Kish, L., and Hess, I. (1958). On noncoverage of sample dwellings. *Jour. Amer. Stat. Assoc.*, **53**, 509–524.

Kish, L., and Hess, I. (1959). A "replacement" procedure for reducing the bias of nonresponse. *Amer. Statistician*, **13**, 4, 17–19.

Kish, L., and Lansing, J. B. (1954). Response errors in estimating the value of homes. *Jour. Amer. Stat. Assoc.*, **49**, 520–538.

Koop, J. C. (1960). On theoretical questions underlying the technique of replicated or interpenetrating samples. *Proc. Soc. Statistics Sect. Amer. Stat. Assoc.*, 196–205.

Lienau, C. C. (1941). Selection, training and performance of the National Health Survey field staff. *Amer. Jour. Hygiene*, **34**, 110–132.

Mahalanobis, P. C. (1946). Recent experiments in statistical sampling in the Indian Statistical Institute. *Jour. Roy. Stat. Soc.*, **109**, 325–370.

Politz, A. N., and Simmons, W. R. (1949, 1950). An attempt to get the "not at homes" into the sample without callbacks. *Jour. Amer. Stat. Assoc.*, **44**, 9–31, and **45**, 136–137.

Sagen, O. K., Dunham, R. E., and Simmons, W. R. (1959). Health statistics from record sources and household interviews compared. *Proc. Social Statistics Sect. Amer. Stat. Assoc.*, 6–15.

Simmons, W. R. (1954). A plan to account for "not-at-homes" by combining weighting and callbacks. *Jour. of Marketing*, **11**, 42–53.

Stephan, F., and McCarthy, P. J. (1958). *Sampling Opinions.* John Wiley and Sons, New York, p. 243.

Sukhatme, P. V., and Seth, G. R. (1952). Non-sampling errors in surveys. *Jour. Ind. Soc. Agr. Stat.*, **4**, 5–41.

Trussell, R. E., and Elinson, J. (1959). *Chronic illness in a large city.* Harvard Univ. Press, pp. 339–370.

Woolsey, T. D. (1956). Sampling methods for a small household survey. *Pub. Health Monographs*, *No.* 40.

Answers to Exercises

1.5 $80,400 and $82,960.

1.6 The confidence probability is about 0.054 (found from $t = -1.67$ with 25 degrees of freedom). This assumes that future receipts follow the same frequency distribution as the sample of 26 receipts.

1.7 When the MSE is due entirely to bias, the estimate is always wrong by $1\sqrt{\text{MSE}}$. The probability of an error $\geq 1\sqrt{\text{MSE}}$ is therefore unity and the probability of an error $\geq 1.96\sqrt{\text{MSE}}$ or $\geq 2.576\sqrt{\text{MSE}}$ is zero. In Table 2.1, $\Pr(\geq 1\sqrt{\text{MSE}})$ tends to $\frac{1}{2}$.

2.4 $\hat{Y} = 51,473$. Probability about 0.9.

2.5 Yes. $v(\hat{Y})$ is 98.4.

2.6 $\hat{Y} = 20,238$, $s(\hat{Y}) = 849$.

2.7 (a) Public: $\hat{R} = 15.46$. Private: $\hat{R} = 12.75$. (b) Public: $s(\hat{R}) = 0.761$. Private: $s(\hat{R}) = 0.727$. For the fpc we take $f = 100/468$. (c) $14.2 < R < 16.7$.

2.8 Diff./s.e._diff $= 2.71/1.186 = 2.28$. P about 0.023. Note that the fpc is not used in computing s.e._diff.

2.9 (a) 9408, s.e. $= 780$; (b) 9472, s.e. $= 1104$.

2.10 S.e. (in 1000's) $= (a)$ 14,800; (b) 3900; (c) 3140.

2.11 9.2. (a) 2.7; (b) 2.4.

2.12 (a) $n = 60$, with 30 from each domain; (b) $n = 80$ will do if the number of owners in the sample lies anywhere between 20 and 60. With $n = 80$, the probability that this will happen is 0.54 (from the binomial tables). With $n = 100$, this probability is 0.94.

2.14 (a) 420; (b) 490; (c) both are unbiased; (d) estimate (b).

3.2 1066, 1334 as given by the normal approximation, equation 3.17.

3.3 Nearly conclusive.

3.6 (a) $76.2 \pm 3.6\%$; (b) 1738 ± 280 families.

3.7 1789 ± 268 families.

3.8 As an exact result,

$$\frac{V(\hat{A}_1)}{V(\hat{A}_1')} = \frac{N_1{}^2 n Q_1}{N^2 n_1 (1 - \pi)(Q_1 + P_1\pi)}$$

395

Now $N_1 = N(1 - \pi)$, and in large samples $n_1 \doteq n(1 - \pi)$. These substitutions give the stated result. In order that $V(\hat{A}_1)/V(\hat{A}_1')$ be small, we must have $\pi(1 - Q_1)/Q_1$ large. This means that Q_1 must be small: in other words, the proportion of domain 1 that lies in class C must be large. For given Q_1, π should be large.

3.9 All give $A_U = 13$. By the hypergeometric, the probability of no units in C in the sample is 0.0601 for $A_U = 12$ and 0.0434 for $A_U = 13$. By the binomial, $P_U = 0.4507$ and $\sqrt{1 - f} P_U = 0.4114$, giving $A_U = 12.3$. Page 59 gives 0.061 and 0.044.

3.11 Estimate (b) seems more precise.

3.12 The highest value is PQ/n as compared with PQ/mn by the binomial formula. This occurs when every cluster consists entirely of 1's or entirely of 0's. The lowest value can be zero if every cluster gives the same proportion P. (This is possible only for certain values of P and m).

3.13 Variance is 0.00184 by the ratio method and 0.00160 by the binomial formula.

3.14 Average size of sample $= m/P$.

4.1 735 houses. This sample size is needed for two-car households if $P = 10\%$.

4.2 About 260 sheets.

4.3 (a) 2475; (b) 4950.

4.4 $n = 21$ (taking $t = 2$).

4.5 $n = 484$. For number of unemployed, the cv would be about 15%.

4.6 62 more.

4.7 (a) $n = 278$; (b) $n = 2315$; (c) $n = 3046$.

4.8 If a rectangular distribution is assumed within each class, we take $S^2 = 0.083h^2$ or $S = 0.29h$. This gives estimates of 230, 580, 2030, and 11,600 in the four classes. If the right-triangular distribution is used in the fourth class, we take $S = 0.24h$, giving 9600 for this class.

4.11 $n_{opt} = \left(\dfrac{UNS}{2c\sqrt{2\pi}} \right)^{2/3}$,

5.1 (a) Neyman allocation gives $n_1 = 0.87$, $n_2 = 3.13$. (b) There are three possible estimates under optimum allocation and nine under proportional allocation. $V_{opt}(\bar{y}_{st}) = \frac{1}{6} = 0.167$: $V_{prop}(\bar{y}_{st}) = \frac{7}{12} = 0.583$. (d) Formula 5.21 gives $V_{opt}(\bar{y}_{st}) = 0.159$.

5.2 (a) $n_1 = 375$, $n_2 = 625$; (b) $n_1 = 750$, $n_2 = 250$.

5.3 $RP = 181\%$ for proportional allocation and 214% for optimum allocation.

5.5 The maximum relative increases when $W_1 = W_2$ equal 0.030 for $r = 2$ and 0.111 for $r = 4$.

5.6 (a) $n_1/n = \frac{1}{3}$, $n_2/n = \frac{2}{3}$; (b) $n = 264$, $n_1 = 88$, $n_2 = 176$; (c) $1936.

5.7 (a) $2288 against $1936. (b) No. The minimum field cost to reduce V to 1 is $2230.

5.8 (a) $n_1 = 384$, $n_2 = 192$; (b) $n_1 = 400$, $n_2 = 1600$; (c) $n_1 = 1200$, $n_2 = 2400$.

5.9 Fractional increase $= \frac{1}{9}$.

5.10 $n_1 = 541$, $n_2 = 313$, $n_3 = 146$.

5.12 In population 1, $V_{prop} = 0.143/n$; $V_{opt} = 0.134/n$. In population 2, $V_{prop} = 0.0491/n$, $V_{opt} = 0.0423/n$. The reduction in variance from optimum allocation is about 6% in population 1 as against 14% in population 2.

5.14 (a) If we guess $P_1 = 45\%, P_2 = 25\%, P_3 = 7.5\%$ as a compromise, this gives $n_1 = 268, n_2 = 116, n_3 = 16$; (b) s.e. $= 0.0225$; (c) s.e. $= 0.0241$.

5A.4 No. In each of the worst cases $[\Sigma(w_h - W_h)\bar{Y}_h]^2$ is $(0.105)^2 = 0.011$. Thus, with stratification, $\text{MSE}(\bar{y}_{st})$, as given by formula (5A.6), is $0.0108 + 0.0110 = 0.0218$. With simple random sampling, $V(\bar{y}) = 0.0177$.

5A.5 (a) $n = 1024$. The optimum allocation for the second variate (average amount invested) satisfies both requirements. (b) The allocation given by equation (5A.14), p. 124, with $\lambda = 0.09$, satisfies both requirements for $n = 1031$.

5A.6 $W_1 = 0.728, W_2 = 0.272$. $S_1 = 1.806, S_2 = 4.698$ (in the coded scale). (a) The optimum sample sizes are $n_1 = 0.507n$, $n_2 = 0.493n$. (b) $V(\bar{y}) = 31.95/n$, $V_{opt}(\bar{y}_{st}) = 6.72/n$.

5A.7 (b) $\int_0^a \sqrt{f(y)}\, dy = \int_0^a \sqrt{2(1-y)}\, dy = 2\sqrt{2}[1 - (1-a)^{3/2}]/3$. Hence we want $[1 - (1-a)^{3/2}] = \frac{1}{2}$.

5A.8 The optima are $L = 7$ for $p = 0.95, L = 5$ for $p = 0.9$, and $L = 4$ for $p = 0.8$. Either $L = 5$ or $L = 6$ is a good compromise.

5A.9 (a) Gain in precision is about 110%. (b) Gain from proportional stratification over simple random sampling is about 90%.

5A.10 (a) 3.733, (b) 1.111, (c) 8.222.

6.1 For the ratio estimate $V(\hat{Y}_R) = N^2(1-f)S_d^2/n$ and for simple expansion $V(\hat{Y}) = N^2(1-f)S_y^2/n$, where $d = (y - Rx)$. For the sample of 21 households the estimates of S_d^2 and S_y^2 are as follows. Number of children, $s_d^2 = 0.49$, $s_y^2 = 1.61$; number of cars, $s_d^2 = 0.41$, $s_y^2 = 0.39$; number of TV sets, $s_d^2 = 0.51$, $s_y^2 = 0.45$. The ratio estimate appears superior for children.

6.2 Gain $= 66\%$. At least 11 units by the ratio method.

6.3 Quadratic limits (27,100, 29,870); normal limits (27,030, 29,700).

6.5 Apply theorem 6.3 to the estimation of $R = \bar{Y}/\bar{X}$. With large samples, use $\bar{y}/\bar{X}$ if $\rho \leq (\text{cv of } x)/2(\text{cv of } y)$, and use $\bar{y}/\bar{x}$ otherwise.

6.6 The MSE's are 46.5 for the separate ratio estimate and 40.6 for the combined ratio estimate. In both cases the contribution of bias to the MSE is negligible.

6.7 For Lahiri's method, $V(\hat{Y}) = 40.1$.

6.8 Estimated population total $= 116.21$ millions. The relative variance is 0.00111, so that the s.e. is $(0.0333)(116.21) = 3.87$ millions. The estimate is within 1 s.e. of the true total.

6.9 The estimates are (a) 1896, (b) 1660, (c) 1689. In (c) we find $w_1 = 2.38, w_2 = -1.38$. Estimated s.e.'s are (a) 256, (b) 36.9, (c) 18.6. For the s.e. in (b) I used the formula s.e. $= \hat{\bar{Y}}_R\sqrt{(1-f)(c_{yy} + c_{11} - 2c_{y1})/n}$, where $\hat{\bar{Y}}_R$ is the ratio estimate of $\bar{Y}$, that is, 1660. For the s.e. in (c) I used $\bar{Y}_{MR} = 1689$.

7.1 Estimate $= 11,080$; s.e. $= 152$ (including the fpc).

7.2 No, since b is very close to 1.

7.3 $\hat{Y}_{lr} = 28,177 \pm 570$. The relative precision is 113%.

7.4 $27,751 \pm 694$.

7.6 For the difference estimate, $V(\bar{y}) = S_e^2/n$, for the linear regression estimate,

$V(\bar{y}_{lr}) = S_e^2 S_y^2 / n(S_e^2 + S_y^2)$. The regression estimate has the smaller variance, but its superiority is unimportant if S_e^2/S_y^2 is small.

7.7 $V(\hat{Y}_{lrs}) = 34.5$, $V(\hat{Y}_{lrc}) = 10.3$.

8.1 Variances are 8.19 (systematic), 11.27 (simple random), 8.25 (stratified, 2), 7.46 (stratified, 1).

8.2 $V_{sys} = 0.00141$, $V_{ran} = 0.00340$.

8.3 The systematic sample should be superior for the proportion of people of Polish descent, since this variable exhibits geographical stratification. It is likely to be inferior for proportion of children because the sampling interval, 1 in 5, coincides with the average size of a household. The same is true, though to a smaller extent, for proportion of males.

8.4 The variances are as follows. Males, $V_{srs} = 0.0204$, $V_{sys} = 0.0216$; children, $V_{srs} = 0.0204$, $V_{sys} = 0.0776$; professional, $V_{srs} = 0.0192$, $V_{sys} = 0.0016$.

8.5 Actual variance $= 8.19$. Method (a) gives 11.29. For method (b) the estimated variance from a single sample is $(1 - f)(\bar{y}_{i1} - \bar{y}_{i2})^2/4$, where $\bar{y}_{i1}$, $\bar{y}_{i2}$ are the means of the two halves. The average is 3.24. The serious underestimation is unexpected.

8.7 Both variances are $(k^2 - 1)/6$.

8.8 Simple random sampling is better unless $n = 1$ or $k = 1$.

9.1 Relative costs of using the four types of unit are as 100, 90.1, 79.7, and 77.8 (taking the first unit as a standard.)

9.2 Relative precision of the household is 211 % for the sex ratio and 38 % for the proportion who had seen a doctor.

9.3 Relative precision of the large unit is 0.566 with simple random sampling and 0.625 with stratified random sampling.

9.5 (a) $M = 5$; (b) $M = 1$.

9.6 The optimum M should decrease because travel cost, which varies as $\sqrt{n}$, becomes relatively less important when n increases.

9.7 (a) 34,242; (b) 5534; (c) 6493.

9.9 (a) If the s.d. among large units in class $h \propto M_h$. (b) If probability $\propto \sqrt{M_h}$.

9.10 $V(\hat{Y}_u) = 1.75$, $V(\hat{Y}_{sys}) = 0.50$, $V(\hat{Y}_{G2}) = 0.33$.

10.1 (a) 2.00; (b) 2.13.

10.3 (a) $165/n$; (b) $148.5/n$; (c) $132/n$.

10.4 (a) $n = 660$ fields; (b) $n = 530$ fields. Protein requires fewer fields than yield.

10.5 $c_1/c_2 = 8$.

10.7 (a) 0.93 %; (b) 0.51 %; (c) 0.36 %.

10.8 (a) Either $m_0 = 7$ or $m_0 = 8$ is suitable; (b) 89 % for $m_0 = 7$ and 93 % for $m_0 = 8$; (c) 86 % for $m_0 = 7$ and 89 % for $m_0 = 8$.

11.2 The relative precision of III to II drops from 3.02 to 2.75. If two sampling plans differ primarily in their between-units contribution to the variance, the relative precision of the superior plan will in general decrease as the ratio of the within-units variance to the total variance increases.

11.3 The explanation is, roughly speaking, that with these data the Y_i/z_i are more stable than the Y_i/M_i. If we took $z_i = \frac{1}{33}, \frac{8}{33}$, and $\frac{24}{33}$, the between-units contribution in method IV would vanish.

11.4 Total variance: 0.00504 (Ia), 0.02358 (II), 0.00554 (III).

11.6 Estimated percentage 14.2 $\pm$ 2.16. Estimated number 3540 $\pm$ 540.

11.7 Estimated percentage 13.9 $\pm$ 2.49.

11.9 (a) Total rooms, 29,400, total persons, 50,550, persons per room, 1.72; (b) s.e.'s: total persons, 2,440, persons per room 0.066.

12.1 $n = 267, n' = 1320$ or $n = 268, n' = 1280$. $V(p_{st})$ with optimum allocation is 6.67 when p_{st} is in %'s. With single sampling, $V(p) = 8.33$.

12.2 $c_n/c_n' > 9$.

12.4 $n' > 16n$.

12.5 By formula (12.29), s.e. $= 1.25$.

12.6 Per cent gains from the second to the sixth occasion are 50, 75, 91, 100, and 105, respectively.

12.8 The values of $nV(\bar{y}_2'')/S^2$ and $nV(\bar{y}_2')/S^2$ are as follows: $\mu = \frac{1}{4}, \rho = 0.8$: 0.885, 0.875; $\mu = \frac{1}{4}, \rho = 0.9$: 0.843, 0.840; $\mu = \frac{1}{2}, \rho = 0.8$: 0.824, 0.810; $\mu = \frac{1}{2}, \rho = 0.9$: 0.752, 0.746.

13.1 (c) 90% response with 1047 completed questionnaires or 95% response with 701 completed questionnaires.

13.2 The method with 90% response costs \$5235. That with 95% response costs \$5.7895 per completed questionnaire, or \$4058 total cost.

13.3 (b) $0.65n_0, 0.815n_0, 0.8915n_0, 0.9351n_0, 0.9611n_0$; ($c$) 100, 104, 108, 112, 117; (d) 300, 288, 277, 267, 256.

13.4 (a) Bias (in %) $= -3.85, -2.15, -1.21, -0.69, -0.40$; ($b$) variances are 8.67, 9.03, 9.39, 9.74, 10.16; (c) four calls.

13.6 Yes. VC for $k = 2$ is only about 2% over the minimum VC.

13.7 Politz-Simmons estimate, 39.7%; binomial, 42.3%.

13.8 (c) Variance $= 0.1$.

13.9 If each enumerator's error of measurement were independent from family to family, the variance of the sample mean would be $(\sigma_{\mu'}^2 + \sigma_d^2 + \sigma_{Is}^2 + \sigma_I^2)/525$ instead of $(\sigma_{\mu'}^2 + \sigma_d^2 + 35\sigma_{Is}^2 + 105\sigma_I^2)/525$. Enumerator biases contribute about 55% of the total variance.

Author Index

Subject Index

405